MESOZOIC MAMMALS

The First Two-Thirds of Mammalian History

**Outcrops of the Nemegt Formation at Nemegt, Gobi Desert.
Photograph by R. Gradziński.**

THE FIRST TWO-THIRDS OF
MAMMALIAN HISTORY

MESOZOIC
MAMMALS

Edited by
Jason A. Lillegraven
Zofia Kielan-Jaworowska
William A. Clemens

UNIVERSITY OF CALIFORNIA PRESS
Berkeley • Los Angeles • London

The following is an example of the
preferred mode of citation of chapters:

Kielan-Jaworowska, Z., Eaton, J. G., and Bown, T. M., 1979, Theria of
    metatherian-eutherian grade, *in* Lillegraven, J. A., Kielan-Jaworowska, Z.,
    and Clemens, W. A., eds., Mesozoic mammals: the first two-thirds of
    mammalian history: Berkeley, Univ. California Press, p. 182-191.

University of California Press
Berkeley and Los Angeles, California

University of California Press, Ltd.
London, England

ISBN 0-520-03582-8
Library of Congress Catalog Card Number: 77-085750
Printed in the United States of America

1 2 3 4 5 6 7 8 9

CONTENTS

CONTRIBUTORS

Thomas M. Bown
>Formerly of the Department of Geology, The University of Wyoming, Laramie, Wyoming (present address: Paleontology and Stratigraphy Branch, United States Geological Survey, Denver, Colorado 80225)

Michael L. Cassiliano
>Formerly of the Department of Geology, The University of Wyoming (present address: Mather Air Force Base, California 95655)

William A. Clemens
>Department of Paleontology, University of California, Berkeley, California 94720

A. W. Crompton
>Museum of Comparative Zoology, Harvard University, Cambridge, Massachusetts 02138

Jeffrey G. Eaton
>The Geological Museum, The University of Wyoming, Laramie, Wyoming 82071

Farish A. Jenkins, Jr.
>Museum of Comparative Zoology, Harvard University, Cambridge, Massachusetts 02138

Zofia Kielan-Jaworowska
>Zakład Paleobiologii, Polska Akademia Nauk, Al. Żwirki i Wigury 93, 02-089 Warszawa, Poland

Mary J. Kraus
>Department of Geology, The University of Wyoming, Laramie, Wyoming 82071

Donald G. Kron
>Department of Geology, The University of Wyoming, Laramie, Wyoming 82071

Jason A. Lillegraven
>Department of Geology and The Geological Museum, The University of Wyoming, Laramie, Wyoming 82071

Everett H. Lindsay
>Department of Geosciences, The University of Arizona, Tucson, Arizona 85721

George Gaylord Simpson
>The Simroe Foundation, 5151 East Holmes Street, Tucson, Arizona 85711

PREFACE AND ACKNOWLEDGMENTS

The idea for this book developed through a course on the subject of Mesozoic mammals offered in the Spring of 1976 in the Department of Geology of The University of Wyoming. Recognition by the students of: (1) the scattered nature of the literature; (2) the lack of recent general reviews; and (3) the fact that knowledge of Mesozoic mammals is expanding rapidly, led to the conclusion that it was opportune to provide a summary of the "state of the art" as of the late 1970's. It was clear, however, that successful development of such a summary would not be possible without contributions from a number of other paleontologists currently conducting research on Mesozoic mammals. Early in the summer of 1976 the editorial board was formed. In the following months several paleontologists agreed to prepare chapters and others made available unpublished information from their own research. We gratefully acknowledge the generosity of all those who have added to this volume. They have contributed of their knowledge, time, and energy, and have also agreed with us to donate all proceeds to a special fund of The Geological Museum of The University of Wyoming, dedicated to the support of graduate education in vertebrate paleontology.

The book is intended to provide a summary assessment of current information available on mammalian life during the Mesozoic Era; no monumental new theories are propounded and few questions have been unequivocally answered. We believe that we have faithfully differentiated between repeatable observation and that which is mere speculation. Equally important, we hope that we have succeeded in showing those areas in which the most glaring voids in knowledge of Mesozoic mammalian life exist. If the summary provides even a modest stimulus toward filling the gaps, we will consider our efforts worthwhile.

References to virtually all modern papers of significance concerning the systematics and evolution of Mesozoic mammals are provided, as are citations to the original descriptions of all formally-named taxa from specific through ordinal levels. Perhaps no single worker would agree with all the taxonomic decisions that have been made, but the arrangement seems at least to be consistent with available knowledge of the day. It is fully appreciated that subsequent finds will profoundly alter the systematic hierarchy used here, and our classification is provided only as a standardized framework useful in facilitating further discussion (see additional comments in Chapter 1).

In addition to the authors themselves and their respective institutions, the following individuals (listed alphabetically) are hereby sincerely thanked for their various contributions in the form of information, constructive criticism, professional advice, or technical assistance: Ms. Marie Andrushuk (University of California, Berkeley); Dr. Miguel T. Antunes (Universidade Nova de Lisboa); Dr. J.

David Archibald (Yale University); Dr. Donald Baird (Princeton University); Dr. Rinchen Barsbold (Academy of Sciences, Mongolian People's Republic); Dr. Percy M. Butler (Royal Holloway College); Mr. Jack M. Callaway (University of Wyoming); Dr. George L. Callison (California State University, Long Beach); Mr. Kenneth Carpenter (University of Colorado); Dr. Demberelyin Dashzeveg (Academy of Sciences, Mongolian People's Republic); Dr. Richard C. Fox (University of Alberta); Mr. Eric F. Freeman (London, England); Dr. William E. Frerichs (University of Wyoming); Dr. Gerhard Hahn (Philipps-Universität); Dr. James A. Hopson (University of Chicago); Dr. Ralph W. Imlay (United States Geological Survey); Mr. James A. Jensen (Brigham Young University); Dr. Erle G. Kauffman (Smithsonian Institution); Dr. Kenneth A. Kermack (University College, London); Dr. John A. W. Kirsch, Jr. (Yale University); Dr. Bernard Krebs (Freie Universität, Berlin); Dr. Georg Krusat (Freie Universität, Berlin); Dr. Wann Langston, Jr. (University of Texas); Dr. Douglas Lawson (University of Southern New Orleans); Mrs. Bernice A. Lillegraven (Laramie, Wyoming); Ms. Augusta Lucas (University of California, Berkeley); Ms. Pat Lufkin (University of California, Berkeley); Dr. Giles T. MacIntyre (Queens College, CUNY); Dr. Edward McCrady, Jr. (University of the South); Mrs. Gloria F. McCabe (National Science Foundation); Dr. Paul O. McGrew (University of Wyoming); Dr. Malcolm C. McKenna (American Museum of Natural History); Dr. Larry G. Marshall (Field Museum of Natural History); Dr. Michael J. Novacek (San Diego State University); Dr. John H. Ostrom (Yale University); Dr. Pamela Parker (Chicago Zoological Park); Dr. F. R. Parrington (University Museum of Zoology, Cambridge); Dr. David C. Parris (New Jersey State Museum); Dr. James L. Patton (University of California, Berkeley); Mr. Jacob A. Reitenbach (University of Wyoming); Rev. Harold W. Rigney, S. V. D. (Divine Word Seminary); Dr. Pamela L. Robinson (University College, London); Mr. Kenneth D. Rose (University of Michigan); Dr. Donald E. Savage (University of California, Berkeley); Dr. Robert J. G. Savage (The University, Bristol); Mr. Charles R. Schaff (Harvard University); Mr. Bob H. Slaughter (Southern Methodist University); Dr. Robert E. Sloan (University of Minnesota); Dr. Maureen B. Steiner (California Institute of Technology); Dr. Boris A. Trofimov (Academy of Sciences, U. S. S. R.); Dr. Leigh Van Valen (University of Chicago); Dr. John A. Wilson (University of Texas); Dr. Robert W. Wilson (University of Kansas); Dr. Michael O. Woodburne (University of California, Riverside).

Mr. George V. Shkurkin (Museum of Paleontology, University of California, Berkeley) must be given special mention for the extensive aid he provided in translating and interpreting information on various Asiatic Mesozoic mammal localities.

Finally, our deepest gratitude goes to Mrs. Jane Love of Laramie, who, without personal remuneration, served as copy editor.

We dedicate the book to the anonymous, ancient stonemason whose discoveries at Stonesfield led to the scientific recognition that mammalian life existed during the "Secondary."

Zdziarka, Poland   Jason A. Lillegraven
March 11, 1977   Zofia Kielan-Jaworowska
                                       William A. Clemens

CHAPTER 1

INTRODUCTION

Jason A. Lillegraven

THE PROBLEM

The Cenozoic Era commonly is referred to as the "age of mammals" and includes that part of earth history between about 64 million years ago and the present. It was the time in which mammals dominated the vertebrate fauna on the earth's dry surface after the extinction of most of the great reptiles. Less generally known, however, is the fact that animals identified as mammals have been a part of the earth's land fauna for most of the Mesozoic Era ("age of reptiles"), as well. The Mesozoic Era includes the Triassic, Jurassic, and Cretaceous periods (see Fig. 2-1) and extended from roughly 240 to about 64 million years before the present; mammals make their first appearance in the fossil record of the Late Triassic, and indicate that mammalian life existed at least 200 million years ago. Thus the designated "age of mammals" comprises less than one-third the total time span of the Class Mammalia.

The literature on Mesozoic mammals is greatly scattered in a large number of publications, some obscure, and in several different languages. Gener-

ally the literature is quite technical and there are no recent overall summaries of the subject available. It is also difficult for those not trained specifically in the field of mammalian paleontology to comprehend the state of present knowledge concerning Mesozoic mammalian history. To help alleviate these problems, the most essential data here are made available in a single publication. The basic purposes of the book are to summarize: (1) the present state of the fossil record in terms of spatial and temporal distribution and known parts of the animals themselves; (2) the scheme of the existing classification systems and their weaknesses; (3) the biological characteristics of the various groups in terms of anatomy, presumed phylogeny, likely ecological roles, extent of adaptive diversifications, modes of reproduction, and relationships with flowering plants; and (4) the known paleogeographic history of the earth during pertinent parts of the Mesozoic in relation to probabilities of intercontinental dispersal of land vertebrates.

The Mesozoic occasionally has been referred to as the "dark ages" of mammalian history. The appellation is well deserved considering the paucity of scientific information now available. Less is known about the entirety of the first 140 million years of mammalian evolution than for any of the various epochs of the Cenozoic except, perhaps, the Paleocene. Thus vast areas of significant paleontological research remain to be completed before documentation of the times of yore of early Mammalia may be considered satisfactory.

MESOZOIC MAMMALS WERE SMALL

Biologically speaking, the all-pervading feature of mammalian life during the Mesozoic was their small body size; most were in the size range of modern shrews to rats. Most of the remainder of the Introduction will revolve about this consideration.

Potential variability in filling adaptive roles at the time was probably constrained by certain mechanical limitations of being minuscule and by the nature of competitor groups. Questions related to possible reasons for the persistent small size among Mesozoic mammals must be approached through consideration of relationships with their contemporaries, the great dinosaurs. Most people tend to think of a sequential relationship between the times of origin of the dinosaurs (developing first) and the mammals (appearing later). In actuality, they were nearly contemporaneous groups, both having originated sometime during the latter half of the Triassic. From their very beginnings, mammals and dinosaurs occupied different adaptive roles. Analysis of dental and jaw morphology of Mesozoic mammals suggests that, except for the multituberculates and perhaps the docodonts (see Chapters 5 and 6) most were small carnivores and probably fed mainly on adult insects and their larvae, various other arthropods, and perhaps small vertebrates. The diverse multituberculates seem to have been predominantly small herbivores. Late in the Cretaceous a variety of marsupial and placental lineages developed into forms that probably were fruit-eaters and/or omnivores. Known dinosaurs, at least as adults, are clearly divisible either into large carnivore or large herbivore adaptive roles. The large herbivores had an especially marked evolutionary radiation during the middle of the Cretaceous, immediately following the first great diversification of the flowering plants.

Dinosaurs tended toward large to gigantic body size, while the mammals maintained small to tiny body size. Few dinosaurs smaller than about 10 kg body weight as adults existed during any part of the Mesozoic (see Bakker, 1971), and no large mammals are known to have developed until the dinosaurs became extinct. The largest known Mesozoic mammal is *Didelphodon vorax,* a badger-sized marsupial

known only from the Late Cretaceous in North America. *Didelphodon* was a true giant amongst the mammals of its day. An undescribed ?amphilestid triconodont, also of comparatively large body size, is known from North American Lower Cretaceous strata. Although there are such exceptions, nearly all Mesozoic mammals were of the shrew- to rat-sized category. Early in the Cenozoic, however, a number of mammalian lineages independently developed that had individuals of large size (even by modern standards). The rate of these evolutionary changes, as well as the rate of development of new mammalian families and orders (see Lillegraven, 1972), was astonishingly rapid through the Paleocene and Eocene. Bakker (1971), as part of his argument for the warm-bloodedness of dinosaurs, suggested that they were physiologically restricted to large body size because of the difficulties experienced by small naked-skinned endotherms in retaining body heat. Why Mesozoic mammals did not "experiment" with larger body size, however, has not yet been adequately explained. Why, through roughly 140 million years, was there no overlap (or even a close approximation) in body size between the largest mammals and small adult dinosaurs?

The question is probably not answerable from the viewpoint of competition from the moderate-sized nondinosaurian reptiles known to have been contemporaries of Mesozoic mammals. Turtles, ichthyosaurs, plesiosaurs, relict cotylosaurs, champsosaurids, crocodilians, and pterosaurs can be eliminated, by nature of their specialized habits, as potentially close competitors with the mammals. I believe the same can be said for the therapsids (a group that markedly declined in numbers and diversity in the latter half of the Triassic and was extinct by the end of the Early Jurassic) and for the rhynchocephalians (a group noted for evolutionary conservatism, modest geographic distribution, and lack of diversity). That leaves only members of the Order Squamata (the lizards, snakes, and amphisbaenians). The oldest known fossil snakes are from Lower Cretaceous rocks, and "worm lizards" are as yet unknown from the Mesozoic. Neither of these groups, in any case, would have had close competitive ties with the mammals; mammals coexist today with lizards, snakes, and amphisbaenians.

Although there are conspicuous exceptions, modern lizards are predominantly carnivorous and diurnal with respect to activity outside their immediate areas of protective habitation. Such was probably the prevailing situation during the Mesozoic, as well. Mesozoic mammals, on the other hand, were probably active mostly at night (see arguments from the point of view of the central nervous system by Jerison, 1973) as are most "primitive" mammals of today. Early mammals had already developed keen senses of hearing (including a complex middle ear and extended labyrinth), touch, and olfaction with communication by sophisticated pheromonal cues. Subdivision of the small carnivore roles between lizards and mammals by the diurnal rhythm was probably at least as effective in the Mesozoic as it is today, and it is therefore unlikely that competition from lizard contemporaries kept the body size of mammals small. Conversely, although lizards are significantly older than mammals as a group (see Carroll, 1977), arguments presented by Pough (1973) from the point of view of food-energy relationships suggest that it is *mammalian* competition that today restricts most lizards to small body size.

Could it have been competition from immature dinosaurs that provided the selective pressure that stopped experimentation toward large body size in mammals? Such a question perhaps will always remain within the realm of speculation. Nevertheless, even assuming the presence of a modicum of protective maternal behavior (see Hopson, 1977), newly-hatched carnivorous dinosaurs probably prowled in search of prey once equilibrated. Extant herbivorous lizards are carnivorous in early life (see review by Pough, 1973); developmental changes in dietary preference may also have characterized young individuals of some herbivorous dinosaur species. Unfortunately, little is known about early growth stages of most dinosaurs.

Jerison (1973) observed that, although the mammalian brain did not change appreciably through the Mesozoic, it had developed roughly to the relative size and proportions characteristic of brains of modern opossums and some living members of the Insectivora as early as the Late Triassic. In light of this, one might question whether a small dinosaurian predator might have been "outwitted" by its potential mammalian prey; Burghardt (1977), however, would argue vigorously against such a proposal. Related to this in terms of escape abilities, Jenkins and Parrington (1976) have demonstrated that the posture of known Late Triassic mammals was already essentially modern and indicative of capability of high mobility over complex surfaces, probably

even in trees. But the bipedal carnivorous dinosaurs also showed postures indicative of great activity, agility, and quickness early in their evolutionary history. Even juveniles probably captured exposed, scampering mammals with ease during daylight hours.

Mammals of today, however, even ones of moderate size, are noted for their behavioral abilities in finding and inhabiting places that are inconspicuous and/or inaccessible to potential predators. There is no reason to believe that this was not also the case during the Mesozoic, and, if so, the dilemma persists as to what restricted Mesozoic mammals to small body size. Most hunting by carnivorous dinosaurs was probably done within the limits of daylight or under conditions of bright moonlight; their auditory, olfactory, tactile, and visual senses undoubtedly did not compare favorably with those of their mammalian contemporaries. One would therefore think that mammals, during the night, could have searched out food with comparative abandon and perhaps even preyed, in turnabout, upon young dinosaurs.

Bakker (1971) suggested that another explanatory factor in the persistent small size of Mesozoic mammals was a probable lack of sophistication in evaporative cooling mechanisms such that high levels of activity (such as grappling with a small dinosaur?) may have raised the core body temperature of the mammals beyond a level that could be equilibrated or tolerated. This argument is not compelling as a major explanatory factor, however, because a number of living Australian marsupials possess only rudimentary abilities in evaporative cooling yet achieve moderate size in hot environments under conditions of normal predatory pressures. In short, questions relating to reasons for the prevailing minuscule nature of mammals during the first two-thirds of their history have yet to be satisfactorily answered.

Because of the small size and generally unimpressive physical nature of Mesozoic mammals, the popular imagination has not been captured as it was by the existence of the great dinosaurs. The Mesozoic seems to have been, comparatively speaking, a time of quiet evolutionary conservatism for mammals rather than an excursion into the large, bizarre, and grotesque, as was the case for the dinosaurs. The question of comparative evolutionary rates, however, is difficult to evaluate. It is true that the dinosaurs, during their roughly 140 millions of years of existence, radiated into a spectacular diversity of body forms. They became variously armored, crested, spiked, clawed, stump-footed, cranially pneumatized, cranially-solidified, or elongated or shortened of neck. Bakker has forcefully argued that they were endothermic (but see Hopson, 1976, and Bouvier, 1977, for alternative views). Importantly, all were of comparatively large body size, and some were immense. The little mammals, on the other hand, showed less variation in body size and general conservatism in dental anatomy. As will be seen, Mesozoic mammal skulls are rare and postcranial skeletons even rarer; from what is known of these parts, however, general conservatism also seems to have been the rule.

One may ask, nevertheless, is the above a realistic measure of comparative "evolutionary rates"? It could be argued that the *real* evolutionary action among Mesozoic mammals was in their communication, maternal behavior, internal "soft" anatomy, and the refinement of sophisticated physiological integration—experimentation within the basic anatomical-physiological-reproductive plan—those things which cannot be fossilized. Jenkins and Parrington (1976, p. 429) hypothesized that early mammals ". . . were probably as specialized in habitat and behavior as were many of their reptilian contemporaries." Could it be that the spectacular adaptations seen among the dinosaurs were of a somewhat more "superficial" nature, having been related primarily to adaptations for predation (or protection from it), sexual displays, and large body size? Perhaps large body size itself provided physiological or mechanical constraints to evolutionary experimentation within more fundamental tissue-, organ-, or system-level adaptations that did not exist for the smaller mammals. These questions may never be answered. Nevertheless, they make the study of Mesozoic mammals a fascinating subject, and are well worth keeping in mind when we study the physical record of their history.

FORMAT INFORMATION

The book, including cited references, follows in most respects the stylistic format of the Bulletin of the Geological Society of America. The metric system of weights and measures is used throughout the text. Page citations are omitted in most cases, but are given when direct quotations are made or when finding the appropriate page in an extensive

monograph may be particularly difficult. No new names are coined, but one emendation of a specific name is provided. Museum specimen numbers are not used. Each chapter (except Chapter 15) dealing with the systematics of a particular mammalian group has two tables dedicated, respectively, to nomenclature and geographic-stratigraphic distributions. For example, Table 4-1 (from Chapter 4, Triconodonta) lists a complete taxonomic hierarchy along with authorships from ordinal to specific levels for all known kinds of triconodonts. Table 4-2 summarizes the known geographic, stratigraphic, and approximate temporal occurrences of all known genera of triconodonts. A listing of taxonomic hierarchies used throughout the text appears in Table 2-1, along with summaries of known temporal and geographic distributions of the families (only Mesozoic records). The publication status (*i.e.*, in press, in preparation, *etc.*) of recent studies is that of January 1, 1978, unless we have personal knowledge to the contrary.

Chapter 2 provides a summary, on a worldwide basis, of the state of the Mesozoic mammalian record involving: (1) faunal lists from each locality (in some cases, each group of localities); (2) brief discussions of geologic age assignments; and (3) information on the parts of the animals that are actually known. Chapters 4 through 8 plus 10 through 12 summarize the detailed record of each major group of Mesozoic mammals from the points of view of anatomy, systematics, phylogenetic history, and ecological adaptations; a general discussion of biogeographical aspects of their histories is deferred to Chapter 14. Information concerning the origin of the tribosphenic molar, a critical step in the evolutionary history of therian mammals, seemed most logically placed immediately following Chapter 8 on eupantotherians. Chapters 3 and 13 are admittedly speculative in their reviews of the origin of mammals and possible modes of reproduction utilized, respectively. The fourteenth chapter is primarily geological in approach, and summarizes new data on Mesozoic world geography that should prove useful to the interpretation of distributions of virtually any group of land organisms of that time. Although the Monotremata of Australia and New Guinea have no known Mesozoic record, they possess many features representative of a reptilian grade of evolution and thus have played an important part in interpreting the biological nature of Mesozoic mammals. Chapter 15 provides notes on historical considerations of the phylogenetic relationships of these curious egg-laying mammals.

A revision of the higher category taxonomy of the Mammalia was not a goal in the development of this book. Rather, emphasis was placed upon summarizing the information available on the particular groups of mammals known from the Mesozoic. The classification utilized here is based in large part upon those presented by Simpson (1945, 1971) and Romer (1966), modified to reflect what we judge to have been significant, subsequent advances in knowledge of phylogenetic relationships; in some cases it also reflects newer uncertainties where near unanimity of agreement prevailed in the past. The classification is a product, unabashedly tentative, of what has been termed an evolutionary taxonomic approach (see Simpson, 1975). Recently McKenna (1975) proposed a major reorganization of mammalian classification based upon rigorous application of cladistic principles and methodology. Subsequently, Szalay (1977) provided both a critique of the values of cladistic classifications and, on other bases, proposed another classification of eutherian mammals. The editors, and our coauthors, have drawn from the research of McKenna and Szalay, but have not adopted their formal taxonomy. The editors questioned the value to communication, in light of the real paucity of hard evidence, of reassessment classifications based upon the concept of strict interpretation of monophyly. We also questioned the value in communication of the resulting cladistic classification which would require formal recognition of every genealogical hypothesis, no matter at what hierarchical level or how well founded, through an astronomical multiplication of new nomina.

As an example of new uncertainties alluded to in the above paragraph, the concept that the early Mammalia underwent a fundamental evolutionary dichotomy into prototherian versus therian lineages is presently coming into significant question (see especially, discussions in Chapters 3, 4, and 6). Therefore, we have used the terms "Prototheria" and "Theria" (see Table 2-1) in informal taxonomic senses. It is the view of the editors that, considering the present inadequacy of information on the evolutionary relationships of Mesozoic mammalian groups (see Fig. 13-1), the formalization of Prototheria and Theria cannot adequately be defended either in phenetic or cladistic senses. The terms are, however, deeply entrenched in the literature, remain generally useful in communication, and thus are retained informally within Table 2-1 and are occasionally used in discussions throughout the text.

The decision not to perpetuate the formality of Prototheria and Theria leads to a series of minor dilemmas within existing nomenclature with respect to taxonomic symmetry. As seen in Table 2-1, for example, the infraclasses Pantotheria, Metatheria, and Eutheria are left stranded without the comforting embrace of a subclass-level name. These three taxa are comparatively well-circumscribed with respect to included animals, and have been used dominantly at the infraclass level. It would, of course, have been a simple matter for us to elevate these taxa to the hierarchy of subclass. However, considering the present flux of opinion on higher-level mammalian taxonomy and in deference to traditional usage, little scientific value was predicted to accrue from invoking such changes. Complementary examples of taxonomic asymmetry, though less obvious, can be seen within the "prototherian" listing and within lower hierarchies discussed throughout the text. Most of the authors of this book would agree that far more information must be wrenched from fossils as yet undiscovered to allow the development of a stable, phylogenetically-oriented higher category classification of mammals.

REFERENCES CITED

Bakker, R. T., 1971, Dinosaur physiology and the origin of mammals: Evolution, v. 25, p. 636-658.

Bouvier, M., 1977, Dinosaur Haversian bone and endothermy: *ibid.,* v. 31, p. 449-450.

Burghardt, G. M., 1977, Of iguanas and dinosaurs: social and behavior communication in neonate reptiles: Amer. Zool., v. 17, p. 177-190.

Carroll, R. L., 1977, The origin of lizards, *in* Andrews, S. M., Miles, R. S., and Walker, A. D., eds., Problems in vertebrate evolution: Linn. Soc. Symp. Ser. 4, p. 359-396.

Hopson, J. A., 1976, Hot-, cold-, or lukewarm-blooded dinosaurs? (book review): Paleobiology, v. 2, p. 271-275.

_____1977, Relative brain size and behavior in archosaurian reptiles: Ann. Rev. Ecol. Syst., v. 8, p. 429-448.

Jenkins, F. A., Jr., and Parrington, F. R., 1976, The post-cranial skeletons of the Triassic mammals *Eozostrodon, Megazostrodon* and *Erythrotherium*: Roy. Soc. London Philos. Trans., B (Biol. Sci.), v. 273, p. 387-431.

Jerison, H. J., 1973, Evolution of the brain and intelligence: New York, Academic Press, *xiv* + 482 p.

Lillegraven, J. A., 1972, Ordinal and familial diversity of Cenozoic mammals: Taxon, v. 21 (2/3), p. 261-274.

McKenna, M. C., 1975, Toward a phylogenetic classification of the Mammalia, *in* Luckett, W. P., and Szalay, F. S., eds., Phylogeny of the primates: New York, Plenum Press, p. 21-46.

Pough, F. H., 1973, Lizard energetics and diet: Ecology, v. 54, p. 837-844.

Romer, A. S., 1966, Vertebrate paleontology (3*rd* ed.): Chicago, Univ. Chicago Press, *ix* + 468 p.

Simpson, G. G., 1945, The principles of classification and a classification of mammals: Amer. Mus. Nat. Hist. Bull, v. 85, *xvi* + 350 p.

_____1971, Concluding remarks: Mesozoic mammals revisited, *in* Kermack, D. M., and Kermack, K. A., eds., Early mammals: Linn. Soc. Zool. Jour., v. 50, suppl. 1, p. 181-198.

_____1975, Recent advances in methods of phylogenetic inference, *in* Luckett, W. P., and Szalay, F. S., eds., Phylogeny of the primates: New York, Plenum Press, p. 3-19.

Szalay, F. S., 1977, Phylogenetic relationships and a classification of the eutherian Mammalia, *in* Hecht, M. K., Goody, P. C., and Hecht, B. M., eds., Major patterns in vertebrate evolution: New York, Plenum Press, p. 315-374.

CHAPTER 2

WHERE, WHEN, AND WHAT
—A SURVEY OF KNOWN MESOZOIC MAMMAL DISTRIBUTION

William A. Clemens

Jason A. Lillegraven

Everett H. Lindsay

George Gaylord Simpson

NOTE: Authors are listed in alphabetical order with no implication as to seniority of authorship.

PURPOSE

The purpose of this chapter is to present a summary, on a worldwide basis, of all Mesozoic mammal localities known to the authors in terms of: (1) where they are: (2) the intervals of geologic time that they are believed to represent; and (3) the nature of the material recovered from the specific localities. The real importance of the chapter is to give the reader an appreciation of the present spotty record of Mesozoic mammals in terms of geographical, temporal, and anatomical representation.

THE TIME SCALE

Figure 2-1 presents the generalized time scale that will be used throughout the book. As far as practicable, ages will be related to European marine stages and corresponding ages, although few of the mammals are in marine beds and correlation with the European sequence is uncertain on other continents. There is no universally accepted nomenclature and subdivision, even in Europe. Different workers have alternative views of the terminology that should be applied to specific cases. For example, Russell (1975) would prefer to use a more local age terminology for Cretaceous mammalian chronology in the Western Interior of North America, and we have followed his system throughout the book. Figure 2-1 was developed using Harland and others (1967), Lambert (1971), Russell (1975), and Van Hinte (1976a, 1976b) as the primary sources. We stress the point that age assignments for most Mesozoic mammal localities should be considered suspect. Many are little more than "best guesses" with respect to contemporaneity with rocks of the classic European stages.

CLASSIFICATION AND DISTRIBUTION

The classification of families in Table 2-1 is expanded and somewhat modified from Simpson (1971). This is an eclectic classification. Known distribution of families is given in Table 2-1 in terms of periods and continents. More precise distributional data are given for each locality in the following text and within the chapters dealing with the specific groups of organisms.

It is emphasized that for the present, negative evidence has little value for Mesozoic mammals. That is, the absence of a group of mammals at a particular time and place generally cannot be taken as an indication that it did not in fact occur then and there. The only areas in which negative evidence may be given some, but not conclusive, weight are those for the Rhaeto-Liassic (Late Triassic or Early Jurassic) of southwestern Britain, the Late Jurassic of southern

England and western United States, the Late Cretaceous of Mongolia, and the Late Cretaceous of the Rocky Mountain and High Plains areas of North America.

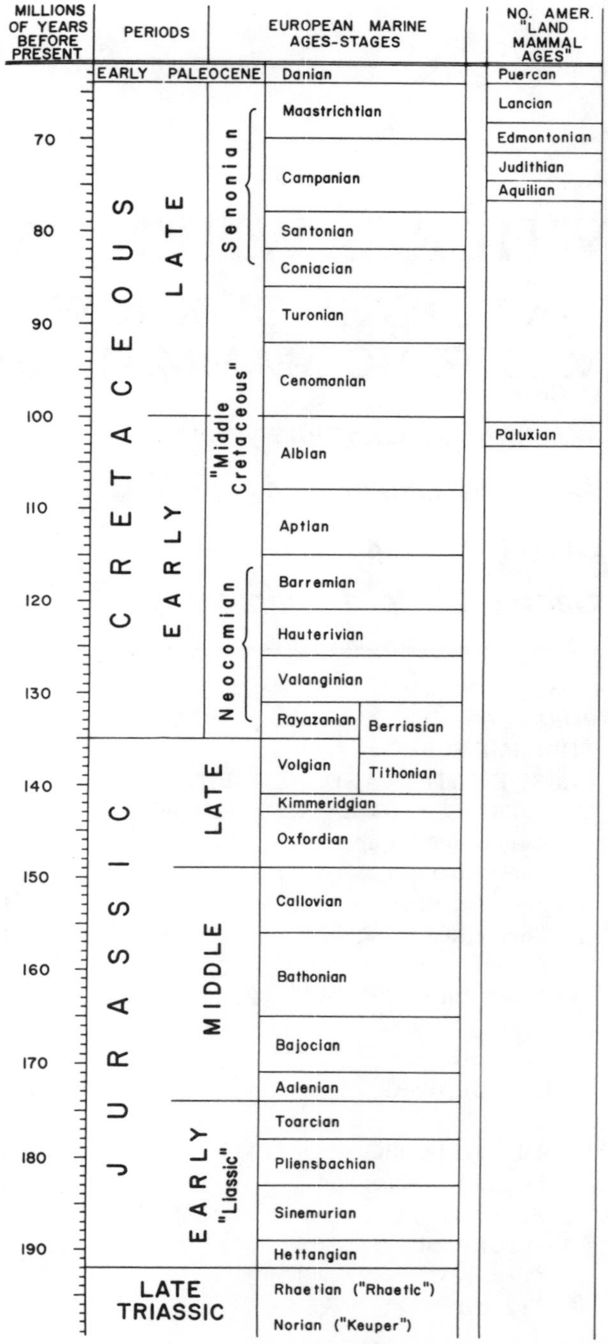

Figure 2-1. Geological time scale used throughout text (see "The Time Scale" for primary sources).

LATE TRIASSIC OR EARLY JURASSIC

Late Triassic or Early Jurassic mammals are known only from near the boundary between the periods and only from a few sites in Europe, South Africa, China, and possibly North and South America. The Late Triassic age conventionally assigned many of the localities yielding these fossils is currently being challenged (Olsen and Galton, 1977, and references therein), so we list them here as being of Late Triassic or Early Jurassic age.

Continental Europe

The oldest presently known record for fossils commonly accepted as mammals comes from a member of the uppermost Middle Keuper "*Plateosaurus* beds" of Halberstadt, Sachsen-Anhalt, now within Bezirk Magdeburg, East Germany (Fig. 2-2), and includes a representative of a group called the "haramiyids." Members of the Haramiyidae are represented only by isolated teeth that show similarity with certain primitive forms of

TABLE 2-1   CLASSIFICATION AND DISTRIBUTION OF MESOZOIC MAMMALIAN FAMILIES

Symbols for chronological distribution: E, Early; M, Middle; L, Late; T, Triassic; RL, Rhaeto-Liassic; J, Jurassic; C, Cretaceous.

Symbols for geographic distribution: A, Asia; Af, Africa; E, Europe; NA, North America; SA, South America.

Class Mammalia
  "Prototherians"
    Subclass Allotheria
      Order Multituberculata
        Suborder Plagiaulacoidea
          Paulchoffatiidae LJ-EC: E
          Plagiaulacidae LJ-EC: E; LJ-EC?: NA;
            EC: A
        Suborder Ptilodontoidea
          Neoplagiaulacidae LC: NA
          ?Neoplagiaulacidae LC: A, NA
          Ptilodontidae LC: NA
          Cimolodontidae LC: NA
         Suborder Taeniolabidoidea
          Taeniolabididae LC: A, NA
          Eucosmodontidae LC: A, NA
          Chulsanbaataridae LC: A
          Sloanbaataridae LC: A
        Suborder *incertae sedis*
          Cimolomyidae LC: NA
        ?Multituberculata *incertae sedis*
          Haramiyidae RL: E
    Subclass Eotheria
      Order Triconodonta
        Morganucodontidae RL-MJ: E; RL: Af, A
        Amphilestidae MJ: E; LJ: NA
        Triconodontidae LJ-LC: NA; LJ: E; EC: A
        ?Triconodonta *incertae sedis* ("Sinoconodon-
          tidae") RL: A
      Order Docodonta
        Docodontidae LJ: NA, E

"Therians"
  Infraclass Pantotheria
    Order Symmetrodonta
      Kuehneotheriidae RL: E
      Amphidontidae LJ: NA; EC: A
      Spalacotheriidae EC-LC: NA; LJ-EC: E
      ?Spalacotheriidae MJ: E; LJ: NA
    Order Eupantotheria
      Amphitheriidae MJ: E
      Peramuridae LJ: E; LJ: Af; EC: A?
      Paurodontidae LJ: NA, E
      Dryolestidae MJ-EC: E; LJ: NA
  Infraclass Metatheria
    Order Marsupialia
      Didelphidae EC?-LC: NA; LC: SA
      Pediomyidae LC: NA, SA?
      Stagodontidae LC: NA
  Infraclass Eutheria
    Orders uncertain or disputed in the Mesozoic. The following eutherian families or superfamilies, also uncertain, have been reported on reasonable authority:
      Endotheriidae (only questionably referable to the Eutheria) EC: A
      Leptictoidea, new family LC: NA, A?
      Palaeoryctidae LC: A; LC: NA
      Zalambdalestidae EC?-LC: A
      ?Paromomyidae LC: NA
      Arctocyonidae LC: NA
  Theria of metatherian-eutherian grade
      Aegialodontidae EC: E, A, NA
      Pappotheriidae EC: NA
      Deltatheridiidae LC: A, NA?
      Family uncertain EC: NA

NOTE: Only the Mesozoic part of the range is given in cases in which the taxon is also known to extend into the Cenozoic. The Order Monotremata (see Chapter 15), usually considered "prototherians," are unknown from Mesozoic rocks.

the Order Multituberculata. The multituberculates are almost universally accepted as mammals, but there is less unanimity about the mammalian affinities of the haramiyids. The arguments will be reviewed more extensively in Chapter 6. In any case, if the Keuper haramiyids are accepted as mammals, they are among the oldest yet known. The Halberstadt finds are restricted to a single isolated tooth referred by Hahn (1973) to *Thomasia* sp. 1 and to a fragmentary ulna of uncertain affinities called *Eoraetica siegerti* by Dietrich (1937).

Latest Triassic ("Rhaetic" or "Rhaetian") mammals and mammal-like reptiles have been found in the Rhaetic bonebeds of Württemberg. The collecting localities, both natural outcrops and exposures in quarries, are in southwestern Germany south of Stuttgart and near Tübingen (Fig. 2-2). The fossils are fragmentary and many are abraded, a result of the winnowing of the sediments that produced the bonebeds (Aepler, 1974). The largest sample of fossils, now housed in the Institut für Geologie

und Paläontologie der Universität Tübingen, is largely the result of the work of Erika von Hüene (1933), O. Schindewolf, and their colleagues. Their primary collecting localities were the bonebeds at Gaisbrunnen, Olgahain, and Degerloch from rocks at several stratigraphic levels that are older than the *Psiloceras planorbis* cephalopod zone.

The composite fauna of the Württemberg bonebeds includes representatives of several tritylodontid mammal-like reptiles: *Oligokyphus triserialis* (including *O. biserialis, Mucrotherium cingulatum,* and *Uniserium enigmatum*), *Tritylodon fraasi,* and *Chalepotherium plieningeri* (see Butler, 1939; Henning, 1922; and Kühne, 1950, 1956). Haramiyids are represented by *Thomasia antiqua* and possibly other taxa (Hahn, 1973). Several teeth of the haramiyid now called *Thomasia* were found near Steinenbronn and described by Plieninger in 1847. *Tricuspes tubingensis,* typified on an isolated tooth found at Gaisbrunnen and possibly represented by a second tooth discovered at Hallau, Switzerland

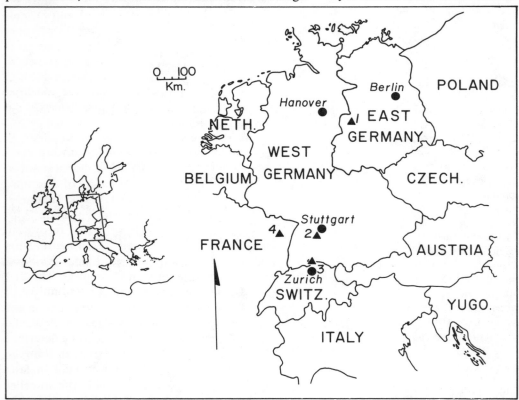

Figure 2-2. Map of central Europe, showing positions (triangles) of Late Triassic localities of mammals or closely mammal-like reptiles: *1*, "*Plateosaurus* beds" of Halberstadt; *2*, Rhaetic bonebeds of Württemberg; *3*, Rhaetic bonebeds of Hallau; and *4*, Rhaetic bonebeds of Saint-Nicholas-du-Port.

(Clemens, research in progress), might be a mammal allied to the Triconodonta.

The largest collection of specimens of mammals and mammal-like reptiles to come from the Rhaetic bonebeds of continental Europe to date is that assembled under the direction of Bernhard Peyer of the Universität Zürich. These fossils, again largely fragmentary isolated teeth, were obtained from a bonebed in Unter-Hallau, which is in the western part of Kanton Schaffhausen, Switzerland, north of Zürich near the German border (Fig. 2-2). In 1956 Peyer published a beautifully illustrated monograph describing teeth of haramiyids, triconodonts, and probable synapsid reptiles. Until his death in 1963 he continued acquisition of material, almost doubling the size of the collection.

Preliminary analysis and comparison with the Rhaetic fauna of Württemberg and the Rhaetic-Liassic faunas of Great Britain (Clemens, research in progress) has already pointed out some intriguing differences and similarities. Unlike the bonebed fauna of Württemberg, *Oligokyphus* or other tritylodonts have not been found at Hallau. This negative evidence carries some weight because Peyer processed large volumes of rock with particular attention to the recovery of microfossils. Even if the teeth of *Oligokyphus* were shattered, their individual crescentic cusps would probably have been recognized. The presence of a tooth closely resembling the type of *Tricuspes tubingensis* has been noted. Haramiyid teeth represent both the *Haramiya* and *Thomasia* patterns. At least two kinds of morganucodontids are present and one closely resembles *Morganucodon watsoni*. Finally, there are several kinds of double-rooted teeth that have crowns of a mammalian grade of complexity but are of sufficiently different pattern to suggest they are not derived from the dentitions of any of the animals cited above. These tantalizing scraps suggest that the Rhaetic mammalian fauna of Switzerland was quite diverse at various taxonomic levels.

An isolated molariform tooth from Rhaetian beds in northeastern France near Saint-Nicholas-du-Port in the district of Meurthe-et-Moselle (Fig. 2-2) was recently described by Russell and others (1976). Although probably representative of a cynodont reptile, all indications suggest that the animal was very near the mammalian level of dental organization. Work at this site is being continued and has already yielded remains of other kinds of vertebrates, some clearly of mammalian affinity (D. Sigogneau and D. E. Russell, pers. comm. to Clemens, 1978). The locality could easily become the most prolific source of Rhaetic mammalian fossils in continental Europe.

Great Britain

Perhaps the most famous Late Triassic or Early Jurassic mammal localities are those from South Wales near Bridgend in Glamorgan (Fig. 2-3). The fossils are found in fissure fillings in commercially-mined Carboniferous limestones. Four quarries (Duchy, Pant, Pont Alun, and Ewenny) have so far yielded mammalian specimens (see Kermack and others, 1973, for aerial photo of general area). The fissures were filled during the Rhaetic or early Liassic (Early Jurassic). The mammals are part of an assemblage of vertebrates and plants, the so-called *Hirmeriella* association found in many fissure fillings. Kermack and others (1973, p. 101) stated: ". . . the *Hirmeriella* association . . . must be either the Lower Lias (Hettangian and Lower Sinemurian) or the Rhaetic. There is insufficient evidence to decide between them." This statement is the most specific, published interpretation known to us on the probable age of the Welsh fissure fillings. Thus significant uncertainty shrouds the localities with respect to antiquity and they are generally referred to as being "Rhaeto-Liassic" in age. C. J. Duffin and David Pacey (students of Kenneth A. Kermack at University College, London) are presently reviewing Rhaetic and Liassic faunal associations in detail with the specific intention of determining the probable geological ages of the mammal-bearing fissure fillings in Wales and England.

At least two genera have been recovered, *Morganucodon watsoni* and *Kuehneotherium praecursoris* (a possible third kind, *Kuhneon duchyense,* will be discussed in Chapter 7). The first species is among the earliest and most primitive of known prototherians, and *Kuehneotherium* is the earliest and most primitive known therian. A second genus of therian from the area is yet to be described (see Kermack and others, 1968). Although the relationships will be discussed in more detail in later chapters, the "prototherians" include the so-called "primitive" mammals (probably including the triconodonts, docodonts, monotremes, and possibly the multituberculates) and the "therians" include the "advanced" mammals (including the symmetrodonts, eupantotheres, marsupials, placentals, and "therians of metatherian-eutherian grade"). Thus the Bridgend localities are extraordinarily significant in that they show that even when mammals made their first appearance in the fossil record, at least two markedly divergent lineages (*i.e.*, prototherian and therian) were already in existence. If one believes that the haramiyids were mammals ancestral to the multituberculates, he must thereby also accept the presence of three major Rhaeto-Liassic mammalian lineages. Most Bridgend mammalian specimens are isolated teeth, but some little damaged jaws have been recovered (see Kermack and others, 1968; Kermack and others, 1973; Gill, 1974; and Parrington, 1971, 1973, 1978). Disarticulated skeletal elements of *Morganucodon* (referred to as *Eozostrodon*) have recently been described in detail by Jenkins and Parrington (1976).

Late Triassic or Early Jurassic mammals are also known from southern England southeast of Bristol at the Holwell Quarry, Frome, in Somerset (Fig. 2-3). Like the Welsh localities, Holwell Quarry also contains several fissure fillings from which fossils were

obtained. It was first collected in 1858 by Charles Moore with further work in 1939 by Walter Kühne. Kühne collected from two fissures, one of which may have been worked by Moore. Most of Kühne's specimens are now at Cambridge University. Two additional haramiyid specimens went to Bristol (Museum and University) where one was destroyed by bombs in World War II. Savage and Waldman (1966; also see Savage, 1971) described a tritylodont reptile from a fissure that might have yielded Kühne's haramiyids. The known mammalian fauna from Holwell includes haramiyids that were referred to *Haramiya moorei, H. fissurae, ?Haramiya* sp., *Thomasia anglica*, and two isolated teeth that were the types and only specimens of *Eozostrodon parvus* and *E. problematicus* (see Parrington, 1941, 1947, and Hahn, 1973). Parrington (1973), in an important review of the dentitions of early mammals, made *E. problematicus* a junior synonym of *E. parvus*. Several paleontologists have concluded that *Morganucodon watsoni* is indistinguishable from *Eozostrodon parvus* and applied the latter name to

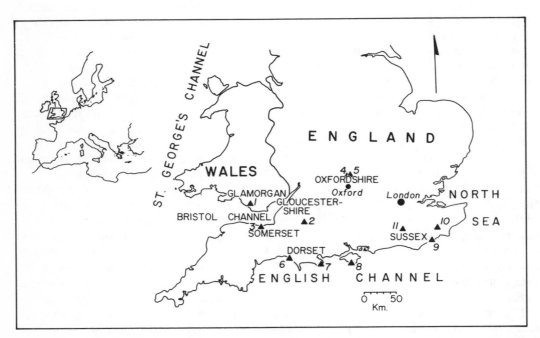

Figure 2-3.   Map of Wales and southern England, showing positions (triangles) of Late Triassic, Middle Jurassic, Late Jurassic, and Early Cretaceous mammal localities: *1*, Late Triassic or Early Jurassic fissure fillings near Bridgend; *2*, Late Triassic or Early Jurassic fissure fillings at Holwell; *3*, Late Triassic beds at Watchet; *4*, Middle Jurassic Stonesfield Slate in Oxfordshire; *5*, Middle Jurassic Forest Marble of Kirtlington and Woodeaten Quarry; *6*, Middle Jurassic Forest Marble at West (or Watton) Cliff; *7*, Late Jurassic beds at the seacliffs of Durlston Bay; *8*, Early Cretaceous Wealden beds on the Isle of Wight; *9*, Early Cretaceous "Cliff End bone bed"; *10*, Early Cretaceous bonebed at Tighe Farm; and *11*, Early Cretaceous bonebed at Paddockhurst Park.

the Welsh morganucodontid. Here separate nomina are retained, *Morganucodon watsoni* for the abundantly represented Welsh morganucodontid, and *Eozostrodon parvus* for the rare, but very significant morganucodontid found only at Holwell Quarry in England (but also see Chapter 4). A review of morganucodontid taxonomy by Clemens has recently been accepted for publication in the Zoological Journal of the Linnean Society.

One isolated, imperfect tooth that is now lost was collected near Watchet in Somerset, southwestern England south of the Bristol Channel (Fig. 2-3), and named *Hypsiprimnopsis rhaeticus* by Boyd Dawkins in 1864. Although Romer (1966) synonymized the genus with *Haramiya,* the tooth in question was exceptionally large (*c.* 4.4 mm in length) for a haramiyid and it may well have been from a tritylodont or some other sort of reptile rather than from a mammal. The only descriptions are by Dawkins (1864) and Owen (1871). The beds are in the lowest part of the Rhaetic section. It is our opinion that the classification of the specimen should not be refined beyond ?tritylodontid, *incertae sedis.*

Southern Africa

Vertebrates now generally considered as mammals are known from southern Africa in Lesotho (Basutoland) and the Orange Free State (Fig. 2-4), about 375 km west of Durban. The generalized stratigraphy of the area is shown below. The beds comprise the Stormberg Group of the famous Karroo Supergroup:

> Drakensberg Volcanics
> Cave Sandstone
> Red Beds
> Molteno Beds

The basal Molteno Beds are mainly coarse-grained clastic sediments overlain by roughly 450 m of redbeds composed of alternating mudstones and siltstones. The Red Beds, in turn, are overlain by or locally interdigitated with the white Cave Sandstone. Until recently, the vertebrates from these strata usually have been accorded a Late Triassic age. On largely biostratigraphic grounds, however, Olsen and Galton (1977) suggested the local faunas of the Red Beds and Cave Sandstone to be of Liassic age; of the

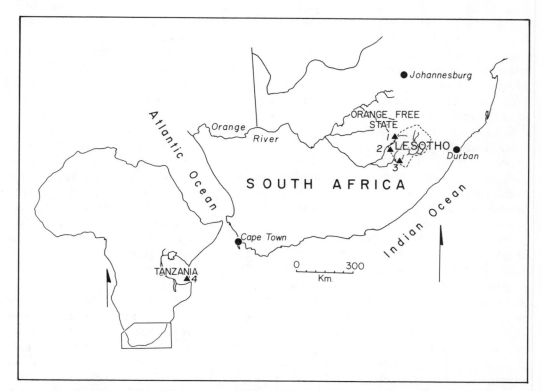

Figure 2-4.   Maps of southern Africa, showing positions (triangles) of Late Triassic and Late Jurassic mammal localities: *1,* **Late Triassic or Early Jurassic "Lady Brand" locality;** *2,* **Late Triassic or Early Jurassic "Mafeteng" locality;** *3,* **Late Triassic or Early Jurassic "Pokane" locality; and** *4,* **Late Jurassic dinosaur beds of Tendaguru.**

units of the Stormberg, only the Molteno is considered by them to have been deposited during the Late Triassic. On the basis of potassium-argon age determinations, Fitch and Miller (1971) suggested that the inception of Drakensberg volcanism in Lesotho began about 187 (± 7) million years ago. Further, they suggest that the upper part of the fossiliferous Red Beds is some 187-193 (± 7) million years old.

The history of collecting in southern Africa records the successes of field parties from many countries, including England, France, South Africa, and the United States (see Crompton, 1968, for summary). Three major mammal-bearing localities have been found. They are at Pokane (near Quthing) and Mafeteng (both in the upper redbeds of Lesotho) and Lady Brand (in the Cave Sandstone of the Orange Free State, South Africa). Two species of morganucodontid mammals (*Erythrotherium parringtoni* and *Megazostrodon rudnerae*) have been found and both are known from remarkably well-preserved upper and lower dentitions (see Crompton, 1974), skull parts, and essentially complete postcranial skeletons (see Jenkins and Parrington, 1976). The former species was recovered from the Mafeteng locality, and is closely related to *Morganucodon* from Great Britain. *Megazostrodon rudnerae* is from the Pokane locality and is a large *Morganucodon*-like animal. The skeleton of *Megazostrodon* represents an adult animal and that of *Erythrotherium* is of a juvenile. Only a few specimens have been recovered from the Cave Sandstone, Lady Brand site, but it is the type locality of Broom's (1932) "Ictidosaurs A and B," generally considered to be advanced mammal-like reptiles. "Ictidosaur B" is now the type of *Diarthrognathus broomi* Crompton, 1958, which previously was classified by some as a mammal.

Ellenberger (1972, 1974) has described a number of trackways from various other localities in beds possibly of Norian and Rhaetian age in the Stormberg group of Lesotho. Some of these, from the Rhaetian at least, seem to be mammalian but cannot be more precisely classified at present.

A dentary fragment with two roots and a part of the crown of a tooth found between the Ugab and Huab rivers of southwestern Africa was described as a mammal by F. von Hüene (1925) and named *Archaeodon* ("*Archaeotherium*") *reuningi*. Romer (1956) referred to it as "ictidosaur or mammal," but omitted it in his 1966 classification.

Southern U.S.S.R.

L. P. Tatarinov (pers. comm. to Kielan-Jaworowska, 1977) currently is studying a complete skeleton of a mammal or small mammal-like reptile found in strata thought to be of Triassic age. Apparently this age determination is based primarily on paleobotanical evidence. The fossil is reported to be from the same locality in the Madygen sector of the Shurab lignite field that yielded the type of the flying reptile *Podopteryx* (see Sharov, 1971, and refs.). This locality, which is not plotted on the maps in this chapter, lies on the northern slope of the Turkestan Range, in the Lyaylak Rayon, Osh Oblast', Kirgiz S.S.R. The discovery gives promise of contributing significantly to our understanding of both the Mesozoic faunas of Asia and possibly an early phase of mammalian evolution.

China

Fossil mammals have been recovered from rocks in sheep grazing areas about 4 km northeast of the city of Lufeng in Yunnan Province, South China (Fig. 2-5), in the lower beds of the lower Lufeng Series. The first collections came from three localities at different stratigraphic levels within this area. These are Yang T'sao Ti (Yancaodi of Pinyin transcription), the lowest; Hei Koa Pen; and Ta Ti, the highest. They have not yet been dated exactly, but on the basis of similarities of the associated therapsid (mammal-like) reptiles with those from South Africa, are thought to be either latest Triassic (Rhaetic) or earliest Jurassic (early Liassic) in age. In the abstract of a paper including the description of *Yunnania,* a new tritylodont from the "lower Lufeng formation," Cui (1976) noted that Chinese geologists and paleontologists currently favor an Early Jurassic correlation. However, Hsing (1976) and Young (1978) continue to refer to the fossils from these sites as being of Triassic age.

The first mammalian specimens from the Lufeng area were discovered by Edgar T. Oehler, S. V. D., then a professor of Chemistry at the University of Peking. The collections were divided into two units. Most of the material went to the University of Chicago where the mammals were studied by Bryan Patterson and Everett C. Olson. They described parts of four skulls, six lower jaws, one humerus, and one femur from Ta Ti and Hei Koa Pen. Patterson and Olson (1961) believed all the material to be representative of but a single species, *Sinoconodon rigneyi.* Association of these specimens has been challenged, and *S. rigneyi,* as currently recognized, is classified as "?Triconodonta *incertae sedis*" (see Chapter 4). Another skull from Yang T'sao Ti, part of Oehler's original collection, was taken to London by Harold W. Rigney, S. V. D., who originally organized the explorations. He provided a brief description of the skull (1963) and used it as the type of *Morganucodon oehleri.* Later, Kermack and others (1973) published a detailed analysis of its lower jaws. A similarly detailed study of the cranium is being prepared by these authors.

Hsing (1976) announced the discovery of additional material in strata of the lower Lufeng Forma- tion in the vicinity of the city of Lufeng. The collec- tions include ten excellently preserved skulls of tritylodonts and mammals. Parts of the vertebral col- umn are associated with at least one mammalian skull. In addition to specimens of *Morganucodon,* Hsing (*ibid.*) writes of others that possibly represent new genera and species. Young (1978) described some of this new material and established a new species, "*Eozostrodon*" *heikuopengensis*, which is probably best allocated to the genus *Morganucodon.* The presence of approximately contemporaneous morganucodontids in Europe, China, and Africa permits the speculation that mammalian faunas in the Late Triassic or Early Jurassic were essentially pangaeic (see Chapter 14).

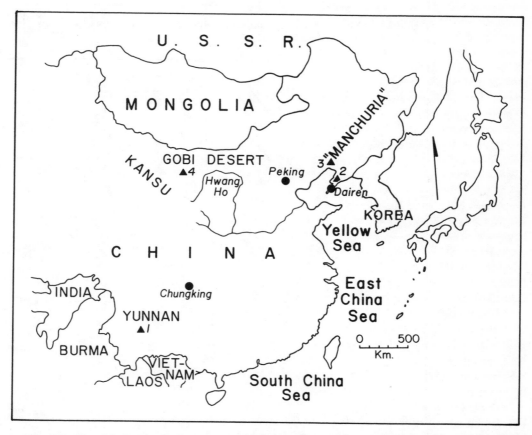

Figure 2-5. Map of eastern Asia, showing positions (triangles) of Late Triassic (or Early Jurassic), Early Cretaceous, and Late Cretaceous mammal localities: *1*, Late Triassic or Early Jurassic beds at Lufeng; *2*, ?Early Cretaceous beds of the "Sakasiyo" coal mine; *3*, ?Early Cretaceous beds of the "Hsinchiu" coal mine; and *4*, Late Cretaceous dinosaur beds at Tsondolein Khuduk (also see Fig. 2-13).

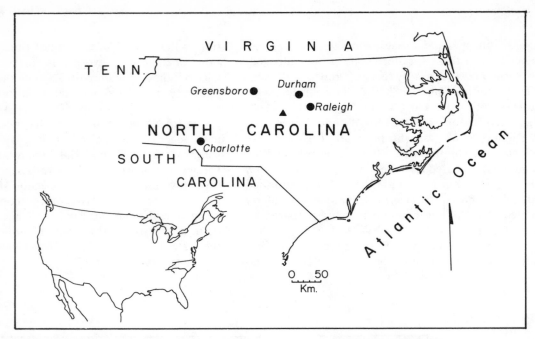

Figure 2-6. Map of North Carolina, showing position (triangle) of the New Egypt coal mine in the Late Triassic Newark Series.

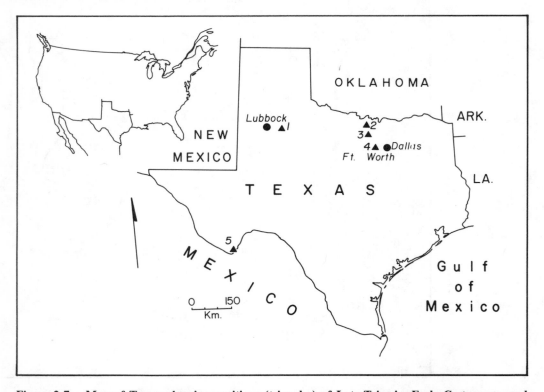

Figure 2-7. Map of Texas, showing positions (triangles) of Late Triassic, Early Cretaceous, and Late Cretaceous localities of mammals or closely mammal-like reptiles: *1*, Late Triassic Dockum Group of Crosby County; *2*, Early Cretaceous "Trinity sands mammals" locality at "Greenwood Canyon"; *3*, Early Cretaceous "Trinity sands mammals" locality at the Butler farm; *4*, early Late Cretaceous Woodbine Formation of Tarrant County; and *5*, Late Cretaceous Javelina Formation at Big Bend National Park.

North Carolina

Two species (*Dromatherium sylvestre* and *Microconodon tenuirostris*) of animals represented by jaws from the New Egypt coal mine in the Chatham coal fields of central North Carolina (Fig. 2-6) were described as mammalian by Ebenezer Emmons in 1857 and Henry Fairfield Osborn in 1886 and 1887. The beds are within the Late Triassic Newark Series. Simpson (1926) refigured the material and, following a thorough restudy, concluded that the animals were more likely representative of advanced cynodont, therapsid reptiles, perhaps phylogenetically near, but certainly not ancestral to any known mammal. However, Kühne (1958) later suggested that *Microconodon tenuirostris* might have been a morganucodontid. It is possible that more complete specimens might indicate that *Microconodon,* at least, meets some current definitions of the Mammalia. Repeated searches in the region of the New Egypt mine have resulted in no new "near-mammalian" specimens.

Texas

New studies, as yet unpublished, have been initiated by Bob Slaughter of the Shuler Museum of Paleontology of Southern Methodist University into the Late Triassic Dockum Group of Crosby County in west Texas (Fig. 2-7). So far Slaughter's efforts, utilizing large-scale acid and heavy-liquid floatation techniques, have resulted in discovery of a partial jaw plus two isolated teeth of a vertebrate similar to *Microconodon* from North Carolina (see Slaughter, 1975a and 1975b). As a result of these recent discoveries, the future seems bright for finding Triassic mammals in North America.

South America

A southern Brazilian skeleton from the Santa Maria Formation (Fig. 2-8) at its type locality (Santa Maria, Rio Grande do Sul) has been named *Therioherpeton* by Bonaparte and Barberena (1975). The postcranial skeleton has not been described, but as

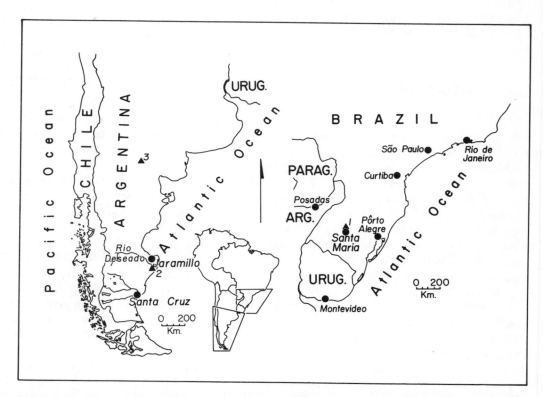

Figure 2-8.   Maps of Argentina and southern Brazil, showing positions (triangles) of ?Late Triassic and ?Middle Jurassic localities of mammals or closely mammal-like reptiles: *1*, **?Late Triassic Santa Maria Formation near Santa Maria;** *2*, **?Middle Jurassic footprint locality in the Estancia Laguna Manantiales; and** *3*, **Late Triassic footprint locality at Los Menucos, Río Negro Province.**

the name "mammal-reptile" suggests, the skull could be classified either as the most reptile-like mammal or as the most mammal-like reptile known, depending on definitions of Reptilia and Mammalia. It seems to be just on the line of transition between the classes in grade of evolution. Bonaparte (1973) put the Santa Maria Formation in his late Chañarian (late Middle Triassic) land reptile age, but it may be closer to the Ischigualastian (early Late Triassic). In either case, if this is considered a mammal, it would be the oldest one known by usual definition. However, this is not necessarily valid evidence for proposing the origin of mammals in South America. Similar cynodont reptiles have been described from the Middle Triassic Chañares Formation of Argentina by Romer (1969).

Footprints and trackways from Los Menucos, Río Negro Province (Patagonia), Argentina (see Fig. 2-8), once thought to be of Middle Jurassic age, are now assigned to the Late Triassic (Casamiquela, 1964, 1975a). In addition to a chirotherioid thecodont and four other apparently reptilian trackways, Casamiquela (*ibid.*) described two types, *Palaciosichnus zettii* and *Stipanicichnus bonnettii,* which he thought might be of therapsid or mammalian origin.

EARLY JURASSIC

India

Just a few weeks before the manuscript of this book was placed in the hands of the University of California Press word was received from P. Yadagiri (pers. comm. to Clemens, 1978) of the discovery of Early Jurassic mammals in central India. A preliminary report of this remarkable discovery has now been published (Datta and others, 1978). This information became available after the texts of this and other chapters were essentially complete, and the discovery site is not plotted on our maps.

Mammalian fossils were recovered by screening marl obtained during the excavation of sauropod skeletal remains. This excavation was in the Yamanpalli area of the Pranhita Godavari Valley, Andhra Pradesh, India. The geology of the area was studied by Kutty (1969), who recognized, among other units, the Kota Formation and underlying Dharmaram Formation. In addition to sandstones and clays, the Kota Formation includes several richly fossiliferous limestones containing remains of both vertebrates and invertebrates. The marl producing the mammalian fossils and associated dinosaurian fossils is within the Kota Formation, just below one of these limestones. Assignment of an early Jurassic (probably Liassic) age to the Kota Formation is based on studies of hypsomid fishes, a flying reptile, prosauropod dinosaurs, ostracods, and conchostracans (see Datta and others, 1978, for references).

Study of the mammalian fossils is being undertaken by P. Yadagiri and P. M. Datta. Their sample includes a variety of well-preserved dental, cranial, and postcranial elements. The few fossils illustrated in the preliminary report (*ibid.*) suggest the presence of a multituberculate or haramiyid and a triconodont or early therian. The report of the recognition of ". . . four to five different types of mammalian pelvic girdles" (*ibid.,* p. 67), indicates a much greater taxonomic diversity. Additional descriptions and analyses are eagerly awaited.

MIDDLE JURASSIC

Except for some Argentinian mammal footprints to be discussed below, only five Middle Jurassic mammal localities are known from the entire world, all from Great Britain.

England and Scotland

Four localities are known from England in the vicinity of Oxford and on the Dorset coast; a fifth is on the Isle of Skye, Scotland. The Stonesfield Quarries west of Woodstock in Oxfordshire produced the Stonesfield Slate (so called from its use in roofing, not its lithology). The commercial mines have been abandoned since 1909. The mined rock is a sandy limestone found stratigraphically near the base of the Great Oolite Series, thought to be of the Bathonian stage. Some of the mines are ancient, and workers commonly found fossils and sold them as curiosities. As far as is known, the first Mesozoic mammalian fossil to be discovered came from there in or about 1764. Its significance, however, was not appreciated until 1828. In 1812 or 1814 "an ancient stonemason" brought two mammalian jaws from Stonesfield to W. J. Broderip, then a student of law at Oxford University. Although he and his professor, W. Buckland, were convinced of the mammalian affinities (and later received confirmation from Cuvier), Buckland waited until 1824 to announce the discovery formally. The paper initially caused an uproar within the natural sciences because mammals were not supposed to occur in the "Secondary" (Mesozoic), contemporary with the dinosaurs! The controversy was settled by the latter 1830s, however, with the general acceptance thereafter of the existence of Mesozoic mammals (see Simpson, 1928a, for further historical background). The mammals recovered from Stonesfield include the following:

Order Triconodonta
  Amphilestidae
    Amphilestes broderipii
    Phascolotherium bucklandi
Order Eupantotheria
  Amphitheriidae
    Amphitherium prevostii

No specimens have been recovered from the mines since Simpson's (1928a) review of the fauna appeared.

Three new mammal-bearing localities in the Forest Marble were recently reported by Freeman (1976a, 1976b). One locality, the Old Cement Works Quarry at Kirtlington, is about 12 km north of Oxford on the east bank of the River Cherwell (Fig. 2-3) and has produced 34 isolated teeth of mammals by the technique of underwater screening. The rock unit

containing mammals at the Old Cement Works Quarry is a nonmarine clay bed within the dominantly marine Forest Marble of the upper part of the Bathonian stage, thought to be slightly younger than the Stonesfield Slate (for references to general geology, see Arkell, 1956; Richardson and others, 1946; and McKerrow and others, 1969). The second locality (Fig. 2-3) is also in the Forest Marble Formation, but on the Dorset coast below West (or Watton) Cliff, west of Bridport Harbour (Freeman, 1976a, and Ensom, 1977). To date, this locality has yielded only a single, damaged mammalian tooth. The third new locality is in a green clay bed that forms part of the so-called "Monster Bed" (see Palmer, 1973) of the Hampen Marly Beds at Woodeaten Quarry, 5 km northeast of Oxford. Although study of the fauna is only in preliminary stages, the following taxa were reported by Freeman:

Order ?Multituberculata
  ?haramiyid or multituberculate, isolated molar
Order Triconodonta
  Morganucodontidae
    morganucodontid lower molar (similar to *Morganucodon watsoni*, but larger)

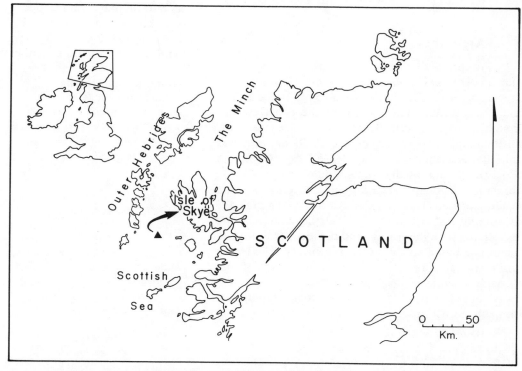

Figure 2-9.   Map of Scotland and adjacent islands, showing the Isle of Skye. Although the precise position of the locality is unknown to the authors, Middle Jurassic mammals have been recovered from coastal exposures of the Great Estuarine Series.

Order Docodonta
  Docodontidae
    new docodontid (represented by numerous teeth)
Order Symmetrodonta
  symmetrodont lower molar (similar to *Kuehneotherium* and Middle Jurassic amphilestids)
Order Eupantotheria
  Dryolestidae
    two dryolestid lower molars
  (?) Peramuridae
    Palaeoxonodon ooliticus (5 molars)
    second species, larger than *P. ooliticus* (upper molar)

The marlstone bands of the Ostracod Limestones of the Great Estuarine Series on the Isle of Skye of Scotland (Fig. 2-9) are of the mid to upper Bathonian Stage and are approximately contemporaneous with the Stonesfield Slate. Probably these deposits were formed in large shallow lagoons not directly open to the sea. Waldman and Savage (1972) described a new docodont, *Borealestes serendipitus,* on the basis of premolar and molar teeth preserved in two mandibles. Subsequently, two partial mammalian skeletons, one certainly referable to *Borealestes,* have been discovered and are now being studied by R. J. G. Savage (written comm. to Clemens, 1977).

Argentina

Footprints described in 1961 as mammalian and named *Ameghinichnus patagonicus* by Casamiquela (see also 1964, 1975b) have been found in the Estancia Laguna Manatiales, south of the Rio Deseado, roughly 140 km southeast of Jaramillo, Santa Cruz, in Patagonia (Fig. 2-8). The age of the deposits was initially described as "Matildense" or "Complejo Porfirico," supposedly "late-middle" or "early-late Jurassic." Subsequent stratigraphic studies suggest a Middle or Late Jurassic, Callovian or Oxfordian age (Casamiquela, 1975b). No skeletal materials are associated with the tracks, and the identification and name are based solely on the footprints. The tracks are interpreted as those of a jumping mammal that Casamiquela (*ibid.*) suggested might be representative of the therian stock ancestral to marsupials and possibly eutherians.

LATE JURASSIC

A much better record is fortunately available from deposits of Late Jurassic age, and so far mammals have been documented from Europe, Africa, and North America. The future looks promising for continued investigation in a number of places.

Portugal

A coal pit at Guimarota just south of Leiria in west-central Portugal (Fig. 2-10) has yielded fossil mammals from deposits dated as lower Kimmeridgian on the basis of ostracodes and charophytes. The mammalian specimens include roughly 1,000 isolated teeth plus miscellaneous jaw and skull fragments that have been recovered by quarrying and screen-washing. A nearly complete pantothere skeleton was discovered in 1976 (see Henkel and Krebs, 1977). Several reasonably complete multituberculate skulls were recently described by Hahn (1977), and a complete docodont skull is being described by Georg Krusat (written comm. to Lillegraven, 1977). The coal-swamp fauna has been discussed by Kühne (1961, 1968b, 1969) and Hahn (1969, 1971, 1977). The assemblage suggests an age somewhat older than those from Purbeck or the Morrison Formation (both discussed below) and is peculiar in that symmetrodonts and triconodonts, major groups common in most other later Jurassic fossil suites, are so far lacking. The taxa described from Guimarota to date include the following listing.

Order Multituberculata
  Paulchoffatiidae
    Paulchoffatia delgadoi
    Pseudobolodon oreas
    Kuehneodon dietrichi
    K. simpsoni
    K. dryas
    K. sp.
    Henkelodon naias
    H. ?guimarotensis
  Family indeterminate (probably Paulchoffatiidae, G. Hahn, written comm. to Clemens, 1977)
    Guimarotodon leiriensis
Order Docodonta
  Docodontidae
    Haldanodon exspectatus
Order Eupantotheria
  Peramuridae
    cf. *Peramus* sp.
  Eupantotheria *incertae sedis*
    Butlerigale sp.
    Guimarota freyi
    Simpsonodon splendens

The deposits are still workable, thus the documented diversity will probably increase in the future.

The Guimarota fauna is especially interesting in that it has the earliest known (non-haramiyid) multituberculates. Although probably only one family is represented, diversity at the generic level is considerable. All are highly specialized, however, and show no ancestral relationships with younger multituberculate groups (*fide* Hahn, 1977). The names *Haldanodon, Simpsonodon, Butlerigale,* and *Guimarota* were used for the first time in Kühne's 1968b paper, and teeth were figured, but only the dentition of *Haldanodon* has been more fully described (see Krusat, 1974, and Kühne and Krusat, 1972). Krusat's study was in the form of a doctoral dissertation, and formal publication of the work on *Haldanodon* (in Portuguese translation) is in process. Krusat is also studying the skull of that genus. It is not clear to which of the families mentioned by Kühne in the 1968b paper (Paurodontidae, Dryolestidae, and Peramuridae) he meant the eupantothere taxa to be assigned. Specimens of definite dryolestids from Guimarota were discussed (without naming them) by Krebs (1971).

Two other Late Jurassic Portuguese localities are known just to the west and southwest of Lourinhã, one at Porto Pinheiro and the other at Porto das Barcas (Fig. 2-10). Information is scanty on these sites (see Krusat, 1969, and Kühne, 1968a). Both seem to be slightly younger (upper Kimmeridgian stage on the basis of ostracodes) than the Guimarota fauna but with considerably less extensive faunal lists. Porto Pinheiro was sampled by the use of a technique of underwater screening (see Kühne, 1968a) and has yielded triconodonts, multituberculates, symmetrodonts, and eupantotheres. The fauna is most similar to that from the Purbeck, described below. Only two teeth are mentioned from Porto das Barcas.

England

The sea-cliffs at Durlston (Durdlestone) Bay near Swanage, Isle of Purbeck, in Dorset (Fig. 2-3) have produced a mammalian assemblage of great interest from the point of view of its diversity and similarity with faunas from distant parts of the

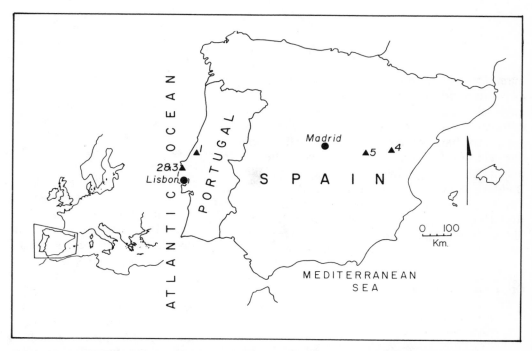

Figure 2-10.   Map of Portugal and Spain, showing positions (triangles) of Late Jurassic and Early Cretaceous mammal localities: *1*, Late Jurassic coal pit at Guimarota near Leiria; *2* and *3*, Late Jurassic localities at Porto Pinheiro and Porto das Barcas; *4*, Early Cretaceous locality near Galve; and *5*, Early Cretaceous locality near Uña.

world. The local geological section at Durlston Bay is given in part below (see Simpson, 1928a, and Arkell, 1933):

	Chief Beef Beds	
	Corbula Beds	
	Upper Building Stone (= Intermarine and Scallop Beds)	
Middle Purbeck Beds		
	Cinder Bed	Durlston Beds

	Lower Building Stone (= Cherty and Marly Freshwater beds. Latter include the Mammal Bed.)	Lulworth Beds
---		
Lower Purbeck Beds	Marls with gypsum, insect beds, and cockle beds *Cypris* Freestone Broken Beds Caps and Dirt Beds	

In 1854 the Rev. P. B. Brodie and a Mr. Wilcox sent a collection of fossils from this locality, including mammalian jaws, to Richard Owen (see Owen, 1871) at the British Museum. Another large collection was made over a period of years and sent to the same destination by S. H. Beckles, and a few other specimens have been found since. All mammals recovered to date are from the Lulworth Beds with only two specimens having come from the Lower Building Stone; all others are from the Mammal Bed. The known fauna from Durlston Bay includes the following taxa (from scattered sources, but mainly Simpson, 1928a; Clemens, 1963c; and Hahn, 1969, 1977):

Order Triconondonta
  Triconodontidae
    Triconodon mordax
    Trioracodon ferox
    T. oweni
    T. major
Order Docodonta
  Docodontidae
    Peraiocynodon inexpectatus (possibly referable to *Docodon*)

Order Multituberculata
  Paulchoffatiidae
    Plioprion minor
    Bolodon crassidens
    B. osborni
    ?*B. elongatus*
  Plagiaulacidae
    Plagiaulax becklesii
    ?*Ctenacodon falconeri*
Order Symmetrodonta
  Spalacotheriidae
    Spalacotherium tricuspidens
    Peralestes longirostris (almost certainly a synonym of *Spalacotherium tricuspidens)*
Order Eupantotheria
  Peramuridae
    Peramus tenuirostris
  Dryolestidae
    Amblotherium nanum
    A. pusillum
    Kurtodon pusillus
    Peraspalax talpoides
    Phascolestes mustelula

The multituberculate fauna is probably taxonomically even more diverse than shown here because, according to Hahn (1971), the species ?*Ctenacodon falconeri* and ?*Bolodon elongatus* are distinct species that may belong in new, as yet unnamed, genera. Fragmentary cranial material, in addition to the dentition, is known for the triconodonts *Trioracodon* and *Triconodon* from Durlston Bay (see Simpson, 1928a, and Kermack, 1963).

Attempts to correlate the Lulworth Beds with the European chronologies (Fig. 2-12) based on marine invertebrates are fraught with difficulties. Toward the close of the Jurassic, enlargement of terrestrial areas divided the European seas into a northern Boreal realm and a southern Tethyan realm. The Purbeck Beds were deposited in a basin within the intervening terrestrial area. Recent work by Casey (1963, 1973) strongly suggests that the "Cinder Bed" was formed during the initial Ryazanian transgression that, coming from the north, flooded parts of eastern England. The Cinder Bed is the base of the Durlston Beds. The Lulworth Beds, source of the mammalian fossils, lie beneath the Cinder Bed and are thought to be a correlative of the Volgian. In the Boreal realm, the Volgian-Ryazanian boundary is used as the Jurassic-Cretaceous boundary. In the Tethyan realm, however, the Tithonian-Berriasian boundary is taken as the division between the Jurassic and Cretaceous. There is a distinct possibility (Casey, 1973; Dodson and others, 1964) that this latter boundary is slightly older than the Volgian-Ryazanian and, by Tethyan standards, deposition of the Lulworth Beds was a Berriasian (*i.e.,* Early Cretaceous) event. Thus although by Boreal standard the Purbeck mammals are of Late Jurassic age, the possibility exists that they are of the Early Cretaceous by Tethyan standards. Because the issue is still moot we will arbitrarily continue to use the Late Jurassic age assignment.

Current studies of the Purbeck Beds, particularly the lower unit (West, 1975), suggest they were formed in and about an extensive, hypersaline gulf rimmed with broad tidal flats. Geological and paleontological data indicate the area probably was semiarid and near or within the warm temperate climatic zone. Forests grew along the margins of the gulf. The Mammal Bed appears to be a deposit formed in a water-logged marsh or swamp dotted with freshwater pools.

In addition to calling this research on the Purbeck Beds of Dorset to our attention, I. M. West pointed out the possibility that mammalian remains had been discovered in Purbeck Beds in Wiltshire, which might be contemporaneous with or older than the oldest Purbeck Beds in Dorset (Barker and others, 1975). On June 5, 1876, Charles Moore directed a Geologists' Association excursion to what is now the Town Gardens Quarry in Swindon. In the circular prepared for the excursion Moore noted the discovery of "*Plagiaulax, Spalacotherium,* and other mammals" in the Purbeck Beds exposed in the quarry. During the tour of the quarry he added "*Paralestes* [*sic*]" to the faunal list (Hudleston, 1876). Many years later a search for these fossils in the museums in Bath and Bristol proved fruitless (Sylvester-Bradley, 1940), but the information at hand indicates that the potential for discovery of mammalian fossils in "dirt beds" of the Swindon facies of the Purbeck Beds is great. (The Swindon locality, which is not plotted on Fig. 2-3, is situated approximately 40 km southwest of Oxford.)

Tanzania

An African Jurassic mammal from Tendaguru in southeastern Tanzania was discovered before World War I about 60 km northwest of Lindi (Fig. 2-4). The sediments have been dated as late Kimmeridgian or early "Tithonian" on the basis of ammonites, and thus would be more or less time-correlative with the Durlston Bay section. The only mammalian specimen known is a toothless (except for the roots) eupantothere mandible tentatively referred to the Peramuridae and named *Brancatherulum tendagurense* (see Dietrich, 1927, and Simpson, 1928b). No Jurassic mammals have since been found in Africa, and no Cretaceous mammals have ever been found there. The beds have been worked mainly for dinosaur remains, and the area is most noted for the huge and magnificently preserved *Brachiosaurus* skeletons. Other land vertebrates are common as well, and further detailed prospecting, washing, and quarrying will undoubtedly result in additional mammalian specimens.

Rocky Mountains of North America

Late Jurassic mammals from North America are known only from the Morrison Formation of Colorado and Wyoming. The Morrison is a geographically widespread rock unit that crops out from Montana southward to New Mexico and western Oklahoma along the eastern Rockies. It is mainly continental, but was deposited during, and a short time after, the regression of the epicontinental Late Jurassic "Sundance Sea" to the east. The thickness of the rock unit varies from 0 to about 300 m, but generally is 60 to 120 m thick. Despite the enormous mass and geographic extent of the Morrison Formation, mammals are recorded from only five almost pinpoint areas. One is at Garden Park in Fremont County, Colorado, north of Canon City (Fig. 2-11) near the Dilly Ranch. These mammalian specimens were found in Marsh's dinosaur quarry (see Simpson, 1929) and include only two species to date:

Order Docodonta
  Docodontidae
    Docodon sp.
Order Eupantotheria
  Dryolestidae
    Kepolestes coloradensis

The age of the deposits is probably close to those from Wyoming discussed below.

A second Colorado locality was discovered in the summer of 1976 by George L. Callison of California State University, Long Beach, northwest of Grand Junction in Mesa County (Fig. 2-11). The site is in the Salt Wash Member of the Morrison Formation in the "Fruita Bowl" at a lower stratigraphic level than either the Garden Park or the Como Bluff (discussed below) localities. Materials recovered to date include three mammalian mandible fragments, one of which is tooth-bearing (probably a triconodont). The locality seems to hold considerable promise for future work, as the mammal specimens were found on the surface in association with partially articulated skeletons of small reptiles.

A third Colorado locality, also in Mesa County, is located about 55 km west of Delta at the so-called "Dry Mesa Quarry" (not plotted on maps in this chapter). The only mammalian record to date is the distal half of a humerus, found in 1977 associated with the world's largest known sauropod dinosaur. The quarry is being worked by James A. Jensen of Brigham Young University. He reports that, in addition to dinosaurian remains, the quarry is also yielding lungfishes, turtles, crocodilians, pterosaurs, and birds. The assemblage is taxonomically very dif-

ferent from other known Morrison sites in surrounding areas of Colorado and Utah and apparently represents a hitherto unsampled paleoenvironmental setting; the probability of discovery there of new kinds of mammals thus seems high.

The Como Bluff fauna from the Morrison Formation in Albany County, southeastern Wyoming (Fig. 2-11), contrasts markedly with the depauperate nature of the Garden Park fauna. Como Bluff is world-famous for its spectacular dinosaur assemblage (about 20 genera), specimens of which were first discovered in 1877; a mammal was found in 1879. Land animals recovered from the area include a pterosaur, salamanders, frogs, turtles, crocodilians, fish, fresh-water invertebrates, and, of course, mammals. The mammals include at least 23 genera and 40 named species (see Simpson, 1929,

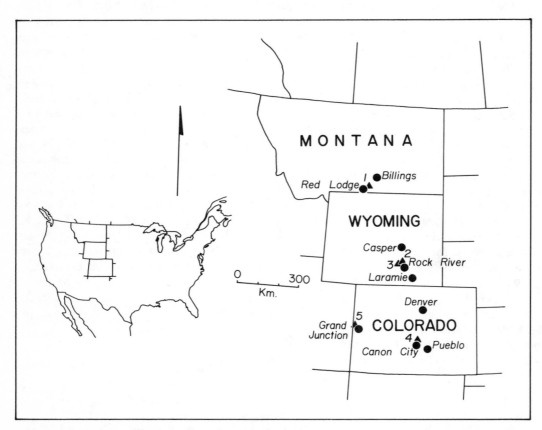

Figure 2-11.   Map of Montana, Wyoming, and Colorado, showing positions (triangles) of Late Jurassic, Early Cretaceous, and some Late Cretaceous mammal localities: *1*, Early Cretaceous Cloverly Formation near Bridger; *2*, Late Jurassic Morrison Formation at Como Bluff and Bone Cabin Draw; *3*, early Late Cretaceous Frontier Formation near Como Bluff; *4*, Late Jurassic Morrison Formation at Garden Park; and *5*, Late Jurassic Morrison Formation near Grand Junction (also see Figs. 2-18 and 2-19).

1937), making it taxonomically the most diverse Mesozoic mammal assemblage yet known from the entire world. Most mammalian specimens were recovered from "Quarry 9," but seven other localities nearby have yielded mammalian specimens. The major collecting efforts were made for O. C. Marsh of Yale University in the late 1800s (see Simpson, 1948, and Ostrom and McIntosh, 1966, for histories of collecting at Como Bluff). Less collecting has been done at Wyoming Morrison exposures during the twentieth century, but undescribed mammalian specimens have been recovered by collaborating parties from Yale University and The American Museum of Natural History led respectively by Charles R. Schaff and Thomas H. Rich at Como Bluff and at the nearby Bone Cabin Draw. Also, Kenneth Carpenter of The University of Colorado in 1976 discovered a fragmentary mammalian tooth (two cusps only) of uncertain affinities from a mudball conglomerate facies of the Morrison Formation in Carbon County on the southern flanks of the Freezout Hills, roughly 25 km northwest of the Como Bluff area. This last site is not plotted on the maps herein.

The recorded mammalian fauna from Quarry 9 is as follows:

Order Triconodonta
  Amphilestidae
    Phascolodon gidleyi
    Aploconodon comoensis
  Triconodontidae
    Trioracodon bisulcus
    Priacodon ferox
    P. robustus
    P. lulli
    P. grandaevus
Order Docodonta
  Docodontidae
    Docodon victor
    D. striatus
    D. crassus
    D. affinus
    D. superus
Order Multituberculata
  Plagiaulacidae
    Ctenacodon serratus
    C. scindens
    C. laticeps
    Psalodon potens
    P. fortis
    ?P. marshi

Order Symmetrodonta
  Amphidontidae
    Amphidon superstes
  Spalacotheriidae?
    Eurylambda aequicrurius
    Tinodon bellus
    T. lepidus
Order Eupantotheria
  Paurodontidae
    Paurodon valens
    Archaeotrigon brevimaxillus
    A. distagmus
    Tathiodon agilis
    Araeodon intermissus
  Dryolestidae
    Dryolestes priscus
    Laolestes eminens
    L. grandis
    Amblotherium gracilis
    A. debilis
    Herpetairus arcuatus
    ?H. humilus
    Melanodon oweni
    M. goodrichi
    Euthlastus cordiformis
    Miccylotyrans minimus
    Malthacolestes osborni
    Pelicopsis dubius

The taxonomic listing is somewhat inflated as some of the species are named on the basis of different parts (*i.e.,* upper dentition *vs.* lowers, anterior parts of tooth-rows *vs.* posterior parts, etc.) that cannot as yet be associated. Nevertheless, the real diversity is great, especially among the therian mammals; the eupantotheres had really come into their own as a major group by the Late Jurassic. *Ctenacodon, Trioracodon, Amblotherium,* and probably *Docodon* (under the guise of *Peraiocynodon*) occur both at Como Bluff and in the Lulworth Beds (part of the Purbeck Beds) at Durleston Bay, England. The generally accepted correlations suggesting contemporaneity of these local faunas were based on faunal similarity, but might be modified when more precise methods of correlation can be utilized.

Colbert (1973) made the point that the dinosaur similarity between the Purbeck, Tendaguru, and Morrison localities is great, suggesting the possibility that major intercontinental dispersal of land vertebrates occurred between North America, Europe, and Africa during the Late Jurassic. Not only were the Morrison and Purbeck formations of nearly the same age, but North America and Europe were probably contiguous in the Late Jurassic. Other evidence suggests that they did not separate until toward the end of the early Eocene. Even with the continents in contact, however, the present sites of Como Bluff and the Isle of Purbeck (now actually a peninsula) would have been distant from each other (see Fig. 14-3), and this could account for some observed faunal differences.

EARLY CRETACEOUS

Mammalian fossils of Early Cretaceous age are from scattered localities in Europe, Asia, and North America. In almost all cases the specimens are extremely rare and hard-won from the sediments.

England

Important Early Cretaceous localities are found in southeastern-most England. The generalized stratigraphic section seen in the area is presented in Figure 2-12.

The Early Cretaceous section in the Wealden district of southeastern England begins with the Durlston beds, the upper part of the Purbeck Beds. These strata pass into the Hastings Beds that are overlain by the Weald Clay. The primarily non-marine strata of the Hastings Beds and Weald Clay are thought to have been deposited in a subsiding graben-basin rimmed by horsts. The basin spasmodically opened northwestward to the sea. According to Allen (1975, p. 389), "The 'normal' environment was a variable-salinity coastal mudplain with lagoons and sandy water-courses." Three mammal-bearing localities have been described (see Clemens, 1963b, and Clemens and Lees, 1971) and a fourth was recently discovered. The most prolific is the "Cliff End bone bed," a unit of the Wadhurst Clay exposed in the sea cliffs northeast of Hastings (Fig. 2-3). On the basis of ostracode faunas it, and the nearby Tighe Farm locality (Fig. 2-3), are of the Valanginian stage (E. R. Shephard-Thorn, *in* Clemens and Lees, 1971). A third locality at Paddockhurst Park (Fig. 2-3) is stratigraphically higher and is of the Valanginian or Hauterivian stage. The

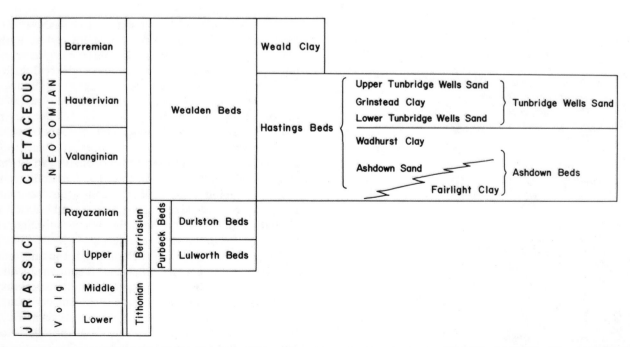

Figure 2-12.   Late Jurassic-Early Cretaceous stratigraphic relationships in the Wealden District of southeastern England. The Grinstead Clay is not present throughout all parts of the district. The Ashdown Sand and Fairlight Clay rock units are at least in part lateral facies equivalents. Combined from Casey (1971), Gallois (1965), and Anderson and Hughes (1964).

fourth locality includes a few teeth from Wealden beds on the Isle of Wight (Fig. 2-3) currently under study by P. M. Butler and R. L. E. Ford. The Cliff End mammalian fauna recorded to date is as follows:

Order Multituberculata
Plagiaulacidae
Loxaulax valdensis
Order Symmetrodonta
Spalacotheriidae
Spalacotherium tricuspidens
Order Eupantotheria
Dryolestidae
Melanodon hodsoni
Therian, order *incertae sedis*
Aegialodontidae
Aegialodon dawsoni

According to Clemens and Lees (1971) and Hahn (1971), multituberculates in addition to *Loxaulax valdensis* are probably present in the fauna. Note that *Spalacotherium tricuspidens* is a species also recorded from the Purbeckian Durlston Bay fauna.

Aegialodon dawsoni (see Kermack and others, 1965) is a very important mammal despite the fact that it is represented by only a damaged and worn isolated lower molar. It is the earliest known therian mammal tooth having a complete three-cusped trigonid and basined heel, comprising a fully tribosphenic design. Such a structure is required in an immediate ancestor for all later marsupial and placental mammals. As will be pointed out in more detail in subsequent chapters, *Aegialodon* may have been close to the ancestry of modern therian mammals.

A second locality in southeastern England is found in the "Telham pebble bed" in the lower part of the Wadhurst Clay cropping out in an abandoned quarry on Tighe Farm near Wittersham on the Isle of Oxney in Kent (Fig. 2-3). Only a few teeth have been recovered, including (Clemens and Lees, 1971):

Order Eupantotheria
Dryolestidae
Melanodon hodsoni

Another mammal-bearing locality for which published documentation is available is the so-called "Paddockhurst Park clay pit" southwest of East Grinstead in north-central Sussex (Fig. 2-3). The mammals come from a lens of grey, shell-rich limestone in the Grinstead Clay. The Paddockhurst Park locality is considerably younger than the other

two Wealden levels and, unfortunately, the fossiliferous lens now seems to have been exhausted. The fauna includes only the following (Clemens and Lees, 1971):

Order ?Multituberculata (one incisor)
Order Symmetrodonta
Spalacotheriidae
Spalacotherium taylori (described as new by Clemens and Lees in 1971, revising Clemens' 1963b identification of an isolated tooth as "cf. *S. tricuspidens*")

In view of the immediate succession of the Wealden localities, it is not surprising that genera persisting from the latest Jurassic are found in all three assemblages. These include *Spalacotherium*, which occurs in the Purbeck fauna, and *Melanodon*, which occurs in the Morrison fauna. The species, however, are different. Although the material is scanty, these faunas seem to have the same taxonomic composition as those of both North America and Europe in the Late Jurassic. *Aegialodon*, known only from a single lower molar, is slightly more advanced than its Jurassic relative, *Peramus*.

Spain

Sediments cropping out near Galve in the Province of Teruel, east-central Spain (Fig. 2-10), have yielded a variety of vertebrate fossils including the remains of fishes, crocodilians, dinosaurs (*Megalosaurus*), and mammals. The fossils appear to have accumulated in a coastal swamp. This deposit has been thought to be of Barremian age, although the possibility that deposition continued into the Aptian cannot be excluded.

The first mammalian fossil from Galve to be described is an enigmatic tooth that Crusafont-Pairó and Adrover (1965; also see 1966) identified as part of the dentition of a pantothere and designated as the type of *Parendotherium herreroi*. *Parendotherium* is certainly a mammal, but more precise identification has been debated. F. S. Szalay, in a personal communication to M. C. McKenna (see McKenna, 1969, p. 225, footnote 3), suggested that the type specimen is probably an upper incisor of a multituberculate. This was contested by Crusafont and Gibert (1976), who maintain that the fossil is a premolar of a dryolestid eupantothere.

Kühne (1966) reported the recovery of a few teeth of multituberculates and pantotheres from the

Galve area. Subsequently, an anonymous news item (Anon., 1975) announced the completion of a study of the multituberculates by Crusafont and Gibert. This was published the following year. Their collections were obtained through washing and screening approximately 15 tons of sediments. The multituberculates, known from isolated teeth, include representatives of undesignated species of *Plagiaulax, Paulchoffatia, Kuehneodon,* and *Bolodon.* This is an interesting mixture of taxa. Prior to these discoveries, *Paulchoffatia* and *Kuehneodon* were known only from the Kimmeridgian, Guimarota local fauna of Portugal, and *Bolodon* and *Plagiaulax* were limited to the Purbeck local fauna from the Volgian, Lulworth Beds of England.

Mammalian fossils have also been found southwest of Galve at Uña (Fig. 2-10) in the Province of Cuenca, central Spain, east-southeast of Madrid (see Kühne and Crusafont-Pairó, 1968). The sediments have been dated as Early Cretaceous, but the age is not precise and it could be as young as the Albian Stage (late Early Cretaceous). The majority of the fauna is now being studied by Siegfried Henkel and Bernard Krebs. The sample of the fauna contains isolated teeth of multituberculates and eupantotheres. Two complete lower jaws of a dryolestid eupantothere have been formally described by Henkel and Krebs (1969) as *Crusafontia cuencana.* Details of dental wear in this species were discussed by Krebs (1971).

Asia

Asiatic records of Early Cretaceous mammalian life are exceptionally tantalizing, but unfortunately very little really usable information is yet available. There are major problems associated with interpreting each of the described finds.

A coal-bearing bed in the "Hsinchiu" or Hsinch'iuyao (Xinqiuyao) coal mine part of the "Husin" or Fuhsin (Fuxin) coal field, about 10 km northeast of the city of Fuhsin, Liaoning Province, northeast China (Fig. 2-5), was originally described by Shikama (1947) as being of Jurassic age. However, on the basis of vertebrate assemblages, and especially the mammalian specimen, the sediments are now thought to be of Early Cretaceous age (see Chow, 1953), perhaps as young as Aptian or Albian stages (late Early Cretaceous; see Patterson, 1956).

An antiquity even this great has been challenged by Fox (1972b). Only one species of mammal has been recovered and was recognized by Shikama (1947) as:

?Eutheria, *incertae sedis*
Endotherium niinomii

Unfortunately, the illustrations of the teeth are less than adequate line drawings, the descriptions are not diagnostic, and the specimens are now lost. Nevertheless, if the illustrations are even vaguely accurate, they depict lower teeth of remarkably advanced morphology that strongly suggest affinities with eutherian (placental) mammals. Thus *Endotherium* remains only as an ambiguous example of a possible early eutherian.

Another mammalian species has been described by Yabe and Shikama (1938) from the "Sakasiyo" or Chatzuyao (Zhaziyao) coal mine, 3.6 km east of the railroad station known as "Gabôten" or Wafangtien (Wafangdian), now known as Fuhsien (Fuxian) city, Liaoning Province (Fig. 2-5), as:

Order Symmetrodonta
  Amphidontidae
    Manchurodon simplicidens

The rock unit is referred to as the "Husin Series" and, like *Endotherium* with which it is probably a time correlative, was originally thought to be of Jurassic age on the basis of plant fossils. The holotype of *Manchurodon simplicidens* is an unnumbered mandible with nearly complete teeth and a fragmentary scapula, possibly of the same individual. The fate of the specimens is unknown to us.

More recent efforts by members of the Soviet-Mongolian Expeditions, as well as by Mongolian paleontologists working alone, have centered on Early Cretaceous deposits in the Mongolian Gobi Desert near the well of Khovboor in the Ubur-Khangai area (Fig. 2-13) on the right bank of a dry river, the Arguyin-gol (see Kalandadze and Reshetov, 1971b). The name Khovboor refers to the matted clump of wool that hangs on the sides of sheep during molting. The work has allowed the compilation of the following faunal list (from Beliajeva and others, 1974, and Dashzeveg, 1975). The locality is given as ". . . Guchin Us somon (county) in the province (aymak) of Arvaykher . . ." by Dashzeveg (1975). According to Shuvalov (1974) the site is about 15 km to the southeast of the county seat of Guchin Us in the eastern part of the extensive Guchin depression.

Order Multituberculata
  Plagiaulacidae
    new genus and species
Order Triconodonta
  Triconodontidae
    "Gobiconodon borissiaki" (referred to in the English abstract by Beliajeva and others, 1974, p. 364, as *Neoconodon borissiaki* Trofimov)
    (for reference to subsequent work see editors' note to Table 4-1)
Order Symmetrodonta
  Amphidontidae
    "Gobiodon infinitus" (referred to in the English abstract by Beliajeva and others, 1974, p. 364, as *Gobion infinitus* Trofimov; according to a personal communication from B. A. Trofimov to M. C. McKenna and Z. Kielan-Jaworowska, he now thinks that the symmetrodont identification may be incorrect)
  Symmetrodonta indet. (personal communication to Z. Kielan-Jaworowska from D. Dashzeveg, 1977)
Order Eupantotheria
  ?Peramuridae
    new genus and species (personal communication to Z. Kielan-Jaworowska from D. Dashzeveg, 1977)
Infraclass Eutheria
  Tenrecidae
    "Prokennalestes kozlovi"
  Zalambdalestidae
    "Prozalambdalestes simpsoni"

Theria of metatherian-eutherian grade
  Aegialodontidae
    Kielantherium gobiensis

Unfortunately, with the exception of *Kielantherium gobiensis* described by Dashzeveg, appearance of the above names was unaccompanied by descriptions or illustrations of the material and they are thus *nomina nuda* (enclosed by quotation marks) and technically invalid. Precious little can be said about most of the fossils at the present time. Details useful in narrowing the likely age of the beds are not given by Beliajeva and others (1974). Crompton and Kielan-Jaworowska (1977) tentatively agreed with Dashzeveg's interpretation of an ?Aptian Stage on the basis of information received from Russian geologists using data from dinosaurs and fossil turtles. Barsbold and others (1971) referred the Khovboor to the Aptian or Albian stages. In any case, although the Khovboor section seems to be significantly older than the Djadokhta and other Mongolian formations discussed below, its age is in considerable question. The Khovboor fauna includes some of the most primitive and perhaps earliest identified eutherians. It also includes the latest known triconodont in Asia. According to Kalandadze and Reshetov (1971a), more than 200 mammalian jaws plus extensive postcranial elements were recovered

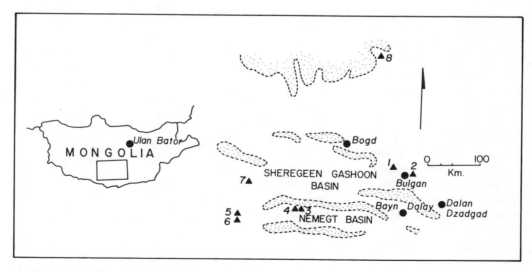

Figure 2-13. Map of southcentral Mongolia, showing positions (triangles) of Early and Late Cretaceous mammal localities: *1*, Late Cretaceous locality of Toogreeg; *2*, Late Cretaceous Djadokhta Formation at Bayn Dzak; *3*, Late Cretaceous Barun Goyot Formation at Khulsan; *4*, Late Cretaceous Barun Goyot Formation at Nemegt; *5* and *6*, localities from Late Cretaceous Barun Goyot Formation of Khermeen Tsav; *7*, Late Cretaceous or earliest Paleocene locality at Khaichin Ula; and *8*, Early Cretaceous locality at Khovboor.

from the screen-washing of about 70 metric tons of rock.

Fox (1976a) argued that Dashzeveg (1975) did not describe any diagnostic features of the solitary lower molar of *Kielantherium gobiensis* that are useful in distinguishing it from the only known tooth (also a lower molar) of *Aegialodon dawsoni* from the Wealden Cliff End fauna of England. Thus Fox synonymized *Kielantherium* with *Aegialodon* and only tentatively accepted the distinctness of the species on the basis of their temporal differences and considerable geographic separation. The Khovboor assemblage is probably significantly younger than the Cliff End fauna. Not only are the two localities geographically disparate, but they were probably isolated by seaways of considerable magnitude during the Early Cretaceous (see Chapter 14). The possibility that the very real similarities between the two known teeth is due to the retention of primitive features from an older common ancestor cannot yet be eliminated. We therefore consider Fox's synonymy to be premature and do not accept it in the formal classification used in this book.

Comments on the Systematics of Cretaceous Eutherians

Not too many years ago, when mammalian fossils of Early Cretaceous age were limited to a few isolated teeth from southeastern England, no difficulties arose in distinguishing Late Cretaceous eutherians from Jurassic pantotheres. This convenient and comfortable state of ignorance has been and continues to be eroded by discoveries of Early Cretaceous mammals documenting early grades in the evolution of the tribosphenic dentition and the diversification of eutherians and metatherians. When reasonably good specimens are available, especially associated parts of dentitions, there is no particular difficulty in sorting them into definable species and genera. However, these mammals all have quite primitive, relatively unspecialized tribosphenic dentitions. The materials in hand commonly do not have characters that can be used in later groups of mammals to distinguish families or even, in some cases, orders. Most of them have in fact been ascribed to particular families and orders, but often on dubious grounds, and taxonomic assignments by different students are sometimes in radical disagreement. In a few cases in this and other chapters where a clear choice cannot be made, we have removed taxa to an *incertae sedis* status but have not created nomina for new groupings.

North America

Recent finds from the Lower Cretaceous Cloverly Formation in the Pryor Mountain Field of Carbon and Bighorn counties, Montana (Fig. 2-11), and Bighorn County, Wyoming, promise to be very important for Mesozoic mammals. The Cloverly Formation directly overlies the Morrison and has yielded a rich dinosaurian fauna, but, until recently, no known mammals. In the 1970s, however, field parties from the Museum of Comparative Zoology led by F. A. Jenkins, Jr., and C. R. Schaff recovered triconodont jaw and skull parts, plus skulls and articulated skeletons of mammals within concretionary nodules (see Chapter 4). The materials are now under preparation and have not yet been described, but it is an understatement to say that the scientific potential of these finds is extraordinary.

More hard-won mammalian specimens have been collected by parties led by Bryan Patterson, formerly of the Chicago Field Museum of Natural History, and B. H. Slaughter, of Southern Methodist University, in north-central Texas from the Paluxy Formation (or more precisely, its lateral equivalent, the upper part of the Antlers Formation; see Langston, 1974, Table 1) of the Trinity Group, Commanchean Series. The Paluxy Formation is a terrestrial and brackish water clay and sand deposit overlying the marine Glen Rose Formation. Age of the Paluxy is based on invertebrate fossils in the Glen Rose Formation, thought to be equivalent with the lower to middle Albian Stage (latest Early Cretaceous). It is younger than the Cloverly Formation, and the mammals have been used by Russell (1975) to define the "Paluxian" land mammal age. Two important areas of localities are known, and mammals from both are commonly referred to as the "Trinity sands mammals." The first locality area is in Greenwood Canyon, a name given for a stream drainage on the land of Virgil Greenwood on Denton Creek, a short distance southwest of the town of Forestburg in Montague County (Fig. 2-7). The fauna was first described by Patterson (1951, 1956) and includes the following taxa:

Order Triconodonta
  Triconodontidae

Astroconodon denisoni
Order Multituberculata
  Plagiaulacidae (reference to this family has recently
    been questioned by Richard C. Fox and Bob H.
    Slaughter, personal communications)
    misc. isolated teeth
Order Symmetrodonta
  Spalacotheriidae
    Spalacotheroides bridwelli
Theria of metatherian-eutherian grade

The multituberculates are the most common elements of the fauna (representing at least two forms), but are as yet undescribed. The so-called "therians of metatherian-eutherian grade" have commonly been referred to in the literature as the "Forestburg therians." Their significance will be discussed in more detail in Chapter 10.

The second important Paluxy locality area is found about 32 km south of Greenwood Canyon on the farm of Lee Butler just northwest of Decatur in Wise County (Fig. 2-7). The mammals comprise the "Butler Farm" fauna. The fossils have been recovered from the bottom few centimeters of an 18-to-20 meters-wide channel fill. The discovery of and collecting at the sites were the accomplishments of B. H. Slaughter, to whom the greatest credit must be given for extraordinary persistence. From the best of his five sites in the area, only about 50 mammal teeth were recovered by screen-washing over 200 tons of rock! The Butler Farm sites represent a freshwater deposit, with fishes and crocodilians being common members of the fauna. The mammalian list from the Butler Farm is as follows (modified from Slaughter, 1971):

Order Triconodonta
  possible occurrence
Order Multituberculata
  undescribed
Theria of metatherian-eutherian grade
  Aegialodontidae
    Kermackia texana
  Pappotheriidae
    Pappotherium pattersoni
  Family uncertain
    Holoclemensia texana

Slaughter (1971) considered *Pappotherium* and *Holoclemensia* to be representatives of the Eutheria and Metatheria, respectively, but we use a different systematic approach that is described in detail in Chapter 10.

In addition to the above localities, the tricono-dont *Astroconodon,* but no other mammal, has been found in freshwater deposits at King's Creek (Montague County), Lewis (Wise County), and Paluxy (Hood County) by Slaughter (1969, further locality data not given).

As an aside, the Texas Cretaceous mammal localities were found in areas that were east of the epicontinental sea dividing North America into eastern and western parts; all other known Cretaceous localities on the continent are to the west of the shoreline of the ancient seaway (see Chapter 14).

LATE CRETACEOUS

Mesozoic mammals are best known from the Late Cretaceous, but only from Europe, South America, Asia, and North America; the record on the first two of these continents is extremely scanty. With a few minor exceptions, the record is restricted to about the last one-third of Late Cretaceous time. Thus major time gaps exist in presently available information concerning Late Cretaceous mammalian evolution.

Europe

The entire Late Cretaceous mammalian record from Europe available in the literature is a report on a single isolated lower molar described by Ledoux and others (1966). The specimen was collected in France at a locality called Champ-Garimond in the valley of Saint-Mamert, 1.3 km northwest of the village of Fons (Gard) in Languedoc (Fig. 2-14). According to a note by Berger (1974) associated with the Le Vigan sheet of the geological map of France, the age of the rocks is now considered to be late Senonian (Valdo-Rognacien).

The tooth has not been formally named, but it is commonly referred to in the literature as the "Champ-Garimond tooth." Affinities of the specimen are uncertain, but it is clearly from a therian and probably a eutherian (placental). Its general morphology suggests similarities with primitive condylarths, the large group of early Cenozoic mammals that ultimately gave rise to the various ungulate (hoofed mammal) groups. McKenna (1969) suggested that the tooth has all the features characteristic of a didelphodontine palaeoryctid insectivore. Relationships, however, cannot be proven with the existing evidence.

Although some collecting by use of screen-washing techniques has been done, further efforts in the area should be strongly encouraged. Large dinosaur eggs are also found at the locality.

Miguel Telles Antunes, in a written communication to Clemens (1977), announced the discovery of Late Cretaceous mammalian fossils in western Portugal. They come from deposits overlying Upper Campanian marine strata containing the ammonite *Hoplitoplacenticeras* that crop out in a belt from north of the city of Aveiro to south of the Mondego River. The associated fauna includes several kinds of invertebrates and various fishes, including *Lepisosteus*. A pelomedusid turtle, *Rosasia soutoi,* is common. Mosasaurs, lizards, a snake, crocodylians, at least two kinds of saurischian dinosaurs, and pterosaurs comprise other elements of the fauna. The locality is not plotted on maps herein.

South America

Mammals have been found by French collectors near Atumcolla in a 300 m² gullied exposure on the northeastern shore of Laguna Umayo in the Peruvian Andes (Fig. 2-15) at an elevation of about 3,900 m. The area is about 20 km northwest of the village of Puno near Lake Titicaca. The rocks are considered equivalent to the Maastrichtian Stage on the basis of charophytes. The fossil-bearing rock unit is referred to the Vilquechico Formation (see Portugal, 1974), but the type section for the formation is about 75 km from Laguna Umayo and the two sections are of quite different lithology. Thus the use of the same formational name in both areas may be questionable. The mammalian fauna is scanty, represented primarily by isolated teeth, tooth parts, and one fragmentary jaw. The material was identified by Grambast and others (1967), and Sigé (1968, 1971, 1972) as follows:

Order Marsupialia
  Didelphidae
    Alphadon austrinum
    didelphid *indet.*
  ?Pediomyidae
    ?pediomyid *indet.*
Infraclass Eutheria

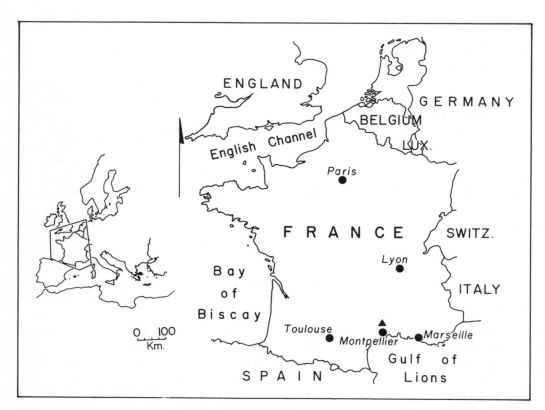

Figure 2-14.   Map of France, showing position (triangle) of Late Cretaceous mammal locality of "Champ-Garimond."

Order ?Condylarthra
    Perutherium altiplanense
Theria *indet.*

The fauna is especially interesting in that *Alphadon* is a genus of marsupial common in the Late Cretaceous of North America. The ?pediomyid record is based upon a single fragmentary lower molar and the query is certainly well deserved. The Pediomyidae are common in North American deposits of Late Cretaceous age and any future confirmation of the identity of the Peruvian animal is eagerly awaited. *Perutherium* is questionably identified as a condylarth, another group common in Holarctic deposits of the early Cenozoic. *Perutherium* is quite unlike anything otherwise known from the Late Cretaceous. Its lower molars are condylarth-like, but not at all close to those of *Protungulatum,* the most common condylarth in some latest Cretaceous local faunas of North America. *Perutherium* does resemble somewhat the Phenacodontidae of the North American and Euro-pean early Cenozoic and also the Didolodontidae of the South American early to middle Cenozoic. Condylarths and marsupials would certainly be expected in the Late Cretaceous or early Paleocene of South America in light of the great evolutionary radiation in or from those groups during the Cenozoic (see Patterson and Pascual, 1968). The interesting aspect of the Peruvian fauna is the apparent affinities with assemblages better known from North America. The fossils indicate that primitive marsupials (didelphines) were present and already somewhat differentiated; they suggest a faunal connection with North America. The marsupials could be used as evidence for almost any of the now numerous speculations about the early dispersal marsupials (see Lillegraven, 1974, and Keast, 1977) but do not particularly support any of the conflicting hypotheses. The presence of a primitive ungulate (*Perutherium*), perhaps closely related to the ancestors of some of the abundant later autochthonous South American ungulates, independently suggests faunal connections with Holarctica. The geographic or lineal origin of this

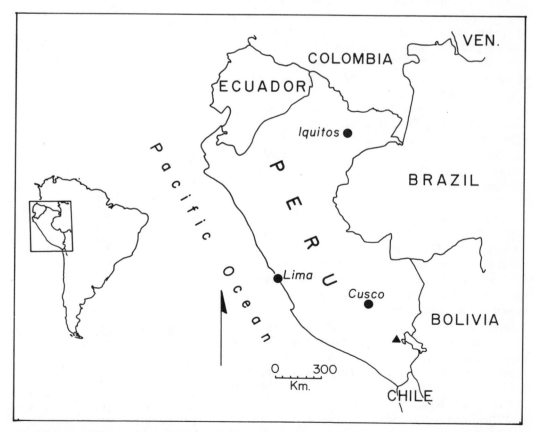

Figure 2-15. Map of Peru, showing position (triangle) of Late Cretaceous mammal locality near Laguna Umayo.

form, however, is completely unknown and is almost beyond reasonable conjecture at present. Further collecting at Laguna Umayo, and in South America in general, is greatly needed.

Asia

Spectacular mammalian finds have been made in rocks of Late Cretaceous age in the Mongolian Gobi Desert by American, Polish, and Russian workers, the latter two in conjunction with scholars of the Mongolian People's Republic. The original discoveries were made during a series of five Asiatic expeditions between 1921 and 1930 organized by personnel from The American Museum of Natural History, especially Roy Chapman Andrews and Walter Granger. Extremely useful information on the expeditions and on geographic place names can be found in the references by Andrews (1932), Gradziński and others (1969), and Gradziński and Jerzykiewicz (1972). The most famous early finds came from the Djadokhta Formation of Bayn Dzak (also spelled Bain-Dzak, meaning "rich in Dzak," referring to *Haloxylon,* a forage plant) in south-central Mongolia in the northern Gobi Desert (Fig. 2-13). The general area was also referred to as Shabarakh Usu, meaning "muddy water." The classic site is along a 10 km escarpment known as the Flaming Cliffs from which the first known Mesozoic mammalian skulls were collected. The early discoveries were described by Gregory and Simpson (especially 1926). Recently, Polish-Mongolian expeditions led by Zofia Kielan-Jaworowska have collected more and better preserved specimens at the same locality. The section is shown in Figure 2-16.

The upper conglomerate layers are known to contain dinosaur eggs. The red sands of the "Flaming Cliffs" have dinosaur eggs and mammalian remains as well. The concretionary zone was originally thought to be relatively unfossiliferous, but the Polish-Mongolian expeditions proved the presence of mammalian specimens. The basal layer has provided skeletons of *Protoceratops* and other dinosaurs, lizards, crocodiles, dinosaur eggs, and skulls of mammals. In total, about 50 mammalian skulls are now known from Bayn Dzak. The mammal fauna from Bayn Dzak is given below, as compiled from Kielan-Jaworowska (1969, 1970, 1971, 1974a, 1975a-d) and Gradziński and others (1977), with slight modifications for consistency with taxonomy used in this book:

Order Multituberculata
  ?Neoplagiaulacidae
    Gobibaatar parvus
  Taeniolabididae
    Catopsalis matthewi (previously known as *Djadochtatherium*)
    Kamptobaatar kuczynskii
  Eucosmodontidae
    Bulganbaatar nemegtbaataroides
    Kryptobaatar dashzevegi
    new genus and species
  Sloanbaataridae
    Sloanbaatar mirabilis
  new family
    new genus and species
Infraclass Eutheria
  ?Leptictoidea, *incertae sedis*
    Kennalestes gobiensis
  Zalambdalestidae
    Zalambdalestes lechei (including *Z. grangeri* and *Z.* sp. as junior synonyms, according to Szalay and McKenna, 1971)

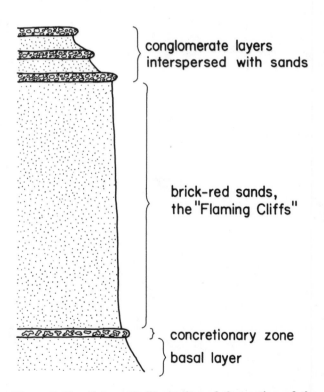

conglomerate layers interspersed with sands

brick-red sands, the "Flaming Cliffs"

concretionary zone

basal layer

Figure 2-16.   Schematic illustration of the section of the Djadokhta Formation at Bayn Dzak (after Lefeld, 1965; for more detail, see Lefeld, 1971). The thickness of the indicated exposed section is about 60 m.

Theria of metatherian-eutherian grade
　Deltatheridiidae
　　Deltatheridium pretrituberculare pretrituberculare
　　Deltatheroides cretacicus
　　Hyotheridium dobsoni

The multituberculate *Catopsalis matthewi* and the therians *Deltatheridium* and *Hyotheridium* have not been found in the area subsequent to the original American expeditions, but a whole suite of other genera have. Differences in the collections are apparently a reflection of a bias toward larger-sized specimens on the part of the Americans; the smaller specimens seem to have been overlooked. The fauna, which may be typical of the uplands in the Late Cretaceous of Asia, includes no clearly definable Metatheria. The Deltatheridiidae, however, according to Butler and Kielan-Jaworowska (1973), combine some metatherian and eutherian characters without being clearly referable to either. The rest of the fauna and of others known from the Late Cretaceous of Mongolia consist of relatively abundant and diverse multituberculates and some primitive proteutherian Eutheria.

As a miscellaneous point, the suffix "baatar" on so many of the multituberculate generic names means "a hero" and alludes to the name of the capital of the Mongolian People's Republic, Ulan Bator (Ulaan Baatar, "red hero," in Mongolian).

The age of the Bayn Dzak fauna was thought by Kielan-Jaworowska in 1970 to be equivalent to ?Coniacian or Santonian stages. Later (1975b), however, she stated that it is more probable that the Djadokhta Formation is closer to the ?Santonian Stage. Unfortunately, no fossiliferous marine interbeds or radiometric ages from any of the Mongolian localities are yet available. The dating is based mainly upon "stages of evolution" of the vertebrate assemblages. Such an approach in dating has been challenged by Fox (1972b, 1974) and he believes the Asiatic faunas to be considerably younger. Recently, Gradziński, Kielan-Jaworowska, and Maryańska (see Gradziński and others, 1977), on the basis of freshwater invertebrate, dinosaur, and mammalian faunas, suggested that the Djadokhta Formation represents the ?late Santonian and/or ?early Campanian Stage. Such an age for the Djadokhta Formation is here tentatively accepted.

A new fossil area (Fig. 2-13) was discovered in 1961 by Rinchen Barsbold and Demberelyin Dashzeveg (see Dashzeveg, 1963) of the Geological Institute of the Mongolian Academy of Sciences. The locality, called Toogreeg (= Toogreegeen Shireh), is about 30 km west-northwest of Bayn Dzak in poorly cemented white and grey-yellow sands (see Gradziński and Jerzykiewicz, 1972). The general region was prospected by Mongolian workers as well as by members of the Soviet-Mongolian Paleontological Expeditions (1969, 1970, and 1976) and briefly in 1971 by the Polish-Mongolian Palaeontological Expedition (Kramarenko, 1974; Kielan-Jaworowska and Barsbold, 1972; Gradziński and Jerzykiewicz, 1972; Gradziński and others, 1977; Kielan-Jaworowska and Dashzeveg, 1978). A list of mammals from Toogreeg has not yet been published. However, a skull of a new genus and species of eucosmodontid multituberculate (*Tugrigbaatar saichanensis*) discovered in 1974 by Dashzeveg has been described by Kielan-Jaworowska and him (1978). Also, members of the Soviet-Mongolian Paleontological Expedition of 1976 found more specimens of multituberculates and a eutherian (information from Rinchen Barsbold). These specimens are housed in Moscow at the Palaeontological Institute of the Academy of Sciences of the U.S.S.R. The occurrences of the dinosaurs *Protoceratops andrewsi* and *Velociraptor mongoliensis* (see Kielan-Jaworowska and Barsbold, 1972) at Toogreeg suggest contemporaneity of the strata with the localities at Bayn Dzak (Gradziński and others, 1977).

Another fossiliferous area was discovered in 1970 by the Polish-Mongolian Palaeontological Expedition. These new localities are in the Nemegt Basin at Khulsan and Nemegt (Fig. 2-13), about 220 km south-southwest of Bayn Dzak in the Barun Goyot Formation (also known as the "Lower Nemegt Beds"). The mammal-bearing sediments are younger than those of Bayn Dzak, and underlie dinosaur-bearing sediments of the Nemegt Formation (also known as the "Upper Nemegt Beds"). So far, the Nemegt Formation has not yielded mammalian fossils. The Barun Goyot Formation has been called ?Middle Campanian Stage by Kielan-Jaworowska (1974a) on the basis of ". . . degree of anatomical differentiation of multituberculates . . . ."

Fossil mammals are also known from two localities at Khermeen Tsav in beds of correlative age with the Barun Goyot Formation, roughly 100 km southwest of Nemegt (Fig. 2-13). About 100 mammalian skulls have been recovered within the combined Nemegt-Khulsan and Khermeen Tsav localities, some being associated with postcranial elements. Thus the

Barun Goyot fossils are of great importance in evaluating the relationships of Mesozoic mammals. The combined Nemegt-Khulsan-Khermeen Tsav mammalian faunal list is presented below (from Kielan-Jaworowska, 1974a, 1975a, 1975b, 1975d):

Order Multituberculata
  Taeniolabididae
    Catopsalis catopsaloides (previously assigned to *Djadochtatherium*)
    ?*Kamptobaatar* sp.
  Eucosmodontidae
    Nemegtbaatar gobiensis
  Chulsanbaataridae
    Chulsanbaatar vulgaris
Infraclass Eutheria
  Palaeoryctidae
    Asioryctes nemegetensis
  Zalambdalestidae
    Barunlestes butleri
Theria of metatherian-eutherian grade
  Deltatheridiidae
    Deltatheridium pretrituberculare tardum

The stratigraphy and sedimentology of the badlands of redbed arkoses making up the Barun Goyot Formation were well described by Gradziński and Jerzykiewicz (1974). They interpreted the Cretaceous local environment as having been desert-like, on a well-elevated continental platform with widespread aeolian dunes alternating with intermittent lakes and streams. We hasten to point out here that such an environment is very different, indeed, from that commonly represented in North American, Late Cretaceous mammal-bearing localities. In the latter, lowland, low-topography, swampy conditions dominated, with most localities not far from the western edge of the Cretaceous epicontinental seas. These dramatic environmental differences must be taken into account when one compares organisms found in Asiatic and North American Late Cretaceous localities.

The body (centrum) of an axis identified as mammalian on the basis of an open suture between the odontoid process and main body was found in association with dinosaurian remains in "Inner Mongolia" during the Sino-Swedish Scientific Expedition of 1929-30. Bohlin (1953) gives the locality as Tsondolein-Khuduk, about 250 km southwest of Ulan-tsonch (Fig. 2-5), in brick-red Late Cretaceous badlands at the eastern side of an extensive lava plateau. The area is in what is now northern Kansu

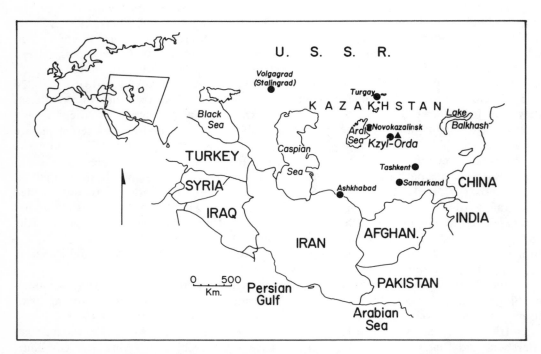

Figure 2-17.   Map of the Middle East, showing position (triangle) of the ?Late Cretaceous mammal locality near Baybolat Well, Dzalagash Rayon, Kzyl-Orda Oblast.

Province, China. Judging by the diversity of dinosaurian remains reported, the paleontological future for Mesozoic rocks of northern China seems excellent.

A fragmentary mammalian dentary with remains of three heavily damaged teeth plus additional alveoli was found in Kazakhstan, U.S.S.R. (Fig. 2-17), in rocks of the Beleutinskaya Svita (= Beleuty Svita, unfortunately a name preoccupied by a lithological unit of unknown age in the Pamir Mountains; see Gradziński and others, 1977, for discussion of usage of the stratigraphic term "svita"). Bazhanov (1972) described the locality as being on the rise (Shakh-Shakh) near Baybolat Well of the Karaysor Farm, Dzalagash Rayon, Kzyl-Orda Oblast at a level designated Cr_2^{kon} (Coniacian), although other interpretations suggest a Cenomanian or Santonian Stage assignment. Probably little weight can be placed upon present age designations, but the specimen represents the only Mesozoic mammal reported from within the Soviet Union. The discovery may indicate a promising area for further collecting, but this fossil is too poorly preserved to be useful. Scrutiny of Figure 1 of Bazhanov (1972) suggests that the anteroposterior orientation of the specimen may have been misinterpreted; the teeth labelled P_3 and P_4 may actually be the last and penultimate molars, respectively. The classification of the specimen according to Bazhanov is as follows:

Theria
"Infraclassis, Ordo [et] Familia incertae sedis"
Beleutinus orlovi

One last Asiatic locality appears in the literature for the Late Cretaceous. This is at Khaichin Ula in the Bugeen Tsav region of the Trans-Altaian Gobi Desert of Mongolia (Fig. 2-13). The area is about 100 km north of Nemegt in the western extreme of the Sheregeen Gashoon Basin. The only known specimen is a partial multituberculate skull with lower jaws found by members of the Soviet-Mongolian Geological Expedition of 1968. The skull (the lower jaws at that time having been misplaced) was described as *Buginbaatar transaltaiensis* (?Cimolomyidae) by Kielan-Jaworowska and Sochava (1969), who then considered the deposits to be of the Maastrichtian (latest Cretaceous) Stage. Subsequently, however, Kielan-Jaworowska (1974a) suggested that the age of the rocks may be either Paleocene or Maastrichtian, with the specimen referable to the Eucosmodontidae. The previously misplaced lower jaws for the

specimen were later found in the collections at the Palaeontological Institute in Moscow and were described by Trofimov (1975), who concurred with the assignment to the Eucosmodontidae. Thus there appears to be no record of the Cimolomyidae from Asiatic rocks.

North America

As was mentioned in the introduction to the section on the Late Cretaceous, we know virtually nothing of mammalian life during the first two-thirds of the Late Cretaceous. Only two exceptions are known, and both are from North America. The first is a record of three mammalian bones (astragalus, distal tibia, and phalanx) found on the surface of an anthill on the Wall Creek Member of the Frontier Formation near Como Bluff in Albany County, Wyoming (Fig. 2-11). The three specimens have not been described, but are in the vertebrate fossil collection of The Geological Museum of The University of Wyoming. The Frontier Formation is equivalent to the Cenomanian or Turonian (early Late Cretaceous) Stage. The second exception is from the Arlington Sandstone Member of the Woodbine Formation of Tarrant County, north-central Texas (Fig. 2-7). Records of "Theria, Multituberculata (eucosmodontid)" are presented in a faunal list by McNulty and Slaughter (1968), but are not discussed further. No published description of the material exists beyond the information that the eucosmodontid record is based on an incisor and that of the therian on a premolar. The Woodbine Formation is considered to be of about the Cenomanian Stage on the basis of marine invertebrates. Thus although these are the oldest known Late Cretaceous mammalian fossils, they really help little in documenting evolutionary events during that interval.

Although a single Late Cretaceous mammal was found in South Dakota by J. L. Wortman in 1882, it remained for J. B. Hatcher and his assistants to make the first significant collections in eastern Wyoming. In 1889-92 collecting was continued by J. B. Hatcher for O. C. Marsh. Since then, collecting has been increasingly intensive and has spread over a wide area of the eastern Rocky Mountain region, especially in New Mexico, Wyoming, Montana, and Alberta. The result has been a fairly continuous sequence of faunas through approximately the last 15 million years of the Late Cretaceous, correlating with the

European Campanian and Maastrictian stages. Russell (1964, 1975), on the basis of these faunas, named the "Aquilan," "Judithian," "Edmontonian," and "Lancian" North American "stages" (see Fig. 2-1) and gave a brief review of this sequence of units. The units lack the rigorous definition and precision of biostratigraphic stages, but have a genesis and character similar to the Cenozoic "land mammal ages" currently used in North America. Here we utilize them in a similar sense.

Most of the early collections were made by sorting through anthills to which the ants had brought teeth and bits of bone along with pebbles from the ground's surface surrounding the colony. John Bell Hatcher (1896) used a flour-sifter for such purposes. Later collections were largely made by mass disintegration of the sediments by dry-screening or underwater screening techniques (the latter was also used by Hatcher). Although these methods have increased collections hundreds-fold, they tend to disintegrate some larger specimens and dissociate weakly held teeth and jaw fragments. A complete skull or skeleton has never been found in Late Cretaceous rocks of North America, although for a single genus (*Mesodma,* a multituberculate) so many isolated parts were found that a partial composite restoration of the skeleton was made (Sloan and Van Valen, 1965). Also, a partial skull of the multituberculate *Meniscoessus* was found by Harley Garbani in the Hell Creek Formation of Montana and was described by J. D. Archibald (1977).

Definite changes occur in the faunas from "Aquilan" to "Lancian" mammal ages, but their broad characteristics are similar. All (except the distinctly different local faunas from the so-called "Bug Creek facies" described below) are dominated both in diversity and in numbers of individuals by multituberculates and marsupials. The multituberculates are usually somewhat more abundant. The earliest known fauna in the Late Cretaceous of North America ("Aquilan") has rare remains of triconodonts and symmetrodonts, but those orders are not known in any later fauna. All the faunas have differentiated metatherians and eutherians, the latter less common than the former except in the latest Cretaceous ("Lancian") localities. Some of the multituberculate groups may be autochthonous to North America, but others may represent dispersal from Asia. The metatherians are quite unlike anything from Asia, including the Asiatic Deltatheridiidae, which have some metatherian-like characters. Fox (1974) identified isolated upper and lower molars from "Judithian" and "Lancian" age faunas as deltatheridiids close to *Deltatheroides* (of probably greater age in Mongolia). He suggested that this group dispersed from one continent to the other, but argued that present evidence does not permit choice as to the direction. Kielan-Jaworowska (1975c) considered that reference to the Deltatheridiidae was not proven, and suggested that resemblance of these isolated teeth could have resulted from convergent evolution. These specimens cannot at present be taken as unequivocally substantiating an Asian-North American faunal connection. Fox (1972a, 1976a) also described teeth of a genus *Potamotelses* in an "Aquilan" fauna that is more primitive than the clearly differentiated Metatheria and Eutheria of this and later ages in North America and is more like the therians of metatherian-eutherian grade in the "Paluxian."

We begin our systematic discussion of North American Late Cretaceous mammal localities with the Upper Milk River beds (of Russell and Landes, 1940) of the Milk River Formation (occasionally incorrectly referred to as the "Upper Milk River Formation") of "Aquilan" age (of Russell, 1975) in southern Alberta, Canada. Fox (1972a and earlier papers cited therein, and 1976a) developed a major collection from three localities in Verdigris Coulee, 29 km east of the village of Milk River (Fig. 2-18). This is the oldest well-documented Late Cretaceous mammalian fauna from North America (or in the world, as argued by Fox, 1976a) and includes the following taxa:

Order Triconodonta
  Triconodontidae
    Alticonodon lindoei
  ?Triconodontidae, new genus and species
Order Multituberculata
  Neoplagiaulacidae
    Mesodma senecta
    ?*M.* sp.
  ?Neoplagiaulacidae
    Cimexomys magister
    C. antiquus
  Cimolodontidae
    Cimolodon electus
    C. similis
  Cimolomyidae
    ?*Cimolomys* sp. A
    ?*C.* sp. B
    Meniscoessus ferox

Family uncertain
  Viridomys orbatus
Order Symmetrodonta
  Spalacotheriidae
    Symmetrodontoides canadensis
Order Marsupialia
  Didelphidae
    Alphadon creber
    A. sp.
    Albertatherium primus
  Pediomyidae
    Pediomys exiguus
    Aquiladelphis incus
    A. minor
  Stagodontidae
    Eodelphis sp.
Infraclass Eutheria
  Order Insectivora
    new genus and species A

new genus and species B
Theria, *incertae sedis*
  Potamotelses aquilensis
  Theria, *incertae sedis*

It is interesting to note that the fauna is multituberculate- and marsupial-rich and placental-poor from a taxonomic point of view. The fauna is most important in showing that the North American mammalian fauna was remarkably diverse from a taxonomic point of view before the end of the Cretaceous and that a number of archaic or relict species persisted nearly to the end of the Mesozoic.

The Judith River Formation of north-central Montana is slightly younger than the upper part of the Milk River Formation and is considered equivalent to a part of the Campanian Stage ("Judithian" land mammal age of Russell, 1975) on

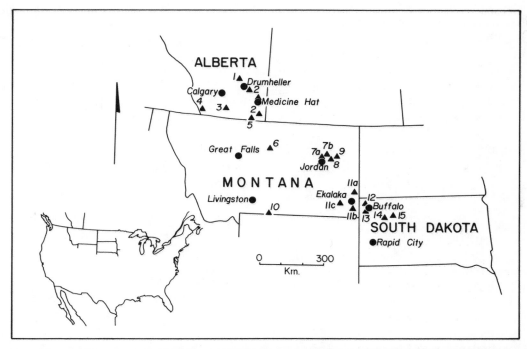

Figure 2-18.   Map of southern Alberta, Montana, and South Dakota, showing positions (triangles) of Late Cretaceous mammal localities: *1*, various localities in the Scollard Formation; *2*, various localities north and south of Medicine Hat in the Oldman Formation; *3*, St. Mary River Formation at Scabby Butte; *4*, St. Mary River Formation north of Lundbreck; *5*, Milk River Formation in Verdigris Coulee; *6*, Judith River Formation at Birch Creek; *7*, Hell Creek Formation (Garfield County), *7a* near Jordan and *7b* at Crooked Creek; *8*, Hell Creek Formation at Flat Creek; *9*, Hell Creek Formation at Bug Creek (McCone County); *10*, "Lance Formation equivalent" near Red Lodge; *11*, Hell Creek Formation, *11a* in Fallon County, *11b* in Carter County, and *11c* in Powder River County; *12*, "Joe Painter Quarry" of the Hell Creek Formation; *13*, "Eureka Quarry" of the Hell Creek Formation; *14*, Fox Hills Formation near Red Owl; and *15*, Fox Hills Formation near Iron Lightning.

the basis of marine invertebrates of the Claggett Shale fauna below and the Bearpaw Shale fauna above. The mammals were studied most recently by Ashok Sahni (1972) at localities divided by the Chouteau and Blaine county lines (Fig. 2-18). The three primary sites are on Birch Creek near the mouth of the Judith River at its junction with the Missouri River and are called "Clayball Hill," "Clambank Hollow" (the richest), and "Ankylosaur Point" (a locality with excellent potential, but difficult to work). The general area was first described by Lewis and Clark, although they reported no fossils. Later, because of the easy access via riverboat, some of the most famous people in the history of North American vertebrate paleontology started fossil explorations there. These included F. V. Hayden and E. D. Cope in the late 1860s and 70s.

Although O. C. Marsh and J. Leidy did not personally visit the area, they studied fossils collected there. Mammals, however, were not collected in the area in the early days, and it remained for Robert E. Sloan to do so in 1963. When the railroads were completed across the West, exploration interests shifted away from the Judith River area. The mammalian faunal list for the Judith River Formation is as follows:

Order Multituberculata
    Neoplagiaulacidae
        Mesodma primaeva (here emended from *M. primaevus* to provide agreement in gender)
    ?Neoplagiaulacidae
        Cimexomys judithae
        C. magnus
    Cimolodontidae
        Cimolodon sp.

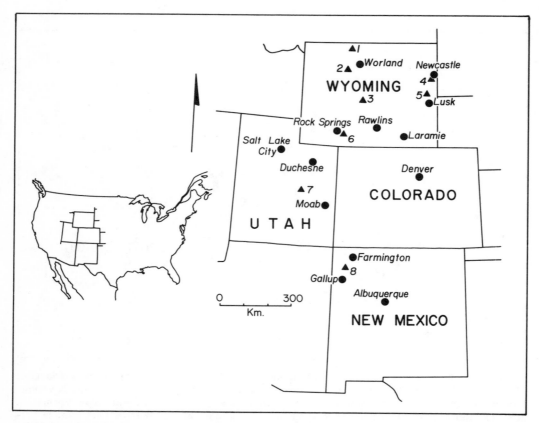

Figure 2-19.   Map of Wyoming, Utah, Colorado, and New Mexico, showing positions (triangles) of Late Cretaceous mammal localities: *1*, "Lance Formation equivalent" at Dumbbell Hill; *2*, "Lance Formation equivalent" localities at Cottonwood Creek and Kirby Creek; *3*, Mesaverde Formation near Alkali Butte; *4*, "Lance Formation equivalent" locality "somewhere north of the Cheyenne River"; *5*, various localities of the type Lance Formation at Lance Creek; *6*, "Lance Formation equivalent" near the Black Buttes stage station; *7*, North Horn Formation at Dragon Canyon; and *8*, Fruitland and Kirtland formations near the former position of the Bisti Trading Post.

Cimolomyidae
  Cimolomys clarki
  Meniscoessus major
Order Marsupialia
  Didelphidae
    Alphadon praesagus
    A. halleyi
    A. cf. *A. rhiaster*
  Pediomyidae
    Pediomys clemensi
  ?Pediomyidae
  Stagodontidae
    "*Boreodon matutinus*" (Sahni, 1972, suggested that *Eodelphis cutleri* is a junior synonym of *Boreodon matutinus,* the latter typified on a damaged premolar, but this proposal was contested by Clemens and Marshall, 1976)
Infraclass Eutheria
  Superfamily Leptictoidea, new family
    Gypsonictops lewisi

Note that placentals remain uncommon and that *Gypsonictops,* a genus of eutherian common in younger Late Cretaceous North American localities, makes its first appearance in the Judith River fauna.

A small undescribed collection of isolated mammalian teeth was recovered after great effort by screen-washing from the "Barwin Quarry." This is in the Mesaverde Formation east of Alkali Butte in the Rattlesnake Hills of Natrona County, central Wyoming (Fig. 2-19), and was worked by Malcolm C. McKenna and Thomas H. Rich of The American Museum of Natural History. According to McKenna, the fauna is similar to that of the Judith River Formation with which it is partly contemporaneous.

The discovery in 1977 of another "Judithian" local fauna containing abundant mammalian fossils is the result of the work of Robert Makela and Larry French of Rudyard, Montana, assisted by Jack Horner of Princeton University. The sites are in outcrops of the Judith River Formation in the north-central part of Montana. They give promise of being the richest "Judithian" microvertebrate localities yet discovered in the United States. The sites are not plotted on the maps herein.

The Oldman Formation of the Belly River Group in southeastern Alberta is also considered a partial equivalent of the Campanian Stage and is, at least in part, a stratigraphic equivalent of the Judith River Formation. It is placed in the "Judithian" land mammal age. The Oldman Formation was a key rock unit in the second great burst of fossil collecting, after the abandonment of riverboats for the

railroads. Early explorers included L. M. Lambe, C. H. Sternberg, W. E. Cutler, and B. Brown. Although major emphasis was on the dinosaur faunas, two species of mammals were described by Lambe in 1902. Mammals have more recently been recovered from the Oldman Formation in outcrops along the Red Deer River near Steveville, along the South Saskatchewan River north of Medicine Hat, and near Manyberries on the Canadian Agriculture Department Range Experiment Farm south of Medicine Hat (Fig. 2-18). Some of the mammalian fossils from the area were reported by Russell (1952) and Fox (1974, 1976b); a sample of several thousand specimens collected by R. C. Fox awaits formal description. All specimens up to 1974 were recovered from the upper parts of the formation and include at least the following taxa:

Order Multituberculata
  Neoplagiaulacidae
    Mesodma primaeva
  Cimolomyidae
    Meniscoessus major
Order Marsupialia
  Didelphidae
    Alphadon praesagus
  Stagodontidae
    Boreodon matutinus
    Eodelphis browni
    Eodelphis cutleri (possibly a synonym of *Boreodon matutinus*; see Clemens and Marshall, 1976, and discussion above for Judith River Formation)
Theria of metatherian-eutherian grade
  cf. *Deltatheroides* sp.

A field party from The University of Alberta discovered mammalian fossils in 1974 in a single locality from the lowest part of the Oldman Formation, and the first results of these finds were reported by Fox (1976b). The site is in rock exposures along the South Saskatchewan River north of Medicine Hat, roughly 4 m above the contact with the Foremost Formation. A large rock sample was collected for pupposes of screen-washing, but the work has not yet been completed. The mammalian fauna reported to date includes the following:

Order Multituberculata
  Cimolomyidae
    Meniscoessus intermedius
Order Marsupialia
  Didelphidae
    Alphadon sp.

The lower part of the St. Mary River Formation, exposed on Scabby Butte 1½ km south of Kehoe Lake, roughly 5 km northeast of Nobleford, Alberta (Fig. 2-18), has yielded a few mammals. The St. Mary River faunal list given by Sloan and Russell (1974) and amended by Russell (1975) is as follows:

Order Multituberculata
   Neoplagiaulacidae
      Mesodma cf. *thompsoni*
   Cimolomyidae
      Cimolomys gracilis
      Meniscoessus conquistus (?, see Chapter 6)
Order Marsupialia
   Pediomyidae
      Pediomys cf. *cooki*
      P. cf. *krejcii*
   Stagodontidae
      Didelphodon? sp.
      Eodelphis? sp.
Infraclass Eutheria
   Superfamily Leptictoidea, new family
      Gypsonictops sp.
   Palaeoryctidae
      Cimolestes sp.
Order Carnivora? (higher category assignments here considered doubtful)
   Miacidae?
      genus and species undetermined

Russell (1964) originally based the "Edmontonian" age on a defining assemblage of terrestrial vertebrates (lacking mammals) and invertebrates from the lower part of the Edmonton Formation (in its original sense as discussed below). He later (1975) referred mammals of the Scabby Butte local fauna from the St. Mary River Formation (thought to be contemporaneous with the lower part of the Edmonton) to the "Edmontonian" age. Other than an isolated protocone of a molar, however, the mammalian fauna of the lower part of the Edmonton Formation remains undocumented. Thus the characterizing faunal assemblage of the "Edmontonian" age is composed of largely terrestrial organisms other than mammals. Sloan and Russell (1974) considered the Scabby Butte local fauna to be of the latest Campanian Stage. Russell's (1975) correlation diagram shows the "Edmontonian" as including both the latest Campanian and the earliest Maastrichtian stages.

The "Miacidae?" record is represented by the trigonid of a lower molar. The trigonid was thought by Clemens (1966, p. 95 in reference to Russell, 1962) to be from a pediomyid marsupial, not a miacid

carnivore. Russell (1975) reiterated his view that the trigonid is referable to the Miacidae, a group generally thought to have had its origin in the Paleocene. Identification of the specimen remains a moot point, and we do not recognize here the existence of Cretaceous miacids.

A single multituberculate M_2 referred to *Cimolodon nitidus* (Cimolodontidae) was found in 1951 by E. T. Tozer about 24 km north of Lundbreck, Alberta, near the top of the St. Mary River Formation on the south bank of the Oldman River. The specimen was referred by Sloan (in Russell, 1975) to a species common in "Lancian" faunas, but Russell refers the specimen and its stratigraphic level to the "Edmontonian" land mammal age.

Farther south in the southwestern part of the San Juan Basin of New Mexico, mammals have been found in the upper part of the Fruitland Formation and the lower part of the Kirtland Formation. Roughly 15 mammal-producing localities are known east of the site of the Bisti Trading Post (now burned) in San Juan County (Fig. 2-19). The best localities are in Hunter Wash, and the following listing of species was presented by Clemens (1973b):

Order Multituberculata
   Neoplagiaulacidae
      Mesodma sp.
   ?Neoplagiaulacidae
      Cimexomys, cf. *C. judithae*
   Ptilodontidae
      cf. *Kimbetohia campi*
   Cimolodontidae
      Cimolodon sp.
   Eucosmodontidae
      new genus and species
Order Marsupialia
   Didelphidae
      Alphadon cf. *marshi*
      Alphadon?, new species
   Pediomyidae
      Pediomys cf. *cooki*
Infraclass Eutheria
   Superfamily Leptictoidea, new family
      Gypsonictops, new species
   Palaeoryctidae
      cf. *Cimolestes* sp.
   eutherian of uncertain ordinal affinities

The fauna, composed almost entirely of isolated teeth, is probably of the "Edmontonian" land mammal age. Genera that are common in the more northern areas are rare or absent in the Hunter Wash fauna. A brief comparison of the Hunter Wash fauna with others of roughly contemporaneous age was provided by Clemens (1973b).

Subsequently Armstrong-Ziegler (1978) reported on samples of four other local faunas found in the Fruitland Formation. The collecting localities are about 50 km southwest of Farmington, New Mexico. Following is a revised faunal list of the mammals found at three of these localities (A, B, and C of Armstrong-Ziegler, *ibid.*):

Order Multituberculata
  Neoplagiaulacidae
    Mesodma? sp.
    new genus? and new species?
  Cimolodontidae
    Cimolodon sp.
  Eucosmodontidae
    new genus and species
  Family *incertae sedis*
    Essonodon? sp.

Order Marsupialia
  Didelphidae
    Alphadon cf. *marshi*
    cf. *Peradectes* sp.

All of the North American localities described above are from the Western Interior, in which the sediments were deposited near the western shore of a Late Cretaceous epicontinental sea. The next two localities, however, are west of the present Rocky Mountains, in areas and environments previously unsampled. The "El Gallo Formation," on the northwest coast of Baja California del Norte, Mexico (Fig. 2-20), crops out mainly to the west and north of the village of El Rosario (Arriba). The beds are equated with the Campanian Stage on the basis of ammonites found in marine deposits within and above the "El Gallo Formation." In addition to a fairly diverse lower vertebrate assemblage, the following list of

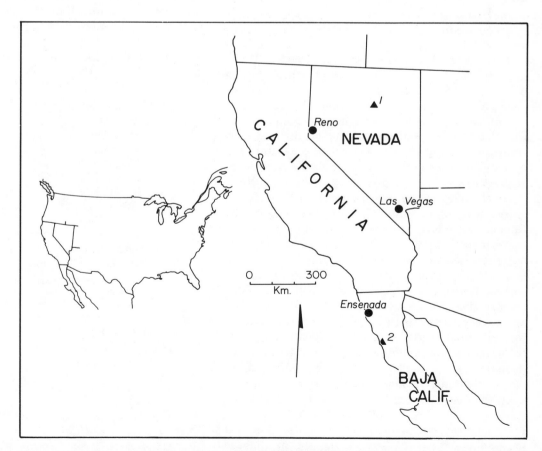

Figure 2-20. Map of Nevada, California, and Baja California del Norte, showing positions (triangles) of Late Cretaceous mammal localities: *1*, Newark Canyon Formation of Eureka County; and *2*, "El Gallo Formation," northwest of El Rosario.

mammals has been established (Lillegraven, 1972, 1976):

Order Multituberculata
  Neoplagiaulacidae
    Mesodma sp. cf. *M. formosa*
  Eucosmodontidae
    ?*Stygimys* sp.
Order Marsupialia
  Pediomyidae
    Pediomys sp.
Infraclass Eutheria
  Order Insectivora, family indefinite
    Gallolestes pachymandibularis

This is the southwesternmost of known North American Cretaceous mammal localities. It was probably distinct ecologically as well as geographically in the Late Cretaceous. With the exception of *Gallolestes,* for which affinities cannot yet be determined, the fauna is quite similar to that of the North American Western Interior; no profound endemism of the "El Gallo" mammal fauna is suggested.

The second locality of westerly geographic interest yielded two undescribed multituberculate teeth from the Newark Canyon Formation (see Smith and Ketner, 1972) of Eureka County, east-central Nevada (Fig. 2-20). The surface of an abandoned anthill was collected by Clemens in 1970, and the teeth were recovered by underwater screening techniques. Unfortunately, neither specimen can be referred with confidence to known taxa. The age of the beds is also in question and cannot be narrowed to a refinement greater than "Late Cretaceous" at the present time.

Returning to the North American Western Interior, taxonomic studies are now in progress by Robert W. Wilson on mammalian specimens collected from the Fox Hills Formation a few kilometers north of Red Owl in Meade County, west-central South Dakota (Fig. 2-18). The Fox Hills Formation was deposited as a predominantly sandy unit along the strand of the Cretaceous epicontinental sea as it made its last eastward regression from the Western Interior. Many teeth and jaw fragments have been recovered, though nothing has yet been found in articulation. The mammal-bearing unit is equivalent to part of the Maastrichtian Stage. Workers from Yale University (see Waage, 1968, pp. 117 and 127) also made a small collection of mammals from the Iron Lightning Member of the Fox Hills Formation near the Indian village of Iron Lightning in Ziebach County, South Dakota, south of the Moreau River (Fig. 2-18). Specimens recovered include unidentified

multituberculates, *Meniscoessus robustus* (Cimolomyidae), an unidentified marsupial, and cf. *Pediomys* (Pediomyidae) (pers. comm. to Lillegraven from J. H. Ostrom, 1976).

The most thoroughly documented mammalian fauna from North American Mesozoic deposits is from the Lance Formation, considered by some to be in part equivalent in age to the Fox Hills Formation. The type area of the Lance Formation is north of the town of Lance Creek in Niobrara County, southeastern Wyoming (Fig. 2-19). Its total thickness exceeds 600 m, and the mammals form the basis for the "Lancian" land mammal age. J. B. Hatcher found mammals there in 1889 and collected them for O. C. Marsh until 1892. Numerous other collections have since been made. The mammalian fauna was most recently described by Clemens (1963a, 1966, 1973a). The faunal assemblage from the type area was recovered from roughly 40 separate localities, all in the valley of Lance Creek and its tributaries. According to Clemens, a single fauna seems to be represented throughout the various localities. Most of the localities are found in the upper one-third of the Lance section. The taxonomic list is as follows (from Clemens, 1973a and Fox, 1974):

Order Multituberculata
  Neoplagiaulacidae
    Mesodma formosa
    M. hensleighi
    M. thompsoni
  ?Neoplagiaulacidae
    Cimexomys minor
  Ptilodontidae
    Kimbetohia campi
  Cimolodontidae
    Cimolodon nitidus
  Cimolomyidae
    Cimolomys gracilis
    Meniscoessus robustus
  Family *incertae sedis*
    Essonodon browni
Order Marsupialia
  Didelphidae
    Alphadon marshi
    A. wilsoni
    A. lulli
    A. rhaister
    A. cf. *rhaister*
    Glasbius intricatus
  Pediomyidae
    Pediomys elegans
    P. cooki

>   *P. krejcii*
>   *P. hatcheri*
>   *P. florencae*
> Stagodontidae
>   *Didelphodon vorax*
> Infraclass Eutheria
> Superfamily Leptictoidea, new family
>   *Gypsonictops hypoconus*
> Palaeoryctidae
>   *Cimolestes incisus*
>   *C. stirtoni*
>   *C. magnus*
>   *Batodon tenuis*
> Palaeoryctidae? *incertae sedis*
>   *Telacodon laevis*
> Theria of metatherian-eutherian grade
>   cf. *Deltatheroides* sp.

Note that this fauna, as those of the other North American Late Cretaceous localities described above, is composed primarily of multituberculates and marsupials. For the first time, however, the diversity of placentals has increased markedly over those of older North American faunas. This may be considered a "typical" latest Cretaceous fauna for the North American eastern Rocky Mountain area, although the relatively advanced genera characteristic of the highest levels at Bug Creek (see below) are absent. Clemens (1973a) pointed out that several of the multituberculates in the Lance fauna (and also at Bug Creek) have close relatives or descendants in the North American Paleocene. Most marsupials became extinct at or about the end of the Cretaceous, but species of *Alphadon* could have been ancestral to the New World and European marsupials. *Gypsonictops* is currently recognized as a leptictoid proteutherian, but Novacek (1977) and others argue that it probably was not ancestral to any known Cenozoic eutherians. *Cimolestes* survived into the early Paleocene (Puercan).

Five mammal-bearing deposits mapped as Lance Formation or "Lance equivalent" should be mentioned here for completeness, although none of the fossils has been fully described. The first "Lance equivalent" area is in the southwestern end of the Big Horn Basin in Hot Springs County, Wyoming (Fig. 2-19). A few teeth have been collected by parties from Princeton and Yale universities on Cottonwood Creek and Kirby Creek. The second "Lance equivalent" mammal locality is at "Dumbbell Hill" on Little Polecat Dome in northeastern Park County, Wyoming (Fig. 2-19), about 19 km north-northeast of Powell. A few molar teeth were discovered and

reported by John Dyer (1948). He also found a coprolite containing three multituberculate jaws (identified by Robert E. Sloan as *Mesodma formosa* and *Cimolodon nitidus*). Further collecting was done for Princeton University by David C. Parris and party in 1971; their collections included the multituberculates *Cimolomys gracilis, Mesodma formosa,* and cf. *Cimexomys* sp. plus the marsupial *Alphadon* cf. *A. marshi* and a possible leptictoid insectivore (identified by W. A. Clemens).

A third "Lance equivalent" locality was mentioned by Jepsen (1931) in a report dealing with dinosaur eggs found near Red Lodge on the northern flank of the Beartooth Mountains in Carbon County, southcentral Montana (Fig. 2-18). Jepsen mentioned only the presence of "a mammal tooth" taken from the Lance beds. Van Valen (1967) reported the presence of arctocyonid, leptictid-like, and *Cimolestes*-like teeth from beds mapped as Lance Formation in northeastern Wyoming. The small collection was made by Wortman and Peterson in 1892 and probably came from somewhere north of the Cheyenne River (Fig. 2-19). It includes forms ". . . all belonging to otherwise unknown species or even genera" (Van Valen, 1967, p. 3). Finally, in 1974 Douglas A. Lawson collected a small sample of teeth (mainly multituberculates and marsupials) from beds in southwestern Wyoming east of Rock Springs and a few kilometers west of the railway station of Bitter Creek. The strata are mapped as Lance Formation, probably erroneously so. The locality is north of the ruins of the Black Buttes stage station (Fig. 2-19), which is on the main line of the Union Pacific Railroad. Lillegraven and his field party discovered two additional mammal-bearing sites in the same general vicinity during the summer of 1977. On the basis of stratigraphic relationships, they are probably older than the localities of the type Lance Formation, but perhaps not so old as to be referred to the "Edmontonian" land mammal age (see below).

In 1977 Kenneth Carpenter discovered mammalian remains in the Laramie Formation of central Weld County of northeastern Colorado. The site is about 110 km northeast of Denver and has so far yielded (pers. comm. to Lillegraven, 1977) multituberculates (*Meniscoessus conquistus, Cimolomys* sp., plus miscellaneous unidentified tooth fragments) and the eutherian *Gypsonictops* sp. Carpenter believes the assemblage to be of earliest "Lancian" affinities. The locality is not plotted on the maps herein.

Another major Late Cretaceous mammalian fauna has been recovered from what was formerly called the upper part of the Edmonton Formation (occasionally referred to incorrectly as the "Upper Edmonton Formation") in Alberta. These deposits crop out extensively along the course of the Red Deer River for many kilometers to the north of the town of Drumheller (Fig. 2-18). Mammal localities were discovered east of the village of Trochu by parties from The University of Kansas and The University of Alberta in the 1960's. In all but the most recent literature the fossils were referred to as representing the "Edmonton fauna." The generalized section, as used previously, is shown in Figure 2-21A.

More recently, following (in part) Irish (1970), the name Edmonton Formation has been elevated to the status of group and confined to the "lower" and "middle" Edmonton. The "upper" Edmonton has become the Scollard Member of the Paskapoo Formation (Fig. 2-21B). The Paskapoo Formation, prior to Irish's (1970) work, was considered to include only the rocks of Paleocene age known to rest unconformably upon the upper member of the Edmonton Formation. Under this interpretation, the "Edmonton fauna" as published (Lillegraven, 1969) is from the Scollard Member of the Paskapoo Formation and is younger than the restricted Edmonton Group, which is believed correlative with the lower part of the St. Mary River Formation and Scabby Butte local fauna; mammals are not known from the restricted Edmonton Group (other than a single isolated protocone from one locality). Thus the "Edmonton fauna" of most of the literature is not of the "Edmontonian"

land mammal age (of Russell, 1975) but is "Lancian" or, in European terms, of the Maastrichtian Stage. The resulting confusion is most unfortunate, and the stratigraphic jumble does not stop here. Gibson (1977) suggested changing the name of Irish's concept of most of the Paskapoo Formation to the Scollard Formation, with the restriction of the Paskapoo Formation to the uppermost part of the rock sequence in the Trochu-Scollard area. The upper limit of the Edmonton Group was elevated to the top of the Scollard Formation, thus including, once again, the mammalian faunas. A discussion of the placement of the Cretaceous-Paleocene boundary is provided by Russell and Singh (1978).

Identifiable mammalian remains have been found only in the lower part of the Scollard Formation at various levels less than 27 m above a volcanic welded ash unit called the Kneehills Tuff. The Kneehills Tuff has yielded an age of 65-66 million years using the potassium-argon technique. Likewise, the marine Bearpaw Formation that underlies the Edmonton Formation (Horseshoe Canyon Formation of Irish, 1970) has been dated at 68 mybp by analyzing the K-Ar content in biotite and sanidine grains in the bentonites. The Scollard mammalian fauna includes the following (from Lillegraven, 1969, and Fox, 1974):

Order Multituberculata
  Neoplagiaulacidae
    Mesodma formosa
    M. hensleighi
    M. thompsoni

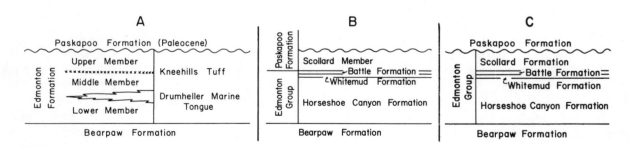

Figure 2-21.   Comparisons of stratigraphic terminology used for latest Cretaceous and Paleocene rocks along the valley of the Red Deer River in Alberta, Canada: *A*, traditionally used names, following Allen and Sanderson (1945); *B*, terminology following Irish (1970); and *C*, terminology adopted by the Geological Survey of Canada following Gibson (1977).

?Neoplagiaulacidae
  Cimexomys priscus
Ptilodontidae
  genus and species *indet.*
Cimolodontidae
  Cimolodon nitidus
Cimolomyidae
  Cimolomys gracilis
  C. trochuus
Order Marsupialia
  Didelphidae
    Alphadon marshi
    A. wilsoni
    A. rhaister
  Pediomyidae
    Pediomys elegans
    P. krejcii
    P. hatcheri
  Stagodontidae
    Didelphodon vorax
Infraclass Eutheria
  Superfamily Leptictoidea, new family
    Gypsonictops hypoconus
    G. illuminatus
  Palaeoryctidae
    Cimolestes cerberoides
    C. propalaeoryctes
    C. magnus
    Batodon tenuis
Theria of metatherian-eutherian grade
  cf. *Deltatheroides* sp.

As in the fauna of the type Lance Formation, that of the Scollard Formation shows a high diversity of eutherians. According to Fox (1974), cf. *Deltatheroides* sp. represents a possible Asiatic invader into North America (or vice versa). Lillegraven (1969, p. 25) postulated that *Cimexomys priscus* may also have had an Asiatic origin. Subsequent to Lillegraven's 1969 paper, Kielan-Jaworowska (1970) formally described *Gobibaatar parvus,* a species similar to *C. priscus* (also see Kielan-Jaworowska, 1974b). Lillegraven also believed that the few eutherians might have descended from Asiatic forms. The recent discoveries in the Gobi Desert had not been described when he studied the Scollard fauna, however, and an exhaustive comparison still has not been made. Overall, the Scollard mammal fauna is essentially a local or ecological variant of the better known Hell Creek and Lance faunas. All genera known from the Scollard fauna are also known from the Hell Creek and/or Lance formations. Several Scollard species, however, have not been recorded from farther south.

The Hell Creek Formation crops out widely across eastern Montana, the western juncture of the two Dakotas, and northeastern Wyoming. It is largely a correlative unit of the Lance Formation to the south (from which it has yet to be distinguished along a mappable, lithologically defined boundary) and the Scollard Formation to the north. Fossil-bearing localities are scattered across most of the area of exposure of the formation.

Mammals were first discovered in the formation by Brown and Kaisen in 1906. Part of their collection came from the valley of Crooked Creek, Garfield County, Montana. Isolated teeth or small fragments of jaws were occasionally found at other sites in subsequent years. Then, in the early 1960s, Donald Beckman, Eugene Kuszmaul, and their families, and Newell Joyner discovered the Bug Creek Anthills. This, and several other localities in the immediate vicinity, have become some of the most productive Mesozoic mammal sites in North America. They are situated in the area of Bug Creek in westernmost McCone County, northeastern Montana, near Fort Peck Reservoir (Fig. 2-18) and about 40 km south of Fort Peck. The quantity of material recovered from a few localities is extraordinary. Literally tens of thousands of mammalian teeth and many more complete specimens and postcranial elements have been collected. The first investigation of the sites began in 1962, and collection, mostly by screen-washing, was carried on largely by R. E. Sloan of the University of Minnesota (Sloan and Van Valen, 1965). Unfortunately, even in the richest locality ("Bug Creek Anthills"), many fossils show marked evidence of predepositional transportation, and nothing is found in articulation. In terms of numbers of specimens, this group of sites is incomparably the richest known deposit of Mesozoic mammals of any age, anywhere in the world. Much of this material, truly an *embarras de richesse,* has not been described.

It is now becoming apparent that at least two faunal facies are represented in the Hell Creek Formation. The "Hell Creek faunal facies" is very similar in composition to the local faunas of the type Lance Formation of Wyoming and the Scollard Formation of Alberta. Its mammalian component is dominated by approximately equal numbers of individuals of multituberculates and marsupials. Eutherians are more rare, forming less than 10 percent of the assemblage of mammalian specimens. The "Bug Creek faunal facies" is characterized by abundant occurrence of species closely related to Paleocene mammals such as the multituberculate

Catopsalis and the eutherian *Protungulatum*. Though rare, species characteristic of the Hell Creek faunal facies usually are present in the large samples of the Bug Creek faunal facies collected from McCone County. The apparent absence of many of these species from the Bug Creek faunal facies of Garfield County probably represents an artifact of the smaller sample size.

An additional complicating factor is the absence of thorough systematic reviews of the collections from the Hell Creek Formation of northeastern Montana. The fossils from McCone County are being studied by R. E. Sloan and L. Van Valen, and those from Garfield County by J. D. Archibald. Their initial analyses indicate some differences in the composition of the faunal facies in the two areas. The cause, or reality, of these differences has yet to be determined. For clarity, faunal lists for each county are presented below. That for McCone County was compiled from Sloan and Van Valen (1965), Van Valen and Sloan (1965), and with modifications by Estes and Berberian (1970). J. D. Archibald provided us with a preliminary compilation of the mammals recorded from sites in Garfield County. In both lists the species limited to the Bug Creek faunal facies are marked with an asterisk.

McCone County

Order Multituberculata
  Neoplagiaulacidae
    Mesodma formosa
    M. thompsoni
    **M.* sp. (Novacek and Clemens, 1977, analyzed the morphology of the posterior premolars of *Mesodma* from Bug Creek Anthills local fauna and found that they appear to be teeth of but one species that is not referable to either *M. formosa* or *M. thompsoni*)
  ?Neoplagiaulacidae
    Cimexomys minor
    **C.,* new species
  Cimolodontidae
    Cimolodon nitidus
  Taeniolabididae
    **Catopsalis joyneri*
  Eucosmodontidae
    **Stygimys gratus*
    **S. kuszmauli*
    **cf. *S.* aff. *S. kuszmauli*
    new genus and species
  Cimolomyidae
    Cimolomys gracilis
    Meniscoessus robustus

Family *incertae sedis*
    Essonodon browni
Order Marsupialia
  Didelphidae
    **Alphadon marshi*
    A. wilsoni
    Glasbius, new species
  Pediomyidae
    Pediomys elegans
    P. hatcheri
    P. krejcii
    P. cooki
    P. florencae
  Stagodontidae
    Didelphodon vorax
Infraclass Eutheria
  Superfamily Leptictoidea, new family
    Gypsonictops hypoconus
    G. illuminatus?
  Palaeoryctidae
    **Batodon tenuis*
    Cimolestes incisus
    C. magnus
    **Procerberus formicarum*
  Arctocyonidae
    **Protungulatum donnae*
    *plus 4 other unnamed new species
  ?Paromomyidae (such affinities are doubted by Bown and Rose, 1976)
    **Purgatorius ceratops*

Garfield County

Order Multituberculata
  Neoplagiaulacidae
    Mesodma cf. *M. formosa*
    M. hensleighi
    M. thompsoni
    **M.* aff. *M. thompsoni*
    ?*Neoplagiaulax,* new species
  ?Neoplagiaulacidae
    **Cimexomys minor*
    **C.,* new species
    genus and species indet.
    *"*Cimexomys*" priscus* (to be defined as a new genus, J. D. Archibald, pers. comm. to W. A. Clemens, 1977)
  Cimolodontidae
    Cimolodon nitidus
  Taeniolabididae
    **Catopsalis* sp.
  Eucosmodontidae
    **Stygimys* aff. *S. kuszmauli*
    *?Eucosmodontidae, genus and species indet.

Cimolomyidae
  Cimolomys gracilis
  Meniscoessus robustus
Family *incertae sedis*
  Essonodon browni
Order Marsupialia
  Didelphidae
    Alphadon marshi
    A. wilsoni
    A. lulli
    A. rhaister
    Glasbius, new species
    *Peradectes cf. *P. pusillus*
  Pediomyidae
    Pediomys elegans
    P. cf. *P. cooki*
    P. krejcii
    P. hatcheri
    P. florencae
  Stagodontidae
    Didelphodon vorax
Infraclass Eutheria
  Superfamily Leptictoidea, new family
    Gypsonictops cf. *G. illuminatus*
  Palaeoryctidae
    Batodon tenuis
    Cimolestes cf. *C. cerberoides*
    C. incisus
    C. propalaeoryctes
    C. stirtoni
    *Procerberus formicarum
  Arctocyonidae
    *Protungulatum cf. *P. donnae*
    *plus 3 other unnamed new species possibly referable to other genera
    *?Oxyclaeninae, genus and species indet.

Sloan and Van Valen (1965) regarded the Bug Creek faunal facies as being a mixture of two contemporary terrestrial vertebrate communities. The rare elements of the Hell Creek faunal facies were thought to document the existence of animals in areas well removed from the site of deposition. The abundant and characteristic mammals of the Bug Creek faunal facies, on the other hand, supposedly lived close to the area of deposition. Also, they recognized that occurrences of the Bug Creek faunal facies were limited to the upper levels of the formation, while the Hell Creek faunal facies was known from sites throughout the section.

Subsequently, several investigators have attributed the differences in faunal composition to differences in age. Research under way by J. David Archibald (part of a project jointly sponsored by the

Natural History Museum of Los Angeles County and the Museum of Paleontology, University of California, Berkeley) indicates that this hypothesis is in part incorrect. The areas of investigation are in the headwaters of the valley of Hell Creek, which includes the type locality of *Tyrannosaurus rex* and lies north of the town of Jordan, and in the valley of Flat Creek, northeast of Jordan, Garfield County, Montana. Archibald (1977) has obtained evidence strongly supporting Sloan and Van Valen's views that the faunal facies were coeval during the closing phases of deposition of the Hell Creek Formation, and that their spatial separation was ecologically controlled.

Four genera are so common at Bug Creek Anthills (BCA) (and absent at lower stratigraphic levels) that there is considerable likelihood they were newcomers to the area when BCA was formed. These include the multituberculates *Stygimys* and *Catopsalis* and the eutherians *Procerberus* and *Protungulatum.* All are also somewhat advanced in evolutionary grade.

Another mammal of advanced evolutionary grade is *Purgatorius ceratops,* the earliest known animal referable to the Order Primates. Within the Hell Creek Formation, *Purgatorius* has been found only at the Harbicht Hill locality, which is stratigraphically the highest in the Bug Creek area. All the localities are below the so-called "Z coal bed." *Triceratops* and bones of other kinds of dinosaurs occur up to about 3 m below the "Z coal" in this area, but no higher. The coal bed is used locally to mark the stratigraphic boundary between the Hell Creek Formation (thought to be entirely of Cretaceous age) and the Tullock Formation (assigned a Paleocene age). Only a single lower molar of *Purgatorius* has been found at Harbicht Hill, but reference to its Paleocene congeners is clear. It is so rare at this site that one can hardly rule out the possibility that its absence at other localities in the Hell Creek Formation is only apparent. There is also a possibility that the Harbicht Hill locality is not of Cretaceous age, but rather earliest Paleocene. If true, however, one must accept the existence of Paleocene dinosaurs, as their teeth and fragmentary bones are not uncommon in the deposit at Harbicht Hill.

Of special interest here is the apparent absence in older North American Cretaceous rock units of fossils representative of species ancestral to the relatively advanced mammals characteristic of the Bug Creek faunal facies. There is, perhaps, some possibility that the advanced forms were immigrants at about this time. Russell (1975) suggested that these species might have been invaders from the north, and during the Lancian did not have time to disperse into what is now Wyoming. It seems equally possible, however, that the environmental differences between the two areas (see Estes and Berberian, 1970) were sufficient barriers. Sampling bias in age of the known local faunas might also account for the absence of certain species to the south, but available techniques for correlation lack the precision to confirm or deny this speculation.

Sloan and Van Valen (1965) pointed out the resemblance of the Bug Creek faunal facies to the Puercan fauna (that followed almost immediately) of the earliest Paleocene. It has even been suggested, if not quite flatly stated, that the whole Paleocene fauna of North America and Europe (or of Laurasia) could have been derived from *Procerberus, Purgatorius,* and *Protungulatum.* Undoubtedly, the eutherians were beginning their basic (ordinal) differentiation in the latest Cretaceous and members of the several different local faunas of the Bug Creek faunal facies document rapid diversification of some groups. There is, however, good evidence that the roster of Late Cretaceous, North American eutherians is far from complete, and that it includes undescribed ancestors of some Puercan mammals. Also, the possibility that some of the mammals found in Puercan faunas of the eastern part of western North America were descendants of immigrants from unknown areas has yet to be disproven.

Other localities document the Hell Creek faunal facies outside of Garfield and McCone counties, Montana. One is "Eureka Quarry" in the "Jumpoff" area southwest of the town of Buffalo in Harding County, South Dakota, just northeast of the East Short Pine Hills (Fig. 2-18). The assemblage was collected by R. W. Wilson, formerly of the South Dakota School of Mines and Technology, and is now under study. Personal communication from Wilson suggests that the suite of animals recovered is typical of those of the Lance-Scollard assemblages. Another South Dakota locality of typical Hell Creek faunal facies is the "Joe Painter Quarry," found northwest of Buffalo (Fig. 2-18). It, too, is now under study by Wilson. Data on the probable locations of the old E. D. Cope and J. Wortman Hell Creek mammal sites in South Dakota (where the type specimens of the large cimolomyid multituberculate *Meniscoessus conquistus* and the stagodontid marsupial *Didelphodon* [= *Thlaeodon*] *padanicus*, and other fossils were collected) were presented by Wilson (1965) and Van Valen (1967).

The final Hell Creek mammalian fossils to be mentioned here were discovered in the northern Powder River Basin of southeastern Montana (Fig. 2-18). Marshall Lambert, Curator of the Carter County Museum of Ekalaka, Montana, and his associates have discovered an important fossiliferous area about 40 to 48 km north-northeast of Ekalaka in Fallon County. The remains of other Hell Creek mammals, including a palate of *Cimolestes magnus* (see Clemens, 1973a, Fig. 24) were found in Carter County, approximately 15 km south of Ekalaka. Farther west in Powder River County, vertebrate fossils were found in the upper part of the Hell Creek Formation, about 8 km south of the Powderville Post Office. A faunal list prepared by C. L. Gazin and D. H. Dunkle was published by Bryson (1952). J. D. Archibald reviewed the collection and provided for use here the following revised listing:

Order Multituberculata
  Neoplagiaulacidae
    Mesodma thompsoni
  Cimolomyidae
    Meniscoessus robustus
Order Marsupialia
  Pediomyidae
    Pediomys elegans or *P. cooki*
    P. cf. *hatcheri*
    P. cf. *florencae*
  Stagodontidae
    Didelphodon vorax
Infraclass Eutheria
  Superfamily Leptictoidea, new family
    Gypsonictops cf. *illuminatus*

Clearly, the outcrops of the Hell Creek Formation in the northern Powder River Basin need further investigation.

Late Cretaceous mammals have been found in the "*Polyglyphanodon* Quarry" of the North Horn Formation in the lower part of Dragon Canyon in Emery County, east-central Utah (Fig. 2-19). An undescribed multituberculate last lower premolar and a single upper molar of a pediomyid marsupial (*Pediomys hatcheri*) were collected from an anthill within the Cretaceous part of the North Horn Formation below the Paleocene Joes Valley Member (Clemens, 1961). Mammalian specimens from the formation are exceptionally rare. Unless those were unusually long-hauling ants, that part of the North Horn Formation is probably "Lancian" in age. The

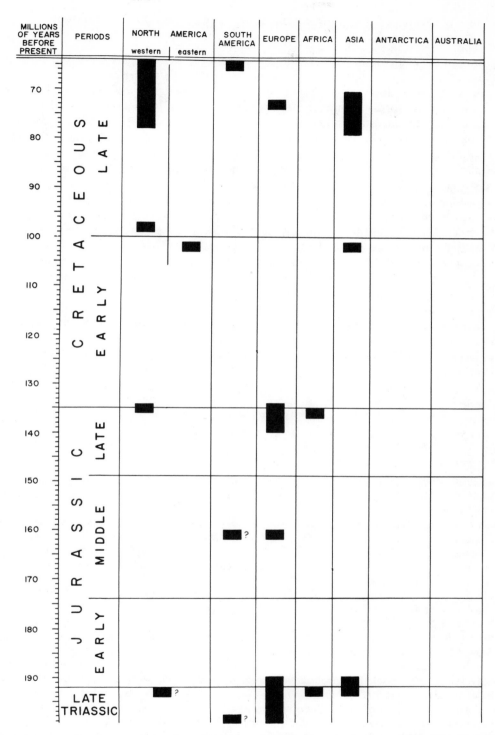

Figure 2-22. The black bands summarize the parts of the Mesozoic time scale that have yielded mammals, or closely mammal-like reptiles. The length of all bands has been more than generously extended, as some should be mere hairlines if drawn to scale. Several of the intervals here represented in terms of millions of years before the present are frankly little more than best estimates (see text for details). Because North America was divided into eastern and western parts by north- to south-running seaways through part of Early and most of Late Cretaceous time, the fossil record for the continent is subdivided on the diagram.

presence of dinosaurs, especially *Alamosaurus,* helps establish the Cretaceous age of the lower part of the North Horn Formation.

The last Mesozoic mammal occurrence with which we are familiar is an isolated lingual part of a eutherian (possibly a condylarth) upper molar from the latest Cretaceous Javelina Formation of the Tornillo Group from Big Bend National Park in Texas (Fig. 2-7). The specimen was found by Wann Langston, Jr., of The University of Texas at Austin and was identified as ?Condylarthra by D. A. Lawson (1972). The Javelina is perhaps most famous for its remains of the giant flying reptile, *Quetzalcoatlus northropi.*

RETROSPECT

Listed above are all the localities known to us that have yielded Mesozoic mammals. Taxa that the localities are known to contain and notes concerning the nature of the fossils themselves are also listed. It will now be clear exactly how meager the record is for the first two-thirds of the time of mammalian existence. Biases of the record (temporal, geographical, and ecological) should give pause to even the most ardent phylogenetic speculator. Temporal ranges and geographical areas containing documented Mesozoic mammals are shown graphically in Figure 2-22; the lengths of the temporal ranges in which fossils are known are shown extremely generously in most cases. Even in those areas and intervals with a record of fossil mammals, few of the possible environments have been sampled, very few articulated skeletons exist in collections, and most identifiable specimens consist of isolated teeth or fragments of jaws. Reasonably complete skulls are rare. Therefore, if in the remainder of this book we seem less than adamant in defending one phylogenetic plan versus another, reasons for our hesitancy will be clear.

REFERENCES CITED

Aepler, R., 1974, Der Rhätsandstein von Tübingen—ein Kondensiertes Delta: N. Jahrb. Geol. Paläont., v. 147, p. 113-162.

Allan, J. A., and Sanderson, J. O. G., 1945, Geology of the Red Deer and Rosebud sheets, Alberta: Res. Council Alberta, Rept. 13, 115 p.

Allen, P., 1975, Wealden of the Weald: a new model: Geol. Assoc. Proc., v. 86, p. 389-437.

Anderson, F. W., and Hughes, N. F., 1964, The "Wealden" of north-west Germany and its English equivalents: Nature, v. 201, p. 907-908.

Andrews, R. C., 1932, The new conquest of central Asia: New York Nat. Hist. Central Asia, v. 1, Amer. Mus. Nat. Hist., *xlix* + 678 p.

Anonymous, 1975, Boletín Informativo: Inst. Prov. Paleont. Sabadell, v. 7 (2), p. 9-10.

Archibald, J. D., 1977, Fossil Mammalia and testudines of the Hell Creek Formation, and the geology of the Tullock and Hell Creek formations, Garfield County, Montana [Ph.D. thesis]: Berkeley, California, Univ. California.

Arkell, W. J., 1933, The Jurassic system in Great Britain: Oxford, Clarendon Press, *xii* + 681 p.

———1956, Jurassic geology of the world: Edinburgh and London, Oliver and Boyd Publ., 806 p.

Armstrong-Ziegler, J. G., 1978, An aniliid snake and associated vertebrates from the Campanian of New Mexico: Jour. Paleont., v. 52, p. 480-483.

Barker, D., Brown, C. E., Bugg, S. C., and Costin, J., 1975, Ostracods, land plants, and Charales from the basal Purbeck Beds of Portesham Quarry, Dorset: Palaeontology, v. 18, p. 419-436.

Barsbold, R., Voronin, Yu. I., and Zhegallo, V. I., 1971, The work of the Soviet-Mongolian paleontological expedition in 1969-1970: Paleont. Jour. (Paleont. Zhur.), 1971, no. 2, p. 272-276.

Bazhanov, V. S., 1972, First Mesozoic Mammalia (*Beleutinus orlovi* Bashanov) from the USSR: Teriologia, Akademiya Nauk SSSR, Sibirskoe Otdelenie, v. 1, p. 74-80 (in Russian with English summary).

Beliajeva, E. I., Trofimov, B. A., and Reshetov, V. J., 1974, General stages in evolution of late Mesozoic and early Tertiary mammalian fauna in central Asia, *in* Kramarenko, N. N., and others, eds., Mesozoic and Cenozoic faunas and biostratigraphy of Mongolia: Moscow, Joint Soviet-Mongol. Paleont. Exped. (Trans., v. 1), p. 19-45 (in Russian with English summary).

Berger, G. M., 1974, Sommières, XXVIII-42: Orléans, Service Géologique National (France), Bureau de Recherches Géologiques et Minières [report associated with geological map], scale 1:50,000.

Bohlin, B., 1953, Fossil reptiles from Mongolia and Kansu:

Sino-Swed. Exped., Publ. 37, VI. Vertebrate Paleontology, 6, p. 1-113.

Bonaparte, J. F., 1973, Edades/reptil para el Triasico de Argentina y Brasil: V Cong. Geol. Argentino Actas, v. 3, p. 93-129.

Bonaparte, J. F., and Barbarena, M. C., 1975, A possible mammalian ancestor from the middle Triassic of Brazil (Therocephalia, Cynodontia): Jour. Paleont., v. 49, p. 931-936.

Bown, T. M., and Rose, K. D., 1976, New early Tertiary primates and a reappraisal of some Plesiadapiformes: Folia Primat., v. 26, p. 109-138.

Broom, R., 1932, The mammal-like reptiles of South Africa and the origin of mammals: London, H. F. & G. Witherby, *xvi* + 376 p.

Bryson, R. P., 1952, The Coalwood Coal Field, Powder River County, Montana: U. S. Geol. Surv. Bull. 973-B, p. 23-141.

Buckland, W., 1824, Notice on *Megalosaurus*: Geol. Soc. London Trans., 2, 1, p. 390-396.

Butler, P. M., 1939, The post-canine teeth of *Tritylodon longaevus* Owen: Ann. Mag. Nat. Hist., London, ser. 11, v. 4, p. 514-520.

Butler, P. M., and Kielan-Jaworowska, Z., 1973, Is *Deltatheridium* a marsupial?: Nature, v. 245, p. 105-106.

Casamiquela, R. M., 1961, Sobre la presencia de un mamífero en el primer elenco (Icnológico) de vertebrados de Jurasico de la Patagonia (Noticia): Physis, v. 22, p. 225-233.

_____1964, Estudios icnológicos. Problems y métodos de la icnología con aplicatión al estudio de pisadas mesozoicas (Reptilia, Mammalia) de la Patagonia: (Ministerio de Asuntos Sociales de la Provincia de Río Negro, Argentina), Buenos Aires, Imprenta del Colegio Industrial, Pío IX.

_____1975a, Nuevo material y reinterpretación de las icnitas mesozoicas (neotriásicas) de Los Menucos, Provincia de Río Negro (Patagonia): Actas del I Congreso Argentino de Paleontologia y Biostratigrafia, Tucumán, v. 1, p. 555-580.

_____1975b, Sobre la significatión de *Ameghinichnus patagonicus,* un mamífero brincador del Jurásico medio de Santa Cruz (Patagonia): *ibid.,* v. 2, p. 71-85.

Casey, R., 1963, The dawn of the Cretaceous Period in Britain: South-eastern Union Scient. Socs. Bull. 117, p. 1-15.

_____1971, Facies, faunas and tectonics in late Jurassic-early Cretaceous Britain, *in* Middlemiss, F. A., Rawson, P. F., and Newall, G., eds., Faunal provinces in space and time: Geol. Jour. Spec. Issue 4, p. 153-168.

_____1973, The ammonite succession at the Jurassic-Cretaceous boundary in eastern England, *in* Casey, R., and Rawson, P. F., eds., The Boreal Lower Cretaceous: *ibid.,* Spec. Issue 5, p. 193-266.

Chow, M. M., 1953, The significance of the finds of Mesozoic fossil Mammalia in the northeast [provinces]: Acta Palaeontologica Sinica, Paleontology Jour., v. 1, p. 150-156 (in Chinese with English abstract).

Clemens, W. A., 1961, A Late Cretaceous mammal from Dragon Canyon, Utah: Jour. Paleont., v. 35, p. 578-579.

_____1963a, Fossil mammals of the type Lance Formation, Wyoming. Part I. Introduction and Multituberculata: Univ. California Pubs. Geol. Sci., v. 48, *vi* + 105 p.

_____1963b, Wealden mammalian fossils: Palaeontology, v. 6, p. 55-69.

_____1963c, Late Jurassic mammalian fossils in the Sedgwick Museum, Cambridge: *ibid.,* v. 6, p. 373-377.

_____1966, Fossil mammals of the type Lance Formation, Wyoming. Part II. Marsupialia: Univ. California Pubs. Geol. Sci., v. 62, *vi* + 122 p.

_____1973a, Fossil mammals of the type Lance Formation, Wyoming. Part III. Eutheria and summary: *ibid.,* v. 94, *vi* + 102 p.

_____1973b, The roles of fossil vertebrates in interpretation of Late Cretaceous stratigraphy of the San Juan Basin, New Mexico: Four Corners Geol. Soc. Memoir Book, 1973, p. 154-167.

Clemens, W. A., and Lees, P. M., 1971, A review of English Early Cretaceous mammals, *in* Kermack, D. M., and Kermack, K. A., eds., Early mammals: Linn. Soc. Zool. Jour., v. 50, suppl. 1, p. 117-130.

Clemens, W. A., and Marshall, L. G., 1976, American and European Marsupialia, *in* Westphal, F., ed., Fossilium catalogus, I: Animalia, Pars 123: Dr. W. Junk B. V. -'s-Gravenhage, p. 1-114.

Colbert, E. H., 1973, Continental drift and the distribution of fossil reptiles, *in* Tarling, D. H., and Runcorn, S. K., eds., Implications of continental drift to the earth sciences: New York, Academic Press, NATO Adv. Study Inst., v. 1, p. 395-412.

Crompton, A. W., 1958, The cranial morphology of a new genus and species of ictidosaurian: Zool. Soc. London Proc., v. 130, p. 183-216.

_____1968, In search of the "insignificant": Discovery, v. 3, p. 23-32.

_____1974, The dentitions and relationships of the southern African Triassic mammals, *Erythrotherium parringtoni* and *Megazostrodon rudnerae*: Brit. Mus. (Nat. Hist.) Bull. (Geol.), v. 24, p. 397-437.

Crompton, A. W., and Kielan-Jaworowska, Z., 1978, Molar structure and occlusion in Cretaceous therian mammals, *in* Butler, P. M., and Joysey, K. A., eds., Studies in the development, function and evolution of teeth: London and New York, Academic Press, p. 249-287.

Crusafont-Pairó, M., and Adrover, R., 1965, El primer mamifero del Mesozoico Español: Fossilia, Publnes Cat. Paleont. Univ. Barcelona, nos. 5-6, p. 28-33.

_____1966, El primer representante de la clase mamíferos hallado en el Mesozoico de España: Teruel, v. 35, p. 139-143.

Crusafont, M., and Gibert, J., 1976, Los primeros Multituberculados de España (Nota preliminar): Acta Geologica Hispanica, Año 11, p. 57-64.

Cui, G., 1976, *Yunnania,* a new tritylodont genus from Lufeng, Yunnan: Vertebrata PalAsiatica, v. 14, p. 85-90 (in Chinese with English abstract).

Dashzeveg, D., 1963, Dinosaur eggs: Priroda, 9, p. 100 (in Russian).

_____1975, New primitive therian from the Early Cretaceous of Mongolia: Nature, v. 256, p. 402-403.

Datta, P. M., Yadagiri, P., and Rao, B. R. J., 1978, Discovery of Early Jurassic micromammals from upper Gondwana sequence of Pranhita Godavari Valley, India: Geol. Soc. India Jour., v. 19, p. 64-68.

Dawkins, W. B., 1864, On the Rhaetic Beds and White Lias of western and central Somerset, and on the discovery of a new fossil mammal in the grey marlstones beneath the bone-bed: Geol. Soc. London Quart. Jour., v. 20, p. 396-412.

Dietrich, W. O., 1927, *Brancatherulum* n. g., ein Proplacentalier aus dem obersten Jura des Tendaguru in Deutsch-Ostafrika: Zbl. Min. Geol. Paläont. (B), 1927, p. 423-426.

_____1937, Über eine Säugetierelle aus dem Rät von Halberstadt: N. Jahrb. Min. Geol. Paläont. (B), Beilage-Band, v. 77, p. 310-319.

Dodson, M. H., Rex, D. C., Casey, R., and Allen, P., 1964, Glauconite dates from the Upper Jurassic and Lower Cretaceous: Geol. Soc. London Quart. Jour., v. 120S, p. 145-158.

Dyer, J., 1948, Paleontology and stratigraphy of the late Cretaceous of Polecat Bench, Park County, Wyoming [senior thesis]: Princeton, New Jersey, Princeton Univ., *ii* + 64 p.

Ellenberger, P., 1972, 1974, Contribution à la classification des Pistes de Vertébrés du Trias: Palaeovertebrata, Mémoire extraordinaire 1972 (pt. 1, 104 p.), 1974 (pt. 2, 141 p.) Montpellier.

Emmons, E., 1857, American geology, containing a statement of principles . . .: Albany, New York, Part 6, p. 1-152.

Ensom, P. C., 1977, A therapsid tooth from the Forest Marble (Middle Jurassic) of Dorset: Geol. Assoc. Proc., v. 88, p. 201-205.

Estes, R. D., and Berberian, P., 1970, Paleoecology of a Late Cretaceous vertebrate community from Montana: Breviora (Harvard Univ.), no. 343, 35 p.

Fitch, F. J., and Miller, J. A., 1971, Potassium-argon radioages of Karroo volcanic rocks from Lesotho: Bull. volcanologique, v. 35, p. 64-85.

Fox, R. C., 1972a, A primitive therian mammal from the Upper Cretaceous of Alberta: Canad. Jour. Earth Sci., v. 9, p. 1479-1494.

_____1972b, An Upper Cretaceous symmetrodont from Alberta, Canada: Nature, v. 239, p. 170-171.

_____1974, *Deltatheroides*-like mammals from the Upper Cretaceous of North America: *ibid.*, v. 249, p. 392.

_____1976a, Additions to the mammalian local fauna from the Upper Milk River Formation (Upper Cretaceous), Alberta: Canad. Jour. Earth Sci., v. 13, p. 1105-1118.

_____1976b, Cretaceous mammals (*Meniscoessus intermedius,* new species, and *Alphadon* sp.) from the lowermost Oldman Formation, Alberta: *ibid.,* v. 13, p. 1216-1222.

Freeman, E. F., 1976a, A mammalian fossil from the Forest Marble (Middle Jurassic) of Dorset: Geol. Assoc. Proc., v. 87, p. 231-235.

_____1976b, Mammal teeth from the Forest Marble (Middle Jurassic) of Oxfordshire, England: Science, v. 194, p. 1053-1055.

Gallois, R. W., 1965, The Wealden District: London, Geol. Surv. Mus., Dept. Scient. Indust. Res., *xii* + 101 p.

Gibson, D. W., 1977, Upper Cretaceous and Tertiary coal-bearing strata in the Drumheller-Ardley region, Red Deer River Valley, Alberta: Geol. Surv. Canad. Paper 76-35, 41 p.

Gill, P., 1974, Resorption of premolars in the early mammal *Kuehneotherium praecursoris:* Arch. Oral. Biol., v. 19, p. 327-328.

Gradziński, R., Kaźmierczak, J., and Lefeld, J., 1969, Geographical and geological data from the Polish-Mongolian Palaeontological Expeditions, *in* Kielan-Jaworowska, Z., ed., Results Polish-Mongol. Palaeont. Expeds., pt. I: Palaeontologia Polonica, no. 19, p. 33-82.

Gradziński, R., and Jerzykiewicz, T., 1972, Additional geographical and geological data from the Polish-Mongolian Palaeontological Expeditions, *in ibid.,* pt. IV: *ibid.,* no. 27, p. 17-32.

_____1974, Dinosaur- and mammal-bearing aeolian and associated deposits of the Upper Cretaceous in the Gobi Desert (Mongolia): Sediment. Geol., v. 12, p. 249-278.

Gradziński, R., Kielan-Jaworowska, Z., and Maryańska, T., 1977, Upper Cretaceous Djadokhta, Barun Goyot and Nemegt formations of Mongolia, including remarks on previous subdivisions: Acta Geol. Polonica, v. 27, p. 281-318.

Grambast, L., Martinez, M., Mattauer, M., and Thaler, L., 1967, *Perutherium altiplanense,* nov. gen., nov. sp., premier Mammifère mésozoïque d'Amérique du Sud: Acad. Sci. Paris C. R., sér. D, v. 264, p. 707-710.

Gregory, W. K., and Simpson, G. G., 1926, Cretaceous mammal skulls from Mongolia: Amer. Mus. Novitates, no. 225, 20 p.

Hahn, G., 1969, Beiträge zur Fauna der Grube Guimarota Nr. 3, die Multituberculata: Palaeontographica, Abt. A, v. 133, p. 1-100.

_____1971, The dentition of the Paulchoffatiidae (Multituberculata, Upper Jurassic): Memória 17 (N. S.) dos Serviços Geológicos de Portugal, Lisboa, p. 1-39.

_____1973, Neue Zähne von Haramiyiden aus der

deutschen Ober-Trias und ihre Beziehungen zu den Multituberculaten: Palaeontographica, Abt. A, v. 142, p. 1-15.

———1977, Neue Schädel-Reste von Multituberculaten aus dem Malm Portugals: Geologica et Palaeontologica, v. 11, p. 161-186.

Harland, W. B., Holland, C. H., House, M. R., Hughes, N. F., Reynolds, A. B., Rudwick, M. J. S., Satterthwaite, G. E., Tarlo, L. B. H., and Willey, E. C., 1967, The fossil record: London, Geol. Soc. London, Burlington House, xi + 827 p.

Hatcher, J. B., 1896, Some localities for Laramie mammals and horned dinosaurs: Amer. Natur., v. 30, p. 112-120.

Henkel, S., and Krebs, B., 1969, Zwei Säugetier-Unterkiefer aus der Untern Kreide von Uña (Prov. Cuenca, Spanien): N. Jahrb. Geol. Paläont. Monatsh., 1969, p. 449-463.

———1977, Der erste Fund eines Säugetier-Skelettes aus der Jura-Zeit: Umschau in Wissenschaft und Technik 77, p. 217-218.

Henning, E., 1922, Die Säugerzähne des württembergischen Rhät-Lias-Bonebeds: N. Jahrb. Min. Geol. Paläont., Beilage-Band, v. 46, p. 181-267.

Hsing, I., 1976, New discoveries of Triassic mammals at Lufeng, Yunnan: Vertebrata PalAsiatica, v. 14, p. 207 (in Chinese).

Hudleston, W. H., 1876, Excursion to Swindon and Faringdon: Geol. Assoc. (London) Proc., v. 4, p. 543-554.

Hüene, E. von, 1933, Zur Kenntnis des Württembergischen Rhätbonebeds mit Zahnfunden neuer Säuger und Säugerähnlicher Reptilien: Jahresh Vereine vaterl. Naturkunde Württemberg, 1933, p. 65-128.

Hüene, F. von, 1925, Triassischer Säugetierzahn aus Südwestafrika: Zbl. Min. Geol. Paläont. (B), 1925, p. 174-181.

Irish, E. J. W., 1970, The Edmonton group of south-central Alberta: Canad. Petrol. Geol. Bull., v. 18, p. 125-155.

Jenkins, F. A., Jr., and Parrington, F. R., 1976, The postcranial skeletons of the Triassic mammals *Eozostrodon, Megazostrodon* and *Erythrotherium*: Roy. Soc. London Philos. Trans., B (Biol. Sci.), v. 273, p. 387-431.

Jepsen, G. L., 1931, Dinosaur egg shell fragments from Montana: Science, v. 73, p. 12-13.

Kalandadze, N. N., and Reshetov, V. Yu., 1971a, Discoveries of the most ancient mammals in the Gobi: Priroda (Akademiya Nauk SSSR), no. 4, p. 106-107 (in Russian).

———1971b, Interesting paleontological finds in Mongolia: *ibid.*, no. 5, p. 83-84 (in Russian).

Keast, A., 1977, Historical biogeography of the marsupials, *in* Stonehouse, B., and Gilmore, D., eds., The biology of marsupials: London, Macmillan Press Ltd., p. 69-95.

Kermack, D. M., and Kermack, K. A., eds., 1971, Early mammals: Linn. Soc. Zool. Jour., v. 50, suppl. 1, *vix* + 203 p.

Kermack, D. M., Kermack, K. A., and Mussett, F., 1968, The Welsh pantothere *Kuehneotherium praecursoris:* Linn. Soc. Zool. Jour., v. 47, p. 407-423.

Kermack, K. A., 1963, The cranial structure of the triconodonts: Roy. Soc. London Philos. Trans., B (Biol. Sci.), v. 246, p. 83-103.

Kermack, K. A., Lees, P. M., and Mussett, F., 1965, *Aegialodon dawsoni,* a new trituberculosectorial tooth from the Lower Wealden: Roy. Soc. London Proc., B (Biol. Sci.), v. 162, p. 535-554.

Kermack, K. A., Mussett, F., and Rigney, H. W., 1973, The lower jaw of *Morganucodon:* Linn. Soc. Zool. Jour., v. 53, p. 87-175.

Kielan-Jaworowska, Z., 1969, Preliminary data on the Upper Cretaceous eutherian mammals from Bayn Dzak, Gobi Desert, *in* Kielan-Jaworowska, Z., ed., Results Polish-Mongol. Palaeont. Expeds., pt. I: Palaeontologia Polonica, no. 19, p. 171-191.

———1970, New Upper Cretaceous multituberculate genera from Bayn Dzak, Gobi Desert, *in ibid.*, pt. II: *ibid.*, no. 21, p. 35-49.

———1971, Skull structure and affinities of the Multituberculata, *in ibid.*, pt. III: *ibid.*, no. 25, p. 5-41.

———1974a, Multituberculate succession in the Late Cretaceous of the Gobi Desert (Mongolia), *in ibid.*, pt. V: *ibid.*, no. 30, p. 23-44.

———1974b, Migrations of the Multituberculata and the Late Cretaceous connections between Asia and North America: So. African Mus. Ann., v. 64, p. 231-243.

———1975a, Late Cretaceous mammals and dinosaurs from the Gobi Desert: Amer. Scient., v. 63, p. 150-159.

———1975b, Preliminary description of two new eutherian genera from the Late Cretaceous of Mongolia, *in* Kielan-Jaworowska, Z., ed., Results Polish-Mongol. Palaeont. Expeds., pt. VI: Palaeontologia Polonica, no. 33, p. 5-16.

———1975c, Evolution of the therian mammals in the Late Cretaceous of Asia. Part I. Deltatheridiidae, *in ibid.*, pt. VI: *ibid.*, no. 33, p. 103-132.

———1975d, Evolution and migrations of the Late Cretaceous Asian mammals, *in* Lehman, J. P., ed., Problèmes Actuels de Paléontologie-Évolution des Vertébrés: Paris, Colloque Internat., C.N.R.S., no. 218, p. 573-584.

Kielan-Jaworowska, Z., and Barsbold, R., 1972, Narrative of the Polish-Mongolian Palaeontological Expeditions 1967-1971, *in* Kielan-Jaworowska, Z., ed., Results of the Polish-Mongol. Palaeont. Expeds., pt. IV: Palaeontologia Polonica, no. 27, p. 5-13.

Kielan-Jaworowska, Z., and Dashzeveg, D., 1978, New Late Cretaceous mammal locality in Mongolia and a description of a new multituberculate: Acta Palaeont. Polonica, v. 23, p. 115-130.

Kielan-Jaworowska, Z., and Sloan, R. E., *in press, Catopsalis* (Multituberculata) from Asia and North America and the problem of taeniolabidid dispersal in the Late Cretaceous: *ibid.*, v. 24.

Kielan-Jaworowska, Z., and Sochava, A. V., 1969, The first multituberculate from the uppermost Cretaceous of the Gobi Desert (Mongolia): *ibid.*, v. 14, p. 355-367.

Kramarenko, N. N., 1974, On the work of the Joint Soviet-Mongolian Paleontological Expedition during the years 1969-1972, *in* Kramarenko, N. N., and others, eds., Mesozoic and Cenozoic faunas and biostratigraphy of Mongolia: Moscow, Joint Soviet-Mongol. Paleont. Exped. (Trans., v. 1), p. 9-18 (in Russian with English summary).

Krebs, B., 1971, Evolution of the mandible and lower dentition in dryolestids (Pantotheria, Mammalia), *in* Kermack, D. M., and Kermack, K. A., eds., Early mammals: Linn. Soc. Zool. Jour., v. 50, suppl. 1, p. 89-102.

Krusat, G., 1969, Ein Pantotheria-Molar mit dreispitzigem Talonid aus dem Kimmeridge von Portugal: Paläont. Zeit., v. 43, p. 52-56.

_____1974, *Haldanodon exspectatus* Kühne & Krusat 1972 (Mammalia, Docodonta): Berlin, Inaugural-Dissertation zur Erlangung der Doktorwurde des Fachbereiches 24 (Geowissenschaften) der Freien Universität Berlin, *iv* + 158 p.

Kühne, W. G., 1950, *Mucrotherium* und *Uniserium* E. v. Huene sind Fragmente unterer Backenzähne eines Tritylodontiers: N. Jahrb. Geol. Paläont. Monatsh., 1950, p. 187-191.

_____1956, The Liassic therapsid *Oligokyphus*: London, Trustees Brit. Mus., *x* + 149 p.

_____1958, Rhaetische Triconodonten aus Glamorgan, ihre Stellung zwischen den Klassen Reptilia und Mammalia und ihre Bedeutung für die Reichart'sche Theorie: Paläont. Zeit., v. 32, p. 197-235.

_____1961, A mammalian fauna from the Kimmeridgian of Portugal: Nature, v. 192, p. 274-275.

_____1966, Découverte de dents de Mammifères dans le Wealdien de Galve (Province de Teruel, Espagne): Teruel, v. 35, p. 159-161.

_____1968a, History of discovery, report on the work performed, procedure, technique and generalities: Contribuição para a Fauna do Kimeridgiano da Mina de Lignito Guimarota (Leiria, Portugal), 1 Parte, Memória 14 (N. S.) dos Serviços Geológicos de Portugal, Lisboa, p. 1-21.

_____1968b, Kimeridge [*sic*] mammals and their bearing on the phylogeny of the Mammalia, *in* Drake, E. T., ed., Evolution and environment: New Haven, Yale Univ. Press, p. 109-123.

_____1969, Säugetiere im Schatten der Dinosaurier: Umschau Wissen. Technik, H. 12, p. 373-377.

Kühne, W. G., and Crusafont-Pairó, M., 1968, Mamíferos del Wealdiense de Uña, cerca de Cuenca: Acta Geológica Hispánica, v. 3, p. 133-134.

Kühne, W. G., and Krusat, G., 1972, Legalisierung des Taxon *Haldanodon* (Mammalia, Docodonta): N. Jahrb. Geol. Paläont. Monatsh., H. 5, p. 300-302.

Kutty, T. S., 1969, Some contributions to the stratigraphy of the Upper Gondwana formations of the Pranhita Godavari Valley, Central India: Geol. Soc. India Jour., v. 10, p. 33-48.

Lambe, L. M., 1902, New genera and species from the Belly River Series (mid-Cretaceous): Geol. Surv. Canada, Contribs. Canad. Palaeont., v. III, pt. II, p. 25-81.

Lambert, R. *St* J., 1971, The pre-Pleistocene Phanerozoic time-scale—a review, *in* Harland, W. B., and Francis, E. H., eds., The Phanerozoic time-scale—A supplement: London, Geol. Soc. London Spec. Publ. 5, Burlington House, Part 1, p. 9-31.

Langston, W., Jr., 1974, Nonmammalian Comanchean tetrapods: Geoscience and Man, v. 8, p. 77-102.

Lawson, D. A., 1972, Paleoecology of the Tornillo Formation, Big Bend National Park, Brewster County, Texas [M. A. thesis]: Austin, Texas, Univ. Texas at Austin.

Ledoux, J.-C., Hartenberger, J.-L., Michaux, J., Sudre, J., and Thaler, L., 1966, Découverte d'un Mammifère dans le Crétacé supérieur à Dinosaures de Champ-Garimond près de Fons (Gard): Acad. Sci. Paris C. R., sér. D, v. 262, p. 1925-1928.

Lefeld, J., 1965, The age of mammal containing beds at Bain-Dzak northern Gobi Desert: Acad. Polon. Sci. Bull., Ser. sci. géol. géogr., v. 13, p. 81-83.

_____1971, Geology of the Djadokhta Formation at Bayn Dzak (Mongolia), *in* Kielan-Jaworowska, Z., ed., Results Polish-Mongol. Palaeont. Expeds., pt. III: Palaeontologia Polonica, no. 25, p. 10-127.

Lillegraven, J. A., 1969, Latest Cretaceous mammals of upper part of Edmonton Formation of Alberta, Canada, and review of marsupial-placental dichotomy in mammalian evolution: Univ. Kansas Paleont. Contribs., Art. 50 (Vertebrata 12), 122 p.

_____1972, Preliminary report on Late Cretaceous mammals from the El Gallo Formation, Baja California del Norte, Mexico: Nat. Hist. Mus. Los Angeles Co. Contribs. Sci., no. 232, 11 p.

_____1974, Biogeographical considerations of the marsupial-placental dichotomy: Ann. Rev. Ecol. Syst., v. 5, p. 263-283.

_____1976, A new genus of therian mammal from the Late Cretaceous "El Gallo Formation," Baja California, Mexico: Jour. Paleont., v. 50, p. 437-443.

McKenna, M. C., 1969, The origin and early differentiation of therian mammals: New York Acad. Sci. Ann., v. 167, p. 217-240.

_____1975, Toward a phylogenetic classification of the Mammalia, *in* Luckett, W. P., and Szalay, F. S., eds., Phylogeny of the primates: New York, Plenum Press, p. 21-46.

McKerrow, W. S., Johnson, R. T., and Jakobson, M. E., 1969, Palaeoecological studies in the Great Oolite at Kirtlington, Oxfordshire: Palaeontology, v. 12, p. 56-83.

McNulty, C. L., Jr., and Slaughter, B. H., 1968, Stratigraphy of the Woodbine Formation, Tarrant County, Texas (Locality 3): Field Trip Guidebook, 2nd Ann. Meet. South-Central Sec. Geol. Soc. America, p. 68-72.

Novacek, M. J., 1977, A review of Paleocene and Eocene Lepticidae (Eutheria: Mammalia) from North America: Paleobios, no. 24, 42 p.

Novacek, M. J., and Clemens, W. A., 1977, Aspects of intrageneric variation and evolution of *Mesodma* (Multituberculata, Mammalia): Jour. Paleont., v. 51, p. 701-717.

Olsen, P. E., and Galton, P. M., 1977, Triassic-Jurassic tetrapod extinctions: Are they real?: Science, v. 197, p. 983-985.

Osborn, H. F., 1886, A new mammal from the American Triassic: *ibid.*, v. 8, p. 540.

_____1887, Observations on the Triassic mammals *Dromatherium* and *Microconodon:* Amer. Philos. Soc. Proc., v. 24, p. 109-111.

Ostrom, J. H., and McIntosh, J. S., 1966, Marsh's dinosaurs—the collections from Como Bluff: New Haven, Yale Univ. Press, *xiv* + 388 p.

Owen, R., 1871, Monograph of the fossil Mammalia of the Mesozoic formations: Palaeontogr. Soc. Monog. 24, 115 p.

Palmer, T. J., 1973, Field meeting in the Great Oolite of Oxfordshire: Geol. Assoc. Proc., v. 84, p. 53-64.

Parrington, F. R., 1941, On two mammalian teeth from the Lower Rhaetic of Somerset: Ann. Mag. Nat. Hist., London, ser. 11, v. 8, p. 140-144.

_____1947, On a collection of Rhaetic mammalian teeth: Zool. Soc. London Proc., v. 116, p. 707-728.

_____1971, On the Upper Triassic mammals: Roy. Soc. London Philos. Trans., B (Biol. Sci.), v. 261, p. 231-272.

_____1973, The dentitions of the earliest mammals: Linn. Soc. Zool. Jour., v. 52, p. 85-95.

_____1978, A further account of the Triassic mammals: Roy. Soc. London Philos. Trans., B (Biol. Sci.), v. 282, p. 177-204.

Patterson, B., 1951, Early Cretaceous mammals from northern Texas: Amer. Jour. Sci., v. 249, p. 31-46.

_____1956, Early Cretaceous mammals and the evolution of mammalian molar teeth: Fieldiana (Geol.), v. 13, p. 1-105.

Patterson, B., and Olson, E. C., 1961, A triconodontid mammal from the Triassic of Yunnan, *in* Vandebroek, G., ed., International colloquium on the evolution of lower and non specialized mammals: Brussels, Kon. Vlaamse Acad. Wetensch., Lett. Schone Kunsten Belgie, pt. 1, p. 129-191.

Patterson, B., and Pascual, R., 1968, The fossil mammal fauna of South America: Quart. Rev. Biol., v. 43, p. 409-451.

Peyer, B., 1956, Über Zähne von Haramiyden [*sic*], von Triconodonten und von wahrscheinlich synapsiden Reptilien aus dem Rhät von Hallau, Kt. Schaffhausen, Schweiz: Schweiz. Paläont. Abh., v. 72, p. 1-72.

Plieninger, T., 1847, Ueber ein Bonebed auf der Gränze von Keuper und Lias: Verh. Ges. Deutsch. Naturforsch. Ärzte, XXIV, 262 p.

Portugal, J. A., 1974, Mesozoic and Cenozoic stratigraphy and tectonic events of Puno-Santa Lucia area, Department of Puno, Peru: Amer. Assoc. Petrol. Geol. Bull., v. 58, p. 982-999.

Richardson, L., Arkell, W. J., and Dines, H. G., 1946 (reprinted in 1963), Geology of the country around Witney: Geol. Surv. Great Britain Mem., Explanation of Sheet 236, p. 150.

Rigney, H. W., 1963, A specimen of *Morganucodon* from Yunnan: Nature, v. 197, p. 1122-1123.

Romer, A. S., 1956, Osteology of the reptiles: Chicago, Univ. Chicago Press, *xxi* + 772 p.

_____1966, Vertebrate paleontology (3*rd* ed.): *ibid., ix* + 468 p.

_____1969, Cynodont reptile with incipient mammalian jaw articulation: Science, v. 166, p. 881-882.

Russell, D. A., and Singh, C., 1978, The Cretaceous-Tertiary boundary in south-central Alberta—a reappraisal based on dinosaurian and microfloral extinctions: Canad. Jour. Earth Sci., v. 15, p. 284-292.

Russell, D., Russell, D., and Wouters, G., 1976, Une dent d'aspect mammalien en provenance du Rhétien Français: Geobios, no. 9, p. 377-392.

Russell, L. S., 1952, Cretaceous mammals of Alberta: Nat'l. Mus. Canada, Ann. Rept. for Fiscal Year 1950-1951, Bull. 126, p. 110-119.

_____1962, Mammal teeth from the St. Mary River Formation (Upper Cretaceous) at Scabby Butte, Alberta: Nat'l. Mus. Canada, Nat. Hist. Pap., no. 14, 4 p.

_____1964, Cretaceous non-marine faunas of northwestern North America: Roy. Ontario Mus. Contrib. 61 (Life Sci.), 24 p.

_____1975, Mammalian faunal succession in the Cretaceous system of western North America: Geol. Assoc. Canada Spec. Paper 13, p. 137-161.

Russell, L. S., and Landes, R. W., 1940, Geology of the southern Alberta plains: Geol. Surv. Canada Mem. 221, *iv* + 223 p.

Sahni, A., 1972, The vertebrate fauna of the Judith River Formation, Montana: Amer. Mus. Nat. Hist. Bull., v. 147, p. 321-412.

Savage, R. J. G., 1971, Tritylodontid *incertae sedis*: Bristol Nat. Soc. Proc., v. 32, p. 80-83.

Savage, R. J. G., and Waldman, M., 1966, *Oligokyphus* from Holwell Quarry, Somerset: *ibid.,* v. 31, p. 185-192.

Sharov, A. G., 1971, New flying reptiles from the Mesozoic of Kazakhstan and Kirgizia, *in* Contemporary problems of paleontology: Trudy Paleontologicheskogo instituta, v. 130, p. 104-113 (in Russian).

Shikama, T., 1947, *Teilhardosaurus* and *Endotherium,*

new Jurassic Reptilia and Mammalia from the Husin Coal-field, South Manchuria: Japan Acad. Proc., v. 23, p. 76-84.

Shuvalov, V. F., 1974, On geology and age of Khobur [Khovboor] and Khurfn-Dukh localities in Mongolia, in Kramarenko, N. N., and others, eds., Mesozoic and Cenozoic faunas and biostratigraphy of Mongolia: Moscow, Joint Soviet-Mongol. Paleont. Exped. (Trans., v. 1), p. 296-304 (in Russian with English summary).

Sigé, B., 1968, Dents de Micromammifères et fragments de coquilles d'oeufs de Dinosauriens dans la fauna de Vertébrés du Crétacé supérieur de Laguna Umayo (Andes péruviennes): Acad. Sci. Paris C. R., sér. D, v. 267, p. 1495-1498.

———1971, Les Didelphoidea de Laguna Umayo (formation Vilquechico, Crétacé supérieur, Pérou), et le peuplement marsupial d'Amérique du Sud: ibid., v. 273, p. 2479-2481.

———1972, La faunule de mammifères du Crétacé supérieur de Laguna Umayo (Andes péruviennes): Mus. Natl. Hist. Natur. Bull., 3e ser., no. 99, Sciences de la Terre 19, p. 375-409.

Simpson, G. G., 1926, Mesozoic Mammalia. V. Dromatherium and Microconodon: Amer. Jour. Sci., v. 12, p. 87-108.

———1928a, A catalogue of the Mesozoic Mammalia in the Geological Department of The British Museum: London, Oxford Univ. Press, x + 215 p.

———1928b, Mesozoic Mammalia. XI. Brancatherulum tendagurense Dietrich: Amer. Jour. Sci., v. 15, p. 303-308.

———1929, American Mesozoic Mammalia: Peabody Mus. (Yale Univ.) Mem., v. 3, pt. 1, Yale Univ. Press, xv + 171 p.

———1937, A new Jurassic mammal: Amer. Mus. Novitates, no. 943, 6 p.

———1948, Como Bluff, in McGrew, P. O., ed., Guidebook to 3rd Ann. Field Conf. Soc. Vert. Paleont. in Southeastern Wyoming, 2-5 Aug. 1948: Laramie, Univ. Wyoming, p. 27-36.

———1971, Concluding remarks: Mesozoic mammals revisited, in Kermack, D. M., and Kermack, K. A., eds., Early mammals: Linn. Soc. Zool. Jour., v. 50, suppl. 1, p. 181-198.

Slaughter, B. H., 1969, Astroconodon, the Cretaceous triconodont: Jour. Mammal., v. 50, p. 102-107.

———1971, Mid-Cretaceous (Albian) therians of the Butler Farm local fauna, Texas, in Kermack, D. M., and Kermack, K. A., eds., Early mammals: Linn. Soc. Zool. Jour., v. 50, suppl. 1, p. 131-143.

———1975a, Progress note: News Bull., Soc. Vert. Paleont., no. 104, p. 10.

———1975b, Progress note: ibid., no. 105, p. 26.

Sloan, R. E., and Russell, L. S., 1974, Mammals from the St. Mary River Formation (Cretaceous) of southwestern Alberta: Roy. Ontario Mus. Life Sci. Contribs., v. 95, p. 1-21.

Sloan, R. E., and Van Valen, L., 1965, Cretaceous mammals from Montana: Science, v. 148, p. 220-227.

Smith, J. F., Jr., and Ketner, K. B., 1972, Generalized geologic map of the Carlin, Dixie Flats, Pine Valley, and Robinson Mountain quadrangles, Elko and Eureka counties, Nevada: U. S. Geol. Surv. Misc. Field Studies Map MF-481, scale 1:125,000.

Sylvester-Bradley, P. C., 1940, The Purbeck Beds of Swindon: Geol. Assoc. (London) Proc., v. 51, p. 349-372.

Szalay, F. S., and McKenna, M. C., 1971, Beginning of the age of mammals in Asia: the late Paleocene Gashato fauna, Mongolia: Amer. Mus. Nat. Hist. Bull., v. 144, p. 269-318.

Trofimov, B. A., 1975, New data on Buginbaatar Kielan-Jaworowska et Sochava, 1969 (Mammalia, Multituberculata) from Mongolia, in Kramarenko, N. N., and others, eds., Fossil fauna and flora of Mongolia: Moscow, Joint Soviet-Mongol. Paleont. Exped. (Trans., v. 2), p. 7-13 (in Russian with English summary).

Van Hinte, J. E., 1976a, A Jurassic time scale: Amer. Assoc. Petrol. Geol. Bull., v. 60, p. 489-497.

———1976b, A Cretaceous time scale: ibid., v. 60, p. 498-516.

Van Valen, L., 1967, The first discovery of a Cretaceous mammal: Amer. Mus. Novitates, no. 2285, 4 p.

Van Valen, L., and Sloan, R. E., 1965, The earliest primates: Science, v. 150, p. 743-745.

Waage, K. M., 1968, The type Fox Hills Formation, Cretaceous (Maestrichtian), South Dakota: Peabody Mus. Nat. Hist. (Yale Univ.) Bull. 27, 175 p.

Waldman, M., and Savage, R. J. G., 1972, The first Jurassic mammal from Scotland: Geol. Soc. London Jour., v. 128, p. 119-125.

West, I. M., 1975, Evaporites and associated sediments of the basal Purbeck Formation (Upper Jurassic) of Dorset: Geol. Assoc. (London) Proc., v. 86, p. 205-225.

Wilson, R. W., 1965, Type localities of Cope's Cretaceous mammals: South Dakota Acad. Sci. Proc., v. 44, p. 88-90.

Yabe, H., and Shikama, T., 1938, A new Jurassic Mammalia from South Manchuria: Imp. Acad. Tokyo Proc., v. 14, p. 353-357.

Young, C. C., 1978, New materials of Eozostrodon: Vertebrata PalAsiatica, v. 16, p. 1-3 (in Chinese with English abstract).

CHAPTER 3

ORIGIN OF MAMMALS

A. W. Crompton

Farish A. Jenkins, Jr.

INTRODUCTION

The history of mammalian origins is a complex story that is only slowly unfolding. The Permo-Triassic mammal-like reptile faunas of southern Africa, and the Jurassic mammalian faunas of Europe and North America, both discovered in the last century, have been central to the development of theories on the reptile-mammal transition. The early work on these faunas was largely descriptive and taxonomic, but as advanced mammal-like reptiles and Jurassic mammals became better known through detailed comparative studies, beginning about 1925, it was possible to perceive the outline of early mammalian history. Yet, until recently, transitional forms were virtually unknown from a period that included the second half of the Triassic and the early part of the Jurassic. The radiation of the most advanced therapsids, the cynodonts, was under way at the beginning of this period; by the end, mammals were represented by at least five major groups. The apparent early diversity of mammals gave Simpson (1928, 1929) reason to propose a polyphyletic origin of various Jurassic groups from cynodonts. Subsequent work on mammal-like reptiles revealed tendencies among certain advanced lineages to develop "mammalian" features in parallel (*e.g.,* a secondary bony palate, enlargement of the dentary, squamoso-dentary jaw articulation). These findings led Olson (1959) and others to support the idea that mammals were derived polyphyletically from different groups of therapsids.

The concept of a polyphyletic derivation of mammals from reptiles originated from limited evidence. About 50 million years separated the records of the last known radiation of mammal-like reptiles and the Jurassic mammalian faunas. Rather than a single transition, multiple transitions of therapsids to a mammalian grade could be envisioned in the intervening time. Such an interpretation strongly influenced later analyses of the reptile-mammal transition, even in the face of the discoveries of Rhaeto-Liassic mammals which made plausible quite different interpretations (Kermack and Mussett, 1959). The spectre of polyphyly in a major vertebrate class elicited much discussion on how such a class might be defined and which taxa were appropriately included (Kühne, 1956, 1958;

Simpson, 1959; Van Valen, 1960; Kermack, 1967; MacIntyre, 1967).

More recently, investigations into mammalian origins have focussed on Rhaeto-Liassic mammals (Parrington, 1971, 1973; see Jenkins and Parrington, 1976, for a review of the literature), now the earliest known representatives of the class, and Middle Triassic cynodonts (Romer, 1970; Crompton, 1972a, 1972b), distinguished among advanced therapsids for their acquisition of a suite of features from which the basic structural plan of mammals could have been derived. Forms much closer to the ''transition'' are thus becoming known. From these studies comes not only a clearer understanding of the transition itself, but a redefinition of the remaining problems to be solved. In this chapter we attempt to recount only the more recent discoveries and theories, cognizant of the fact that future work will continue to unfold this complex story of mammalian origins. For a review of this subject prior to 1973, see Crompton and Jenkins (1973).

MORGANUCODONTIDS AND THE ADAPTATIONS OF RHAETO-LIASSIC MAMMALS

Of the several kinds of early mammals known from Rhaeto-Liassic deposits, the triconodont family Morganucodontidae is best represented in the fossil record. Thus, much of current opinion on the origin of mammals is based on *Eozostrodon*[1] [*Morganucodon*], *Megazostrodon,* and *Erythrotherium.* For reasons outlined elsewhere (Chapter 4), morganucodontids are possibly ancestral to later triconodonts, another extinct lineage (Docodonta), and the unknown group from which monotremes arose; all are probably removed from the ancestry of placentals and marsupials (Fig. 3-1).

Many morganucodontid features appear to have originated in parallel among various lineages of mammal-like reptiles. Nonetheless, morganucodontids achieved a level of structural organization well advanced beyond that of any therapsid. All of their features, considered together, clearly set them apart from any known therapsid stock. A synopsis of these features is as follows:

1. The jaw joint is formed in part by the squamosal and dentary (Kermack and others, 1973), as in mammals, but also by the quadrate and articular (the typical reptilian condition) which lie medially adjacent to the squamoso-dentary articulation (Fig. 3-2*F*).

2. The postcanine teeth are differentiated into premolars and molars (Fig. 3-2*D*). The premolars appear to have been preceded by deciduous teeth (Parrington, 1971), but there is no evidence for replacement of the molars. Hopson (1973) suggested that this type of limited tooth replacement is related to rapid growth rate of juveniles and to dependence upon maternal milk for nourishment (see Chapter 13). A functional set of teeth is not essential in the immediate postpartum period. Consequently, considerable postnatal growth in mammals can take place before the eruption of the milk teeth. In contrast, juvenile reptiles are independent as hatchlings and must feed themselves. During maturation, many series of tooth replacements are required to match the relatively large size increase from hatchling to adult.

3. During occlusion, the buccal or outer surface of the lower molars shear against the lingual or inner surface of the uppers, forming a consistent pattern of clearly defined wear facets (Crompton, 1974) (Fig. 3-2*E*).

4. Jaw movement during occlusion is guided in a dorsomedial direction by the structure of the molars. This movement is part of a masticatory pattern common to most mammals in which the jaw moves ventrally during opening, dorsolaterally during the early phase of closing, and dorsomedially during the final stage of intermolar occlusion (*ibid.*). Normally, only one side of the jaw is brought into occlusion during a single chewing cycle. This triangular masticatory route and differential use of the two postcanine tooth rows was first developed in early mammals.

5. The cavum epiptericum is partially floored below the trigeminal and geniculate ganglia. This floor joins the anterior lamina in front of and behind the mandibular branch of the trigeminal nerve to form a foramen pseudovale. The VIIth nerve leaves this enclosed space by two separate foramina. In other aspects, however, the structure of the lateral wall of the braincase is almost identical to that in some cynodonts (such as *Thrinaxodon* and *Probainognathus*) and very different from that of monotremes.

---

1. Editors' note: Elsewhere in this book the generic name *Eozostrodon* is referred to as *Morganucodon* (see fourth footnote to text of Chapter 4 for further discussion).

6. A well-developed fenestra rotunda is present lateral to the jugular foramen (Kermack, 1963).

7. The cochlear region of the inner ear is large relative to skull size when compared with that of cynodonts, and is a dominant feature on the ventral surface of the braincase.

8. All known Triassic mammals were small. Their body weight, estimated at 20 to 30 g, is an order of magnitude smaller than that of any known middle Triassic cynodont.

9. The presence of an anticlinal vertebra and major structural differences between thoracic and lumbar vertebrae represent specializations for dorso-ventral flexure of the trunk. Thus, morganucodontids appear to have achieved the basic adaptations for truncal posture and movement which distinguish mammals (Jenkins and Parrington, 1976).

10. The atlanto-axial joint possesses a large, protuberant dens, one of several typically mammalian specializations for rotary movement. The double occipital condyles lie at the ventrolateral margins of the foramen magnum. Although the atlas arches and intercentrum do not fuse into an annular structure as in later mammals, the atlanto-occipital

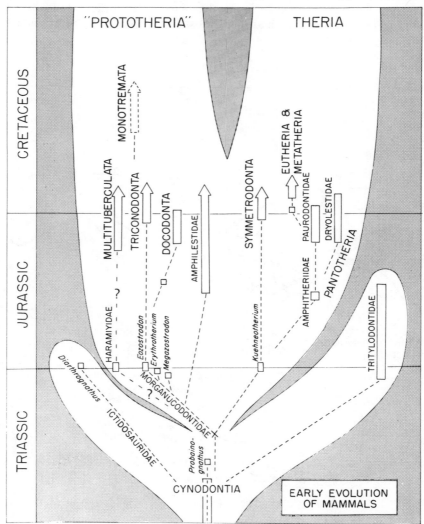

Figure 3-1. Current interpretation of the evolution and relationships of early mammals. The Order Pantotheria is here used *sensu* Simpson (1929), and includes three families (Amphitheriidae, Paurodontidae, and Dryolestidae). Elsewhere in the book the term Eupantotheria is used for essentially the same taxonomic grouping, with the addition of the Family Peramuridae (represented by *Peramus*, which Simpson, *ibid.*, considered a paurodontid).

joint is specialized for movements of flexion-extension.

11. The pelvis is that of a pattern basic to mammals, with a narrow, rod-like ilium directed antero-dorsally, a large obturator foramen, and a reduced pubis.

The fossil record of Morganucodontidae is sufficient to establish these and other structural features of mammals as present in at least the earliest known members of the class; indeed, the development of many major and interrelated features of the skull and postcranial skeleton was under way in their cynodont ancestors. Several therapsid groups that survived into Late Triassic times, such as the ictidosaurs and tritylodontids (Kühne, 1956; Crompton, 1964), independently attained certain mammalian features to an extent comparable to those in morganucodontids. Among these were a squamoso-dentary articulation, an externally visible fenestra rotunda, an anteriorly directed, rod-like ilium, and a reduced pubis. However, the ictidosaurs, tritylodontids, and other advanced therapsids were highly specialized in other features, and in no case appear to have developed the remaining suite of mammalian characteristics listed above.

The fossil record is quite deficient in evidence for other kinds of adaptations (behavioral, physiological, reproductive, and anatomical) among

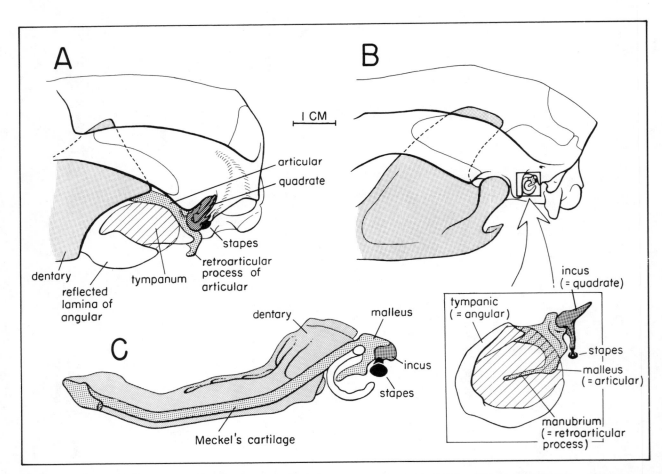

Figure 3-2. Interrelationship between the masticatory apparatus and the middle ear in mammalian evolution: *A*, reconstruction of a cynodont, *Thrinaxodon liorhinus*, in which the quadrate and articular not only formed the jaw joint, but also conducted vibrations from the tympanum (supported by the reflected lamina of the angular) to the stapes; *B*, the middle ear in the North American opossum (*Didelphis virginiana*), as in other mammals, lies behind the squamoso-dentary joint, and retains elements of the sound-conducting system of mammal-like reptiles; *C*, medial view of the jaw in a fetal mammal to show the developmental parallels of the middle ear and jaw joint complex with the phylogenetic origin of these

which are found fundamental mammalian features. Some of these may be inferred by extrapolation from both paleontological and neontological studies, although at present such conclusions are weighted with variable degrees of uncertainty.

Jenkins and Parrington (1976) view the small Triassic triconodonts as insectivores adapted to active foraging in an arboreal/terrestrial habitat. This model is based upon considerations of their size and shearing dentition, as well as of adaptations in the axial and appendicular skeleton for a postural and locomotor repertoire comparable to that in many Recent small mammals. For example, the structural modifications of the hallux which permit independent movement of this digit, and which in the tree

shrew *Tupaia* are employed for hallucal prehensity in climbing, are present in *Megazostrodon*.

Jerison (1973) recently revived the idea that the earliest mammals were nocturnal. The evidence for nocturnal habits derives both from paleontological and neontological sources, although neither can be considered definitive. Jerison cites the relative increase in brain size among Mesozoic mammals (based on a nearly complete cranial endocast of *Triconodon* and partial endocasts of *Amblotherium* and *Sinoconodon rigneyi*), and argues that this relates to enhanced auditory and olfactory acuity as adaptations for nocturnal rather than diurnal activity. More recently, Crompton and Jenkins (1978) have determined that the relative brain to body size is at least

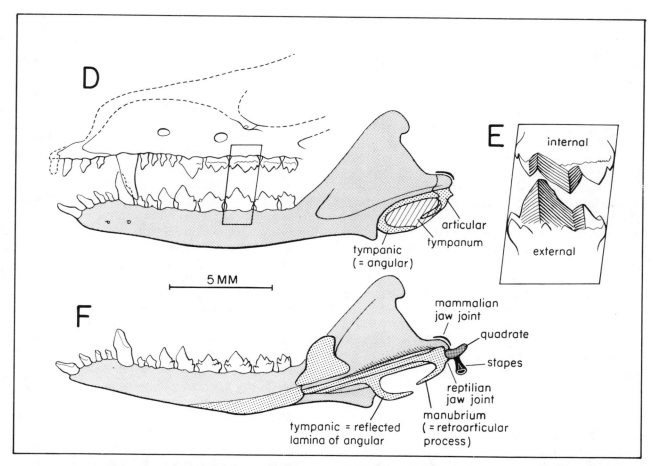

structures (compare with *A* and *F*); *D*, reconstruction of the teeth and jaws of a Rhaeto-Liassic mammal, *Eozostrodon*, in lateral view (compare the disposition of the tympanum with that in *A*, above); *E*, the molar occlusal pattern of *Eozostrodon* (in order to illustrate both the intercuspal relationships and the wear facets, the internal surface of the upper molar is viewed as if the tooth were transparent); and *F*, reconstruction of the lower jaw of *Eozostrodon* in medial view, illustrating relationships of postdentary bones to the squamoso-dentary (mammalian) jaw joint. (*C* and ear ossicles in inset modified after Gaupp, 1913; *D* and *F* modified after Parrington, 1971, Kermack and others, 1973, and Allin, 1975) very similar, and perhaps identical, in morganucodontids and Cretaceous triconodonts, and that the ratio represents a three- to fourfold increase over that in the most advanced mammal-like reptiles. Refined musculoskeletal coordination, together with greater auditory and olfactory acuity, are possibly all represented in this volumetric increase.

Auditory and olfactory acuity alike would have been critical adaptations for small, nocturnal insectivores. The gradual reduction of the quadrate and incus in advanced therapsids, and their divestment from the masticatory system in mammals, can be interpreted in this framework, especially if these bones were already involved in sound conduction in therapsids (Allin, 1975; Crompton and Parker, 1978) (Fig. 3-2). Although the separation of the masticatory and auditory complexes was apparently not completed until post Rhaeto-Liassic times, the enlarged cochlear housing of the Rhaeto-Liassic mammals is evidence that greater auditory sensitivity accompanied the establishment of a secondary, or squamoso-dentary, jaw articulation. In later forms the postdentary bones and quadrate no longer filled the dual roles of jaw hinge and sound conductors and were freed for increasing specialization as an auditory device. The evidence for the evolutionary development of olfactory acuity is rather tenuous, and rests chiefly on Simpson's (1927) comparison of the endocranial cast of *Triconodon* and the cynodont *Nythrosaurus*. Both have relatively large olfactory bulbs and nasal chambers, as well as cartilaginous ethmoturbinals. On other than Jerison's interpretation of increased brain size in Mesozoic mammals, the evidence for an increase in olfactory acuity appears insufficient (such a trend, however, perhaps will be discerned from recently discovered but as yet unpublished materials).

Comparative anatomical studies of the vertebrate eye also have provided indirect evidence which supports Jerison's hypothesis. Walls (1942) concluded that some of the unique specializations of the retina in mammals are derivatives of a nocturnally adapted visual system.

Crompton and others (1978) have recently summarized the evidence for endothermy in the earliest mammals. Indeed, endogenous thermoregulation is consistent with the interpretation of nocturnal habits among the small Rhaeto-Liassic mammals that would have been active over a wide range of low ambient temperatures. As in various "primitive" living nocturnal mammals, such as tenrecs and hedgehogs, the early mammals probably regulated their body temperature below 30° C. Furthermore, they were able to maintain a constant body temperature in ambient temperatures lower than that of the body, despite a lower metabolic rate than would be encountered in a diurnal mammal of the same size. As in the case of tenrecs, the early mammals probably lacked the complex physiological mechanisms necessary to cope with the high heat loads that can accompany a diurnal existence.

THERAPSID ANCESTORS OF MAMMALS

The process of identifying the therapsid ancestors of mammals must begin with reference to the morganucodontid characters discussed above and proceed to the determination of which therapsid lineage evolved such characters as a complex. Isolating characters for comparison is, of course, a somewhat artificial procedure, and at the very least engenders the risk that any particular character may be misinterpreted either in its adaptive significance or its phylogenetic development. It is worthwhile noting, therefore, that most "mammalian" characters as identified from fossil material are osteological and represent only a fraction of the anatomical, physiological, and behavioral complexes undergoing phylogenetic change. Furthermore, these characters are interrelated in a more complicated manner than can ever be reconstructed from the fossil record alone. Any attempt to establish the relationships between morganucodontids and antecedent therapsids is seriously constrained by the nature of this evidence. For the moment, we exclude from consideration other early mammalian groups (Kuehneotheriidae, Haramiyidae) for which anatomical evidence is still very limited; the significance of these taxa to the question of mammalian ancestry is potentially important, however, and they are discussed separately below.

A feature of primary importance is the structure of the jaw joint which in morganucodontids and all other known mammals is comprised of a squamoso-dentary contact. The primitive reptilian condition is that of a joint between the articular (one of the so-called postdentary bones of the lower jaw) and the quadrate (hinged in variable fashion on the squamosal); in the total composition of the jaw and its suspensorium, the dentary is large but is not the major element. The relative increase in size of the dentary relative to that of the postdentary bones is a well-known phenomenon of therapsid evolution, and is especially characteristic of the cynodont, therocephalian, and bauriamorph lineages (Fig. 3-3).

Only in cynodonts, however, does this structural alteration reach advanced stages, *i.e.,* in ictidosaurs (Fig. 3-3*D*), traversodontids (Fig. 3-3*C*), tritylodontids, galesaurids, cynognathids, and chiniquodontids (Crompton, 1972a; Hopson, 1969). In certain cynodont families, notably traversodontids, cynognathids, and chiniquodontids, a secondary contact between the surangular and squamosal is developed.

Such a contact possibly served to impede excessive backward movement of the jaw, and thus acted much as a postglenoid process in higher mammals in buttressing the joint against forces that might result in posterior dislocation. The question of function aside, the establishment of a surangular-squamosal contact appears to have been an intermediate stage in the development of the definitive mammalian jaw joint. No therapsid groups other than cynodonts are known to have attained this level of organization.

Further development of the jaw joint complex took place in the chiniquodontids, and notably in

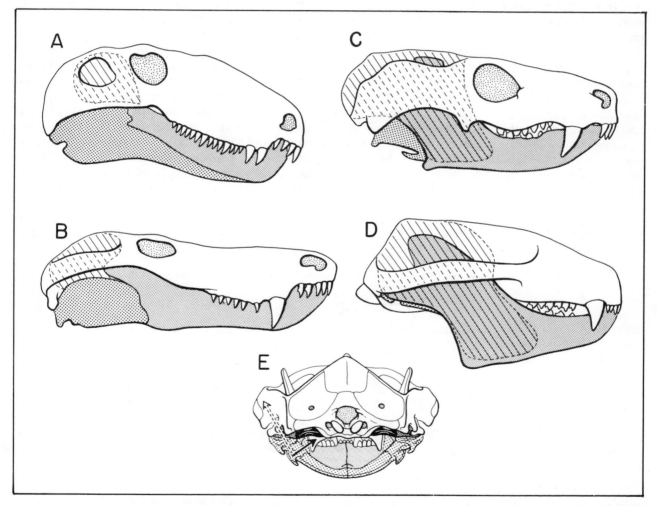

Figure 3-3. **Skulls of primitive mammal-like reptiles (***A***,** *Dimetrodon***, Early Permian;** *B***,** *Pristerognathoides***, Late Permian) and advanced mammal-like reptiles (***C***,** *Trirachodon***, Early Triassic;** *D***,** *Diarthrognathus***, Late Triassic). From the Permian to the Triassic, the dentary (light stippling) progressively enlarged relative to the postdentary bones (heavy stippling). This trend was accompanied by an increase in the mass of adductor muscles (oblique hatching).** *E***, occipital view of the skull of a cynodont (***Thrinaxodon***, Early Triassic), depicting an essentially mammalian organization of the masseteric (dashed arrow) and pterygoideus (dark arrow) musculature. The stapes is black, the postdentary bones stippled; the darkly stippled quadrate is seen lateral to stapes. Not to scale.**

Probainognathus (Fig. 3-4). Here a clearly defined glenoid fossa, presumably associated with articular cartilage and synovial tissue, was established in the squamosal. Alongside the surangular, which articulated with the glenoid, lies the "articular process" of the dentary, which at least buttressed the surangular and possibly invaded the joint capsule as well. The final stage in the evolution of this joint is exemplified by morganucodontids, in which the dentary extended more posteriorly, excluded the surangular from the joint, and alone represents the articular contact of the jaw with the squamosal.

In other groups of advanced cynodonts, similar modifications of the jaw joint occurred. For example, in ictidosaurs (Crompton, 1972a) a well-defined dentary condyle for articulation with the squamosal is present although a glenoid fossa is not; the latter, however, may have been formed principally by cartilaginous tissue. Among tritylodontids, which combine many mammalian features with some obvious specializations for herbivory, a glenoid fossa in the squamosal and a condyle on the dentary have not yet been identified; the discovery of a mammalian joint upon further study, however, would not be unexpected, although clearly the tritylodontids are removed as a group from mammalian ancestry.

Most interpretations of the reduction of postdentary bones in cynodonts relate to changes in masticatory efficiency (Crompton, 1963; Barghusen and Hopson, 1970; Kermack and others, 1973). Allin (1975), however, has suggested that the postdentary bones of cynodonts not only formed part of the jaw joint, but were also involved in transmission of vibrations to the inner ear. According to his reconstruction, the reflected lamina of the angular supported a tympanic membrane. Diminution of the postdentary bones would improve their sensitivity as transmittors of tympanic membrane vibrations. Thus, the reduction of the postdentary bones in cynodonts and the concomitant increase in the size of the dentary involved selection for auditory acuity rather than an evolutionary development in mastication alone. If, indeed, the postdentary bones of early cynodonts were involved in hearing, the independent and parallel decrease in the size of these bones and accompanying increase in the size of the dentary would not be unexpected in different cynodont lineages.

A second feature of importance is the configuration of the adductor muscles of the jaw. Cynodonts, apart from all other groups of mammal-like reptiles, progressively developed masseteric muscles. These adductor muscles passed from the temporal or infratemporal fossa between the jaw and a laterally bowed zygomatic arch, and inserted onto the lateral surface of the lower jaw (masseteric fossa) (Fig. 3-3C, D) (Barghusen, 1968). The elaboration of this

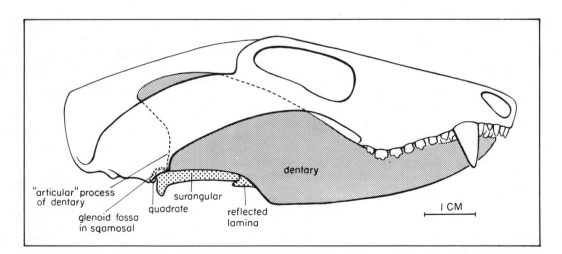

Figure 3-4.   **Reconstruction of the skull of *Probainognathus jenseni* (a Middle Triassic cynodont) in lateral view to show relationships of bones forming the jaw joint. The glenoid fossa in the squamosal, the "articular" process of the dentary (the site of the condyle in mammals), and the surangular condyle are not exposed in lateral view, but are here indicated in broken lines as if the zygomatic arch were transparent.**

part of the adductor complex has been interpreted as having several effects. First, jaw movements, especially in the transverse plane, were brought under more delicate control; each side of the jaw was in effect suspended in a muscular sling composed of the pterygoids medially and the masseter laterally. Second, the addition of masseteric musculature increased the force of the bite. Third, the stress on the jaw joint was reduced as the resultant muscle forces changed their orientation and were directed through the point of bite rather than through the articular-quadrate fulcral point. In neither the therocephalians nor the bauriamorphs, two groups of advanced therapsids which at one time or another have been considered to be mammalian ancestors, is there any indication of adductor muscle migration to the surface of the dentary.

In addition to the postdentary complex and adductor musculature, there are other features developed only in cynodonts that further link them phylogenetically with mammals. Among these are the following: (1) in certain more primitive forms (*e.g.,* *Thrinaxodon*) postcanine teeth are basically tricuspid and structurally very similar to those in morganucodontids (Crompton and Jenkins, 1968); (2) in advanced forms, postcanine teeth became increasingly complex and double rooted (*i.e.,* tritylodontids), and even developed precise occlusion and limited replacement (Crompton, 1972b); and (3) an epipterygoid with an extensive contact with the anterior border of the periotic, a lateral process of the periotic which abuts the quadrate rami of the epipterygoid, and a well-developed recess in the periotic for the trigeminal ganglion. All these features are seen in *Eozostrodon*, probably the oldest known morganucodontid (Kermack, 1963; Kermack and Kielan-Jaworowska, 1971).

The question remains as to which group of cynodonts gave rise to mammals. There is no clear answer at present. Some groups (*e.g.,* tritylodontids) that acquired decidedly mammalian structures both in cranial and postcranial anatomy are, in other features (such as dentition), so specialized as to remove them from consideration. The question of ancestry is clouded by the fact that at least one important family of early mammals (the kuehneotheriids) is known only from dental remains, and even their relationship to morganucodontids (much less to cynodonts) has been debated on the basis of the available evidence. The Chiniquodontidae in-

clude the most advanced forms of cynodonts that did not evolve the peculiar specializations typical of tritylodontids and ictidosaurs. For the present, the chiniquodontid *Probainognathus* appears to be the closest known representative of the pre-mammalian lineage. It is unlikely, however, that *Probainognathus* was directly ancestral to the Morganucodontidae, because of the relative reduction of cingular cusps on the postcanine teeth. Despite this, *Probainognathus* was probably closely related to the group that gave rise to these mammals, for the following reasons: (1) the glenoid fossa is developed in the squamosal (although the dentary did not contact the squamosal, it lies very close to this joint); (2) the postcanine dentition consists of teeth that are longitudinally ovate in crown view and possess small cingular cusps; (3) the structure of the periotic and its relationship to the alisphenoid in triconodontids (as well as in the Morganucodontidae) could have been derived from that of cynodonts such as *Probainognathus;* (4) the frequency of tooth replacement in *Probainognathus* was lower than in more primitive cynodonts, such as *Thrinaxodon*; and (5) there are no obvious specializations in the skeleton of *Probainognathus* that would preclude it from having been ancestral to the morganucodontids.

If *Probainognathus* is a representative of the group from which mammals arose, the major changes that took place during the reptile-mammal transition would have been: (1) reduction in body size; (2) invasion of the squamoso-surangular joint by the articular process of the dentary, and further reduction of the postdentary bones, quadrate, and stapes; (3) enlargement of the brain, with particular increase in the volume of the cranial cavity in the region between the orbits; (4) increase in size of the cochlear housing within the periotic, decrease in size of the paroccipital processes, ventral exposure of the fenestra rotunda, and development of a bony wall external to the trigeminal ganglion; (5) differentiation of the postcanine tooth row into molars and premolars, with reduction of tooth replacement to two sets (milk and permanent); (6) development of a tongue-and-groove mechanism between successive molars (this is required for precise occlusion, and is lacking in cynodonts such as *Probainognathus*); (7) acquisition of typically mammalian jaw movements, involving a triangular excursion with a dorsomedially directed occlusal phase; and (8) further development of mammalian features in the postcranial axial skeleton (*e.g.*, structural differentiation of the cervical, thoracic, and lumbar series) and appendicular skeleton (*e.g.*, reduction of the procoracoid and pubis, reorientation of the ilium).

KUEHNEOTHERIIDAE AND THE MONOPHYLY-POLYPHYLY QUESTION

Kuehneotheriids are small Rhaeto-Liassic mammals, associated with *Eozostrodon* in several faunas, which at present are known only from isolated upper and lower teeth and jaws (Kermack and others, 1968; Parrington, 1971, 1973). Other skeletal parts have not been recovered, or at least have not yet been identified. As a result, the prevailing interpretation of their relationships, which links them to later symmetrodonts, pantotheres, and other therians, is based solely on their postcanine tooth structure.

Kuehneotherium praecursoris was a small insectivore that probably had attained the same grade of mammalian organization as contemporary morganucodontids. The similarities and differences in molar structure between *Kuehneotherium* and that typical of morganucodontids have been documented elsewhere (Kermack and others, 1968; Parrington, 1973; Crompton, 1974). Here it suffices to note that the two major differences are the position of the secondary cusps relative to the primary cusp on each molariform tooth, and the relative position of upper and lower cusps during occlusion (see Chapter 9). Despite these differences, the wear facets on the teeth reveal that the lower jaw moved through a triangular route, an excursion which is a fundamental characteristic of the mammalian masticatory system. Furthermore, the well-developed dentary condyle, the retention of a groove for the much reduced postdentary bones, and the persistence of the quadrate (incus) and articular (malleus) as part of the jaw articulation are all features shared by *Kuehneotherium* and morganucodontids.

The simultaneous occurrence both of reptilian (quadrate-articular) and mammalian (squamoso-dentary) types of jaw joints in individuals of at least two groups of early mammals is not unexpected. Essentially the same level of organization was achieved by certain advanced cynodonts (Fig. 3-2*A*, *D*), and thus this represents the retention of an ancestral condition. However, the quadrate and articular in the early mammals are relatively smaller than in any known cynodont, and this diminution represents a further advance toward dissociation of the middle ear and jaw joint complexes.

If the currently proposed ancestral relationships of morganucodontids to nontherian mammals and kuehneotheriids to therians is correct, then the structural and functional separation of a three-boned middle ear from the jaw must have occurred as the result of later, independent evolution. The existence of a well-developed dentary condyle in both lineages was prerequisite to further reduction of the articular (versus auditory) function of the quadrate and articular bones. The fact that the ossicular chain in later therians and nontherians evolved to such structural and functional similarity is explicable in terms of the presumed auditory association of postdentary bones in therapsids (Allin, 1975) and the continuing development of the ear during and after the reptile-mammal transition.

The similarities and differences between *Kuehneotherium* and the morganucodontids have alternatively been cited to support either polyphyletic or monophyletic interpretations of mammalian origins. In the literature, however, the term "polyphyly" has been used with different meanings. An analysis of the various contexts in which polyphyly is discussed is therefore necessary to understand the major problems that remain to be solved in reconstructing the origin of mammals.

One use of the term "polyphyly" principally concerns the taxonomic recognition of a character (or characters) that defines the class. In this case the focus of debate is on the consequences of making some more or less arbitrary taxonomic division between reptiles and mammals. Given the evidence that one taxon of mammal-like reptile gave rise both to *Kuehneotherium* and to morganucodontids, the important question is where to draw the boundary. If the reptile-mammal distinction is made on the basis of independently evolved structures (*e.g.*, a three-boned middle ear dissociated from the jaw joint), the result would, by definition, yield polyphyly or at least diphyly. Alternatively, if the boundary were drawn on a character shared by common ancestry (*e.g.*, a squamoso-dentary articulation), the result is monophyly. Neither choice can be supported over the other on the basis of presently available evidence. More important, however, in this use of the term "polyphyly" is the underlying interpretation that mammals share a common ancestor among advanced cynodonts. Such a viewpoint is fundamentally mono-phyletic.

A second and quite different use of the term "polyphyly" concerns the phylogenetic relationships of mammals to mammal-like reptiles. In this context the taxonomic division between the two classes is acknowledged to be arbitrary and of secondary importance. Polyphyly here is used to signify that different groups of mammals (*e.g.*, kuehneotheriids and morganucodontids) are derived from *separate* therapsid stocks which also gave rise to other lineages of mammal-like reptiles. The assemblage of mammalian characters in "prototherians" and therians is therefore largely convergent in the sense of being independently derived. Such a viewpoint is truly polyphyletic.

Monophyly and polyphyly imply quite different evolutionary events, and variations of opinion on the subject in fact reflect different interpretations of the incomplete fossil evidence bearing on mammalian origins. Although the evidence is as yet insufficient to settle definitively the question of mono- or polyphyly, a review of some current viewpoints is provided below to clarify this and related issues.

One group of workers (Kermack and others, 1973; Mills, 1971) has maintained that therians and nontherians arose from quite disparate lineages of therapsids. Thus, mammals are polyphyletic in the sense that their independent evolution to a mammalian grade is more of a convergent phenomenon than the result of parallel development from a single protomammalian ancestor. Olson (1959), for example, considered the common ancestor of all mammals to have also given rise to other groups of mammal-like reptiles. In his view, two descendent lineages of such a common ancestor (therians and nontherians) independently acquired sufficient mammalian characters that they are now classified as mammals, whereas others did not and are regarded as therapsids. Mills (1971) also attributed a similar significance to the differences between the therian and nontherian lineages. In his opinion the common ancestor of *Kuehneotherium* and the morganucodontids must lie early in cynodont or therapsid history.

Another group of paleontologists finds evidence to support their contention that *Kuehneotherium* and the morganucodontids are closely related (Parrington, 1971; Crompton and Jenkins, 1968; Hopson and Crompton, 1969). They view similarities in molariform tooth structure, shape of the jaws, and configuration of the postdentary bones as indicative of close relationship among the earliest known mammals and between these mammals and advanced cynodonts. The differences that did evolve early in mammalian evolution represent a modest adaptive radiation of a structural pattern, the rudiments of which were established only in the most advanced cynodonts. The occlusal pattern of the molars discussed below illustrates this point.

The common ancestor of both groups of early mammals was probably characterized by molariform teeth that were brought into intimate contact during mastication. From this stage, the structure and position of teeth developed to permit fitted occlusion between upper and lower molars, although the precise occlusal relationship was slightly different in the line leading to *Eozostrodon* than in that leading to *Kuehneotherium*. In the morganucodontids, the main cusp of the lower molar occluded between the main cusp of the upper and the anterior accessory cusp. In the *Kuehneotherium* line, the main cusp of the lower lay adjacent to or slightly in front of the anterior accessory cusp. This difference could have been brought about by a slight relative displacement of tooth positions in the upper and lower jaws. At the same time, the surfaces between adjacent molars developed a tongue-and-groove structure, a mechanism that ensured both contiguity and alignment of the tooth rows (the tongue-and-groove structure also differed slightly in the two lineages). Although initially minor, the difference in occlusal relations between kuehneotheriids and morganucodontids was of crucial significance to the later evolution of mammals; the type of occlusion established in *Kuehneotherium* offered the possibility of development of a pattern of reversed triangles above and below and ultimately the emergence of the tribosphenic molar (Chapter 9).

Discussion of the relationships among early mammals has not been confined to evidence from jaws and teeth. Kermack (1967), referring to basic differences between therians and nontherians in the structure of the braincase, concluded that nontherian mammals (Docodonta, Triconodonta, Multituberculata, and Monotremata) ". . . seem to have had a common ancestor at the reptilian level of evolution. The Theria are completely isolated." He suggested that the alisphenoid (the epipterygoid of cynodonts and other reptiles) of *Eozostrodon* resembles that of *Bauria* or a scaloposaurid more closely than that of a

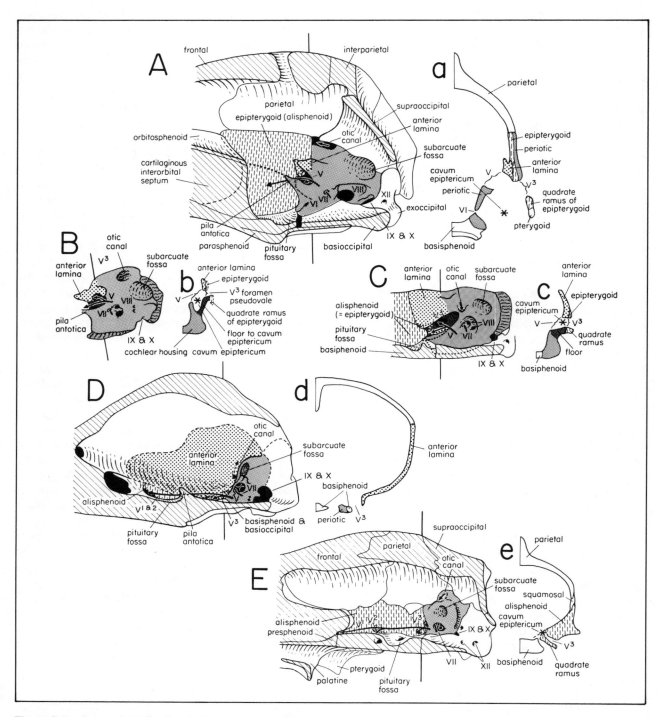

Figure 3-5. Internal views of periotic bones in: *A*, *Thrinaxodon liorhinus* (an Early Triassic cynodont); *B*, *Eozostrodon* (a Rhaeto-Liassic morganucodontid); *C*, a triconodontine (based in part on data from Kermack, 1963, and on undescribed material from the Early Cretaceous Cloverly Formation); *D*, *Ornithorhynchus anatinus* (a monotreme); and *E*, *Didelphis virginiana* (a marsupial). Vertical lines indicate the location of transverse sections represented in *a-e*. The periotic is indicated by grey shading, the floor of the cavum epitericum by dark grey shading, the anterior lamina by stippling, and the epipterygoid (or alisphenoid) by vertical hatching. Not to scale.

cynodont. Subsequently, Kermack and Kielan-Jaworowska (1971) fully documented the differences in braincase structure which differentiate therians and nontherians. This fundamental distinction, especially between monotremes and therians, is unquestionably valid. The interpretation of a separate derivation of therian and nontherian mammals from different therapsid stocks, however, is not supported by more recent studies of braincase elements in cynodonts, *Eozostrodon,* and triconodontines. Some of the results of these studies may now be reviewed.

In monotremes and multituberculates the side wall of the braincase is formed in part by a large anterior extension of the periotic, the so-called anterior lamina, and only to a limited extent by the alisphenoid (Fig. 3-5*D*). The reverse is true for therian mammals where the alisphenoid is greatly expanded and the anterior lamina of the periotic is absent (Fig. 3-5*E*). The main body of the periotic, however, is almost identical in both groups. While it is true that the periotics of *Eozostrodon* (Fig. 3-5*B*) and triconodontines (Fig. 3-5*C*) show the beginnings of the enlargement of the anterior lamina (clearly a monotreme feature), it is also true that these periotics are very similar to those of cynodonts such as *Thrinaxodon* (Fig. 3-5*A*).

In *Thrinaxodon* a small anterior lamina above the incisura prootica formed part of the side wall of the braincase, together with the epipterygoid (alisphenoid) (Fig. 3-5*A*). The facial nerve (VII) passed through the periotic between the vestibular portion of the inner ear and incisure prootica and exited through a single foramen. The trigeminal and geniculate ganglia lay in an extracranial space (the cavum epiptericum) bordered internally by the pila antotica and periotic, and externally by the epipterygoid (Fig. 3-5*a*). This extracranial space is open ventrally. The ophthalmic and probably the maxillary branches of the trigeminal nerve ran forwards in this space and emerged around the anterior margin of the epipterygoid.

The principal innovations of *Eozostrodon* are the anterior extension of the anterior lamina and the formation of a floor to the cavum epiptericum (Fig. 3-5*B, b*). This floor joins the anterior lamina in front of and behind the mandibular branch of the trigeminal nerve (V^3) to form a foramen pseudovale. This new extension of the periotic enclosed the geniculate and trigeminal ganglia in an intercranial space. Thus, there are now two foramina for the VIIth nerve, one for the greater petrosal (palatine) branch and one for

the facial (hyomandibular) branch, rather than the single foramen as in cynodonts. As a result of the enlargement of the anterior lamina, the ascending process of the epipterygoid in *Eozostrodon* is narrower than that in cynodonts.

In triconodontines (Fig. 3-5*C*) the anterior lamina further increased in size. The geniculate ganglion and greater petrosal nerves were surrounded by the periotic and completely separated from the cavum epiptericum. Monotremes are characterized by an even further increase in the extent of the anterior lamina and a reduction of the floor of the cavum epiptericum. The alisphenoid is considerably reduced in size and forms a posterior border to the foramen pseudovale.

The therian condition (Fig. 3-5*E*) is also readily derivable from that of cynodonts. In this group the small anterior lamina is reduced and a floor to the trigeminal ganglion is formed by that part of the alisphenoid which is homologous to the quadrate ramus of epipterygoid in cynodonts. As the quadrate ramus borders the floor of cavum epiptericum in *Eozostrodon* (Fig. 3-5*b*), this change does not require a major reorganization of this region. With the increase in brain size the alisphenoid, rather than the anterior lamina, forms part of the lateral wall of the braincase.

In all therians there are separate foramina for the main branches of the VIIth nerve. The geniculate ganglion is contained within the periotic. As these features are shared with nontherian or ‘‘prototherian’’ mammals, it is probable that therians were derived from forms which initially floored the cavum epiptericum in the same fashion as in *Eozostrodon* and triconodontines. In therians, part of this floor was replaced by the alisphenoid, whereas in monotremes it was reduced. It is not clear why part of the side wall of the braincase in therian and nontherian mammals is formed by different structures. It may be related to the independent and parallel increases in brain size in the two lineages.

The formation of the side wall of the braincase supports the taxonomic division of mammals into nontherian and therian lineages, and also supports the view that *Eozostrodon* should be included in the nontherian group. However, insofar as the therian braincase can also readily be derived from that of cynodonts, the comparative anatomy of this region in mammals does not support the view that early therians and nontherians *(Eozostrodon* and *Kuehneotherium)* are distantly related or that they arose from different therapsid groups. On the contrary, the structure of the side wall tends to confirm the conclusion based on the structure of the jaws and teeth that both groups of Rhaeto-Liassic mammals arose from a Middle to Late Triassic cynodont.

HARAMIYIDAE

Haramiyids are known from isolated molariform teeth from the Rhaeto-Liassic of Europe (see Chapters 2 and 6). Hahn (1969) has suggested that they were related to or ancestral to multituberculates. It is not possible to establish with certainty the orientation and position of the individual haramiyid teeth, and it is therefore very difficult to assess their relationships to other Triassic mammals or mammal-like reptiles.

CONCLUSIONS

The earliest mammals were cynodont descendents, very probably from a form allied to *Pro-bainognathus*. The cynodont-mammal relationship is firmly established on the basis of structural similarities in the dentition, jaw articulation, braincase, and postcranial skeleton. During Late Triassic times, a marked decrease in both the size and diversity of cynodonts was accompanied by an increase in the diversity and abundance of archosaurs (especially dinosaurs), lepidosaurian, and rhynchocephalian reptiles. The early mammals may well have been nocturnal, and the sensory and physiological adaptations that opened this niche to them ensured their survival in competition with diverse and successful groups of diurnal reptiles. Although some morphological trends (*e.g.,* enlargement of the dentary, reduction of the postdentary bones) may be traced from cynodonts to mammals, other developments (*e.g.,* brain enlargement, alterations in tooth replacement pattern, reorganization of the braincase) represent innovations. The sum of all known changes in this transition clearly separates early mammals from therapsids, and it is likely that other features which cannot be documented directly from the fossil record (*e.g.,* lactation, endothermy) were being developed at least by this time.

REFERENCES CITED

Allin, E. F., 1975, Evolution of the mammalian middle ear: Jour. Morph., v. 147, p. 403-438.

Barghusen, H. R., 1968, The lower jaw of cynodonts (Reptilia, Therapsida) and the evolutionary origin of mammalian adductor jaw musculature: Postilla (Yale Univ.), no. 116, 49 p.

Barghusen, H. R., and Hopson, J. A., 1970, Dentary-squamosal joint and the origin of mammals: Science, v. 168, p. 573-575.

Crompton, A. W., 1963, The evolution of the mammalian jaw: Evolution, v. 17, p. 431-439.

———1964, On the skull of *Oligokyphus*: Brit. Mus. (Nat. Hist.) Bull. (Geology), v. 9, p. 69-82.

———1972a, The evolution of the jaw articulation in cynodonts, *in* Joysey, K. A., and Kemp, T. S., eds., Studies in vertebrate evolution: Edinburgh, Oliver and Boyd Publ., p. 231-251.

———1972b, Postcanine occlusion in cynodonts and tritylodontids: Brit. Mus. (Nat. Hist.) Bull. (Geology), v. 21, p. 27-71.

———1974, The dentitions and relationships of the southern African Triassic mammals, *Erythrotherium parringtoni* and *Megazostrodon rudnerae*: ibid., v. 24, p. 397-437.

Crompton, A. W., and Jenkins, F. A., Jr., 1968, Molar occlusion in Late Triassic mammals: Biol. Rev., v. 43, p. 427-458.

———1973, Mammals from reptiles: a review of mammalian origins: Ann. Rev. Earth Planet. Sci., v. 1, p. 131-155.

———1978, Mesozoic mammals, *in* Cooke, H. B. S., and Maglio, V., eds., Evolution of African mammals: Cambridge, Harvard Univ. Press, p. 46-55.

Crompton, A. W., and Parker, P., 1978, Evolution of the mammalian masticatory apparatus: Amer. Sci., v. 66, p. 192-201.

Crompton, A. W., Taylor, C. R., and Jagger, J. A., 1978, Evolution of homeothermy in mammals: Nature, v. 272, p. 333-336.

Gaupp, E., 1913, Die Reichertsche Theorie (Hammer-, Amboss- u. Kieferfrage): Arch. Anat. Physiol., Anat. Abt., Suppl.-Band 1912, *xiii* + 416 p.

Hahn, G., 1969, Beiträge zur Fauna der Grube Guimarota Nr. 3, die Multituberculata: Palaeontographica, Abt. A, v. 133, p. 1-100.

Hopson, J. A., 1969, The origin and adaptive radiation of mammal-like reptiles and non-therian mammals: New York Acad. Sci. Ann., v. 167, p. 199-216.

———1973, Endothermy, small size, and the origin of mammalian reproduction: Amer. Natur., v. 107, p. 446-452.

Hopson, J. A., and Crompton, A. W., 1969, Origin of mammals, in Dobzhansky, T., Hecht, M. K., and Steere, W. C., eds., Evolutionary biology: New York, Appleton-Century-Crofts, v. 3, p. 15-72.

Jenkins, F. A., Jr., and Parrington, F. R., 1976, The postcranial skeletons of the Triassic mammals *Eozostrodon, Megazostrodon* and *Erythrotherium*: Roy. Soc. London Philos. Trans., B (Biol. Sci.), v. 273, p. 387-431.

Jerison, H. J., 1973, Evolution of the brain and intelligence: New York, Academic Press, *xiv* + 482 p.

Kermack, D. M., Kermack, K. A., and Mussett, F., 1968, The Welsh pantothere *Kuehneotherium praecursoris*: Linn. Soc. Zool. Jour., v. 47, p. 407-423.

Kermack, K. A., 1963, The cranial structure of the triconodonts: Roy. Soc. London Philos. Trans., B (Biol. Sci.), v. 246, p. 83-103.

———1967, The interrelations of early mammals: Linn. Soc. Zool. Jour., v. 47, p. 241-249.

Kermack, K. A., and Kielan-Jaworowska, Z., 1971, Therian and nontherian mammals, in Kermack, D. M., and Kermack, K. A., eds., Early mammals: Linn. Soc. Zool. Jour., v. 50, suppl. 1, p. 103-115.

Kermack, K. A., and Mussett, F., 1959, The first mammals: Discovery, London, v. 20, p. 144-151.

Kermack, K. A., Mussett, F., and Rigney, H. W., 1973, The lower jaw of *Morganucodon*: Linn. Soc. Zool. Jour., v. 53, p. 87-175.

Kühne, W. G., 1956, The Liassic therapsid *Oligokyphus*: London, Trustees Brit. Mus., *x* + 149 p.

———1958, Rhaetische Triconodonten aus Glamorgan, ihre Stellung zwischen den Klassen Reptilia und Mammalia und ihre Bedeutung für die Reichart'sche Theorie: Paläont. Zeit., v. 32, p. 197-235.

MacIntyre, G. T., 1967, Foramen pseudovale and quasi-mammals: Evolution, v. 21, p. 834-841.

Mills, J. R. E., 1971, The dentition of *Morganucodon, in* Kermack, D. M., and Kermack, K. A., eds., Early mammals: Linn. Soc. Zool. Jour., v. 50, suppl. 1, p. 29-63.

Olson, E. C., 1959, The evolution of mammalian characters: Evolution, v. 13, p. 304-353.

Parrington, F. R., 1971, On the Upper Triassic mammals: Roy. Soc. London Philos. Trans., B (Biol. Sci.), v. 261, p. 231-272.

———1973, The dentitions of the earliest mammals: Linn. Soc. Zool. Jour., v. 52, p. 85-95.

Romer, A. S., 1970, The Chañares (Argentina) Triassic reptile fauna. VI. A chiniquodontid cynodont with an incipient squamosal-dentary jaw articulation: Breviora (Harvard Univ.), no. 344, 18 p.

Simpson, G. G., 1927, Mesozoic Mammalia. IX. The brain of Jurassic mammals: Amer. Jour. Sci., v. 14, p. 259-268.

———1928, A catalogue of the Mesozoic Mammalia in the Geological Department of The British Museum: London, Oxford Univ. Press, *x* + 215 p.

———1929, American Mesozoic Mammalia: Peabody Mus. (Yale Univ.) Mem., v. 3, pt. 1, Yale Univ. Press, *xv* + 171 p.

———1959, Mesozoic mammals and the polyphyletic origin of mammals: Evolution, v. 13, p. 405-414.

Van Valen, L., 1960, Therapsids as mammals: *ibid.*, v. 14, p. 304-313.

Walls, G. L., 1942, The vertebrate eye and its adaptive radiation: Bloomfield Hills, Cranbrook Inst. Sci., Bull. 19, *xiv* + 785 p.

CHAPTER 4

TRICONODONTA

Farish A. Jenkins, Jr.
A. W. Crompton

INTRODUCTION

Triconodont phylogeny spans the entire Mesozoic history of mammals from the Late Triassic to the Late Cretaceous (see Tables 4-1 and 4-2). As the name implies, their basic dental structure comprises three major cusps mesiodistally[1] aligned, although some advanced forms enlarged a fourth (originally cingular) cusp on the distal margin. Triconodonts, like other Mesozoic mammals, are known princi-

pally on the basis of jaws and teeth. However, current work on the cranial and postcranial remains of Late Triassic forms, as well as the recent discoveries of skeletons of Early Cretaceous age from the Cloverly Formation of Montana, offer substantial potential for increasing our understanding of the structure and relationships of this group.

In terms of dental structure, triconodonts diversified little in comparison with other Mesozoic groups. Moreover, no lineage of Tertiary or Recent mammals can be traced to them. The adaptations of advanced mammals as we know them today are certainly not of triconodont heritage.

For several reasons, however, triconodonts represent an important aspect of early mammalian evolution. First, the primitive pattern of triconodont molar structure is present in the best known and most widespread of Triassic mammal groups, the Morganucodontidae. This pattern, characterized by a large central cusp flanked by two lower cusps (one mesial, the other distal), was presaged among

---

1. Editors' note: Reflecting current diversity in usage, one standard dental nomenclature has not been employed by authors of this and other chapters. A number of terms utilized in the book are wholly or partially synonymous. Mesial, toward the symphysis of the mandibles, is usually synonymous with anterior, but note the orientation of the incisors. Distal, away from the symphysis, usually is synonymous with posterior. Labial, toward the lips, and buccal, toward the cheeks, frequently are used interchangeably. Lingual, toward the tongue, is universally employed.

cynodont mammal-like reptiles and was retained with certain modifications in Jurassic and Cretaceous forms. At the present time, the most significant differences among triconodont taxa are apparent in cusp structure and molar occlusion. With the better information on dental formulae,

tooth replacement, and other aspects of cranial as well as postcranial anatomy that is becoming available as a result of recent discoveries, a more accurate assessment of their phylogeny and early relationships is guaranteed. There is currently no doubt, however, that the Order Triconodonta is

TABLE 4-1 CLASSIFICATION OF TRICONODONTA

Subclass Prototheria Gill, 1872 [editors' note: taxon not used formally elsewhere in book]
Infraclass Eotheria Kermack and Mussett, 1958 [editors' note: taxon considered at subclass level elsewhere in book]
Order Triconodonta Osborn, 1888
  Family Morganucodontidae Kühne, 1958. (Retained as a family under Article 40 of the International Code of Zoological Nomenclature although *Morganucodon* Kühne, 1949, is a junior synonym of *Eozostrodon* Parrington, 1941)
    Eozostrodon Parrington, 1941 [editors' note: *Morganucodon* considered the valid name elsewhere in book]
      Eozostrodon parvus Parrington, 1941 (*E. problematicus* Parrington, 1941 considered a junior synonym)
      Eozostrodon ("*Morganucodon*") *watsoni* Kühne, 1949 (*Morganucodon* Kühne, 1949, considered a junior synonym of *Eozostrodon* Parrington, 1941)
      Eozostrodon ("*Morganucodon*") *oehleri* Rigney, 1963
      Eozostrodon ("*Morganucodon*") *heikuopengensis* Young, 1978 [editors' note: a new species published after the text of this chapter was completed]
    Erythrotherium Crompton, 1964
      Erythrotherium parringtoni Crompton, 1964
    Megazostrodon Crompton and Jenkins, 1968
      Megazostrodon rudnerae Crompton and Jenkins, 1968
  Family Triconodontidae Marsh, 1887
    Alticonodon Fox, 1969
      Alticonodon lindoei Fox, 1969
    Astroconodon Patterson, 1951
      Astroconodon denisoni Patterson, 1951
    Priacodon Marsh, 1887
      P. robustus (Marsh, 1879)
      P. ferox (Marsh, 1880)

      P. grandaevus Simpson, 1925b
      P. lulli Simpson, 1925b
    Triconodon Owen, 1859
      T. mordax Owen, 1859
    Trioracodon Simpson, 1928
      T. ferox (Owen, 1871)
      T. major (Owen, 1871)
      T. bisulcus (Marsh, 1880)
      T. oweni Simpson, 1928
    unnamed genus and species
  Family Amphilestidae Osborn (1888). (Proposed as a subfamily; raised to family rank by Kühne, 1958. See International Code of Zoological Nomenclature, Article 36)
    Amphilestes Owen, 1871
      A. broderipii (Owen, 1845)
    Aploconodon Simpson, 1925b
      A. comoensis Simpson, 1925b
    Phascolodon Simpson, 1925b
      P. gidleyi Simpson, 1925b
    Phascolotherium Owen, 1838
      P. bucklandi (Broderip, 1828).
    undescribed genus and species

[Editors' note added in proof: The following paper (in Russian) was published after submission of copy for the present book to the printers (Trofimov, B. A., 1978, First triconodonts [Mammalia, Triconodonta] from Mongolia: Akad. Nauk SSSR, Doklady, v. 243, p. 213-216). Two genera of amphilestids from the Khovboor locality area are described and figured. These are *Gobiconodon* Trofimov, 1978 (with a single species, *G. borissiaki* Trofimov, 1978) and *Guchinodon* Trofimov, 1978 (with a single species, *G. hoburensis* Trofimov, 1978). Elsewhere throughout the present book *Gobiconodon* is referred to as a *nomen nudum*.]

      Gobiconodon borissiaki Trofimov, 1978
  ?Triconodonta *incertae sedis*
    Sinoconodon Patterson and Olson, 1961
      S. rigneyi Patterson and Olson, 1961

phylogenetically one of the earliest mammalian groups to appear and is, in molar structure at least, a conservative group.

A second consideration that must be accorded triconodonts in Mesozoic mammal history concerns the dichotomy between therian and nontherian groups. Although living nontherians (*i.e.,* the monotremes) form an insignificant part of Recent faunas, such was not the case during Mesozoic times when nontherians (triconodonts, docodonts, multituberculates) were numerous and widespread. With the possible exception of multituberculates, for which there is tenuous evidence for independent

evolution since the Late Triassic, nontherian mammals appear to represent a once flourishing but now nearly extinct major branch of mammalian phylogeny. Triconodonts, by virtue of certain aspects of their anatomy and their early appearance in the fossil record, are possibly on or near the ancestry of later appearing nontherian groups.

Finally, for what triconodonts lacked in diversity, they made up in size. The earliest forms, the morganucodontids, were small (10 to 20 g estimated body weight; Fig. 4-1); indeed, most groups of Mesozoic mammals did not exceed rat size. Later triconodonts, in contrast, included the largest of

TABLE 4-2   AGE AND OCCURRENCE OF GENERA OF TRICONODONTA

GENUS	OCCURRENCE	AGE OR STAGE
Eozostrodon ("*Morganucodon*")	fissure fillings near Bridgend, Wales, and Holwell Quarry, Frome, Somerset, England;	Late Triassic[2]
	possibly in Rhaetic bonebed, Hallau, Kanton Schaffhausen, ὶ., Switzerland (pers. comm. from W. A. Clemens, 1977);	Late Triassic[2]
	Lower Lufeng Series, Yunnan Province, China	Late Triassic[2]
Megazostrodon	Pokane locality, Stormberg Group, Lesotho, southern Africa	Late Triassic[2]
Erythrotherium	Mafeteng locality, Stormberg Group, Lesotho, southern Africa	Late Triassic[2]
editors' note[3]		
Amphilestes	Stonesfield Slate, Oxfordshire, England	Bathonian
Phascolotherium	Stonesfield Slate, Oxfordshire, England	Bathonian
Phascolodon	Morrison Fm., Como Bluff, Wyoming, U.S.A.	Late Jurassic
Aploconodon	Morrison Fm., Como Bluff, Wyoming, U.S.A.	Late Jurassic
Trioracodon	Morrison Fm., Como Bluff, Wyoming, U.S.A.;	Late Jurassic
	Lulworth Beds, Durlston Bay, England	Volgian
Priacodon	Morrison Fm., Como Bluff, Wyoming, U.S.A.	Late Jurassic
Triconodon	Lulworth Beds, Durlston Bay, England	Volgian
unnamed genus and species (triconodontid)	Cloverly Fm., Montana and Wyoming, U.S.A.	Early Cretaceous
unnamed genus and species (amphilestid)	Cloverly Fm., Montana and Wyoming, U.S.A.	Early Cretaceous
Gobiconodon	Fm.?, Khovboor, near Guchin Us, province (aymak) of Arvaykher, Mongolian People's Republic	?Aptian or ?Albian
Guchinodon	Fm.?, Khovboor, near Guchin Us, province (aymak) of Arvaykher, Mongolian People's Republic	?Aptian or ?Albian
Astroconodon	Paluxy (= Antlers Fm.) Fm., Texas, U.S.A.	"Paluxian"
Alticonodon	upper part of Milk River Fm., Alberta, Canada	"Aquilan"

EDITORS' NOTES:
    2. Referred to as Rhaeto-Liassic elsewhere in book (see Chapter 2 for discussion).
    3. Although only questionably a triconodont, for purposes of completeness we add reference to *Sinoconodon*, Lower Lufeng Series, Yunnan Province, China, Rhaeto-Liassic.

Mesozoic mammals, some attaining the size of the Virginia opossum and possessing a skeletal build that was proportionally more robust.

Triconodonts not only had a long phylogenetic history, they also played a central role in the development of paleontological theories. Among the first fossil mammals to be discovered in Mesozoic rocks was a triconodont, and the group subsequently figured prominently in the writings of Richard Owen, O. C. Marsh, H. F. Osborn, W. K. Gregory, and others concerned with the origin and evolution of mammals. A review of earlier work, principally systematic and descriptive in nature and spanning a century prior to 1925, is given by Simpson (1929).

DIAGNOSIS

Members of the Triconodonta are characterized by the following: the one to three or four incisors are usually small; canines and two to five premolars are present; molars, three to five in number (for further data on dental formulae, see Table 4-3), bear three main cusps aligned mesiodistally; on lower molars the central cusp (*a*) is usually moderately or substantially larger than cusps (*b*) in front and (*c*) behind, a small cingular cusp (*d*) occurs on the distal cingulum, and a lingual cingulum is variably developed; on upper molars the central cusp (*A*) is usually relatively lower than the corresponding cusp (*a*) on the lowers, and lingual and buccal cingula plus a distal cingular

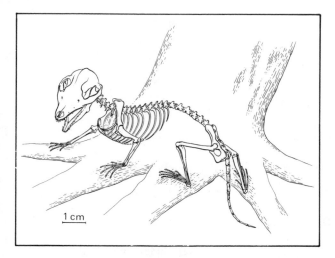

Figure 4-1.   Skeletal reconstruction of a Triassic triconodont based principally on the proportions of *Megazostrodon rudnerae*. (From Jenkins and Parrington, 1976; used with permission of The Royal Society)

cusp (*D*) are present; lower molars wear an oblique facet(s) along the lingual aspect of uppers; the posterior part of the maxilla bearing the distal molar is continued as the zygoma; and the zygoma is stout.

ANATOMY

Cranial

Knowledge of the cranial anatomy of triconodonts has been severely limited by the sparsity of fossil material. Simpson (1925b) described the maxilla and jugal of *Priacodon ?ferox* which, together with a nearly complete lower jaw, permitted a partial reconstruction of the skull (Fig. 4-2) and palate. Simpson (1928) also described fragmentary cranial bones associated with *Triconodon mordax*, including a partial maxilla (which resembles that of the Morrison *Triconodon*), parietals, a frontal, basisphenoid and part of an alisphenoid, and both periotics (petrosals). From the relative proportions of the frontal, parietal, and lower jaw, Simpson concluded that a substantial part of the braincase (perhaps a fourth or more) lay behind the glenoid and ". . . that specialization of the basicranial structure was proceeding on lines quite different from those seen in monotremes, marsupials, or multituberculates" (1928, p. 84). Although Simpson expressed some reservations about his interpretation of the basisphenoid, he made a comparison with the same bone in *Ornithorhynchus* and noted the similar position of the foramen ovale. This interpretation, however, was subsequently questioned by Crompton (*fide* Kermack, 1963) who suggested that the bone had structural similarities with the sphenoid complex of an advanced mammal-like reptile, a view supported by Kermack's (1963) study of triconodont and cynodont cranial structure. The periotic in *T. mordax* reveals several features of interest, including a deep, well-defined floccular fossa (resembling that in certain primitive living mammals) and an uncoiled cochlea (representing a reptilian grade of organization).

In 1958 Kermack and Mussett described and figured a petrosal of a morganucodontid from Pant Quarry in Wales. Later, Kermack (1963) made a comparative survey of this and the petrosals of *Triconodon mordax* (which were further prepared after Simpson's study), together with a petrosal associated with *Trioracodon ferox*. He concluded that triconodonts possessed a persistent cavum

TABLE 4-3   TRICONODONT DENTAL FORMULAE (LETTERS IN PARENTHESES REFER TO SOURCES, IDENTIFIED BELOW)

	Morganucodontidae		Triconodontidae		Amphilestidae	
INCISORS	(a) *Eozostrodon watsoni*	$\frac{3}{4}$	(d) *Priacodon*	?	(e) *Amphilestes*	$\frac{?}{3 \text{ or } 4}$
	(b) *Eozostrodon oehleri*	$\frac{4}{4}$	(e) *Triconodon*	?	(d) *Aploconodon*	?
	(c) *Erythrotherium*	$\frac{4+?}{3+?}$	(d) *Trioracodon*	?	(d) *Phascolodon*	?
	(c) *Megazostrodon*	?	(f) Undes. triconod. Cloverly Fm.	$\frac{2}{1}$	(g) Undes. amphilestid Cloverly Fm.	$\frac{1+?}{2}$
CANINES	(a) *Eozostrodon watsoni*	$\frac{1}{1}$	(d) *Priacodon*	$\frac{1}{1}$	(e) *Amphilestes*	$\frac{?}{1}$
	(b) *Eozostrodon oehleri*	$\frac{1}{1}$	(e) *Triconodon*	$\frac{?}{1}$	(d) *Aploconodon*	?
	(c) *Erythrotherium*	$\frac{1}{1}$	(d) *Trioracodon*	$\frac{1}{1}$	(d) *Phascolodon*	?
	(c) *Megazostrodon*	?	(f) Undes. triconod. Cloverly Fm.	$\frac{1}{1}$	(e) *Phascolotherium*	$\frac{?}{1}$
					(g) Undes. amphilestid Cloverly Fm.	$\frac{1}{1}$
PREMOLARS	(a) *Eozostrodon watsoni*	$\frac{5}{4}$	(d) *Priacodon*	$\frac{3}{3}$	(e) *Amphilestes*	$\frac{?}{4}$
	(b) *Eozostrodon oehleri*	$\frac{4}{3\text{-}4}$	(e) *Triconodon*	$\frac{?}{4}$	(d) *Aploconodon*	?
	(c) *Erythrotherium*	$\frac{4}{4}$	(d) *Trioracodon*	$\frac{4}{4}$	(d) *Phascolodon*	?
	(c) *Megazostrodon*	$\frac{5}{5}$	(f) Undes. triconod. Cloverly Fm.	$\frac{4}{4}$	(e) *Phascolotherium*	$\frac{?}{2}$
					(g) Undes. amphilestid Cloverly Fm.	$\frac{2+?}{2}$
MOLARS	(a) *Eozostrodon watsoni*	$\frac{4}{4\text{-}5}$	(d) *Priacodon*	$\frac{4}{4}$	(e) *Amphilestes*	$\frac{?}{5}$
	(b) *Eozostrodon oehleri*	$\frac{3}{4}$	(e) *Triconodon*	$\frac{4}{4}$	(d) *Aploconodon*	$\frac{?}{2+?}$
	(c) *Erythrotherium*	$\frac{3+?}{4}$	(d) *Trioracodon*	$\frac{3}{3}$	(d) *Phascolodon*	$\frac{?}{4+?}$
	(c) *Megazostrodon*	$\frac{4}{4}$	(f) Undes. triconod. Cloverly Fm.	$\frac{5}{5}$	(e) *Phascolotherium*	$\frac{?}{5}$
					(g) Undes. amphilestid Cloverly Fm.	$\frac{4 \text{ or } 5}{5}$

SOURCES: (a) Parrington, 1973; (b) Kermack and others, 1973; (c) Crompton, 1974; (d) Simpson, 1929; (e) Simpson, 1928; (f) A. W. Crompton and F. A. Jenkins, Jr., unpublished; and (g) F. A. Jenkins, Jr., and C. R. Schaff, unpublished.

epiptericum which lay lateral to the braincase wall formed by the petrosal; the lateral boundary of the cavum was formed by the alisphenoid, which did not, in this region, contribute to the braincase. Thus, the braincase in this respect was apparently of an essentially reptilian pattern. It should be noted that the materials available to Kermack were dissociated and, in some cases, damaged. However astute his observations were, it is now certain that a much clearer understanding of triconodont braincase structure can be achieved with reference to the recently discovered skulls from the Cloverly Formation. Our preliminary study of the material leads us to conclude that the triconodont braincase was more mammalian than was previously appreciated.

Dental

A distinctive feature of mammalian teeth is the precision of occlusion; upper and lower cusps are positioned consistently, and thus produce patterns of wear, or facets, that are characteristic of a taxon. In general structure, triconodont molars may appear to be much alike. However, a significant difference between taxa is revealed by study of the facets; upper and lower molars, and accordingly the homologous cusps, occlude in several distinct types of patterns.

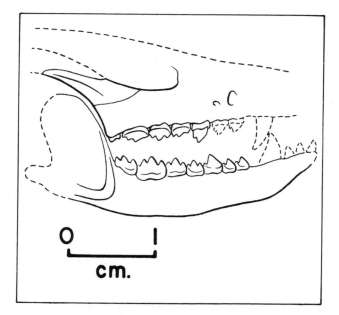

Figure 4-2. Composite reconstruction of right side of skull and jaw of _Priacodon_, based principally on specimens of _P. ferox_. Dashed lines indicate restored areas. (After Simpson, 1925b)

Data on the microstructure of the enamel are presented in Chapter 11.

The morganucodontid occlusal pattern, as developed in _Eozostrodon_[4] _watsoni_, has been determined by a number of workers (Crompton and Jenkins, 1968; Parrington, 1971; Mills, 1971; Butler, 1972). The central cusp (a) of the lower molars occludes with the lingual side of the notch between upper cusps B and A. The central cusp (A) of the upper molars occludes with the buccal side of the notch between lower cusps a and c (Fig. 4-3A). During initial stages of wear, however, cusp a only contacts the lingual cingulum of the corresponding upper molar, and cusp A contacts the buccal surface of the lower. Only with further wear do intercuspal facets develop. Therefore, the eruption locus of the molars is the determinant of the occlusal pattern, rather than the placement of the cusps. The development of complementary shearing edges is produced mechanically rather than ontogenetically.

Known triconodontids of the Jurassic retained the same molar occlusal pattern as in _Eozostrodon watsoni_ (see Mills, 1971; Crompton, 1974; and Fig. 4-3C). Structurally, a typical triconodontid molar differs from that in _E. watsoni_ in having the three principal cusps more evenly spaced, and in equalizing the height of B, b and C, c relative to A, a. This apparent trend, evident in Jurassic forms, was further advanced among triconodontids (as yet undescribed) from the Early Cretaceous Cloverly Formation and in the Late Cretaceous _Alticonodon_ (Fox, 1969, 1976), in which the molars are evenly serrated blades. Concomitantly, the distal cingular cusp (d), on posterior molars at least, becomes enlarged and forms part of the crown's cutting edge. This cutting edge is thus comprised of a series of cusps and V-shaped embrasures between. The molars are positioned so that individual cusps are opposed to embrasures; during occlusion, each cusp passes through its corresponding embrasure and along the groove

---

4. Editors' note: Proper utilization of the generic names _Eozostrodon_ and _Morganucodon_ is currently a contentious point. In other chapters of this book and in an article recently accepted for publication in the Zoological Journal of the Linnean Society, Clemens has argued that a nomenclature restricting the genus _Eozostrodon_ to the species _parvus_ (including _problematicus_) and allocating the species _watsoni_ and _oehleri_ to the genus _Morganucodon_ is appropriate. Of much greater biological significance, and in this we are agreed, _parvus_, _watsoni_, and _oehleri_ should be recognized as separate species of morganucodontids.

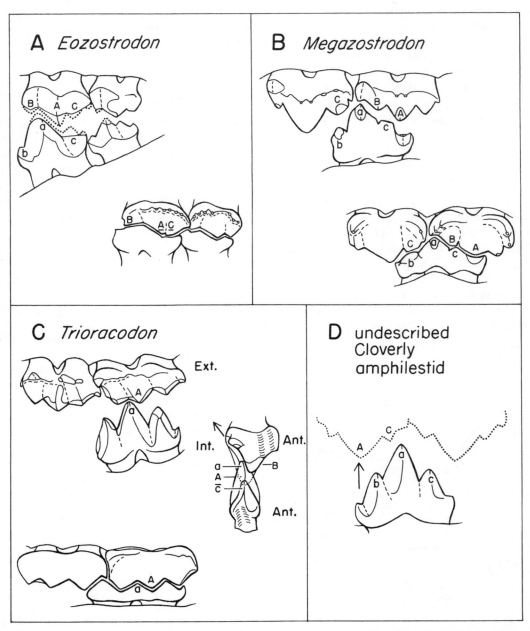

Figure 4-3. Occlusal patterns in left triconodont molars. Differences in the intercuspal relationships (anterior to left) are depicted in buccal (top) and inferobuccal (bottom) views; occlusion in *Trioracodon* is also shown in anterior (or mesial) view. The occlusal pattern of the undescribed amphilestid from the Cloverly Formation is a tentative reconstruction based on study in progress by F. A. Jenkins, Jr., and C. R. Schaff. Not to scale. (Modified from Crompton, 1974)

formed by the shoulders of adjacent cusps on the opposing molar (Mills, 1971; Crompton, 1974).

The morganucodontid *Megazostrodon rudnerae* possesses a different occlusal pattern. Here the cusp *a* of the lower molars lies to the lingual side, or slightly in front of, cusp *B* of the uppers; cusp *A* is positioned somewhat behind cusp *c* (Crompton, 1974; Fig. 4-3*B*). Although the intercuspal relations thus more closely resemble those of *Kuehneotherium* (a Late Triassic symmetrodont) and certain later therians, *Megazostrodon* is undoubtedly related to the European and Chinese morganucodontids by virtue of fundamental similarities of crown structure. As in *Eozostrodon watsoni,* well-defined cutting edges are not present in the newly erupted *Megazostrodon* molar, but presumably developed as the result of wear which began on the cingula.

The occlusal pattern of amphilestid triconodonts differs from that in triconodontids, and bears certain similarities to that in *Megazostrodon* and even *Kuehneotherium.* Mills (1971) reconstructed the occlusion in *Phascolotherium,* and concluded that cusp *A* of an upper sheared behind lower cusp *c* and against the cingular cuspule *d* (rather than in front of *c* as in *Eozostrodon watsoni*). He believed *Amphilestes* to be much the same, with the exception that cusp *A* occluded with the mesial cingular cuspule of the next posterior lower molar because of the reduction in the size of *d.* Based on an examination of stereophotographs of *Amphilestes broderipii,* Crompton (1974) interpreted upper cusp *A* as occluding between *f* (a mesiobuccal cingular cusp) and *b*; in suggesting a slightly more posterior position of lowers relative to uppers, he believed that the occlusion more closely resembled that in the Late Jurassic symmetrodont *Tinodon* than that in *Kuehneotherium.* The views of Crompton and Mills do not represent major disagreement, and both point to a basically similar occlusal pattern in symmetrodonts (including *Kuehneotherium*) and amphilestids. Preliminary study of the recently discovered amphilestid from the Cloverly Formation in Montana reveals that upper cusp *A* wore a deep facet on the anteromesial surface of lower cusp *b*; the principal lower cusp *a* opposed the distobuccal part of the upper cingulum as well as cusp *C* (Fig. 4-3*D*). Thus, in this more advanced amphilestid, lower molars are positioned slightly more distally relative to uppers than is the case in *Amphilestes* and *Phascolotherium.*

Molar occlusal patterns in triconodont mammals fall into two basic categories. In the first, ex-

emplified by some Triassic morganucodontids and all known Jurassic and Cretaceous triconodontids, upper and lower molars are opposed more or less one-to-one. Lower cusp *a* occludes between upper *A* and *B*; upper cusp *A* occludes between lower *a* and *c*. In the second, characteristic of the morganucodontid *Megazostrodon* and Jurassic and Cretaceous amphilestids, upper and lower molars are opposed more or less two-to-one. Lower cusp *a* may occlude in a relatively anterior position (*i.e.*, against the distal aspect of *C* in the undescribed Cloverly amphilestid) or in a relatively posterior position (*i.e.*, against the mesial aspect of *B* in *Megazostrodon*). An intermediate position between these has been suggested by Mills (1971) for *Phascolotherium.* However, all are clearly similar and distinctly different from the one-to-one relationship of *Eozostrodon* and triconodontids.

Postcranial

Until recently, the postcranial skeleton of triconodonts was virtually unknown. Simpson (1928) noted that *Triconodon mordax* possessed an axis with a stout odontoid process; the other fragmentary bones associated with this specimen were not identifiable. The availability of morganucodontid postcranial materials from the Late Triassic of Britain and southern Africa (Jenkins and Parrington, 1976), together with the recent discovery of triconodontid and amphilestid skeletons from the Early Cretaceous of North America, now provides a basis for analyzing postcranial evolution in nontherian mammals.

Morganucodontids

Preliminary accounts of some British morganucodontid postcrania were given by Kermack and Mussett (1959), who figured a scapulocoracoid, and Parrington (1971), who described an ilium and several femoral heads. These and other materials were recovered in abundance from fissure fillings in which the bones for the most part were dissociated and broken, or became so in the process of dissolving the matrix. This fact, together with the intermixture of reptilian remains, hampered a confident assessment of the material. The availability of two nearly complete skeletons of related forms (*Megazostrodon rudnerae* and *Erythrotherium parringtoni*), however, made a comparative survey possible (Jenkins and

Parrington, 1976). The British material is better preserved in structural details, especially the articular surfaces. The African skeletons confirm the identity of the British material as well as establish proportional relationships.

Triassic triconodonts possess two occipital condyles. The atlas arches are not synostosed into the ring-like structure of later mammals, but are separate as in cynodonts and other synapsids. The atlanto-occipital articulation is nonetheless ginglymoid, the typical mammalian specialization of this joint for flexion and extension. The robust, protuberant dens and the absence of any evidence on the atlas arches of an atlanto-axial zygapophyseal joint is evidence that this joint was adapted for rotation as in later mammals. Postaxial cervical vertebrae in *Megazostrodon* bear short, tapering spinous processes; the zygapophyses are broadly set apart, and the laminae and pedicles are anteroposteriorly narrow. Middle cervical vertebrae have enlarged vertebral foramina at levels corresponding to the cervical intumescence and the origin of the brachial plexus. Wide zygapophyseal spacing and cervical canal enlargement is typical of later mammals, and is probably related to both the large size of the cervical intumescence of the spinal cord (a concomitant of the increased neuromuscular control of the forelimb) and increased flexibility of the neck (and hence a requirement for ample space within the vertebral canal at this level). Narrow laminae and reduced spinous processes are also found in modern mammals, but these features are adaptations for pronounced cervicothoracic flexure whereby the cervical series is inclined anterodorsally to support the head in an elevated position. Broad laminae and long spinous processes would interfere with such flexion, and apparently Triassic mammals had already adopted such a posture.

The thoracic and lumbar vertebrae give clear evidence of a structural differentiation found in later mammals which was only incipiently developed in cynodonts. An articulated series of three vertebrae in *Eozostrodon watsoni* preserves an anticlinal region with the characteristics of advanced mammals (Fig. 4-4*I*). First, the spinous processes, gracile and posteriorly directed in the thoracic series, become robust and vertically oriented in the lumbar series. Second, the orientation of the articular facets shifts from more or less horizontal (thoracic) to approximately 40° (lumbar). Third, the lumbar vertebrae bear short, anterolaterally directed transverse processes. All of these features are typical of the

thoracolumbar transition in advanced mammals, and relate to musculoskeletal specializations for flexion and extension of the spine during locomotion.

Thus, for movements of the head, neck, and trunk, Triassic triconodonts already appear to have acquired the basic adaptations which characterize most later mammals.

The pectoral girdle retains basically a cynodont pattern, especially in the shape of the scapular blade, the deep infraspinous fossa, the lack of any supraspinous fossa, and the configuration of the two coracoids (see Fig. 4-4*B* and *C*). The posterior of the two coracoids bears a posteriorly directed process, as in cynodonts and monotremes. The small anterior coracoid is excluded from the glenoid fossa, which is relatively narrow, shallow, and symmetrical; these features represent advances beyond a cynodont level. As a whole, however, the pectoral girdle shows little reorganization in the direction of a therian structure, and instead represents a pattern from which the monotreme girdle (Fig. 4-4*D*) could have been derived.

The humeral head is hemispherical and flanked by tuberosities resembling those of therians (Fig. 4-4*A*). The most interesting feature is a spiral ulnar condyle (rather than a trochlea as in therians) that wraps around the distal end of the humerus from dorsolateral to ventromedial aspects. An ulnar condyle is found in cynodonts and multituberculates and is retained in somewhat modified form by monotremes; functionally, the spiral configuration is an adaptation to accommodate complex movements of the humerus and ulna in different planes.

The pelvis (Fig. 4-4*F*), in contrast to the pectoral girdle, is well advanced toward a mammalian structure. The iliac blade is elongate and anterodorsally directed; on its lateral aspect is a low crest separating the origins of the gluteal muscles (above) from those of the iliacus (below). Such features are unknown in cynodonts (Fig. 4-4*G*), although they are present in tritylodontids and are characteristic of mammals. Other features, such as the enlarged obturator foramen and apparent reduction of the anterior part of the pubis, represent further development of trends already established among cynodonts. The pubes are only incompletely known from available materials, but the essentially complete skeletons of *Megazostrodon* and *Erythrotherium* show no conclusive evidence for the presence of epipubic bones.

The femoral head (Fig. 4-4*E*) is spherical, as in later mammals. A fovea, together with a well-developed acetabular notch on the pelvis (continuous with an incisure beneath the ischial facet), is evidence of a typically mammalian ligamentum capitis femoris. The fovea lies on the ventromedial aspect of the head; assuming that the fovea and its attached ligament moved within the deepest (*i.e.*, nonarticular acetabular fossa) part of the acetabulum, the femur must have been directed anterolaterad at about 45° to sagittal (as in generalized modern mammals). However, the acetabulum retains two primitive features. First, the contour of the lateral margin is not circular, but instead is irregular by virtue of the projecting facets of the ilium, ischium, and pubis (as

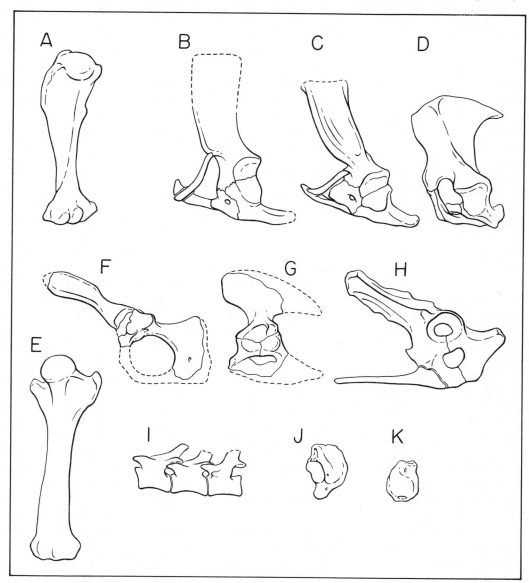

Figure 4-4.   Postcranial bones of a Triassic triconodont, a cynodont, and a monotreme: *A*, **left humerus of** *Eozostrodon watsoni*, **dorsal view (X3.1);** *B* **and** *C*, **lateral views of reconstructed left pectoral girdles of** *E. watsoni* (*B*) **and a cynodont** (*C*) **compared with that of** *Tachyglossus* (*D*) (*B*, **approximately X5.0;** *C*, **X0.2;** *D*, **X0.7);** *E*, **dorsal view of left femur of** *E. watsoni* **(X3.6);** *F* **and** *G*, **lateral views of reconstructed left pelvic girdles of** *E. watsoni* (*F*) **and a cynodont** (*G*) **compared with that of** *Tachyglossus* (*H*) (*F*, **approximately X2.8;** *G*, **approximately X0.5;** *H*, **X0.7);** *I*, **three articulated vertebrae from the thoracolumbar region of** *E. watsoni* **(approximately X3.6, anterior to left); and** *J* **and** *K*, **dorsal views of right calcaneus** (*J*) **and left astragalus** (*K*) **of** *E. watsoni* **(both approximately X3.9). (After Jenkins and Parrington, 1976)**

in cynodonts). Second, the articular surface of the acetabulum is a simple cup-shaped depression, like that of monotremes, rather than the inverted U-shape of therians.

The astragalus (Fig. 4-4*K*) is somewhat hemispherical, as in cynodonts, and possesses a bulbous tibial facet rather than a trochlea as in therians. Two features appear here for the first time among mammals. First, an astragalar head occurs as a well-ossified, protuberant process for articulation with the navicular. Second, a sulcus between the calcaneal facets on the astragalus is enclosed posteriorly to form an astragalar canal (and foramen). Although the calcaneal tuber is as well developed as in cynodonts, the sustentaculum tali is not (Fig. 4-4*J*); only a modest degree of astragalar superposition appears to have occurred by elevation of the medial margin of the calcaneus, thus allowing the ventral aspect of the astragalus to lie against it. In neither the ankle nor subtalar joints is there evidence that Triassic triconodonts had progressed substantially toward a therian level of organization. The specializations of the monotreme tarsus, particularly the bulbous articular surfaces for the tibia and fibula, and the lack of superposition, are more readily derived from the structure of Triassic triconodonts than from any form in which recognizably therian characters had developed.

The phalanges of Triassic triconodonts provide evidence of well-developed prehensile abilities, specifically considering the flanges for digital fibrous sheaths of the flexor tendons, the extensive trochleae at the distal interphalangeal joints, the large ungual flexor tubercles, and the structure of the distal phalanges which indicate narrow, pointed claws. Of particular interest is the asymmetrical condyle on the distal end of the hallucal metatarsal. In *Tupaia glis*, a similarly asymmetrical joint permits independent abduction and flexion-extension in a plane different from that of the other digits; the independent movement and pseudo-opposition thus achieved augments pedal stability on uneven and arboreal surfaces. The same functional adaptation may be inferred from the hallucal structure of Triassic triconodonts.

Jenkins and Parrington (1976) were unable to detect significant differences in postcranial structure between *Eozostrodon watsoni* and the African morganucodontids.

Triassic triconodonts were small (approximately 10 cm in head-body length) and probably weighed between 20 and 30 g. Other than somewhat longer humeri and femora, *Megazostrodon* (Fig. 4-1) ap-

pears to have had skeletal proportions much like those in medium-sized shrews (*e.g.*, *Suncus murinus*, *Crocidura baluensis*).

Amphilestids and Triconodontids

Postcranial skeletons both of amphilestids and of triconodontids were recovered from the Early Cretaceous Cloverly Formation in Montana during 1974 and 1975. This material, currently being prepared and studied at Harvard University, offers the first opportunity to examine the postcranial anatomy of triconodontids and provides the basis for comparing developments among nontherian mammals of the Cretaceous with those of the Late Triassic.

A complete account of these forms would be premature at present, but one obviously important feature may be noted. The amphilestid, represented by two individuals, had an essentially therian scapular structure. Only the scapular bases are preserved, but they clearly show a spine separating infra- and supraspinous fossae. The coracoid (missing in both specimens) may have been large, judging from the size of the articular surface on the scapulae, although the configuration of the glenoid fossa is such that the coracoid probably contributed at most a quarter of the articular surface. In contrast to the scapulocoracoid of *Eozostrodon watsoni,* the shoulder girdle of this Cretaceous amphilestid is significantly advanced toward a therian grade. The scapular structure of the Cloverly triconodontid is based on circumstantial association. To date, some twenty dental specimens have been recovered from one quarry, all triconodontids, ranging from fragmentary jaws to complete skulls; each of these specimens was encased in a nodule, and parts of the postcranial skeleton were associated with some. Dissociated postcranial bones, including the only complete scapula thus far recovered, occur in separate nodules; the fact that no other mammalian orders are yet known to be represented at this site leads us to conclude, at least tentatively, that the scapula is that of a triconodontid. If this assumption is correct, triconodontids of the Early Cretaceous possessed an essentially therian type of scapula. The infra- and supraspinous fossae, spine, acromion, and coracoid are comparable in size and structure with those of modern, generalized therians.

These unexpected findings necessitate reexamination of widely held views of therian and nontherian evolution. The lack of a supraspinous fossa in morganucodontids, multituberculates, and monotremes, together with other structural similarities in the pectoral girdle, supported the notion (originally based on cranial evidence) of an early phylogenetic dichotomy of nontherian and therian mammals. However, the occurrence of a therian scapulo-coracoid in nontherian mammals now requires consideration of two alternatives. First, the therian scapula was independently evolved by the two groups, but without all nontherians participating in this acquisition. Alternatively, amphilestids are neither triconodonts nor nontherians, but in fact are more closely allied to therians. Acceptance of the second hypothesis is contingent upon rejecting the presumed association of a therian scapula with the Cloverly triconodontids. At the present time, we favor the first hypothesis, but recognize that definitive evidence is not yet available.

A further point of interest arising from the discovery of the Early Cretaceous amphilestid is its size and robustness. The majority of Mesozoic mammals described thus far were shrew to rat-sized or a little larger. The amphilestid is at least 35 cm in head-body length (excluding tail) and was heavily built (a preliminary reconstruction in Ostrom, 1976, portrays its basic features). A mammal of these proportions very probably had invaded a different niche from the archetypal role usually assigned the small, rat-like Mesozoic mammals.

ANCESTRY

Triconodonts first appear in rocks of Late Triassic age on three continents (Europe, Africa, and China) and, with kuehneotheriids, are the earliest known mammals. Their ancestry is to be found among the cynodonts, advanced mammal-like reptiles of the Early and Middle Triassic. Only cynodonts (together with their closely related derivatives the Tritylodontia and Ictidosauria) evolved a suite of cranial and postcranial features from which the adaptations of the earliest mammals could have developed. An account of the reptile-mammal transition and an analysis of these features was given by Crompton and Jenkins in Chapter 3 of this volume.

SYSTEMATICS AND PHYLOGENY

Triconodonts were first assigned ordinal rank by Osborn (1907). The term Triconodonta had previously been used (Osborn, 1888) to designate the hypothetical ancestors of triconodonts and some other fossil forms. Later, Simpson (1928) provided a more complete diagnosis based on his survey of the then available American and European forms, all from the Jurassic (also see Simpson, 1925a, 1925b, 1929). As presently understood, triconodonts represent a more broadly construed group, including the earliest known relatives (Morganucodontidae) of the Rhaetic and the relatively advanced forms of the Cretaceous.

The characteristic feature of triconodonts is a tricuspid alignment on the molars (Fig. 4-5). In most forms the central cusps (a, A) are higher than the accessory cusps (b, c, B, C). Some advanced triconodontids, however, have cusps that are all approximately equal in height (e.g., *Triconodon*, Fig. 4-5G, H). Other characters of the incisors, canines, and postcanine teeth are variable, as might be expected of a group with such a long phylogenetic history. Simpson's (1928) diagnosis cited a lack of an angular process, the presence of distinct masseteric and pterygoid crests, and a "high, strong coronoid." Reference to these features is omitted from the diagnosis presented here because the earliest triconodonts (i.e., morganucodontids) possessed an angular process and lacked masseteric and pterygoid crests; furthermore, the relative shape of the coronoid is not sufficiently distinct to be useful in the present context. Simpson also diagnosed triconodonts as having zygomata that were ". . . stout, not expanded laterally, arising from posterior ends of alveolar processes of maxillae" (1928, p. 67). The subsequent discovery of Late Triassic and Early Cretaceous triconodont skulls reveals that a robust zygoma is a consistent feature. The degree of lateral expansion demonstrable on the basis of available cranial material, however, is too uncertain to be used as a definitive diagnostic character for the order.

At the present time, diagnoses of the three families of triconodonts may be based reliably only on the size and position of the three major cusps on the molars. In morganucodontids, the relative height of these cusps is $a > c > b$ (Fig. 4-5A, B). Triconodontids have cusps more or less equal in height, although in some genera where there is a slight disparity (e.g., *Priacodon*) the relative height is $a > b > c$. In amphilestids the relative cusp height is $a > b \cong c$, and in this family lower cusps b and c are shifted lingually relative to a, and upper cusps B and C are shifted buccally relative to A. Simpson's (1928, 1929) diagnoses of amphilestids and triconodontids (originally these groups were considered subfamilies)

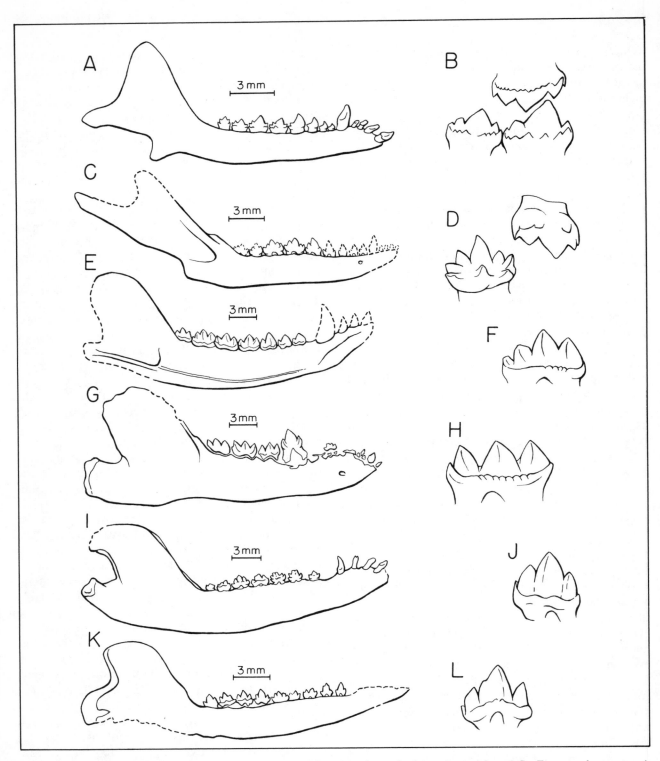

Figure 4-5. Lower jaws and representative upper and lower molars of triconodonts: *A* and *B*, *Eozostrodon watsoni*, medial views of left jaw and left molars; *C* and *D*, *Megazostrodon rudnerae*, medial views of left jaw and left molars; *E* and *F*, *Priacodon*, medial views of left jaw and left lower molar; *G* and *H*, *Triconodon*, lateral view of right jaw and medial view of left lower molar; *I* and *J*, *Phascolotherium*, medial views of left jaw and left lower molar; and *K* and *L*, *Amphitherium*, medial views of left jaw and left lower molar. Enlarged molars to various scales. (*A*, modified after Kermack and others, 1973; *B* and *D*, after Crompton, 1974; *C*, original; *E*, *F*, *H*, and *J*, after Simpson, 1929; *G*, *I*, *K*, and *L*, modified after Owen, 1871)

referred also to premolar structure and molar number. Amphilestids were characterized as having symmetrical and submolariform premolars and more than four molars, in contrast to triconodontids with asymmetrical, more or less recurved premolars and three or four molars. Recent discoveries of both amphilestids and triconodontids from the Early Cretaceous of Montana reveal that neither premolar form nor molar number is useful in making suprageneric distinctions between these groups.

The systematic classification of the triconodonts (Table 4-1) is based in part on that proposed by Hopson (1970). In presenting this classification, we recognize that there are several interpretive problems with the incomplete evidence presently available; these problems, when resolved, may require substantial systematic revision and thus are of greater current interest than the classification itself. In relative order of importance, they are the relationship of triconodonts to monotremes and other nontherian mammals (*i.e.*, the validity of the Subclass Prototheria), the relationship of the Amphilestidae to other triconodonts, and the nature of morganucodontid diversity (including the question of synonomy of *Eozostrodon* and *Morganucodon*). Each of these problems is discussed below.

Hopson (1970) included three infraclasses within the Subclass Prototheria: Eotheria (triconodonts and docodonts), Ornithodelphia (Monotremata), and Allotheria (multituberculates). He summarized the principal features that united the subclass: (1) an anterior extension of the periotic, rather than the alisphenoid, forming the greater part of orbitotemporal region of the braincase; (2) molar teeth with principal cusps aligned anteroposteriorly; and (3) retention of certain primitive features such as an uncoiled cochlea, lateral head vein in the adult, and a lack of a supraspinous fossa on the scapula. Previous studies of the braincase, including those of Kermack (1967), Hopson and Crompton (1969), and Kermack and Kielan-Jaworowska (1971), appear to support the view that prototherians evolved an orbitotemporal wall structure fundamentally different from that in therians. Monotremes certainly differ from therians in this respect, and Kielan-Jaworowska (1971) has shown that Cretaceous multituberculates fit the prototherian pattern. However, we note that a triconodont-prototherian relationship, on the basis of braincase structure, has been interpreted only on the relatively limited evidence of dissociated petrosals, with the exception of a brief discussion and diagram of a morganucodontid given by Kermack

and Kielan-Jaworowska (1971). Study of the complete triconodont skulls from the Early Cretaceous of Montana and a full account of available morganucodontid material are needed to confirm this crucial aspect of the evidence linking triconodonts to prototherians. We regard the question as open because the vestigial teeth of the monotreme *Ornithorhynchus* do not provide convincing evidence of their affinities and because at least one therian feature (a supraspinous fossa) is present in amphilestids and is possibly present in triconodontids.

The second major problem in triconodont classification is the relationship of the amphilestids. They were originally grouped as a subfamily in the Triconodontidae (Osborn, 1888, 1907), and later elevated to familial rank by Kühne (1958). Simpson's (1928, p. 70) diagnosis refers to ". . . premolars symmetrical and submolariform. Molars more than four in number, with anterior and posterior cusps small relative to the main cusp." With the material available to Simpson, this diagnosis was adequate to differentiate the group from triconodontids, which possessed asymmetrical premolars and three or four molars with cusps of more or less equal height. Discovery of additional amphilestid and triconodontid material from the Cretaceous reveals that premolar form and molar number are no longer useful diagnostic features. Differences in molar structure, therefore, remain as the primary feature by which the relationships of amphilestids and triconodontids may be assessed. Inclusion of the amphilestids in the Triconodonta has been questioned by Simpson (1961), Patterson and Olson (1961), and Kermack (1967). More recently, Mills (1971) expressed the opinion that amphilestid dentitions are most similar to those of *Kuehneotherium* and such "obtuse-angled" symmetrodonts as *Tinodon*; in so doing, he drew attention to the major structural and occlusal similarities between these groups, and suggested that the amphilestids be removed to the "Infraclass Pantotheria." Granting the validity of Mills' morphological observations, we are not persuaded that there is sufficient evidence to warrant formal reclassification at this time. The anteroposterior alignment of the three principal cusps is a basic triconodont feature which distinguishes these forms from *Kuehneotherium* and symmetrodonts. It is true, of course, that the occlusal pattern is similar to that in symmetrodonts, but the same intercuspal relationships are also found in *Megazostrodon*, which structurally is an undoubted morganucodontid triconodont. Thus, although amphilestids may well be regarded as a separate and early offshoot of the primitive triconodont stock, we do not feel justified in removing them from the Triconodonta on present evidence.

A third problem concerns the nature of diversity within the Morganucodontidae. Conflicting viewpoints on the subject abound in the literature and most frequently focus on questions of *Eozostrodon-Morganucodon* synonymy and the systematic position of *Sinoconodon*. We do not propose to recapitulate the detailed arguments on either question (see Parrington, 1971, and Kermack and others, 1973), but will simply emphasize the principal conclusions that appear to be most reasonable on the available evidence. In so doing, we recognize that studies of available materials now under way at several institutions may well require modification of our current opinions. Morganucodontid materials have now been recovered from three continents (Europe, Africa, Asia) and, on the basis of comparisons of dental structure, appear to represent a closely related group. The differences among morganucodontid teeth from the various localities in Europe and China are not of the order that ordinarily warrants generic distinction, and we are persuaded that *Morganucodon* Kühne, 1949, is a junior synonym of *Eozostrodon* Parrington, 1941. *Megazostrodon* Crompton and Jenkins, 1968, has undoubted generic identity, although *Erythrotherium* Crompton, 1964, is a juvenile and is similar to, if not congeneric with, *Eozostrodon* (Crompton, 1964, Mills, 1971). However, Crompton (1974) reported that further preparation of the type and only specimen of *Erythrotherium* revealed several characters that warrant generic distinction. *Sinoconodon rigneyi*, originally described by Patterson and Olson (1961) from fragmentary skull and post-cranial material, is difficult to classify with confidence. Some of the material originally referred to *Sinoconodon* has subsequently been identified as that of a morganucodontid (Rigney, 1963; Kermack, 1967). Crompton (1964) found that the dentary of *Sinoconodon* bears many resemblances to that of a galesaurid cynodont, and later reiterated (Crompton, 1974) differences between *Sinoconodon* and morganucodontids. In view of the relatively poor preservation of available material and current doubts on its affinities, we judge that *Sinocodon* is best ascribed as ?Triconodonta *incertae sedis* and does not warrant separate familial rank. We currently subscribe to the opinion of Hopson and Crompton that *Sinoconodon* may represent an early offshoot of the morganucodontid stock ". . . that lost the molar cingula, evolved a wide diastema in front of the molar teeth through early loss of the premolariform teeth during ontogeny, and developed a more specialized interlocking mechanism between adjacent molars than occurs in typical [morganucodontids]" (Hopson and Crompton, 1969, p. 32).

ECOLOGY

In attempting to reconstruct the habits and habitats of triconodonts, at least three types of evidence should be considered: detailed taphonomic data from triconodont localities, faunal associations, and the anatomical adaptations of specific triconodont taxa. With the exception of faunal association, there is actually very little information bearing on triconodont ecology. It is well known that faunal assemblages may be modified by many factors, with the resulting thanatocoenoses differing in important respects from related biocoenoses. Furthermore, there are no recent small mammals with a dentition comparable with that of triconodonts. Cognizant of this situation, we discuss triconodont ecology in frankly speculative terms.

Jurassic and Cretaceous triconodonts occur in a variety of faunal associations. At Como Bluff, Wyoming, the Morrison fauna includes a distinctly aquatic component of molluscs, fish (including ganoids and lungfish), amphibians, turtles, and a crocodilian. Terrestrial elements (rhynchocephalians, lizards, saurischian and ornithischian dinosaurs), as well as more than twenty genera of mammals (including two of triconodonts), are also present (Simpson, 1926). The Purbeck Formation of England has yielded a comparable fauna, the principal differences being the absence of lungfish, the preservation of diverse insects, and a lesser diversity and abundance of dinosaurs. The Purbeck also contains intercalated beds of a marine or brackish water facies (Simpson, 1928), and thus would appear to represent a more proximally coastal marine environment than the Morrison. Both, however, give evidence of a lowland, low-energy setting. The heterogeneity of life forms preserved in these deposits suggests complex food chains and niche diversity, partitioned among vertebrates, invertebrates, and plants. However, nothing learned from these faunal associations helps to differentiate the ecological role of triconodonts from that of other contemporary mammals.

Slaughter (1969) has cited evidence of faunal

association with *Astroconodon* in support of his suggestion that triconodonts may have been semiaquatic and piscivorous. Of the five Texas localities yielding Albian faunas, two contain the triconodont *Astroconodon*, multituberculates, and therians, together with such freshwater or terrestrial forms as frogs, salamanders, and lizards; no picnodonts or rayfishes are recorded. The three other localities do not yield amphibians or lizards, but picnodonts and rayfishes are common, and among mammals, only *Astroconodon* is known. We are not persuaded, however, that *Astroconodon* was semiaquatic and fed on small fish simply because it is associated locally with sediments deposited in shallow bays and brackish water lagoons. Similar associations of marine and terrestrial elements are well known (*e.g.*, the Purbeck fauna, Simpson, 1928, Milk River fauna, Fox, 1968, and Shotgun fauna, McGrew, 1963) and each simply represents a coastal thanatocoenose.

Slaughter's (1969) principal argument centers on a comparison of the teeth of triconodonts with those of more recent marine mammals. Recognizing that modern odontocetes and some pinnipeds that are almost strictly piscivorous have conical, pointed teeth, he notes that archaeocetes and many phocid pinnipeds have triconodont-like molars. Although the suggested functional correlation is intriguing, we doubt that it is sufficient to support the claim that triconodonts were piscivorous. If, for example, the insectivorous aardwolf (*Proteles cristatus*) were known only from fossils, one might then wrongly argue for dietary similarity with those odontocetes and pinnipeds that possess conical, pointed teeth. Gross similarity of structure can be most deceptive, especially when comparisons are made between taxa that are widely separated both phylogenetically and temporally.

We think the evidence at hand is sufficient to support the hypothesis that the earliest triconodonts (morganucodontids) were insectivorous *sensu lato*, and that the later triconodontids developed more restricted carnivorous specializations. The amphilestid and triconodontid dentitions both were essentially shearing devices, and in both families the tendency to relatively larger size can be interpreted as having been advantageous in predatory roles.

BIOGEOGRAPHY

Table 4-2 summarizes the continental and stratigraphic occurrence of triconodonts. Congeneric and probably contemporaneous species occur on different continents in at least two cases: *Eozostrodon* (Late Triassic, Europe and Asia) and *Trioracodon* (Late Jurassic, North America and Europe). Preliminary information indicates that the undescribed amphilestid from the Early Cretaceous Cloverly Formation is similar to a named ("*Gobiconodon borissiaki*") but undescribed form from Lower Cretaceous deposits in Mongolia. Available evidence thus points to relatively rapid and widespread dispersal of certain representatives of each of two triconodont families.

REFERENCES CITED

Beliajeva, E. I., Trofimov, B. A., and Reshetov, V. J., 1974, General stages in evolution of late Mesozoic and early Tertiary mammalian fauna in central Asia, *in* Kramarenko, N. N., and others, eds., Mesozoic and Cenozoic faunas and biostratigraphy of Mongolia: Moscow, Joint Soviet-Mongol. Paleont. Exped. (Trans., v. 1), p. 19-45 (in Russian with English summary).

Broderip, W. J., 1828, Observations on the jaw of a fossil mammiferous animal found in the Stonesfield Slate: Zool. Jour. London, v. 3, p. 408-412.

Butler, P. M., 1972, Some functional aspects of molar evolution: Evolution, v. 26, p. 474-483.

Crompton, A. W., 1964, A preliminary description of a new mammal from the Upper Triassic of South Africa: Zool. Soc. London Proc., v. 142, p. 441-452.

_____1974, The dentitions and relationships of the southern African Triassic mammals, *Erythrotherium parringtoni* and *Megazostrodon rudnerae*: Brit. Mus. (Nat. Hist.) Bull. (Geol.), v. 24, p. 397-437.

Crompton, A. W., and Jenkins, F. A., Jr., 1968, Molar occlusion in Late Triassic mammals: Biol. Rev., v. 43, p. 427-458.

Fox, R. C., 1968, Early Campanian (Late Cretaceous) mammals from Alberta, Canada: Nature, v. 220, p. 1046.

_____1969, Studies of Late Cretaceous vertebrates. III. A triconodont mammal from Alberta: Canad. Jour. Zool., v. 47, p. 1253-1256.

_____1976, Additions to the mammalian local fauna from the Upper Milk River Formation (Upper Cretaceous), Alberta: *ibid.*, v. 13, p. 1105-1118.

Hopson, J. A., 1970, The classification of nontherian mammals: Jour. Mammal., v. 51, p. 1-9.

Hopson, J. A., and Crompton, A. W., 1969, Origin of mammals, *in* Dobzhansky, T., Hecht, M. K., and Steere, W. C., eds., Evolutionary biology: New York, Appleton-Century-Crofts, v. 3, p. 15-72.

Jenkins, F. A., Jr., and Parrington, F. R., 1976, The postcranial skeletons of the Triassic mammals *Eozostrodon*, *Megazostrodon* and *Erythrotherium*: Roy. Soc. London Philos. Trans., B (Biol. Sci.), v. 273, p. 387-431.

Kermack, K. A., 1963, The cranial structure of the triconodonts: *ibid.*, v. 246, p. 83-103.

_____1967, The interrelations of early mammals: Linn. Soc. Zool. Jour., v. 47, p. 241-249.

Kermack, K. A., and Kielan-Jaworowska, Z., 1971, Therian and nontherian mammals, *in* Kermack, D. M., and Kermack, K. A., eds., Early mammals: Linn. Soc. Zool. Jour., v. 50, suppl. 1, p. 103-115.

Kermack, K. A., and Mussett, F., 1958, The jaw articulation of the Docodonta and the classification of Mesozoic mammals: Roy. Soc. London Proc., B (Biol.), v. 148, p. 204-215.

_____1959, The first mammals: Discovery, London, v. 20, p. 144-151.

Kermack, K. A., Mussett, F., and Rigney, H. W., 1973, The lower jaw of *Morganucodon*: Linn. Soc. Zool. Jour., v. 53, p. 87-175.

Kielan-Jaworowska, Z., 1971, Skull structure and affinities of the Multituberculata, *in* Kielan-Jaworowska, Z., ed., Results Polish-Mongol. Palaeont. Expeds., pt. III: Palaeontologia Polonica, no. 25, p. 5-41.

Kühne, W. G., 1949, On a triconodont tooth of a new pattern from a fissure-filling in South Glamorgan: Zool. Soc. London Proc., v. 119, p. 345-350.

_____1958, Rhaetische Triconodonten aus Glamorgan, ihre Stellung zwischen den Klassen Reptilia und Mammalia und ihre Bedeutung für die Reichart'sche Theorie: Paläont. Zeit., v. 32, p. 197-235.

McGrew, P. O., 1963, Environmental significance of sharks in the Shotgun fauna, Paleocene of Wyoming: Contribs. Geol., Univ. Wyoming, v. 2, p. 39-41.

Marsh, O. C., 1879, Notice of new Jurassic mammals: Amer. Jour. Sci., ser. 3, v. 18, p. 396-398.

_____1880, Notice of Jurassic mammals representing two new orders: *ibid.*, ser. 3, v. 20, p. 235-239.

_____1887, American Jurassic mammals: *ibid.*, ser. 3, v. 33, p. 326-348.

Mills, J. R. E., 1971, The dentition of *Morganucodon*, *in* Kermack, D. M., and Kermack, K. A., eds., Early mammals: Linn. Soc. Zool. Jour., v. 50, suppl. 1, p. 29-63.

Osborn, H. F., 1888, On the structure and classification of the Mesozoic Mammalia: Acad. Nat. Sci. Philadelphia Jour., ser. 2, v. 9, p. 186-263.

_____1907, Evolution of mammalian molar teeth: New York, Macmillan Co., 250 p.

Ostrom, J. H., 1976, The triumph of the mammals, *in* Fishbein, S. L., ed., Our Continent—a natural history of North America: Washington, D. C., National Geographic Society, p. 118-141.

Owen, R., 1938, On the jaws of the *Thylacotherium prevostii* (Valenciennes) from Stonesfield: Geol. Soc. London Proc., v. 3, p. 5-9.

_____1845, Odontography; or, a treatise on the comparative anatomy of the teeth: London, Hippolyte Bailliere, Publ., *viic* + 655 p.

_____1859, Palaeontology: Encycl. Brit., 8th ed., v. 17, p. 156-161.

_____1871, Monograph of the fossil Mammalia of the Mesozoic formations: Palaeontogr. Soc. Monog. 24, 115 p.

Parrington, F. R., 1941, On two mammalian teeth from the Lower Rhaetic of Somerset: Ann. Mag. Nat. Hist., London, ser. 11, v. 8, p. 140-144.

_____1971, On the Upper Triassic mammals: Roy. Soc. London Philos. Trans., B (Biol. Sci.), v. 261, p. 231-272.

_____1973, The dentitions of the earliest mammals: Linn. Soc. Zool. Jour., v. 52, p. 85-95.

Patterson, B., 1951, Early Cretaceous mammals from northern Texas: Amer. Jour. Sci., v. 249, p. 31-46.

Patterson, B., and Olson, E. C., 1961, A triconodontid mammal from the Triassic of Yunnan, *in* Vandebroek, G., ed., International colloquium on the evolution of lower and non specialized mammals: Brussels, Kon. Vlaamse Acad. Wetensch., Lett. Schone Kunsten Belgie, Brussels, pt. 1, p. 129-191.

Rigney, H. W., 1963, A specimen of *Morganucodon* from Yunnan: Nature, v. 197, p. 1122-1123.

Simpson, G. G., 1925a, Mesozoic Mammalia. I. American triconodonts, Part 1: Amer. Jour. Sci., ser. 5, v. 10, p. 145-165.

_____1925b, Mesozoic Mammalia. I. American triconodonts: Part 2: *ibid.*, ser. 5, v. 10, p. 334-358.

_____1926, The fauna of Quarry Nine: *ibid.*, ser. 5, v. 12, p. 1-11.

_____1928, A catalogue of the Mesozoic Mammalia in the Geological Department of The British Museum: London, Oxford Univ. Press, *x* + 215 p.

_____1929, American Mesozoic Mammalia: Peabody Mus. (Yale Univ.) Mem., v. 3, pt. 1, Yale Univ. Press, *xv* + 171 p.

_____1961, Evolution of Mesozoic mammals, *in* Vandebroek, G., ed., International colloquium on the evolution of lower and non specialized mammals: Brussels, Kon. Vlaamse Acad. Wetensch., Lett. Schone Kunsten Belgie, pt. 1, p. 57-95.

Slaughter, B. H., 1969, *Astroconodon*, the Cretaceous triconodont: Jour. Mammal., v. 50, p. 102-107.

Young, C. C., 1978, New materials of *Eozostrodon*: Vertebrata PalAsiatica, v. 16, p. 1-3 (in Chinese with English abstract).

CHAPTER 5

DOCODONTA

Donald G. Kron

INTRODUCTION

The Order Docodonta was a Middle and Late Jurassic mammalian group having certain persistently primitive features and unique dental specializations. The order is known primarily from isolated jaws and teeth; few cranial and no postcranial remains have yet been described. Docodonts have been found at six areas in the Northern Hemisphere. A possible ancestral group existed in the Late Triassic, but no descendants of the order are known. The classification of docodonts, as currently recognized, is presented in Table 5-1.

DIAGNOSIS

The nontherian mammalian Order Docodonta is ". . . a very small, highly specialized group in which the molar teeth have attained a complex type of crown-to-crown occlusion superficially resembling that of advanced therians" (Hopson and Crompton,

TABLE 5-1   CLASSIFICATION OF DOCODONTA

Subclass Eotheria Kermack and Mussett, 1958
  Order Docodonta Kretzoi, 1946
    Family Docodontidae (Marsh, 1887)
      Docodon Marsh, 1881
        D. victor (Marsh, 1880)
        D. striatus Marsh, 1881
        D. affinis (Marsh, 1887)
        D. crassus (Marsh, 1887)

        D. superus Simpson, 1929
      Peraiocynodon Simpson, 1928a
        P. inexpectatus Simpson, 1928a
      Haldanodon Kühne and Krusat, 1972
        H. exspectatus Kühne and Krusat, 1972
      Borealestes Waldman and Savage, 1972
        B. serendipitus Waldman and Savage, 1972
  unnamed docodont reported by Freeman (1976)

1969, p. 32). The docodonts achieved areal enlargement of the molars (and hence increased masticatory efficiency) by a broad expansion of the internal cingula in upper and lower teeth accompanied by inflation of the internal cusps and the development of transverse ridges connecting the cusps. Docodonts therefore, independently from all other mammals, developed an advanced subquadrate molar pattern quite early in their history. The premolars show only modest changes from what was probably the primitive triconodont condition. The posterior upper premolars in *Docodon* and *Haldanodon* have a slight "talonid," but the lowers are almost unmodified.

Docodonts are also distinguished by their jaw structure, which retains vestiges of the primitive reptilian articular-quadrate suspension pattern. The primary hinge, however, is the dentary-squamosal unit, a feature commonly considered diagnostic of mammals.

ANATOMY

Skull and Mandible

Docodonts were mouse-sized mammals with a long, narrow snout. A complete skull of *Haldanodon* is known, but to date only some damaged cranial fragments have been illustrated and described (Krusat, 1974, written communication, 1977). The skeletal structure is still unknown, but Jenkins and Parrington (1976) described morganucodontid material from the Upper Triassic. If the docodonts were as conservative in their bodies as they were in their jaw structure (discussed below), they probably looked much like morganucodontids.

The docodont mandible is generally long and rather slender (Fig. 5-1), with the condyle located nearly at the level of the tooth row. The low placement of the condyle would have allowed sequential occlusion of the teeth. A stout coronoid process arises just behind the tooth row and partly overhangs the condyle. The ventral border of the jaw is distinguished by a prominent triangular-shaped process that descends well forward of the condyle. Simpson (1928a) regarded it as a homologue of the therian angular process, although its relative position is much farther forward in docodonts. Patterson (1956) disagreed on the basis of detailed comparisons of probable muscular relationships. He compared the process in docodonts to the "echidna angle" of the monotremes, and concluded that the process served

to anchor a depressor muscle homologous with the monotreme detrahens muscle. This interpretation was supported by Krusat (1974). Kermack and others (1973) described the jaw of *Morganucodon* (Order Triconodonta) and came to the opposite conclusion; they called the flange a genuine angular process homologous to that in the Theria. In this they supported Parrington (1959, 1971), who felt that the function of the process was to give the adducting masseter and pterygoid muscles maximum leverage at the time the jaw was nearly closed. Parrington also noted that shifting the muscular leverage forward reduced strain on the primitive and rather weak jaw articulation.

A trough is present on the postero-internal surface of the jaw. Comparative studies of the mandible of *Docodon* by Simpson (1928b) and that of *Morganucodon* by Kermack and others (1973), resulted in interpretations of the function of the docodont trough. Simpson (1928b) thought that the recess in *Docodon* had contained major nerves and blood vessels. The more complete material of *Morganucodon*, however, shows that the trough contained vestigial and splinter-like angular and articular bones, arranged subparallel to one another and to the jaw itself. Although Krusat (1974) believed that the bones had been lost in the docodonts, the trough is still rather prominent in these animals and may also have held minute "reptilian" accessory mandibular bones to form a secondary jaw suspension. Recognition of the possible double jaw articulation led Simpson (1959) to suggest that the Docodonta (and those morganucodontids which shared this feature) might belong to the Mammalia, but only with the status of *incertae sedis*. Kermack and Mussett (1958) discussed

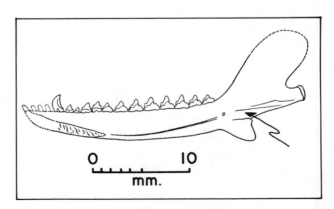

Figure 5-1. Lingual view of reconstructed right mandible of *Docodon* sp. Arrow points to location of postero-internal trough. (Modified from Simpson, 1929)

the problem and concluded that a "mammal" can be defined as an animal in which the *major* articular elements of the jaws are the dentary and squamosal.

Dentition

In the dental evolution of the Docodonta, the presumably ancestral triconodont molar with its longitudinally arranged cusps was modified both in the upper and lower teeth by the expansion of the internal cingulum accompanied by addition of a transverse ridge. The result was a dentition possessing considerably increased shearing capabilities due to the added ridges and crenulations. The pattern, however, was developed in a fashion quite different from that of the therians (Simpson, 1961; Gingerich, 1973). The docodonts were also unusual in their retention of the principal upper cusp in its ancestral buccal position; the cusp migrated lingually in symmetrodonts and eupantotheres as molar enlargement progressed (Patterson, 1956). Data on microstructure of the enamel are presented in Chapter 11.

Figures 5-2 through 5-4 illustrate, respectively, the molar teeth of *Borealestes*, *Haldanodon*, and *Docodon*, and are provided in part to allow better understanding of Figure 5-5, which shows occlusal relationships as interpreted by Jenkins (1969).

The changes involved in the evolution of the docodont molar from the primitive triconodont condition were probably as set forth in the following discussion. An initial lingual broadening of the upper molars would have occluded posterior to the protoconid and the main internal cingular cusp of the lower molars. Equivalent widening of the lower molars associated with the buildup of transverse connecting crests in upper and lower teeth would have been necessary to increase occlusal contact. Cusp "B" on the upper molars and cusp "c" on the lowers were lost during this process. Wear facets and striae were studied by Jenkins (1969). He suggested that the cusp loss either brought about, or was the result of, a shift from tooth occlusion that would be described as being nearly "opposite" (Fig. 5-5A) to an "alternate" occlusion. The newly developed "talon" ("internal extension" of terminology by Hopson and Crompton, 1969) occluded between the transverse crests of opposing lower molars (Fig. 5-5B). The proposed transition from *Haldanodon* to *Docodon* involved an anteroposterior broadening of the "talon," resulting in increased occlusal area and complexity (Fig. 5-5C; also see Hopson and Crompton, 1969, for more detail of inferred evolutionary changes). Gingerich (1973) reviewed Jenkins' (1969) study and concluded that mastication in *Docodon* involved two stages of movement of the lower jaw.

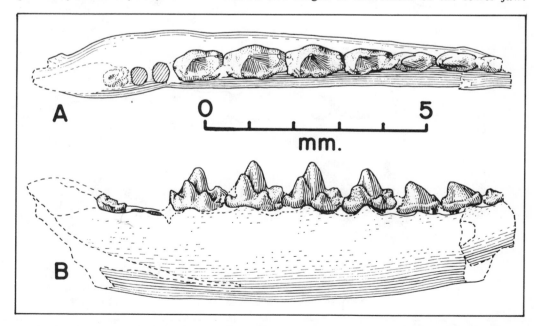

Figure 5-2. Left mandible of *Borealestes serendipitus* in occlusal (*A*) and lingual (*B*) views. (From Waldman and Savage, 1972; published with permission of The Geological Society and Scottish Academic Press Limited)

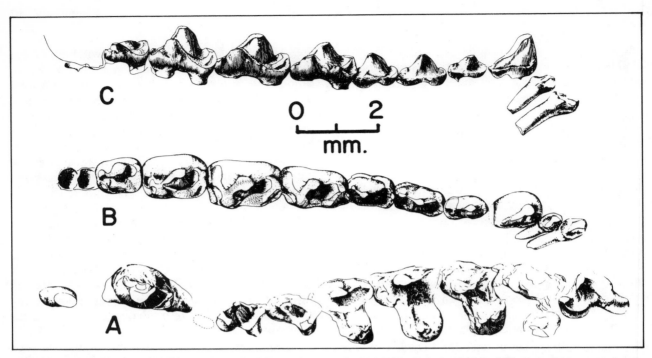

Figure 5-3.   Teeth of *Haldanodon*: *A*, occlusal view of reconstructed left upper dentition of *H. exspectatus*, anterior to left; and *B*, occlusal and *C*, lingual views of reconstructed left lower dentition of *H. exspectatus*, anterior to right. (Illustrations courtesy of G. Krusat).

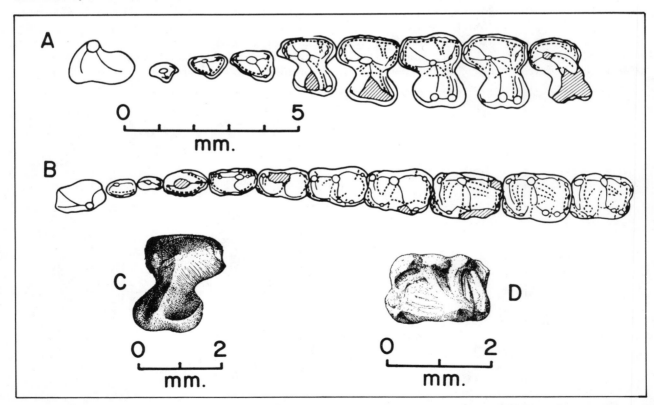

Figure 5-4.   Teeth of *Docodon*: *A* and *B*, semidiagrammatic reconstructions in occlusal view of left upper dentition (based upon *D. superus*) and right lower dentition (based upon *D. victor*), respectively (from Jenkins, 1969). *C*, right M³ of *D. superus*, and *D*, right M$_x$ of *D.* sp. (*C* and *D* from Simpson, 1929).

These were, first, an upward and backward puncturing stroke and, second, an upward and forward shearing motion. Analysis of the wear facets did not reveal convincing signs of major grinding movement, although neither Gingerich (1973) nor Mills (1971) ruled out minor function of this sort.

SYSTEMATICS

Several species of *Docodon* were named from O. C. Marsh's famous "Quarry 9" site at Como Bluff, Wyoming. One tooth was also found in Colorado at Marsh's Garden Park dinosaur locality. Quarry 9 and Garden Park are both in the Late Jurassic Morrison Formation. The dental formula of *Docodon* is $I^?_{3+}C^1_1P^3_{3-4}M^{6+?}_{7-8}$, known from a fair assortment of jaws and maxillary fragments. Marsh (1880, 1881, 1887), on the basis of lower dentitions, described three genera and four species of docodonts (*Diplocynodon victor, Docodon striatus, Enneodon affinis*, and *E. crassus*). *Diplocynodon* and *Enneodon* were preoccupied names later replaced by *Dicrocynodon* and *Ennacodon*, respectively. The name *Diacynodon* was a later replacement for *Diplocynodon*, but both are synonymous with *Dicrocynodon*. Simpson (1929) revised the group and put *Dicrocynodon* and *Ennacodon* in synonymy with *Docodon*, while retaining Marsh's original species names. Simpson, at the same time, added *D. superus* as a "convenience" species to include all upper teeth of the genus. Jenkins (1969) restudied all available material of *Docodon* and came to the conclusion that the genus may actually be monospecific, although he did not formally synonymize the names.

Peraiocynodon inexpectatus is known from a single left mandibular ramus recovered from the uppermost Jurassic Lulworth Beds of Durlston Bay, England. Simpson (1961) expressed doubts that *Peraiocynodon*, described by him in 1928a, is distinct from *Docodon*. The original description of *Peraiocynodon* was based upon what has since been interpreted as a milk dentition, and the teeth may be referable to *Docodon*.

Haldanodon exspectatus was found in the Guimarota coal pits in Portugal. The deposits are presumed to be of the early Kimmeridgian Stage, and the overall aspect of the fauna appears more primitive than that from Durlston Bay. The dental formula of *Haldanodon* is $I^5_{2+}C^1_1P^3_3M^5_5$. The described

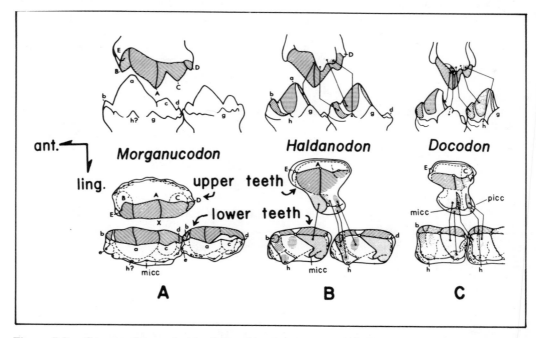

Figure 5-5. Comparative occlusal relationships between teeth of *Morganucodon* **sp.** (*A*), *Haldanodon* **sp.** (*B*), **and** *Docodon* **sp.** (*C*). **Lingual views above, occlusal views below.** *micc*, **main internal cingular cusp;** *picc*, **postero-internal cingular cusp (terminology from Jenkins, written communication, 1976; other letters signify arbitrary cusp designations used by Hopson and Crompton, 1969). (Modified from Hopson and Crompton, 1969; reproduced with permission of Appleton-Century-Crofts, Educational Division, Meredith Corporation, Plenum Publishing Corporation)**

material includes cranial elements as well as jaws and maxillary fragments. A complete skull is now being described by Krusat. *Haldanodon* was first reported in 1968 (Kühne, 1968b) but remained a *nomen nudum* until 1972 when a formal description and diagnosis was published (Kühne and Krusat, 1972). Kühne (1968a) suggested that two other, unnamed, genera of docodonts occur at Guimarota, but Krusat (1974) regarded them as morphologic variants of *Haldanodon.*

Freeman (1976) reported an unnamed docodont from the upper Bathonian Forest Marble formation in Oxfordshire, England. A number of teeth were found, but only a single upper molar was complete enough to merit being figured. The molar appears typical for docodonts, but is primitive in that the breadth/length ratio is less than in later forms. The characteristic pinched waist seen in *Docodon* and *Haldanodon* is lacking, and the postero-internal cingular cusp is relatively larger than in either of those genera.

Borealestes serendipitus was described from a right mandibular ramus found in the Ostracod Limestone on the Isle of Skye, Scotland (Waldman and Savage, 1972). The fossil-bearing stratum was dated at mid-upper Bathonian, or about upper Middle Jurassic. The known dental formula is $I_7C_1P_{3+?}M_6$. Only one other specimen of *Borealestes* has been reported, a left mandibular ramus from the same locality, but a partial skeleton of *Borealestes* from the Isle of Skye is now under study by R. J. G. Savage (written communication to W. A. Clemens, 1977).

The higher category classifications of the Docodonta have undergone a number of changes.

Marsh (1887) placed them as a family (Diplocynodontidae) in the Order Pantotheria. Simpson (1929) changed the family name to Docodontidae. Patterson (1956) followed Kretzoi (1946) by placing the docodonts in a separate order allied with the Triconodonta and in an uncertain subclass. Patterson (*ibid.*) also included *Morganucodon* in the Docodontidae. Kermack and Mussett (1958) proposed the Subclass Eotheria to hold the Docodonta and *Morganucodon,* but left the Triconodonta as Order *incertae sedis.* Hopson (1970) changed the level of the hierarchy to Infraclass Eotheria, Subclass Prototheria. Simpson (1971) followed Kermack and Mussett (1958), but regarded the triconodonts as definitely belonging to the Subclass Eotheria. Simpson also placed the morganucodontids (and their possible close relatives, the sinoconodonts) firmly in the Triconodonta.

PHYLOGENY

The docodonts did not achieve great diversity (Table 5-2). Even within the comparatively large collections from Como Bluff and Guimarota they fail to approach the modest diversity achieved by their triconodont "cousins." Nevertheless, there are questions about their phylogeny. Prior to the discovery of *Borealestes, Haldanodon* was regarded as a direct or nearly direct ancestor of *Docodon* (*e.g.,* by Hopson and Crompton, 1969). Waldman and Savage (1972), however, felt that *Borealestes* was allied with *Haldanodon,* and that neither was in a direct lineage to *Docodon.* They cited differences in relative arrangement of cusps and basins as their reasons.

TABLE 5-2   AGE AND OCCURRENCE OF GENERA OF DOCODONTA

GENUS	OCCURRENCE	AGE OR STAGE
Borealestes	Ostracod Limestones, Isle of Skye, Scotland	middle to late Bathonian
unnamed docodont	Forest Marble, Oxfordshire, England (Freeman, 1976)	late Bathonian
Haldanodon	Guimarota coal pits, Guimarota, Portugal	?early Kimmeridgian
Peraiocynodon (probably synonymous with *Docodon*)	Lulworth Beds, Durlston Bay, England	Volgian
Docodon	Morrison Fm., Como Bluff, Wyoming, and Garden Park, Colorado, U.S.A.	Late Jurassic

Krusat (1974) compared *Haldanodon* with the better-known *Docodon*, and did not comment upon their relationships with *Borealestes*. Similarly, Freeman (1976) did not suggest an interpretation of the phylogenetic significance of the Forest Marble docodont.

The Upper Triassic triconodont *Morganucodon* was once regarded as a suitable ancestor for the docodonts (Kühne, 1950). In part because of this, the morganucodontids were included in the Order Docodonta for a number of years before being reassigned to the Triconodonta by Hopson (1970). Current opinion on the triconodont-docodont relationship was summed up by Crompton (1974, p. 428) who preferred to consider ". . . an as yet unknown eozostrodontid [morganucodontid] . . ." as the evolutionary base for the docodonts. Crompton (*ibid.*) cited specializations in the dentition of *Morganucodon*, particularly in the upper molars, as reasons for eliminating that particular genus from consideration as a probable ancestor of the docodonts. Jaw structure thus remains the primary morphological link between the docodonts and triconodonts.

Freeman (1976) reported an unusual (and late) morganucodontid lower molar from the Middle Jurassic Forest Marble formation. The tooth differs from earlier forms in having a more inflated shape, and the main internal cingular cusp has migrated forward to a position opposite cusp "*a*," as in docodont lower molars. Although this particular species could not have given rise to the Docodonta, we may be seeing a relict of an ancestral form that was somewhat more specialized in the direction of the docodonts than the morganucodont stock of the Upper Triassic.

The docodonts have no known descendants. Patterson (1956) felt they might have been ancestral to the monotremes, but a comparative discussion of nontherian skull structure by Kielan-Jaworowska (1971) allied the monotremes more closely with the multituberculates (also see Chapter 6). There is no reason to suspect that multituberculates were closely related to the docodonts.

ECOLOGY

Little can be said about ecological relationships of the Docodonta. They lived when the giant sauropod dinosaurs ruled the earth, and among early mammals they seem to have been fairly successful. They have been found at most of the Jurassic mammal sites in the Northern Hemisphere; those collections not known to include docodonts are relatively depauperate (*e.g.*, Stonesfield, Porto Pinheiro, and Porto das Barcas). Thus members of the group must have had good powers of dispersal. With the exception of the Lulworth Beds, docodonts form a significant fraction of the total number of mammalian specimens recovered, leading to the possible conclusions that they either were very numerous or lived in habitats that favored burial and preservation.

The exact diet of the docodonts remains a mystery. Kühne (1968b) commented that the teeth of *Haldanodon* were generally more worn than those of other mammals collected at Guimarota and a few teeth were reduced to knoblike remnants. If this wear was not the result of damage through the processes of preservation, it seems that, although the docodonts were specialized to increase the shearing function of the molars, their diet, at least in the later stages of an individual's life, must have been amenable to processing by simple crushing and grinding. Simpson (1933) made an analogy between teeth of *Docodon* and those of much later omnivorous-frugivorous primates. This is rather tenuous, but Krusat (1974) agreed with the conclusion that docodont teeth were adapted to an omnivorous diet. It is possible that the docodonts enjoyed more flexible food habits than did their primarily insectivorous peers. A wider tolerance of individual habitat is also suggested by their widespread occurrence and comparatively low generic and specific diversity.

REFERENCES CITED

Crompton, A. W., 1974, The dentitions and relationships of the southern African Triassic mammals, *Erythrotherium parringtoni* and *Megazostrodon rudnerae*: Brit. Mus. (Nat. Hist.) Bull. (Geology), v. 24, p. 397-437.

Gingerich, P. D., 1973, Molar occlusion and function in the Jurassic mammal *Docodon*: Jour. Mammal., v. 254, p. 1008-1013.

Freeman, E. F., 1976, Mammal teeth from the Forest Marble (Middle Jurassic) of Oxfordshire, England: Science, v. 194, p. 1053-1055.

Hopson, J. A., 1970, The classification of nontherian mammals: Jour. Mammal., v. 51, p. 1-9.

Hopson, J. A., and Crompton, A. W., 1969, Origin of mammals, *in* Dobzhansky, T., Hecht, M. K., and Steere, W. C., eds., Evolutionary biology: New York, Appleton-Century-Crofts, v. 3, p. 15-72.

Jenkins, F. A., Jr., 1969, Occlusion in *Docodon* (Mammalia, Docodonta): Postilla (Yale Univ.), no. 139, 24 p.

Jenkins, F. A., Jr., and Parrington, F. R., 1976, The postcranial skeletons of the Triassic mammals *Eozostrodon, Megazostrodon* and *Erythrotherium*: Roy. Soc. London Philos. Trans., B (Biol. Sci.), v. 273, p. 387-431.

Kermack, K. A., and Mussett, F., 1958, The jaw articulation of the Docodonta and the classification of Mesozoic mammals: Roy. Soc. London Proc., B (Biol.), v. 148, p. 204-215.

Kermack, K. A., Mussett, F., and Rigney, H. W., 1973, The lower jaw of *Morganucodon*: Linn. Soc. Zool. Jour., v. 53, p. 87-175.

Kielan-Jaworowska, Z., 1971, Skull structure and affinities of the Multituberculata, *in* Kielan-Jaworowska, Z., ed., Results Polish-Mongol. Palaeont. Expeds., pt. III: Palaeontologia Polonica, no. 25, p. 5-41.

Kretzoi, M., 1946, On Docodonta, a new order of Jurassic mammals: Hist.-Nat. Mus. Nat'l. Hungarici Ann., v. 39, p. 108-111.

Krusat, G., 1974, *Haldanodon exspectatus* Kühne & Krusat 1972 (Mammalia, Docodonta): Berlin, Inaugural-Dissertation zur Erlangung der Doktorwurde des Fachbereiches 24 (Geowissenschaften) der Freien Universität Berlin, *iv* + 158 p.

Kühne, W. G., 1950, A symmetrodont tooth from the Rhaeto-Lias: Nature, v. 166, p. 696-697.

———1968a, History of discovery, report on the work performed, procedure, technique and generalities: Contribuição para a Fauna do Kimeridgiano da Mina de Lignito Guimarota (Leiria, Portugal), 1 Parte, Memória 14 (N. S.) dos Serviços Geológicos de Portugal, Lisboa, p. 1-21.

———1968b, Kimeridge [*sic*] mammals and their bearing on the phylogeny of the Mammalia, *in* Drake, E. T., ed., Evolution and environment: New Haven, Yale Univ. Press, p. 109-123.

Kühne, W. G., and Krusat, G., 1972, Legalisierung des

Taxon *Haldanodon* (Mammalia, Docodonta): N. Jahrb. Geol. Paläont. Monatsh., H. 5, p. 300-302.

Marsh, O. C., 1880, Notice of Jurassic mammals representing two new orders: Amer. Jour. Sci., ser. 3, v. 20, p. 235-239.

———1881, New Jurassic mammals: *ibid.*, ser. 3, v. 21, p. 511-513.

———1887, American Jurassic mammals: *ibid.*, ser. 3, v. 33, p. 326-348.

Mills, J. R. E., 1971, The dentition of *Morganucodon, in* Kermack, D. M., and Kermack, K. A., eds., Early mammals: Linn. Soc. Zool. Jour., v. 50, suppl. 1, p. 29-63.

Parrington, F. R., 1959, The angular process of the dentary: Ann. Mag. Nat. Hist., London, ser. 13, v. 2, p. 505-512.

———1971, On the upper Triassic mammals: Roy. Soc. London Phil. Trans., B (Biol. Sci.), v. 261, p. 231-272.

Patterson, B., 1956, Early Cretaceous mammals and the evolution of mammalian molar teeth: Fieldiana (Geology), v. 13, p. 1-105.

Simpson, G. G., 1928a, A catalogue of the Mesozoic Mammalia in the Geological Department of The British Museum: London, Oxford Univ. Press, *x* + 215 p.

———1928b, Mesozoic Mammalia. XII. The internal mandibular groove of Jurassic mammals: Amer. Jour. Sci., ser. 5, v. 15, p. 461-470.

———1929, American Mesozoic Mammalia: New Haven, Peabody Mus. (Yale Univ.) Mem., v. 3, pt. 1, Yale Univ. Press, *xv* + 171 p.

———1933, Paleobiology of Jurassic mammals: Palaeobiologica, v. 5, p. 127-158.

———1959, Mesozoic mammals and the polyphyletic origin of mammals: Evolution, v. 13, p. 405-414.

———1961, Evolution of Mesozoic mammals, *in* Vandebroek, G., ed., International colloquium on the evolution of lower and non specialized mammals: Brussels, Kon. Vlaamse Acad. Wetensch., Lett. Schone Kunsten Belgie, pt. 1, p. 57-95.

———1971, Concluding remarks: Mesozoic mammals revisited, *in* Kermack, D. M., and Kermack, K. A., eds., Early mammals: Linn. Soc. Zool. Jour., v. 50, suppl. 1, p. 181-198.

Waldman, M., and Savage, R. J. G., 1972, The first Jurassic mammal from Scotland: Geol. Soc. London Jour., v. 128, p. 119-125.

CHAPTER 6

MULTITUBERCULATA

William A. Clemens

Zofia Kielan-Jaworowska

INTRODUCTION

Multituberculates are frequently described as the "rodents of the Mesozoic." A superficial examination of their dentitions, which for many years was all that was known of these mammals, highlights some rodent-like features, such as the pair of enlarged, procumbent lower incisors. But, unlike rodents, these are usually opposed by more than a single pair of upper incisors. The battery of low-cusped molariform teeth at the posterior ends of the jaws formed a grinding mechanism similar to those of many rodents.

In the mid-regions of the multituberculate's dentition teeth are obviously specialized in ways unlike those found in any rodent. Particularly the upper premolariform teeth usually are not separated from the incisors by long, clear diastems indicative of the presence of a highly mobile tongue. Also, as many as four lower premolariform teeth are modified to form blade-like structures. The closest dental analogs among modern mammals are to be found in the small "musk-rat kangaroos" (*Hypsiprymnodon*), the "rat kangaroos" (*Bettongia*), and the "Mountain Pigmy Possum" (*Burramys*). All are omnivorous. *Hypsiprymnodon* is reported to feed on insects, worms, and plant material (Troughton, 1962). The bettongs apparently have similarly broad diets with one species reported to be a scavenger of marine refuse (*ibid.*; Ride, 1970; Shortbridge, 1910). *Burramys* feeds on both plants and invertebrates (Dimpel and Calaby, 1972).

The dentition is divisible into three functional units. The incisors acted in grasping and puncturing; only in taeniolabidoids were they modified for gnawing. The mid-section was another functional unit for the holding and cutting of food. At the back is a grinding mill formed by the molariform teeth. Dental morphology and other lines of evidence discussed below suggest that multituberculates, like many rodents, were adapted to feed on vegetable material. However, as Landry's (1970) analysis demonstrates, modern rodents are not all herbivores, and there is a diversity of diets among them that is not obviously reflected in dental morphology.

The only known associated postcranial materials of Mesozoic multituberculates are partial skeletons from rocks of Late Cretaceous age in Mongolia. An incomplete skeletal restoration of one North American Cretaceous multituberculate, *Mesodma*, was prepared utilizing bones that were not preserved in association (Sloan and Van Valen, 1965). The record of postcranial structure of Tertiary multituberculates is amost equally slim. What is known of skeletal structure and proportions of these few multituberculates gives no indication of highly derived modes of locomotion. There is no evidence that they evolved saltatorial, fossorial, aquatic, or volant modes of locomotion. They probably made their way quad-rupedally utilizing their rather long hind legs for the occasional leap. However, in light of the large known species diversity of multituberculates and recognizing their general convergences with rodents, it would not be surprising to discover Mesozoic species with one or more of these specializations. None of the known Mesozoic multituberculates would be considered to be a large mammal by modern standards. They ranged in size from that of very small mice to animals as large as pikas or small rabbits.

From the Late Jurassic onward through the Cretaceous every well-sampled Holarctic local fauna contains one or more species of multituberculates (see Tables 6-1 and 6-2); knowledge of mammals in the Southern Hemisphere during this period is essentially nonexistent. Particularly in the Late Cretaceous multituberculates typically made up more than half of the mammals represented in the local faunas. Their diversity apparently was the product of a major evolutionary radiation linked to the rapid spread and diversification of angiosperms in the middle of the Cretaceous. Also this change in the terrestrial floras, through its impact on the coevolving terrestrial invertebrate fauna, probably helped to spark a radiation of therian mammals (Chapters 10-12 and 14).

At the end of the Cretaceous some lineages of multituberculates became extinct. During the early Paleocene the numerous surviving stocks rapidly speciated, and the fossil record suggests that at this time the acme of multituberculate diversity was reached. Subsequently increasing competitive pressure from primates, small condylarths, and, by the close of the Paleocene, rodents took its toll (Van Valen and Sloan, 1966; Hopson, 1967). Multituberculates are absent from most middle and late Eocene faunas of Holarctica, but in North America they survived in restricted areas until at least the close of the Eocene.

Ancestry of the multituberculates is still an open question. As will be shown, shared derived cranial characters link the multituberculates, placed in the Allotheria, with members of the Eotheria. Together these subclasses contain the "prototherian" mammals of the Mesozoic. However, dental specializations easily separate the Allotheria and Eotheria. The haramiyids, known only from isolated teeth of Late Triassic, Rhaetic, and Rhaeto-Liassic age found in Europe (see Chapter 2), might be the ancestral stock of the multituberculates. Today, as in years past, strong proponents and opponents of this hypothesis are not hard to find. Without reflecting strong con-

TABLE 6-1   CLASSIFICATION OF MESOZOIC MULTITUBERCULATA

Subclass Allotheria (Marsh, 1880)
  Order Multituberculata Cope, 1884
    Suborder Plagiaulacoidea (Simpson, 1925)
      Family Paulchoffatiidae Hahn, 1969
        Subfamily Paulchoffatiinae Hahn, 1971
          Paulchoffatia Kühne, 1961
            P. delgadoi Kühne, 1961
            P. sp. Crusafont and Gibert, 1976
          Pseudobolodon Hahn, 1977
            P. oreas Hahn, 1977
            P. sp. Hahn, 1977
        Subfamily Kuehneodontinae Hahn, 1971
          Bolodon Owen, 1871
            B. crassidens Owen, 1871
            B. osborni Simpson, 1928a
            B. sp. Crusafont and Gibert, 1976
            ?*B. elongatus* Simpson, 1928a
          Henkelodon Hahn, 1977
            H. naias Hahn, 1977
            ?*H. guimarotensis* (Hahn, 1969)
          Kuehneodon Hahn, 1969
            K. dietrichi Hahn, 1969
            K. dryas Hahn, 1977
            K. simpsoni Hahn, 1969
            K. sp. Crusafont and Gibert, 1976
            ?*K.* sp. Hahn, 1977
          Plioprion Cope, 1884
            P. minor (Falconer, 1857)
        Subfamily *incertae sedis* (Hahn, pers. comm. to Clemens, 1977)
          Guimarotodon Hahn, 1969
            G. leiriensis Hahn, 1969
      ?Paulchoffatiidae (Hahn [1971] suggested that two of the isolated teeth from the Early Cretaceous, Wealden, Cliff End bonebed of England referred to *Loxaulax valdensis* by Clemens [1963a] were more likely teeth of a paulchoffatiid.)
      Family Plagiaulacidae Gill, 1872
        Ctenacodon Marsh, 1879
          C. laticeps (Marsh, 1881)
          C. scindens Simpson, 1928a
          C. serratus Marsh, 1879
          ?*C. falconeri* (Owen, 1871)
        Loxaulax Simpson, 1928a
          L. valdensis (Woodward, 1911)
        Plagiaulax Falconer, 1857
          P. becklesii Falconer, 1857
          ?*P. dawsoni* Woodward, 1891 (probably not a mammal [Clemens, 1963a])
          P. sp. Crusafont and Gibert, 1976
        Psalodon Simpson, 1925
          P. fortis (Marsh, 1887)
          P. potens (Marsh, 1887)
          ?*P. marshi* Simpson, 1929

?Plagiaulacoidea *incertae sedis*
  Plagiaulacidae, new genus and species (Khovboor local fauna, Mongolia; Beliajeva, Trofimov, and Reshetov, 1974)
  Plagiaulacidae, new genus and species (Possibly two forms, Greenwood Canyon and Paluxy local faunas, Texas, Patterson [1956]. Reference to the Plagiaulacoidea has been challenged by both Richard C. Fox and Bob H. Slaughter [pers. comms., 1976, 1977].)
  ?Plagiaulacidae. (Kühne and Crusafont-Pairó [1968] announced the discovery of multituberculates at a site near Uña, Spain)
  ?Multituberculata, Plagiaulacoidea (but see Crusafont and Gibert, 1976)
    Parendotherium Crusafont-Pairó and Adrover, 1965
      P. herreroi Crusafont-Pairó and Adrover, 1965
    Suborder Ptilodontoidea Sloan and Van Valen, 1965
      Family Neoplagiaulacidae Ameghino, 1890
        Mesodma Jepsen, 1940
          M. formosa (Marsh, 1889b)
          M. hensleighi Lillegraven, 1969
          M. primaeva (Lambe, 1902)
          M. senecta Fox, 1971
          M. thompsoni Clemens, 1963b
          M. sp., cf. *M. formosa* (*fide* Lillegraven, 1972)
          M. sp., cf. *M. formosa* (*fide* Novacek and Clemens, 1977)
          M. sp., cf. *M. formosa* (*fide* Archibald, 1977)
          M. sp. aff. *M. thompsoni* (*fide* Archibald, 1977)
          M. sp. Clemens, 1973b
          ?*M.* sp. Fox, 1971
        ?*Neoplagiaulax* Lemoine, 1880
          ?*Neoplagiaulax*, new species Archibald (1977)
      ?Neoplagiaulacidae (These genera are grouped here to recognize their primitive grade of evolution and not, necessarily, to imply close phylogenetic relationship [Kielan-Jaworowska, 1974, and Archibald, 1977].)
        Cimexomys Sloan and Van Valen, 1965 (J. D. Archibald [1977] suggests that the last four species in the following list are referable to a new genus.)
          C. antiquus Fox, 1971
          C. minor Sloan and Van Valen, 1965
          C. sp. Sloan and Van Valen, 1965
          C. new species Archibald (1977)
          C. judithae Sahni, 1972

C. cf. *judithae* Clemens, 1973b
C. magister Fox, 1971
C. magnus Sahni, 1972
C. priscus Lillegraven, 1969
Gobibaatar Kielan-Jaworowska, 1970b
    C. parvus Kielan-Jaworowska, 1970b
Genus and species indet. of Archibald (1977)
Family Ptilodontidae Gregory and Simpson, 1926
    Kimbetohia Simpson, 1936
        K. campi Simpson, 1936
        cf. *K. campi* Clemens, 1973a
    genus and species indet. of Lillegraven, 1969
Family Cimolodontidae Marsh, 1889a
    Cimolodon Marsh, 1889a
        C. electus Fox, 1971
        C. nitidus Marsh, 1889a
        C. similis Fox, 1971
        C. sp. Sahni, 1972
        C. sp. Clemens, 1973b
Suborder Taeniolabidoidea Sloan and Van Valen, 1965
Family Taeniolabididae Granger and Simpson, 1929
    Catopsalis Cope, 1882 (includes *Djadochtatherium* Simpson, 1925, following Kielan-Jaworowska and Sloan, *in press*)
        C. catopsaloides (Kielan-Jaworowska, 1974)
        C. joyneri Sloan and Van Valen, 1965
        C. matthewi (Simpson, 1925)
        C. sp. Archibald (1977)
    Kamptobaatar Kielan-Jaworowska, 1970b
        K. kuczynskii Kielan-Jaworowska, 1970b
Family Eucosmodontidae (Jepsen, 1940)
    Subfamily Eucosmodontinae Jepsen, 1940
        Buginbaatar Kielan-Jaworowska and Sochava, 1969
            B. transaltaiensis Kielan-Jaworowska and Sochava, 1969
        Bulganbaatar Kielan-Jaworowska, 1974
            B. nemegtbaataroides Kielan-Jaworowska, 1974
        Kryptobaatar Kielan-Jaworowska, 1970b
            K. dashzevegi Kielan-Jaworowska, 1970b
        Nemegtbaatar Kielan-Jaworowska, 1974
            N. gobiensis Kielan-Jaworowska, 1974
        Stygimys Sloan and Van Valen, 1965
            S. gratus (Jepsen, 1940)
            S. kuszmauli Sloan and Van Valen, 1965
            S. sp. aff. *S. kuszmauli* (*fide* Archibald, 1977)
            ?*S.* sp. Lillegraven, 1972
        Tugrigbaatar Kielan-Jaworowska and Dashzeveg, 1978
            T. saichaenensis Kielan-Jaworowska and Dashzeveg, 1978

Subfamily Microcosmodontinae Holtzman and Wolberg, 1977
    Genus and species indet. of Archibald (1977)
Eucosmodontidae (*fide* McNulty and Slaughter, 1968)
Eucosmodontidae, new genus and species Clemens, 1973b
Eucosmodontidae, new genus and species Kielan-Jaworowska, 1975b
?Eucosmodontidae, genus and species indet. of Archibald (1977)
Family Chulsanbaataridae Kielan-Jaworowska, 1974
    Chulsanbaatar Kielan-Jaworowska, 1974
        C. vulgaris Kielan-Jaworowska, 1974
Family Sloanbaataridae Kielan-Jaworowska, 1974
    Sloanbaatar Kielan-Jaworowska, 1970b
        S. mirabilis Kielan-Jaworowska, 1970b
Suborder *incertae sedis*
Family Cimolomyidae Marsh, 1889b
    Cimolomys Marsh, 1889a
        C. clarki Sahni, 1972
        C. gracilis Marsh, 1889a
        C. trochuus Lillegraven, 1969
        ?*C.* sp. A Fox, 1971
        ?*C.* sp. B Fox, 1971
    Meniscoessus Cope, 1882
        M. borealis Simpson, 1927 (a synonym of *M. robustus fide* J. D. Archibald [1977])
        M. conquistus Cope, 1882
        M. ferox Fox, 1971
        M. intermedius Fox, 1976
        M. major (Russell, 1937)
        M. robustus (Marsh, 1889a)
Family *incertae sedis*
    Essonodon Simpson, 1927
        E. browni Simpson, 1927
Family *incertae sedis*
    Viridomys Fox, 1971
        V. orbatus Fox, 1971
new family
    new genus and species Kielan-Jaworowska, 1975b
?Multituberculata *incertae sedis*
Family Haramiyidae Simpson, 1947
    Haramiya Simpson, 1947
        H. moorei (Owen, 1871)
        H. fissurae (Simpson, 1928a)
    Thomasia Poche, 1908
        T. anglica Simpson, 1928a
        T. antigua (Plieninger, 1847)
        T. sp. 1 Hahn, 1973
        T. sp. 2 Hahn, 1973

victions on the matter, we have treated the haramiyids as "?Multituberculata, *incertae sedis.*" The haramiyids were excluded from consideration in drawing up the generalizations on "Diagnosis" and "Anatomy." A review of the haramiyids is included in the section on systematics as a preamble to consideration of multituberculate phylogeny.

We gratefully and especially acknowledge the help of five colleagues in preparation of this chapter. J. D. Archibald gave us full access to his study of Late Cretaceous multituberculates, part of his un-

published doctoral dissertation (Archibald, 1977). Gerhard Hahn provided copies of the proofs of two papers on new specimens of multituberculates from the Guimarota local fauna, Portugal. P. M. Butler and G. T. MacIntyre gave us the opportunity to read a draft of their report on an analysis of the functional anatomy of the haramiyid dentition. A draft of the section on ecology was reviewed by J. H. Calaby, whose comments on the feeding habits of modern Australian marsupials added valuable data and insights.

TABLE 6-2   AGE AND OCCURRENCE OF GENERA OF MESOZOIC MULTITUBERCULATA AND HARAMIYIDAE

GENUS	OCCURRENCE	AGE OR STAGE
Paulchoffatia	Guimarota Coal Pits, Guimarota, Portugal; Galve local fauna, Spain	?early Kimmeridgian through Early Cretaceous
Pseudobolodon	Guimarota Coal Pits, Guimarota, Portugal	?early Kimmeridgian
Bolodon	Lulworth Beds, Durlston Bay, England; Galve local fauna, Spain	Volgian through Early Cretaceous
Henkelodon	Guimarota Coal Pits, Guimarota, Portugal	?early Kimmeridgian
Kuehneodon	Guimarota Coal Pits, Guimarota, Portugal; Galve local fauna, Spain	?early Kimmeridgian through Early Cretaceous
Plioprion	Lulworth Beds, Durlston Bay, England	Volgian
Guimarotodon	Guimarota Coal Pits, Guimarota, Portugal	?early Kimmeridgian
Ctenacodon	Morrison Fm., Como Bluff, Wyoming, U.S.A.; Lulworth Beds, Durlston Bay, England	Late Jurassic Volgian
Loxaulax	Wadhurst Clay, Cliff End, England	Valanginian
Plagiaulax	Lulworth Beds, Durlston Bay, England; Galve local fauna, Spain	Volgian through Early Cretaceous
Psalodon	Morrison Fm., Como Bluff, Wyoming, U.S.A.	Late Jurassic
Mesodma	Upper part of Milk River Fm., Oldman Fm., St. Mary River Fm., and Scollard Fm., Alberta, Canada; Judith River Fm. and Hell Creek Fm., Montana; Lance Fm., Wyoming; Fruitland Fm. and Kirtland Fm., New Mexico, U.S.A.: "El Gallo Fm.," Baja California, Mexico	"Aquilan" through "Lancian"
Cimexomys	Upper part of Milk River Fm., St. Mary River Fm., and Scollard Fm., Alberta, Canada; Judith River Fm. and Hell Creek Fm., Montana; Lance Fm., Wyoming; Fruitland Fm. and Kirtland Fm., New Mexico, U.S.A.	"Aquilan" through "Lancian"
Gobibaatar	Djadokhta Fm., Bayn Dzak (Shabarakh Usu), Mongolian People's Republic	?late Santonian and/or ?early Campanian
Kimbetohia	Lance Fm., Wyoming; Fruitland Fm. and Kirtland Fm., New Mexico, U.S.A.	"Edmontonian" through "Lancian"
Cimolodon	Upper part of Milk River Fm., St. Mary River Fm., and Scollard Fm., Alberta, Canada; Judith River Fm. and Hell Creek Fm., Montana; Lance Fm., Wyoming; Fruitland Fm. and Kirtland Fm., New Mexico, U.S.A.	"Aquilan" through "Lancian"
Catopsalis	Djadokhta Fm., Bayn Dzak (Shabarakh Usu) and Barun Goyot Fm., Nemegt Basin; beds of Khermeen Tsav, Khermeen Tsav, Mongolian People's Republic; Hell Creek Fm., Montana, U.S.A.	"Lancian," North America, and ?late Santonian to ?middle Campanian, Asia

TABLE 6-2   CONTINUED

GENUS	OCCURRENCE	AGE OR STAGE
Kamptobaatar	Djadokhta Fm., Bayn Dzak (Shabarakh Usu), Mongolian People's Republic	?late Santonian and/or ?early Campanian
Buginbaatar	Khaichin Ula local fauna, Bugeen Tsav, Mongolian People's Republic	?Maastrichtian or ?Paleocene
Bulganbaatar	Djadokhta Fm., Bayn Dzak (Shabarakh Usu), Mongolian People's Republic	?late Santonian and/or ?early Campanian
Kryptobaatar	Djadokhta Fm., Bayn Dzak (Shabarakh Usu), Mongolian People's Republic	?late Santonian and/or ?early Campanian
Nemegtbaatar	Barun Goyot Fm., Nemegt Basin; beds of Khermeen Tsav, Khermeen Tsav, Mongolian People's Republic	?middle Campanian
Stygimys	Hell Creek Fm., Montana, U.S.A.; "El Gallo Fm.," Baja California, Mexico	"Edmontonian" through "Lancian"
Tugrigbaatar	"Toogreeg beds," Toogreegeen Shireh, Mongolian People's Republic	?late Santonian and/or ?early Campanian
Chulsanbaatar	Barun Goyot Fm., Nemegt Basin; beds of Khermeen Tsav, Khermeen Tsav, Mongolian People's Republic	?middle Campanian
Sloanbaatar	Djadokhta Fm., Bayn Dzak (Shabarakh Usu), Mongolian People's Republic	?late Santonian and/or ?early Campanian
Cimolomys	Upper part of Milk River Fm. ?, Oldman Fm., St. Mary River Fm. and Scollard Fm., Alberta, Canada; Judith River Fm. and Hell Creek Fm., Montana; Lance Fm., Wyoming, U.S.A.	?"Aquilan" through "Lancian"
Meniscoessus	Upper part of Milk River Fm., Oldman Fm., and St. Mary River Fm., Alberta, Canada; Judith River Fm. and Hell Creek Fm., Montana; Lance Fm., Wyoming, U.S.A.	"Aquilan" through "Lancian"
Essonodon	Hell Creek Fm., Montana; Lance Fm., Wyoming, U.S.A.	"Lancian"
Viridomys	Upper part of Milk River Fm., Alberta, Canada	"Aquilan"
Haramiya	Rhaetic bonebed, Hallau, Kanton Schaffhausen, Switzerland; Holwell Quarry, Frome, Somerset, England	Rhaeto-Liassic
Thomasia	"*Plateosaurus* beds," Halberstadt, Sachsen-Anhalt, East Germany; Rhaetic bonebeds, Württemberg, West Germany; Rhaetic bonebed, Hallau, Kanton Schaffhausen, Switzerland; Holwell Quarry, Frome, Somerset, England	Late Triassic and Rhaeto-Liassic
?haramiyid	Forest Marble, Oxfordshire, England (Freeman, 1976)	late Bathonian

DIAGNOSIS

Members of the Multituberculata (excluding the family Haramiyidae) are characterized by the following. As many as three pairs of upper incisors but only one pair of lowers are present. Premolars are differentiated from the molars on morphological criteria. Posterior lower premolars are blade-like in plagiaulacoids, ptilodontoids, and some other multituberculates. At least the lower incisors and some premolars are diphyodont. Cusps of molars are of essentially uniform height and ordered in longitudinal rows. Upper molars are offset so that anteroposterior midline of M^2 is lingual to the midline of M^1, except in the Paulchoffatiinae. Skull is depressed dorsoventrally and is comparatively short and wide with strong zygomatic arches. The braincase is short and wide with the glenoid fossa situated lateral to the petrosal. Orbit is not floored but roofed, and closed anteriorly by maxilla and frontal; consequently the eyes faced laterally. Lacrimals are large, but jugals are lacking. Tabular bones, ectopterygoid bones, and posttemporal fossae are present. The lateral wall of the braincase is formed essentially by the ascending lamina of the petrosal and large orbitosphenoid; the alisphenoid contributes little. The cochlea is straight. The middle ear is open ventrally. None of the tympanic ossicles have been found. Supraspinous fossa of the scapula is lacking. Humeral head forms a greater portion of a sphere than in other mammals and is flanked by the trochanters of subequal size. Humero-ulnar articulation is of condylar type.

Sacrum, where known, is composed of three vertebrae. Ischial arc is very narrow. The femur resembles that of therian mammals in general proportions. Tibia and fibula are not fused. The tibia is U-shaped proximally in cross section. Calcaneum is of therian type with a long tuber calcanei. Astragalus is short, wide, and incompletely superimposed over the calcaneum. The hind foot is long and plantigrade; the pollex is opposable.

Members of the Haramiyidae, which are known only from isolated teeth, differ from multituberculates in (after Hahn, 1973): (1) greater variation in heights of molar cusps; (2) presence of transverse crests linking the rows of cusps and blocking the median, anteroposteriorly oriented groove or basin; and (3) absence of grooving in the enamel.

ANATOMY

Cranial

Available Sample

The oldest known multituberculate cranial material, found in Kimmeridgian beds of Portugal (Hahn, 1969), consisted of a crushed skull of *Paulchoffatia*, a rostrum of *Kuehneodon*, and mandibles of both genera. Hahn (*ibid.*) provided a tentative reconstruction of the skull of *Paulchoffatia*; it resembles those of known Late Cretaceous and Tertiary multituberculates, differing only in having a somewhat more elongated snout. Subsequently Hahn (1977a) described five paulchoffatiid cranial fragments that document variation in the shape of the snout. Unlike *Paulchoffatia*, the snout of *Kuehneodon* is relatively shorter and broader. Available fossils of other Jurassic genera provide no information on cranial anatomy. Similarly, almost all specimens of North American Cretaceous multituberculates consist only of isolated teeth or tooth-bearing jaw fragments. The only well-preserved North American multituberculate skulls known are those of the Paleocene genera *Taeniolabis* and *Ptilodus* described by Simpson (1937a). Because of the nature of their preservation, it has been impossible to recognize details of the structure of the braincase in specimens of *Taeniolabis*. Simpson was able, however, to determine some of the structural details of the braincase of *Ptilodus*. His reconstruction is essentially correct for the foramina in the basicranial region, but because the occipital plate was not preserved and sutures were obliterated, Simpson hypothetically reconstructed the braincase on essentially therian lines. This was challenged by Kielan-Jaworowska (1971).

The most useful multituberculate cranial material collected to date comes from the Mongolian Late Cretaceous Djadokhta and Barun Goyot formations. A large part of this collection, derived from the Polish-Mongolian Paleontological Expeditions, has been described (see Kielan-Jaworowska, 1970a, 1970b, 1971, 1974a). The discussion of multituberculate cranial structure that follows is based largely upon this Mongolian material.

Description

The main differences between the multituberculate and therian skulls will be pointed out as a prologue. The multituberculate skull (Fig. 6-1) is depressed dorsoventrally. It is comparatively short and wide, has a blunt snout, strong zygomatic arches, and a comparatively short braincase that is widely expanded laterally. In primitive therians the snout is strongly elongated, and the braincase is rather narrow and high. In ventral view the glenoid fossa of multituberculates is situated lateral to the petrosal, but in therian mammals it is placed anterolateral to the petrosal. In the multituberculates the orbit has no floor, but is partially roofed by the maxilla and the frontal. Consequently, the anterior root of the zygomatic arch is set more anteriorly than in the therian mammals, and the eyes of multituberculates faced laterally. In contrast, therian mammals have a floored orbit without a roof and the eyes faced more anteriorly. Several reptilian structures lost in therians were retained in the multituberculate skull, for example, the tabular bones, ectopterygoid bones, and posttemporal fossae.

Nasals are large, expanded posteriorly, and contact the lacrimals. Lacrimals are moderately large in the Jurassic *Paulchoffatia* (see Hahn, 1969) and very large in known Cretaceous genera. The lacrimal has a roughly rectangular and extensive wing on the dorsal side of the skull in known Asian Late Cretaceous multituberculates. The reported absence of lacrimals in skulls of *Kamptobaatar* and *Sloanbaatar* (see Kielan-Jaworowska, 1971) was corrected by the same author (1974a) after making comparisons with better preserved material from the Barun Goyot Formation.

The premaxilla has an extensive palatal process but is comparatively small laterally. The margin between the ventral and lateral walls of the premaxilla is thickened and forms a sharp edge. The large maxilla contributes extensively to the structure of the zygomatic arch. The infraorbital foramen is usually large. A jugal is lacking, and the maxilla directly contacts the squamosal. The glenoid fossa of the squamosal is large, flat, roughly triangular or oval, and has a weak postglenoid process set posterolaterally. Frontals are extensive and have a transversely-aligned posterior margin in all known Asian genera, but taper posteriorly in *Taeniolabis* and *Ptilodus* from North America (see Simpson, 1937a). Parietals are extensive and form the entire posterior cranial roof. Palatal vacuities are absent in some families (*e.g.*, Taeniolabididae and Chulsanbaataridae), but are present in others (*e.g.*, Eucosmodontidae and Ptilodontidae). Within the Paulchoffatiidae the presence or absence of anterior palatal vacuities is a matter of intergeneric variation. Palatine fissures,

major and minor palatine foramina, and palatonasal foramina are present. Choanae are separated by the vomer. The most peculiar feature of the choanal region, found in various Asian representatives of the Taeniolabidoidea, is the position of the pterygoids. They do not form the lateral walls of the choanae, but divide each choanal opening into two channels. Thus the choanae are subdivided both by the vomer and the pterygoids so that four channels are present above the nasopharyngeal region. The inner pair of channels (on either side of the vomer) served for air passages, whereas the lateral ones end in cul-de-sacs. They possibly served as areas for muscle origins. Lateral to the choanae are the ectopterygoid bones that taper anteriorly at the palatonasal foramen and contact the alisphenoids posteriorly.

Only a small part of the ectopterygoid is exposed below the orbit on the ventrolateral wall of the skull. The orbitosphenoid has a large exposure in the orbit,

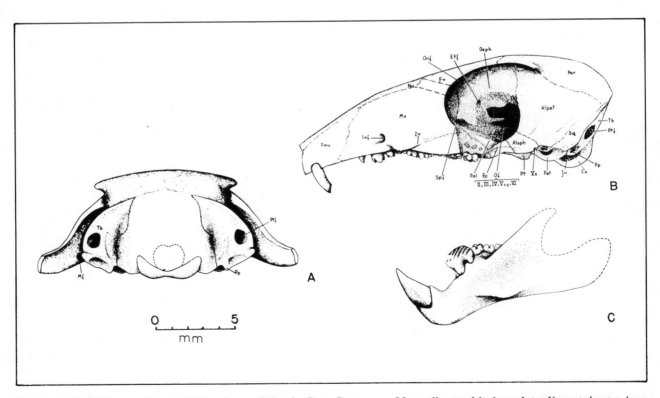

Figure 6-1.   Reconstruction of skull and mandible of a Late Cretaceous Mongolian multituberculate, *Kamptobaatar kuczynskii*: *A*, **posterior, skull;** *B*, **lateral, skull;** *C*, **lateral, left mandible;** *D*, **dorsal, skull;** *E*, **ventral, skull, views (After Kielan-Jaworowska, 1971, Figs.** *B* **and** *D* **emended). Abbreviations:** *Alpet*, **ascending lamina of petrosal;** *Alsph*, **alisphenoid;** *Bo*, **basioccipital;** *Bs*, **basisphenoid;** *Ce*, **?cavum epitericum;** *Co*, **condyle;** *Ec*, **ectopterygoid;** *Etf*, **ethmoid foramen;** *Fc*, **fenestra cochleae (rotunda);** *Fr*, **frontal;** *Fv*, **fenestra vestibuli (ovalis);** *H*, **hamulus;** *HF*, **hiatus canalis Fallopii;** *Ic*, **internal carotid foramen;** *Inf*, **infraorbital foramen;** *Jf,* **jugular foramen;** *Jn*, **jugular notch;** *La*, **lacrimal;** *Lf*,

forming most of the intraorbital wall. Spheno-palatine foramina are large and placed at the junctions of the maxillary, frontal, orbitosphenoid, and palatine bones. An ethmoid foramen is also present. In some genera part of the intraorbital wall was possibly membranous during life. The shape of the unossified area was tentatively reconstructed for *Kamptobaatar* in Figure 6-1. No definite foramina are recognizable in this region, but probably this large orbital fissure allowed passage of cranial nerves II, III, IV, V_{1-2} and VI. A skull of *Henkelodon* described by Hahn (1977a) preserves a large sphenorbital fissure. Interpretation of the limits of the alisphenoid is to some extent tentative in all known multituberculates; the position of the suture between the petrosal and alisphenoid is uncertain. The alisphenoid, as recognized by Kielan-Jaworowska (1971), is reduced to a small ventral element contributing little to the lateral wall of the braincase. In

lateral view, it is exposed between the ectopterygoid and ascending lamina of the petrosal.[1] The ventral margin of the alisphenoid is slightly thickened and forms a "wing" protruding somewhat ventrally below the basicranial region. In ventral view this

---

1. Watson (1916) introduced the term "anterior lamina of the petrosal" (processus anterior periotici) for the bone that forms most of the lateral wall of the monotreme braincase. This bone has also been called the "ascending lamina of the petrosal" or "lamina obturens." Kermack (1963) wrote of the "anterior lamina of the petrosal" in triconodonts. Kielan-Jaworowska (1971) interpreted the large bone forming the lateral wall of the multituberculate braincase as being homologous with the "anterior lamina" of the monotremes. She pointed out, however, that because of spatial relationships, the term "anterior lamina" is not appropriate for use in multituberculates. The bone in question in the multituberculate skull consists of two parts arranged at right angles to one another, and neither is anterior to the cochlea. Therefore, it is descriptively more accurate to refer to this bone in multituberculates as the "ascending lamina of the petrosal."

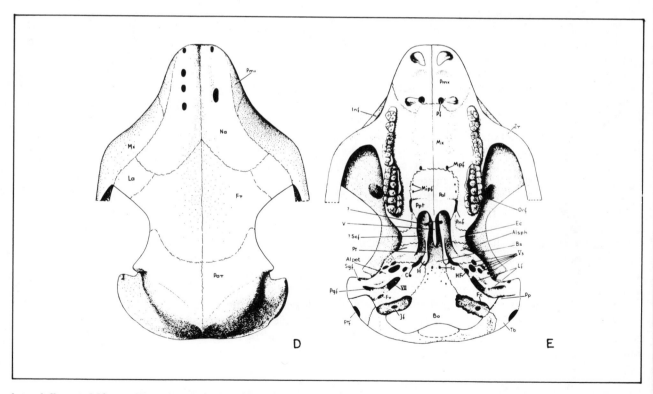

lateral flange; *Mf*, maxillary foramen; *Mipf*, minor palatine foramen; *Mpf*, major palatine foramen; *Mx*, maxilla; *Na*, nasal; *Of*, orbital fissure; *Onf*, orbitonasal foramen; *Osph*, orbitosphenoid; *Pal*, palatine; *Par*, parietal; *Pet*, petrosal; *Pf*, palatine fissure; *Pgf*, postglenoid foramen (canalis prooticus); *Pmx*, premaxilla; *Pnf*, palatonasal foramen; *Pp*, paroccipital process; *Ppt*, postpalatine torus; *Pt*, pterygoid; *Ptf*, post-temporal fossa; *Scf*, scaphoid fossa; *Sgf*, supraglenoid foramen (possibly anterior opening of post-temporal fossa); *Spf*, sphenopalatine foramen; *Sq*, squamosal; *Tb*, tabular; *V*, vomer; and *Zr*, zygomatic ridge. II, III, IV, V_1, V_2, V_3, VI, and VII are foramina for the respective cranial nerves.

wing is crescent-shaped and surrounds the foramina For V_3 anterolaterally. Most of the lateral wall of the braincase is formed by the ascending lamina of the petrosal. Kielan-Jaworowska (*ibid.*) interpreted the horizontal suture between the ascending lamina and the parietal as being situated near the middle of the height of the lateral wall of the braincase. Comparison with a better preserved skull of *Nemegtbaatar* from Mongolia, however, later allowed her to show (1974a) that both in *Kamptobaatar* and *Nemegtbaatar* the suture is situated more dorsally. It extends posteriorly as a roughly horizontal line from the posterior prolongation of the postorbital process, just below the rounded edge set between the cranial roof and lateral wall of the braincase. Figure 6-1 is an emended reconstruction of the lateral wall of the braincase of *Kamptobaatar*, showing the extensive ascending lamina. The squamosal is narrow and contributes little to the structure of the lateral wall of the braincase.

The basicranial region is comparatively short and quite wide. The junction of the alisphenoid and petrosal on the ventral aspect of the skull is tentatively identified in *Kamptobaatar*. A comparatively large opening, interpreted as a remnant of the cavum epitericum, is present on the anterolateral corner of the promontorium; it presumably lies along the suture between the alisphenoid and the petrosal. The internal carotid foramina, if correctly identified, are small in *Kamptobaatar*. The opening for V_3 is divided into two foramina in many multituberculates (*e.g.*, *Ptilodus*, *Sloanbaatar*, and *Kryptobaatar*). In *Kamptobaatar*, however, it is divided into five foramina. When two foramina for V_3 are present, one faces ventrally, the other ventrolaterally. In *Kamptobaatar*, four foramina face ventrally and the fifth ventrolaterally. One of these foramina is situated in the suture between the alisphenoid and the petrosal; the others pierce the petrosal. The cochlea is straight and the middle ear is completely open ventrally. Tympanic ossicles have not been found. The fenestra vestibuli lies at the base of the promontorium and faces anterolaterally. The fenestra cochleae is situated close to the fenestra vestibuli and faces in the opposite direction. The recess of the tympanic cavity extends laterally from the fenestra vestibuli and passes laterally into the external auditory meatus. Recess and meatus are delimited posteriorly by the paroccipital process (see below), that is, placed just lateral to the base of the promontorium. The recess also extends anteromedially, demarking the anterolateral side of the promontorium anterolaterally. The

recess of the tympanic cavity contains a foramen, probably for a branch of cranial nerve VII, and the recess ends anteromedially at the hiatus canalis Falopii. The remaining foramina of the basicranial region (Fig. 6-1) include the jugular foramina (possibly confluent with the hypoglossal foramen), postglenoid foramina (for canalis prooticus), and supraglenoid foramina (possibly the anterior opening of the post-temporal fossa).

Kielan-Jaworowska and Dashzeveg (1978) note that *Kryptobaatar* differs from all described multituberculates (as well as from all other known mammals) in the structure of the basicranial region. The basioccipital in *Kryptobaatar* strongly protrudes ventrally, forming a structure informally designated the basioccipital box. The basioccipital box, which is empty inside, forms a ventral extension of the braincase. A detailed description of this structure and interpretation of its function will be published by Kielan-Jaworowska.

The occipital region in multituberculates has a structure unusual for mammals. The entire region between the occipital bone and lambdoidal crest is occupied by an extensive tabular bone. On the lower part of the tabular there is a large post-temporal fossa. A triangular paroccipital process is present on the lower edge of the occipital surface lateral to the occipital condyle. A suture separating the tabular from the paroccipital process has not been recognized. A suture is present along the ventral edge of the paroccipital process, but it is difficult to state with certainty which bone actually forms the process.

The mandible of multituberculates is rodent-like in general appearance. An angular process is absent, and the posterior border of the horizontal ramus of the dentary forms an almost complete semicircle. The mandibular symphysis is unfused in all known genera, and each ramus probably could move with considerable independence. Hahn (1977b) has discovered that a rudimentary coronoid bone is present on the mandibles of the paulchoffatiid *Kuehneodon*. Among the multituberculates this is the only known instance of the presence of bones other than the dentaries in the lower jaws.

Discussion

As mentioned above, Simpson (1937a) interpreted the multituberculate braincase in terms of the characteristic anatomy of therians. Kermack (1963) was the first to note the similarities in the structure of the petrosal in triconodonts and multituberculates. He (Kermack, 1967) suggested that the four nontherian orders (Triconodonta, Docodonta, Multituberculata, and Monotremata) be grouped as a taxon of equal rank with the Theria.

Since the early 1960s many teeth, jaws, and isolated bones of multituberculates have been collected from the Late Cretaceous Hell Creek Formation of Montana. Scattered bits of information from the unpublished studies of Giles T. MacIntyre on the structure of the well-preserved multituberculate petrosals found at these sites have entered the literature (*e.g.*, Hopson and Crompton, 1969, and Hopson, 1970). The conclusions of these authors concerning the interrelations of the Triconodonta, Docodonta, and Multituberculata were similar to those of Kermack (1967). About the same time, Kielan-Jaworowska (1970b, 1971) published the first detailed descriptions of well-preserved multituberculate braincases. She demonstrated the similarities in structure of the petrosal between the triconodonts and multituberculates but suggested some modifications of Kermack's (1963) interpretation of the triconodont petrosal. She proposed that, as far as the braincase is concerned, the Multituberculata are more similar to the Monotremata than to the Triconodonta.

Kermack and Kielan-Jaworowska (1971) discussed the structure of the lateral wall of the braincase in therian and nontherian mammals. They demonstrated that while in the therian mammals the lateral wall of the braincase is formed by the alisphenoid and squamosal bones, in the known nontherian mammals it is essentially formed by the anterior (ascending) lamina of the petrosal. The lateral wall of the braincase of a skull of *Morganucodon* from China (*ibid.*, Fig. 3) shows the large petrosal and comparatively narrow alisphenoid. It should be noted that, although comparatively narrow, the alisphenoid of *Morganucodon* contributes to the lateral wall of the braincase to a much greater degree than in multituberculates and monotremes.

It is interesting that Kermack (1967), Hopson and Crompton (1969), Hopson (1970), Kielan-Jaworowska (1970b, 1971), and Kermack and Kielan-Jaworowska (1971) independently, and more or less simultaneously, developed similar ideas concerning the relationships of early mammals. Their conclusions differ only in details. Currently, Jenkins and Crompton (see Chapter 4) are studying a well-preserved skull of an Early Cretaceous triconodont

from the Cloverly Formation of Montana. The alisphenoid in this animal is comparatively larger than in *Morganucodon*, and contributes extensively to the structure of the lateral wall of the braincase (Crompton, pers. comm. to Clemens, 1977). This discovery challenges the currently accepted idea of basically different patterns of structure of the lateral wall of the braincase in therian versus nontherian mammals.

The question arises whether the interpretation of the structure of the braincase in Multituberculata should be revised in light of Crompton's and Jenkins' discovery. Unfortunately, the bones of the multituberculate braincase tended to fuse early in life, and many sutures were obliterated. The skull of *Kamptobaatar* illustrated in Figure 6-1 probably belongs to a young individual and the position of most of the sutures is clear. Nevertheless, recognition of the suture between the alisphenoid and petrosal is uncertain (see Kielan-Jaworowska, 1971, for further discussion). Identification of the large bone forming

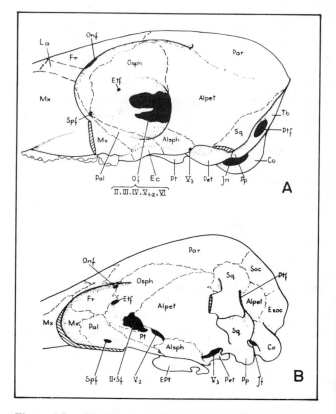

Figure 6-2. Diagrammatic illustrations of lateral aspect of braincase of *Kamptobaatar* (*A*) and *Ornithorhynchus* (*B*). Not to scale. *Ept*, Echidna pterygoid; *Exoc*, exoccipital; *Sf*, sphenorbital fissure; *Soc*, supraoccipital; other abbreviations as in Fig. 6-1. (After Kielan-Jaworowska, 1971, Fig. *A* emended)

the lateral wall of the braincase in multituberculates as the ascending lamina of the petrosal was based in part on comparisons with the skull of *Ornithorhynchus*. As shown in Figure 6-2 and the discussion by Kielan-Jaworowska (*ibid.*), similarities between multituberculate and monotreme braincases are striking. They include not only general proportions and position of particular bones, but several minor details as well. If Watson's (1916) interpretation of the structure of the monotreme skull is correct, the large bone forming the lateral wall of the multituberculate braincase is probably an ascending lamina of the petrosal. In such a case, the multituberculate and monotreme braincases would differ significantly not only from the therian mammals, but also from that of the triconodont from the Cloverly Formation.

Dental

The dominant theme of dental evolution in multituberculates was a shift away from complete dependence upon the primitive mammalian mode of mastication. In primitive mammals preparation of food was accomplished by orthal movements (in a vertical plane with slight transverse components) of the mandible. Mastication in most multituberculates appears to have been accomplished both by orthal movements of the mandible (when the incisors and premolars were being utilized) and by propalinal movements (anteriad and posteriad movements in a horizontal plane), sliding the cusps of the lower molars across those of the uppers.

The potential for great mobility of the mandible is illustrated by the structure of the glenoid fossae of the skulls. The fossae are ovoid, shallow basins, encircled by low crests and situated on the zygomatic arches, well removed from the walls of the narrow braincase. The mandibular condyle is large, forming most of the posterior end of the horizontal ramus. There is no angular process. In lateral view the condyle is transversely widest dorsally, becoming narrower ventrally. With such flexible, unrestrictive articulations of the mandibles and the unfused mandibular symphysis, precision in occlusion of the dentition must have been accomplished by interaction between cusps and crests of upper and lower teeth and coordination of large, specialized mandibular muscles. Though limited dorsally and ventrally by ridges, the masseteric fossae of primitive multituberculates are not delimited anteriorly. Their floors

gradually merge with the lateral sides of the mandibles (Hahn, 1969; Ride, 1957, 1959). In some later multituberculates the masseteric fossae were sharply delimited anteriorly, ending in a basin below the posterior premolars or the molars (Jepsen, 1940, contrast *Mesodma ambigua*, Pl. I, with *Mimetodon churchilli*, Pl. II) or at the rim of an "elevated" table (*ibid.*, *Pentacosmodon pronus*, Pl. V). A deep pterygoid fossa is characteristic.

Although not certainly established in known Late Jurassic multituberculates, in later forms the length of the upper dentition (occlusal tip of anteriormost upper incisor to posterior end of M^2) was greater than that of the lower dentition (occlusal tip of lower incisors to posterior end of M_2). The mandible had to be protruded and lowered to bring the tips of the lower incisors into contact with the uppers (probably I^{2-3}). This change in position held the molars and premolars out of occlusion when the incisors were in use. When the molars were in occlusion the lower incisor lay behind I^2. In species with an I^3 situated on the palate, the lower incisor might have occluded with it. Essentially the same derived pattern of masticatory movements evolved convergently in Eocene and more recent rodents.

All known multituberculates have but one pair of lower incisors. In plagiaulacoids, and probably primitively, they are stout teeth with high, broad bases and relatively short, curved crowns with the concave surface dorsal. Their crowns are fully covered with enamel. General trends of evolution of the lower incisors of later multituberculates fall into two categories. In some the lower incisors were elongated and their bases reduced in diameter. The tip and most of the body of the crown are covered with enamel, but frequently near the base of the crown dentine is exposed on the dorsal surface. In some of the most derived forms the lower incisors were long, thin, saber-like teeth (see, for example, Jepsen, 1940, *Ectypodus laytoni*, Pl. III), not unlike the lower incisors of the modern "grasshopper mouse," *Onychomys*, which is largely insectivorous. The other general trend is the evolution of gliriform (rodent-like) incisors, and is used as a diagnostic feature of the taeniolabidoids. The lower incisor is not tapered, but of relatively uniform diameter throughout its length. Enamel is limited to a band on the anteroventral surface. The teeth, which can be "ever-growing" and self-sharpening, are the only type of multituberculate incisors apparently specifically adapted for gnawing. In some genera the lower incisor has been shown to be diphyodont (Szalay, 1965; Kielan-Jaworowska, 1970b).

Although isolated upper incisors are well represented in the fossil record, very few skulls preserving the premaxillaries with incisors in place have been recovered. In the paulchoffatiids I^1 is small with a single cusp; the closely approximated I^2 is larger with a principal anterior cusp and a small, hook-like posterior basal cusp; I^3 is about the same size as I^2, carries three or four cusps, and is set slightly medial to the edge of the palate. The upper incisors of plagiaulacids differ from those of paulchoffatiids in the presence of only two cusps on I^3.

In known Cretaceous multituberculates only two pairs of upper incisors are present. Possibly these are homologous with I^2 and I^3 of the paulchoffatiids. I^2 is large, often carrying accessory cusps behind the principal cusp; I^3 is variously developed but usually of simpler morphology. In all Mongolian multituberculates in which the tooth-bearing part of the premaxilla is preserved (i.e., in *Gobibaatar*, assigned to the ?Neoplagiaulacidae, and members of the Eucosmodontidae, Taeniolabididae, Chulsanbaataridae, and Sloanbaataridae) I^3's are small, peg-like teeth. Their position is unusual for mammals. They are situated not at the edge of the premaxilla but on the palatal process near the midline of the skull. No trace of wear has been found on them. In North American Cretaceous and Tertiary multituberculates this part of the palate is rarely preserved. In the best-known skulls of the Tertiary multituberculates *Taeniolabis* and *Ptilodus* (see Simpson, 1937a), small, peg-like I^3's are preserved. Unlike the Mongolian multituberculates, they are placed more buccally on the premaxilla nearer the edge of the palate. In a skull of *Meniscoessus* from the Hell Creek Formation, Montana (being described by J. D. Archibald) the I^3's are situated in a similar buccal position.

The most anterior upper and lower premolariform tooth is single-rooted in at least some paulchoffatiid plagiaulacoids (*Paulchoffatia, Pseudobolodon,* and *Kuehneodon*); all other cheek teeth have two or more roots. Hahn (1969, 1977a) suggested that the anterior upper "premolar" might be a premolariform upper canine. He (1977a) noted that in addition to its single root and its position as the first maxillary tooth, the tooth behind it (conventionally designated P^2) is the first tooth to be lost from the paulchoffatiid dentition. Using Hahn's

(*ibid.*) revised terminology, in *Paulchoffatia* and *Pseudobolodon* "C" and "P^1" are present. In *Kuehneodon*, "P^1" is missing, and "C" and "P^2" are separated by a diastema. Otherwise, canines are not known to occur in multituberculate dentitions. In the course of multituberculate evolution the diastemata separating incisors from premolars, particularly in the lower dentition, tended to become enlarged.

In his influential monographs on Mesozoic mammals, Simpson (1928a, 1929) did not attempt to establish a dental formula for the premolars of multituberculates that would suggest homology and occlusal relationships in the way they are reflected in the dental formulae of eutherian and metatherian mammals. In view of the paucity of information available, this was clearly a wise decision.

Five upper premolars were present in the plagiaulacoid dentitions known to Simpson in 1928-1929. The anterior three have crowns bearing three or four large, conical cusps arranged in triangular or rectangular patterns and did not occlude with the lower premolars. The posterior two premolars have six to eight cusps arranged in two longitudinal rows. Usually their lingual sides occluded with the labial sides of the lower premolars to produce a shearing action. These posterior premolars differ from molars in the absence of a distinct longitudinal valley. Simpson (1928a) designated these premolars P^1 through P^5. *Paulchoffatia*, described more than thirty years later, and the new genus *Pseudobolodon*, have six upper premolariform teeth. At first Hahn (1969) designated these teeth of *Paulchoffatia* P^1 through P^6, but later with his study of *Pseudobolodon* Hahn (1977a) changed the designations to C, P^1 through P^5.

No skull fragments containing upper premolars are known of Early Cretaceous multituberculates and it is only toward the end of the Late Cretaceous in ?late Santonian to ?middle Campanian Mongolian and "Lancian" North American samples that specimens document the upper premolar sequence. By this time the upper premolar dentition had been reduced to four premolars of which only the posterior occludes with a lower premolar. These teeth are traditionally designated P^1 through P^4. Clemens (1963b) suggested they might be homologues of P^1, P^2, P^3, and P^5 of plagiaulacoids with five premolars.

The Late Cretaceous multituberculates exhibit two evolutionary trends in modification of the upper premolars that continued in the evolution of their

Cenozoic descendants. In ptilodontoids and cimolomyids the four upper premolars tend to be retained. P^4 functions as part of the shearing mechanism while P^{1-3}, with the tongue, served as a holding device helping to manipulate and steady material for shearing (Clemens, 1963b). In some taeniolabidoid multituberculates the premolars were modified from double- to single-rooted teeth and their number was reduced when the shearing function of the posterior premolars was lost.

The lower premolar dentition of plagiaulacoids is made up of three or four teeth. Simpson (1928a) designated the four lower premolars of *Ctenacodon* as P_1 through P_4. The most anterior premolar is much smaller than the others and has a bulbous crown. The other premolars are blade-like with up to eight serrations along their dorsal rim. P_4 and P_3 are known to carry one or more buccal cusps near the base of their crowns, and usually functioned with the last two upper premolars to form a shearing mechanism. The Kimmeridgian genera *Paulchoffatia,* *Kuehneodon,* and *Pseudobolodon* differ from all other multituberculates in the early development of large, horizontal wear facets on the crests of their lower premolars and on the crowns of the upper premolars and molars. This peculiar pattern of wear suggests that the premolars performed a crushing-grinding action akin to that of the molars.

No dentulous jaws of multituberculates found in deposits of Early Cretaceous age have yet been described. This absence of data also is characteristic of most of the early Late Cretaceous. Thus, interpretations of the nature of the dentitions characterizing primitive members of families of later multituberculates are not substantiated by direct evidence. Within the known ptilodontoids and cimolomyids, the primitive condition appears to have been the presence of two premolars, a peg-like P_3 and the blade-like P_4, which has a low number of serrations (between 5 to 10 at most) and is approximately the same length as M_1. These numerical designations, at least P_4, probably indicate homologies with elements of the plagiaulacoid dentition. In several descendant lineages P_3 was lost, P_4 enlarged, and the number of serrations increased. Within the taeniolabidoids P_3 was frequently lost. In some lineages P_4 became enlarged relative to M_1, in others it was reduced to a peg-like tooth with a small, bulbous, triangular crown.

There is evidence from Late Cretaceous and Tertiary multituberculates that some anterior upper premolars, those not directly involved in the shearing function, were diphyodont (Szalay, 1965; Kielan-Jaworowska, 1970b). Even though mandibles of juvenile multituberculates in which the last lower premolar had not fully erupted are known (see Clemens, 1963b), there is no evidence in ptilodontoids, cimolomyids, or taeniolabidoids that the blade-like premolars or their functional counterparts in the upper dentition were diphyodont. Hahn (1969) described a series of isolated teeth that he identified as lower deciduous premolars (dP_{1-4}) of paulchoffatiids, and recently (Hahn, 1978) announced the discovery of fragmentary mandibles containing premolars of these types. Presence of diphyodont premolars in paulchoffatiids can be interpreted as a plesiomorphous retention. Samples of other families of multituberculates are now large enough so that the negative evidence begins to carry some weight. The absence of evidence of deciduous posterior premolars suggests that these premolars were monophyodont.

Dental formulae for the premolars, particularly the upper premolars, of multituberculates are poorly understood. Unlike the dental formulae of other mammals, similarity in designation probably does not indicate homology. For example, P^6 (after Hahn, 1969) of paulchoffatiids, P^5 of plagiaulacids, and P^4 of ptilodontoids and taeniolabidoids might well be homologous teeth. R. E. Sloan (pers. comm. to Clemens, 1977) has suggested that posterior upper and lower premolars of multituberculates should be designated M^b and M_b to reflect their apparent monophyodont ontogeny. The system of numbering the other premolars would remain unchanged. We have not followed this reasonable suggestion because it only picks at an edge of the larger problem of establishment of a system of premolar designations fully reflecting their homologies. We retain a current inadequate, and somewhat illogical, system to promote communication until the entire problem can be resolved. Unless otherwise indicated, the premolars of: (1) paulchoffatiids (possibly including a premolariform upper canine) are designated as $P^{\frac{1-2-3-4-5-6}{1-2-3-4}}$; (2) those of plagiaulacids as $P^{\frac{1-2-3-4-5}{1-2-3-4}}$; and (3) those of the other multituberculates as $P^{\frac{1-2-3-4}{3-4}}$.

The common morphological pattern of multituberculate molars is that of two parallel rows of anteroposteriorly oriented cusps. In known plagiaulacoid multituberculates the maximum numbers of cusps (divided equally, or approximately so, between the two rows) are M_1, 6; M_2, 6; M^1, 7; and M^2, 5. Within each row the cusps tend to be of approximately equal height. This morphological pattern differs from that of haramiyids in which transverse ridges link the longitudinal rows and there is greater variation in the height of cusps within each row.

Again paulchoffatiids provide exceptions to these generalizations. Except M^2, all the molars have been found in place either in mandibular or skull fragments in at least one species of paulchoffatiid (Hahn, pers. comm. to Clemens, 1977). The M_1's and upper molars of paulchoffatiids conform to the generalization just given; M_2's do not. M_2's have crowns with a central basin surrounded by a crenulated rim. Only one distinct cusp, which Hahn (1969) concluded is at the anterolingual corner of the crown, is present.

The pattern of occlusion of the molars has appeared to be a firm, diagnostic character of the Multituberculata. In the lower dentitions of all known multituberculates the labial and lingual rows of M_1 and M_2 are aligned, one directly behind the other. In contrast, in all multituberculates possibly excepting paulchoffatiines, M^1 and M^2 are laterally offset with the labial cusp row of M^2 aligned behind the lingual row of M^1 (Figure 6-3). M^2 of paulchoffatiines is known only from isolated teeth. However,

on the basis of the position of its alveolus, Hahn (1969) concluded the M^2 was not offset lingually relative to M^1; but this reconstruction has been questioned.

Mills (1971) reviewed various hypotheses for the origin of the occlusal pattern found in most multituberculates. It is obviously too early to make a choice between alternatives. However, as will be discussed at some length in the section on phylogeny, if confirmed, the difference in occlusal pattern of the molars of paulchoffatiines and all other multituberculates should be given considerable weight. Probably the difference arose at the time that the second row of cusps was being added to the molar crowns, and therefore would trace back to a very early stage in multituberculate evolution.

Evolution of multituberculate molars in the Late Cretaceous is characterized by increase in the number of cusps on each molar. This occurred both by the multiplication of the number of cusps in each row and by the addition of a third row of cusps to the upper molars. On M^1, the addition of this third row began at the posterolingual end of the crown, aligned with the lingual row of cusps of M^2. In most ptilodontoids and cimolomyids additional cusps were added anteriorly, but rarely was this new (third) row as long and its anterior cusps as large as those of the original (now medial) and labial rows. Evolutionary modification of M^2 followed a similar but a reversed pattern. The third row of M^2 started with the addition of a labial cusp aligned posterior to the labial cusp row of M^1. In more derived forms this third row of M^2 was elongated posteriorly by the addition of cusps. Elongation of these "third" rows of cusps, almost fully masking the upper molars' primitive asymmetry, was greatest in some lineages of taeniolabidoids in which they became as long as the other rows and there was little difference in size of the cusps.

Morphology of the individual molar cusps and the grooves that separate the cusp rows also underwent evolutionary change. Excluding the basined crown of M_2 of *Paulchoffatia*, the anteroposterior groove separating adjacent rows of cusps on plagiaulacoid molars is broadly V-shaped. Individual cusps tend to be conical; some are modified by the presence of small grooves in the enamel. In the Late Cretaceous, the primitive conical shape of the cusps and V-shaped cross-section of interrow grooves is maintained in many lineages. However, in some ptilodontoids and cimolomyids the conical shape of the molar

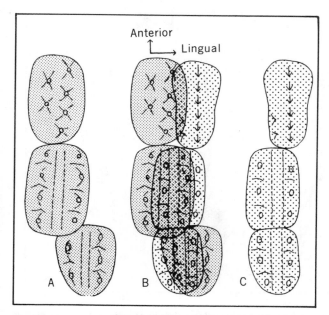

Figure 6-3. Diagrammatic illustrations of occlusal surfaces of the last premolar and molars of a hypothetical plagiaulacid: *A*, **upper partial dentition;** *B*, **upper and lower partial dentitions in occlusion;** *C*, **lower partial dentition. Not to scale.**

cusps was modified by evolution of a lateral ridge or crest on each side of the cusp. In frontal section these cusps have a crescentic outline with the concave side oriented posteriorly in lower molars and anteriorly in uppers. In lateral view the crests on the slopes of the cusps are not straight but are also crescentic. Again, the concave sides of the crests are oriented posteriorly on lower molars and anteriorly on the uppers.

Clemens (1963b) suggested that during mastication the mandible was drawn forward while upper and lower molars were in occlusion. If M_1 had been drawn forward of M^1, the wedge-like posterior slope of P^4 would have forced M_1 (and thus the entire mandible) ventrally. This would prevent damaging contact of the serrate crest of P_4 with the anterior upper premolars, and of the lower incisors against the posterior surfaces of I^2 or I^1. Wear facets on P^4's of several species show that such movement did occur,

but probably it was not part of the most powerful masticatory movement of the jaw. In light of subsequent investigations by Every (1970), Crompton (1971), and others the orientation of the crescentic blades suggests that the power stroke in mastication involved closure and retraction of the mandible. During movement in this direction the oppositely oriented crests of the molar cusps would form a series of trap-shearing mechanisms (see Chapter 9). By this interpretation the dental positioning mechanism formed by the contact of M_1 with the back of P^4 would have been advantageous in insuring sufficient retraction of the mandible to a position where P_4 and the incisors would not have been damaged during the mastication of food.

Opposite extremes in modification of cusp and groove morphology are illustrated by a comparison of the taeniolabidids and the curious multituberculate *Essonodon*. In the Cretaceous genus *Catop-*

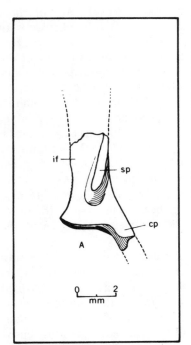
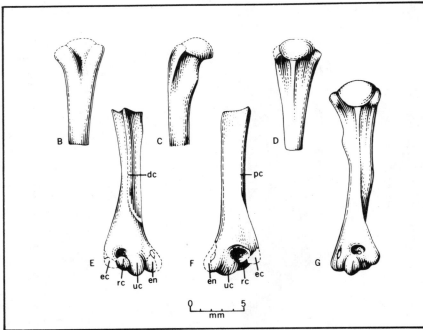

Figure 6-4. Semidiagrammatic illustrations of postcranial elements of multituberculates drawn at various scales (scales of all illustrations within each box are the same). *A*, lateral view of fragment of right scapula of a multituberculate, possibly *Cimolodon nitidus* (see Clemens, 1963b), from the Lance Formation, Wyoming (redrawn from McKenna, 1961). Abbreviations: *cp*, posterior coracoid; *if*, infraspinous fossa; and *sp*, spine. *B-F*, *Tugrigbaatar saichaenensis*, "Toogreeg beds," Mongolia. *B-D*, reconstruction of proximal part of left humerus (*B*, anterior; *C*, lateral; and *D*, posterior views). *E-F*, reconstruction of distal part of right humerus (*E*, anterior and *F*, posterior views). *G*, reconstruction of right humerus, pos-

salis (and to a greater extreme in the Puercan *Taeniolabis*) the individual cusps became more numerous, more closely packed, and the interrow grooves were greatly reduced in width. Another, but less well known, extreme is exhibited by molars of the Late Cretaceous, North American genus *Essonodon* (Clemens, 1964; Archibald, 1977). On these teeth the body of the original cusp has been reduced and the crests strengthened to a degree that, at first glance, most of the crown appears to be made up of a series of individual basins divided by high narrow ridges.

Data on the microstructure of the enamel are presented in Chapter 11.

Postcranial

Available Sample

The multituberculate postcranial skeleton is incompletely known. Gidley (1909) described a humerus, radius, incomplete pelvis, nearly complete femur, proximal ends of tibia and fibula, and a terminal phalanx of *Ptilodus gracilis* from Paleocene

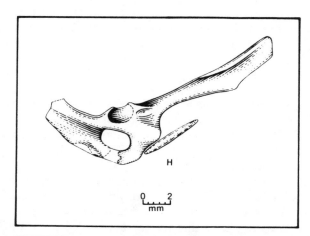

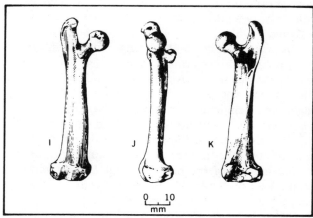

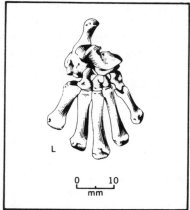

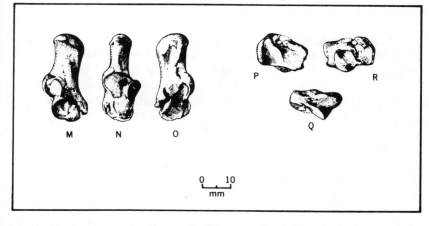

terior view. Abbreviations: *dc*, deltopectoral crest; *ec*, ectepicondyle; *en*, entepicondyle; *rc*, radial condyle; and *uc*, ulnar condyle (redrawn from Kielan-Jaworowska and Dashzeveg, 1978). *H*, lateral view, right pelvis of *Kryptobaatar dashzevegi*, Djadokhta Formation, Mongolia (redrawn from Kielan-Jaworowska, 1969). *I-R*, *Eucosmodon* sp., Nacimiento Formation, New Mexico (redrawn with some restoration from Granger and Simpson, 1929). *I-K*, right femur (*I*, anterior; *J*, internal; and *K*, posterior views). *L*, right pes, lacking phalanges. *M-O*, right calcaneum (*M*, medial; *N*, dorsal; and *O*, lateral views). *P-R*, right astragalus (*P*, dorsal; *Q*, anterior; and *R*, ventral views).

strata (Fort Union Formation) of Montana. He mentioned the existence of a nearly complete cervical vertebra (sixth or seventh) and two caudals, but did not figure them. Broom (1914) redescribed the pelvis of *Ptilodus gracilis* and concluded that it was a shoulder girdle. Broom's interpretation was shown by Granger (in a note to Broom's paper) to be erroneous. Simpson (1928b) described fragments of the postcranial skeleton of *Catopsalis matthewi* (= *Djadochtatherium matthewi*, see Kielan-Jaworowska and Sloan, 1978) from the Late Cretaceous Djadokhta Formation of Mongolia. They consist of five lumbar vertebrae, a partial scapula, partial humerus, metacarpals, a few phalanges, and fragments of ribs. The scapula of *Catopsalis* was redescribed in greater detail by McKenna (1961), together with two unidentified scapulae from the Lance Formation of Wyoming. Clemens (1963b) tentatively assigned the scapulae described by McKenna (1961) to *Mesodma formosa* and *Cimolodon nitidus* (Fig. 6-4). Granger and Simpson (1929) referred a postcranial skeleton (consisting of most of the pelvis, almost complete hind limbs, and four lumbar and six caudal vertebrae) from the Paleocene Nacimiento Formation of New Mexico to *Eucosmodon* sp. and described it in detail. On the basis of this skeleton, Simpson and Elftman (1928) reconstructed the probable musculature, posture, and movements of the hind limbs of *Eucosmodon*. Kielan-Jaworowska (1969) described a pelvis and articulated epipubic ("marsupial") bones from the Djadokhta Formation. Sloan and Van Valen (1965) reported a rich collection of isolated multituberculate postcranial bones from the Late Cretaceous Hell Creek Formation of Montana. An analysis of the collection has not been published, but Sloan and Van Valen (*ibid.*) reproduced an incomplete reconstruction of the postcranial skeleton of *Mesodma thompsoni* prepared by D. G. Deischl on the basis of this material. Jenkins (1973) figured the distal end of the humerus and the proximal end of the ulna of unidentified multituberculates from the Hell Creek Formation and discussed the humero-ulnar joint. Kielan-Jaworowska and Dashzeveg (1978) described the proximal and distal ends of a humerus of the eucosmodontid *Tugribaatar* (Fig. 6-4).

An almost complete postcranial skeleton of *Chulsanbaatar vulgaris* and partial skeletons of *Nemegtbaatar gobiensis*, *Kryptobaatar dashzevegi*, and *Sloanbaatar mirabilis* were collected by the Polish-Mongolian Palaeontological Expeditions

from rocks of Late Cretaceous age in the Gobi Desert. Other than the pelvis of *Kryptobaatar dashzevegi* (see Kielan-Jaworowska, 1969), the material has not been described.

The following description of the postcranial skeleton is based mainly on published data. Information from undescribed fossils housed in the Zakład Paleobiologii in Warsaw is included in a few cases.

Vertebral Column

Cervical and thoracic vertebrae have not been described. In the undescribed material from the Djadokhta Formation housed in Warsaw there is an incomplete skeleton of an animal the size of *Kryptobaatar*. The axis of this skeleton is completely fused with the third vertebra. Fusion of the neck vertebrae, however, is not characteristic of other multituberculate skeletons known from Mongolia.

The lumbar vertebrae of *Catopsalis* and *Eucosmodon* were described by Granger and Simpson (1929). Those of *Eucosmodon* have nearly circular bodies, strong pleurapophyses with truncated ends, and extensive articular processes. The majority of the posterior vertebrae have neural spines directed anteriad, but on the most anterior it is directed dorsad.

Granger and Simpson (*ibid.*) mentioned a crushed fragment of a sacrum of *Eucosmodon*, consisting of at least two fused vertebrae. An undescribed specimen of *Chulsanbaatar vulgaris* housed in Warsaw shows that the sacrum was composed of three vertebrae. The first few caudal vertebrae of *Eucosmodon* have transverse processes forming horizontal plates. Posteriorly, the bodies become more elongated and the various processes disappear, as is generally characteristic of mammals. Granger and Simpson (*ibid.*) concluded that the tail was long and heavy.

Forelimb

The coracoid is fused to the scapula, and the scapulocoracoid suture is obliterated. The composite bone, as in mammals in general, could well be referred to as scapulocoracoid (*e.g.*, see McKenna, 1961). A supraspinous fossa is lacking. The infraspinous fossa is deep, and the scapular spine is situated anteriorly, projecting laterad. The multituberculate scapula is similar to that of known Rhaeto-Liassic triconodonts in the absence of a supraspinous fossa (see Jenkins and Parrington, 1976), but in the latter, sutures between procoracoid, coracoid, and scapula are visible. The supraspinous fossa is also absent from the monotreme scapulo-coracoid, but, as was pointed out by McKenna (1961), multituberculate and monotreme shoulder girdles differ greatly in other respects. The coracoid process projects antero-ventro-mediad in known multituberculates and not postero-ventro-mediad as in monotremes. In multituberculates, the shoulder girdle was situated lateral to the anterior ribs. It did not form a yoke around the neck as in monotremes. Lastly, the lateral face of the monotreme scapulocoracoid is flat, without the spine and trough-like infraspinous fossa found in known multituberculates.

Lack of a supraspinous fossa clearly distinguishes the multituberculate, most triconodont (see Chapter 4), and monotreme scapulae from those of adult therian mammals, but this fossa is absent during part of the embryological development of therians. For example, the foetus of *Didelphis* possesses only an infraspinous fossa until it reaches 7.5 mm in crown-rump length (Cheng, 1955).

All known humeri are long and rather slender. A large head projects laterad from the proximal part of the shaft forming a smooth, spherical surface. It is flanked anteriorly by the greater tuberosity and posteriorly by the lesser tuberosity, which are of subequal size. A characteristic feature of the multituberculate humerus is that its head forms a greater portion of a sphere than in triconodonts or most therians. This points to the possibility of extensive flexibility of movements of the forelimb upon the scapula.

Another characteristic feature of the multituberculate humerus is the presence of a posterior crest (Fig. 6-4), which extends along the posterior surface of the shaft. This crest starts proximally below the middle of the head and becomes less prominent distally as it reaches the ectepicondyle. The surface between the posterior crest and the ridge of the deltopectoral crest is strongly concave proximally, forming a deep sulcus differing from the usual morphology of therian mammals. A similarly developed posterior crest occurs in a triconodont, *Morganucodon* (see Jenkins and Parrington, 1976), but is not developed in comparable form in known therian mammals. A posterior crest occurs in the housecat, *Felis domestica*, but it is much less prominent than in the multituberculates, and divides posteriorly into two branches which extend to the entepicondyle and ectepicondyle.

The deltopectoral crest is prominent. The distal end of the humerus is strongly enlarged and the entepicondyle is more prominent than the ectepicondyle. The entepicondylar foramen is large and rounded. Between the entepicondyle and ectepicondyle there are distinct radial and ulnar condyles. The radial condyle (capitulum) is large and rounded. The ulnar condyle is narrower, with a sharp keel. Jenkins (1973) recognized two types of humero-ulnar articulations in mammals, the condylar and trochlear types. He demonstrated that in the multituberculates the articulation is of a condylar pattern. The distal parts of the radius and ulna, and the carpus have not yet been described. Simpson (1928b) described four metacarpals (two complete) and three proximal phalanges of *Catopsalis*. On the basis of these fragments he concluded that the forefoot of *Catopsalis* was mobile and slender, with an opposable pollex.

Hindlimb

Incomplete pelves are known for *Ptilodus* (see Gidley, 1909) and *Eucosmodon* (see Granger and Simpson, 1929), and a complete pelvis of *Kryptobaatar* has been discovered (see Kielan-Jaworowska, 1969). All are of the same pattern, and it seems likely that this pattern is characteristic of the Multituberculata as a whole. The ilium is long. The acetabulum is surrounded by a high rim anteriorly and a less prominent rim posteriorly. Dorsally this rim is lacking and the femoral head is uncovered (*ibid.*). The obturator foramen is situated posteroventral to the acetabulum; its longitudinal diameter exceeds that of the acetabulum.

The dorsal border of the ischium is strongly concave and curves up to a prominent tuber ischii. The posterior ends of the ischia are directed steeply ventrad and meet at a very acute angle. They are completely synostosed in *Kryptobaatar*. Seen ventrally, the symphysis has the appearance of a narrow, prominent ridge. Shallow concavities receive the epipubic bones along the anterior margins of the pubes. The epipubic bones are about half the length of the ilium, peglike, and sharply tapered.

The pelvis of multituberculates differs from those of other mammals (see Kielan-Jaworowska, 1975a) in having an extremely acute ischial arc and completely synostosed ischia. In the oviparous Monotremata, the ischial arc is U-shaped. In

Eutheria and Metatheria the angle at which the ischia meet may vary, but it is rarely as acute as in the multituberculates. There would be no room for young to be born via a route below the coccygeal vertebrae if the multituberculate pelvis was placed at an angle with the sacrum similar to that characteristic of the therian mammals. This suggests that the angle at the iliosacral joint between the ventral border of the sacrum and the dorsal border of the ischium was greater in multituberculates.

The femur is long and straight. The neck for its head is long and well defined, and the head forms more than a half of a sphere. A pit for a ligamentum teres is lacking. The greater trochanter is long and extends parallel to the axis of the femoral shaft. The lesser trochanter is prominent and has a well-defined neck and expanded head. It is situated in the middle of the posterior face of the femur. There is no third trochanter. Between the lesser trochanter and the gluteal crest there is a deep fossa, not seen in other known mammals. Simpson and Elftman (1928) suggested that this is a part of a subdivided gluteal fossa. A broad intercondylar notch is present on the distal end of the femur. Articular surfaces of the condyles are small, and the lateral epicondyle is larger than the medial one.

The multituberculate femur is very different from those of the monotremes. There are also conspicuous differences from those of triconodonts (Jenkins and Parrington, 1976) in which the neck of the head is less clearly defined and the two trochanters diverge on more or less opposite sides of the neck. The multituberculate femur resembles that of therian mammals in general pattern and in the structure of the head and greater trochanter. It differs in lack of the teres pit, in structure and position of the lesser trochanter, and in division of the gluteal fossa into two parts.

The tibia and fibula are not fused, and the fibula does not articulate with the femur. The most distinguishing feature of the multituberculate tibia is the U-shaped cross-section of its proximal end. This shape results from the development of a deep fossa on the posterior surface of the tibial shaft for the origin of the gastrocnemius muscle.

The tarsus consists of seven bones and shows a mixture of primitive and advanced characters. The calcaneum is similar to that of specialized therian mammals in having a long tuber calcanei and being compressed laterally. The sustentacular facet does not protrude from the body of the bone. The astragalus has an unusual structure. It is short and wide, the astragalar neck is not developed, but there is a short distal process, homologous with the astragalar head. A tibial trochlea is not developed, but there are two oblique grooves on the dorsal surface of the astragalus. There is a facet for articulation with the navicular on the distal margin. Proximally there is an astragalar foramen. A primitive feature of the multituberculate tarsus is the small degree of superposition of the astragalus over the calcaneum with the astragalus set medial to the calcaneum. The navicular is small and transversely elongated. The cuboid (as reconstructed for *Eucosmodon* by Granger and Simpson, 1929) is wedged proximally between calcaneum and navicular. Three cuneiforms articulate proximally with the navicular. Another distinctive feature of the multituberculate pes is the saddle-like joint between the mesocuneiform and the first metatarsal, indicating that the hallux was opposable (*ibid.*). The foot is long and plantigrade. The multituberculate tarsus differs from that of known Triassic triconodonts (Jenkins and Parrington, 1976), in which the calcaneum is broad, thin, and hemispherical as in cynodont reptiles. An astragalar head is developed in triconodonts but not in known multituberculates.

SYSTEMATICS

Introduction

Early studies of the systematic relationships of the Multituberculata were reviewed by Simpson (1928a, 1929). At that time, in addition to mammals now recognized as multituberculates, the tritylodonts were included in the Multituberculata. Simpson (*ibid.*) recognized the major dichotomy within the Multituberculata and divided it into two suborders, Tritylodontoidea and Plagiaulacoidea. Tritylodonts, Triassic and Jurassic vertebrates exhibiting many derived characters also found in the younger "plagiaulacoids," were not thought to be their direct ancestors.

In the 1940's, when the research of Young and Watson revealed the reptilian character of their jaw articulations, tritylodontids were removed from the Mammalia, and the Multituberculata was restricted to the "plagiaulacoids" (see Simpson, 1945). The hypothesis of ancestor-descendant relationships between tritylodonts and multituberculates currently is thought improbable. For example, the tritylodont cheek tooth battery is interpreted as being more specialized than those of the earliest multituberculates in the presence of three linearly organized rows of cusps on the upper cheek teeth. Probably the broadly similar patterns of dental morphology in tritylodonts (foreshadowed in earlier gomphodont cynodonts) and multituberculates are products of parallel evolution.

Until very recently interpretations of the phylogenetic relationships of the constituents of the Multituberculata changed little from those presented by Simpson in 1928a and 1929. Dentally, Late Jurassic and Early Cretaceous multituberculates are plesiomorphous, relative to other multituberculates, in the presence of: (1) stout, procumbent incisors; (2) many premolars; and (3) molars with no more than two rows of cusps. They were grouped in the Plagiaulacidae by Simpson. During the passage of the Cretaceous, multituberculate dentitions were modified by changes in form and function of the incisors, with some species evolving special modifications for piercing or gnawing. The premolar dentition was modified by concentration of the shearing function in the posterior premolars, and, especially in the lower dentition, by reduction in numbers of premolars. The number of cusps and degree of complexity of their morphology increased.

Simpson (1945) divided the Late Cretaceous and Tertiary multituberculates into two families, Ptilodontidae and Taeniolabididae, and thought both probably were derived from a plagiaulacid ancestry. In his choice of nomina for families Simpson (*ibid.*, p. 169) allowed ". . . convenience and common sense [to dictate] rejection of priority in some family names."

Field work directed specifically toward the recovery of microvertebrates has greatly added to our knowledge of the diversity of Mesozoic multituberculates. It has begun to fill the great lacuna in the record that once separated English, Early Cretaceous plagiaulacids from the later Cretaceous multituberculates discovered in the Djadokhta Formation of Mongolia and the Judith River and Oldman formations of North America. Studies of these new materials show that the tripartite division of Simpson's classification does not give adequate recognition to the diversity of multituberculates or parallelism in their evolution.

The plagiaulacoids, as redefined, are still thought to include or be representative of the ancestral stocks of later multituberculates. However,

it is now clear that their descendants are not readily divisible into two major lineages. Multituberculates were one of the groups that underwent major evolutionary radiations during the latter half of the Cretaceous, probably in response to the new, diverse food sources provided by the angiosperms and co-evolving terrestrial invertebrates. As was to be the case in the evolutionary radiation of the rodents during the Eocene, the Late Cretaceous diversification of multituberculates was characterized by considerable parallelism and geographic provincialism. The phylogenetic relationships of many lineages are still mysteries. Thus, the classification adopted here differs from that of Simpson (1945) in recognition of new families and suprafamilial groups and relegation of more taxa to *incertae sedis* status.

Haramiyidae

Haramiyidae, a family known previously by the names Microlestidae and Microcleptidae, is represented in British and continental European local faunas of Rhaetic and Rhaeto-Liassic age. A heavily damaged tooth from Dorset (Freeman, 1976) might record the presence of haramiyids in England during the Bathonian (Middle Jurassic). The only fossils referred to the Haramiyidae are isolated teeth that, even counting the more complete fragmentary teeth from Hallau, Switzerland, number no more than fifty.

Since publication of Simpson's (1928a) monograph on European Mesozoic mammals, three papers have added significantly to our knowledge of haramiyid morphology: Parrington, 1947; Peyer, 1956; and Hahn, 1973. We also acknowledge the opportunity to read a preliminary draft of an analysis of the haramiyids by P. M. Butler and G. T. MacIntyre.

In occlusal view the crowns of the majority of the teeth allocated to the Haramiyidae are ovoid in outline and consist of a central basin bordered by two approximately parallel rows of cusps. Of these, one row usually containing three high cusps is designated "Row A" (Hahn, 1973). The other, "Row B," usually consists of one large, high cusp linked to a terminal cusp of "Row A" by a ridge or saddle, and followed by four or five smaller cusps. At the end of the crown, opposite the saddle, the two rows are linked by a U-shaped ridge. At the other end of the crown a low ledge or cingulum can be present adjacent to the terminal cusp of "Row B." The width of the valley separating the two rows of cusps varies from narrow to broad and basin-like. The surface of the enamel normally is smooth and does not show the striations or grooves frequently found in plagiaulacoids. Most teeth of this pattern are supported by two roots, but three or four can be present. Teeth fitting this description are usually considered to be molariform. Several other teeth of simpler coronal morphology have been tentatively identified as elements of haramiyid dentitions.

In all attempts to reconstruct the haramiyid dentition it is assumed that the albeit modest sample of isolated teeth includes both upper and lower molariform teeth. The presence of interdental wear facets on some teeth indicates that the long axis of their crowns is also their anteroposterior axis. Simpson (1928a) adopted a convention of distinguishing the wider, higher, more prominent end of the crown as the anterior end, but clearly qualified this as a choice made for convenience of description. Parrington (1947) utilized this convention. However, from his study of the patterns of wear of the teeth, "It appears clear . . . that the microcleptid molars of the two jaws had crown patterns which, in their main features at least were mirror images of each other, and that the teeth were opposed with the rows of five cusps working in the centre valley of the opposing tooth, the valleys opening in opposite directions" (*ibid.*, p. 719). If the upper molars were both anteroposterior and labiolingual mirror images of the lowers, then the convention used for identification of the anterior end of the crown would be incorrect for either the upper or the lower teeth. Although calling for labiolingual reversal of pattern, Hahn (1973) thought it most probable that on all haramiyid molariform teeth the U-shaped ridge formed the posterior end of the crown. From their detailed study of patterns of wear Butler and MacIntyre (pers. comm. to Clemens, 1977) essentially support Parrington's reconstruction of the orientation of the molariform teeth. They also note that, when chewing, haramiyids moved the lower jaw in an upward and diagonally backward direction. In contrast to many other Mesozoic mammals, multituberculates are a notable exception in that they did not have a transverse component of mandibular movement.

Two genera of haramiyids, *Haramiya* (= *Microlestes* and *Microcleptes*) and *Thomasia* are currently recognized. They and the included species are diagnosed on minor differences in coronal morphology that might well reflect only differences in position within the dental arcade. The type and only

referred specimen of *Hypsiprymnopsis* from the Rhaetic of Somerset (see Chapter 2) has been lost. What little information can be garnered from the description of the specimen suggests that it was a tooth of a tritylodontid.

The broader systematic relationships of haramiyids remain as Simpson (1928a) aptly described them, "painfully uncertain." Haramiyid teeth show the mammal-like traits of multiplication of cusps and roots. With both the tritylodontids and multituberculates they also share the features of an anteroposterior, linear organization of multiple cusps and varying degrees of propalinal motion of the jaws during mastication.

Our decision to categorize haramiyids as "?Multituberculata, *incertae sedis*" rests upon the following, far from conclusive lines of evidence. The paulchoffatiids, described in detail by Hahn (1969, 1977a, 1977b), are known from many cranial fragments and clearly show apomorphous characters shared with other multituberculates; their reference to the Multituberculata appears well justified. Additionally, in the morphology of their teeth paulchoffatiids exhibit characters that are strongly reminiscent of the haramiyids, for example, the basined crown of M_2, and the large labial cusps on the lower premolars, which increase their morphological similarity to the molars. The latter takes some of the sting out of Simpson's observation that the lack of blade-like teeth among fossils referred to the Haramiyidae argues against their multituberculate affinities. Furthermore, current theories of mammalian origins (Chapter 3) suggest that evolution of small body size was one of the adaptations involved in the origin of the Mammalia. Haramiyid teeth are small; their lengths (between 1.0 and 3.0 mm) are comparable to those of the majority of Late Triassic and Jurassic mammals. Although the teeth of juveniles of the smaller tritylodontids do fall into this size range, the teeth of the adults of even the smaller species of *Oligokyphus* and *Bienotherium* are distinctly larger (Kühne, 1956). To repeat the all too common refrain, more material is needed before the question of the systematic affinities of the haramiyids can begin to be resolved.

Plagiaulacoidea

General Features

As presently used (following Hahn, 1969), the Suborder Plagiaulacoidea includes the oldest and most plesiomorphous (primitive) of the multituberculates. Until recently most records of plagiaulacoids were from Late Jurassic sites in the Morrison Formation in North America and the Purbeck Beds in England. A few isolated teeth documented the presence of the group in England during the Early Cretaceous. Plagiaulacoids are now also known from Early Cretaceous faunas in other parts of Europe, Asia, and, possibly, North America. Among the most significant recent discoveries are those made at Kimmeridgian localities in Portugal by Kühne and his associates (Chapter 2). In addition to providing detailed studies of these Kimmeridgian multituberculates, Hahn (1969, 1971, and 1977a) has undertaken a thorough systematic revision of the Plagiaulacoidea. Also noteworthy are the descriptions by Crusafont and Gibert (1976) of the first

Early Cretaceous paulchoffatiids and plagiaulacids discovered in Spain.

Following Hahn (1969) the Plagiaulacoidea includes multituberculates with a dental formula of $I_1^3 C_0^0 P_{3-4}^{4-6} M_2^2$ (Fig. 6-5). Subsequently Hahn (1977a) suggested the homologies of the premolariform teeth would be correctly expressed by the formula $C_0^{0-1} P_{3-4}^{4-5}$. I^1 is unicuspid. I^2 is strikingly larger and bicuspid. The morphology of I^3 differs between families; in plagiaulacids it is similar to I^2, while in paulchoffatiids it carries three or four cusps. The lower incisors are large and procumbent.

Of the upper premolariform teeth the anterior bear three or four cusps that, like the cusps of all the other cheek teeth, are of a simple, conical shape. Each of the posterior upper premolariform teeth and molars usually has two rows of cusps with three or

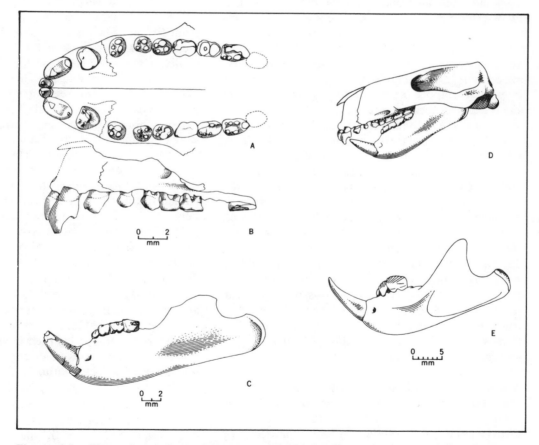

Figure 6-5. Illustrations of plagiaulacoid multituberculates drawn at various scales. *A-B*, *Kuehneodon simpsoni* (redrawn and reversed from Hahn, 1969), palate with dentition lacking M²s and one posterior premolar (*A*, ventral view, *B*, lateral view showing I¹⁻³, P¹ (? = C), P²⁻⁴ [P⁵ missing], and M¹ [M² missing]. *C*, *Paulchoffatia delgadoi* (redrawn from Hahn, *ibid*.), lateral view of left mandible showing I and P₁₋₄; molars missing. *D*, lateral view of largely hypothetical restoration of a paulchoffatiid skull. *E*, *Plagiaulax becklesii* (redrawn and reversed from Simpson, 1928a), lateral view of left mandible showing I and P₁₋₄; molars missing.

four cusps per row. On the last upper premolariform the beginnings of a third row can be present. The crowns of the lower premolars (particularly those most posterior) are relatively high, blade-like, and tipped with a series of cusps, and thus are easily distinguished from the lower molars.

The anterior lower premolar (usually P_1) has a small, buttress-like crown. In species with P_1, P_2 is blade-like, but smaller and with fewer serrations than P_3. In species lacking P_1, the crown of P_2 is buttress-like. The number of serrations on P_3 and P_4 varies from three to eight. Buccal cusps on P_{3-4} might be vestiges of a second row of cusps. Function of the posterior premolars appears to have differed among plagiaulacoids. Flat apical wear facets on the premolars of Kimmeridgian paulchoffatiids indicate that these teeth made direct contact with the upper premolars and functioned with the molars in crushing or grinding. Currently this occlusal pattern is interpreted as a plesiomorphous trait. In post-Kimmeridgian paulchoffatiids and plagiaulacids the labial surfaces of the posterior lower premolars, especially P_{3-4}, occluded with the lingual surfaces of the posterior upper premolars to produce a shearing action between their serrate apices.

Hahn (1969) divided the plagiaulacoids into two families, Paulchoffatiidae and Plagiaulacidae, known primarily from North American, Late Jurassic, and European, Late Jurassic and Early Cretaceous fossils. Subsequently knowledge of the Old World record has been substantially increased. *Guimarotodon*, still represented only by an isolated tooth of Kimmeridgian age found at Guimarota, Portugal, was first tentatively referred to the Plagiaulacoidea (Hahn, *ibid.*), but now is thought to be a paulchoffatiid (Hahn, pers. comm. to Clemens, 1977). Teeth from Early Cretaceous deposits near Galve, Spain (see Chapter 2), have been identified by Crusafont and Gibert (1976) as representatives of three genera of paulchoffatiids (*Paulchoffatia, Bolodon,* and *Kuehneodon*) and the plagiaulacid, *Plagiaulax*. Systematic allocation of *Parendotherium*, a taxon based on a single, isolated tooth from Galve remains a moot point. Initially it was described as a dryolestid by Crusafont-Pairó and Adrover (1965). F. S. Szalay (in McKenna, 1969, p. 225, footnote 3) suggested that it was an upper incisor of a multituberculate. Crusafont and Gibert (1976) continue to hold for dryolestid affinities of *Parendotherium*. The multituberculates from an Early Cretaceous locality near Uña, Spain, reported by Kühne and Crusafont-Pairó (1968) might be plagiaulacoids. Finally, Beliajeva and others (1974) announced the presence, but have yet to describe a new genus of plagiaulacoid in the Early Cretaceous, Khovboor local fauna of Mongolia.

Future studies may invalidate the current North American, Early Cretaceous fossil record of plagiaulacoids. Multituberculates are members of the Greenwood Canyon and Paluxy local faunas of Texas. They have been tentatively referred to the Plagiaulacidae (*e.g.*, Patterson, 1956), but this allocation has been challenged by Richard C. Fox and Bob H. Slaughter (pers. comms. to Clemens, 1976, 1977), who suggest that these multituberculates are too derived to be included in the Plagiaulacoidea.

Paulchoffatiidae

Seven genera including at least eleven species from European Late Jurassic and Early Cretaceous local faunas are included in this family. I^3 of paulchoffatiids is a large tooth and differs from I^2 in bearing three or four cusps. There are four to six upper premolariform teeth (possibly including a premolariform canine) and three or four lowers. Because horizontal or near horizontal wear facets were developed on their premolars, it is assumed that the Kimmeridgian paulchoffatiids utilized their premolars in crushing or grinding. Independently of other multituberculates, the geologically younger paulchoffatiids evolved a shearing mode of occlusion between the posterior premolars. M_1^1 are of typical plagiaulacoid pattern with crowns bearing two rows of two to five cusps. M^2 also carries two rows of cusps, but in *Paulchoffatia* there is a hint of the development of a third (labial) row. In contrast, the crown of M_2 is basin-like with only one distinct cusp at the anterolingual corner. Another peculiar character of both M^2 and M_2 is the frequent fusion of the two roots supporting their crowns. Hahn (1977b) noted the presence of small coronoid bones on the mandibles of paulchoffatiids.

Paulchoffatia and *Pseudobolodon* are placed in a separate subfamily, the Paulchoffatiinae. In paulchoffatiines the long axes of the lower cheek tooth battery and the body of the mandible are parallel. In the other paulchoffatiids (members of the Kuehneodontinae) and other multituberculates, the molars lie lingual to the long axis of the mandible, and the two axes intersect anteriorly. Paulchoffatines also differ from the kuehneodontines in: (1) that they exhibit

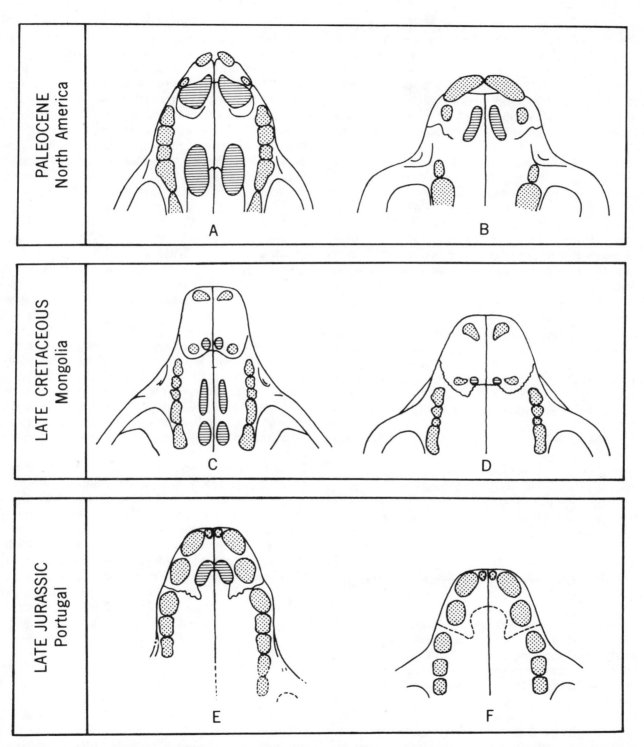

Figure 6-6. Views of palates of multituberculates to illustrate variation in positions of teeth (crowns stippled) and palatal openings (ruled horizontally). Drawn at various scales (redrawn from Hahn, 1977a). *A*, *Ptilodus montanus*. *B*, *Taeniolabis taoensis*. *C*, *Sloanbaatar mirabilis*. *D*, *Kamptobaatar kuczynskii*. *E*, ?*Paulchoffatia delgadoi*. *F*, *Kuehneodon dryas*.

less differentiation in the lengths of P_3 and P_4; (2) that the lower incisor is implanted in a more vertical position; (3) that there are six upper premolariform teeth (four or five are present in kuehneodontines); and (4) that only the last upper premolar of *Paulchoffatia* has an anteroposteriorly elongated, molar-like crown (in *Pseudobolodon* and kuehneodontines the last two premolars are molar-like). Hahn (1969, 1977a) noted that *Paulchoffatia* (and by inference other paulchoffatiines) differs from all other multituberculates in the positioning of M^2 directly behind M^1; it is not offset with the labial cusp row of M^2 aligned behind the lingual row of M^1 (Figs. 6-3, 6-6). However, a specimen of *Paulchoffatia* or *Pseudobolodon* preserving M^{1-2} *in situ* has yet to be discovered and described. Van Valen (1976) and others have questioned Hahn's reconstruction of the position of M^2.

Plagiaulacidae

As redefined (following Hahn, 1969, in large part), the known Plagiaulacidae contains a total of four genera and nine species from North American (Late Jurassic) and European (Late Jurassic and Early Cretaceous) sites. Plagiaulacids are distinguished from paulchoffatiids by at least the following dental criteria. I^3 is similar to I^2 in being bicuspid. The premolars, as many as five upper and four lower, functioned as a holding-shearing mechanism; there is no evidence of the crushing-grinding function found in paulchoffatiines. M^2 is offset lingually relative to M^1. The crown of M_2 consists of two anteroposteriorly oriented rows of cusps each made up of three cusps.

Comments on Late Cretaceous-Tertiary Grade

In comparison with plagiaulacoids, Late Cretaceous and Tertiary multituberculates are united by many apomorphous characters of the dentition. However, because of the middle Cretaceous gap in the mammalian fossil record (see Chapter 2), we do not know if these characters were inherited from a single ancestral stock or are products of parallel evolution. These derived features include at least the following: Modification of the incisors, probably increasing their efficiency for piercing or gnawing. The premolars were reduced to at most four upper and two lower (following customary usage, which well

might not indicate homology with the premolars of their plagiaulacoid ancestors, they are arbitrarily designated $P^{1-2-3-4}$ and $P_{3,4}$). Shearing function of the premolar dentition was either concentrated in one pair of teeth (P^4_4) or lost. Apparently the known lineages of the Late Cretaceous and Tertiary were characterized by initial enlargement of M^1_1 relative to M^2_2 and P^4_4. Later, in some more derived forms, P^4_4 or, possibly, M^2_2, were enlarged relative to M^1_1. On molars the number of cusps per row is usually greater than in plagiaulacoids. Also, the upper molars were characterized by addition of first a cingulum and then, in more derived forms, a third row of cusps on the lingual side of M^1 and on the labial side of M^2.

We recognize two suborders within this grade, Ptilodontoidea and Taeniolabidoidea, and assign several taxa to *incertae sedis* status. Their phylogenetic interrelationships are unknown or, at best, poorly understood. Although a few lineages died out at the close of the Cretaceous, most appear to have had Paleocene descendants. During the Paleocene there was a significant evolutionary radiation. As presently known, the group reached its acme of diversity about the middle of the Paleocene. Then, during the remainder of the epoch and into the early Eocene, the group went into a decline that probably resulted from competition with primates, small condylarths, and, finally, rodents (Van Valen and Sloan, 1966).

During the past decade or two, a number of workers, particularly R. E. Sloan, have been at work on systematic analyses of Tertiary multituberculates. The results of only a few of these studies have been published. In preparing the descriptions of the families included in this grade, we have restricted full coverage to their Mesozoic members. Thus, in most cases, our accounts probably do not fully describe the Cenozoic diversity of the family. In summary, the suprageneric classification offered here is in large measure a convenient analgesic, not a thoroughly tested pattern of organization.

Ptilodontoidea

The history of the taxon Ptilodontoidea is illustrative of the problems currently bedeviling the suprageneric taxonomy of the later Multituberculata. The name Ptilodontidae appeared in print in 1926 and 1927 without benefit of formal definition or diagnosis (Gregory and Simpson, 1926; Simpson,

1927). The following year a diagnosis was provided by Simpson (1928a), but he did not present a full exposition of his classification of the Multituberculata until 1929 (Simpson, 1929). The next major step in evolution of the taxonomy and, to the best of our knowledge, the last involving considered redefinition of all suprageneric taxa, was Jepsen's (1940) establishment of the subfamilies Ptilodontinae and Eucosmodontinae. The current concept of Ptilodontoidea stems from the Ptilodontinae of Jepsen. Of the nine genera he included in this subfamily, three are now recognized in the Cretaceous record (*Mesodma, Kimbetohia,* and *Cimolomys*). Of these, *Cimolomys* has been excluded from the Ptilodontoidea, *Kimbetohia* retained in a narrowly defined Ptilodontidae, and *Mesodma* placed in another ptilodontoid family.

Late Cretaceous multituberculates included in the Ptilodontoidea share many apparently apomorphous characters. The lower incisors, in comparison with those of the plagiaulacoids, are slenderer, more elongated teeth (Fig. 6-7). They retain the plesiomorphous features of an extensive enamel cap covering a large part of the crown and ontogenetic closure of their roots, although eruption might have continued after root closure. Jepsen (1940) suggested that the upper incisors (I^2) of ptilodontines had a simple, single tip. This is the case in *Gobibaatar*, but might not be true of the Cretaceous species of *Mesodma* and *Cimolodon*.

The number of upper premolars is reduced to a maximum of four, all of which are supported by two roots. In comparison with plagiaulacoids the last premolar (P^4) is relatively longer than any of those preceding it (P^{1-3}). P_4 is always a large, laterally compressed, trenchant tooth with lateral ridges and a serrate edge that is on line with or rises above the molar cusps. The number of serrations (8-16) usually exceeds that found on any lower premolars of a plagiaulacoid (6-8). P_3, when present, is little more than an enamel-covered button supported by a single root. The shearing function is concentrated in the interaction between P_4^4. P^{1-3} appear to have functioned with the tongue in holding or manipulating food. P_3 appears to be a vestige that served no function other than filling a gap in the base of the leading edge of P_4.

The upper molars differ from those of plagiaulacoids in the addition of cingula or, in more derived forms, a third row of cusps. In general, the number of cusps per row on the upper and lower molars of ptilodontoids tends to be greater and the cusps tend to be crescentic in shape with distinct crests on their slopes. The length of M^1_1 is distinctly greater than that of M^2_2. During their wear the molars of ptilodontoids, in contrast to taeniolabidoids, retain the plesiomorphic trait of tending to maintain the anteroposteriorly oriented rows of cusps and intervening grooves.

Neoplagiaulacidae

Sloan and Van Valen (1965) proposed a grouping of small members of the Ptilodontoidea under the name Ectypodidae, later modified to Ectypodontidae, and now known by the senior synonym, Neoplagiaulacidae (see Ameghino, 1890). Sloan (in Van Valen and Sloan, 1966) included *Cimexomys* and *Mesodma*, which range from the Cretaceous into the Paleocene; the Tertiary multituberculates *Neoplagiaulax, Ectypodus, Parectypodus,* and *Mimetodon*; and three undescribed genera in the family. Subsequently, study by Kielan-Jaworowska (1974a, 1975b) and Archibald (1977) indicated that *Cimexomys* should be removed from the family. Except for a possible record of *Neoplagiaulax* in the Hell Creek faunal-facies, Hell Creek Formation, Montana (Archibald, *ibid.*), *Mesodma* is the only genus known from the Cretaceous.

Species of *Mesodma* are known from all well-sampled local faunas of "Aquilan" through "Lancian" age in the Western Interior and West Coast of North America. The named species include: *M. senecta* ("Aquilan"); *M. primaeva* ("Judithian"); *M. thompsoni* (possibly "Edmontonian" and "Lancian"); *M. hensleighi* ("Lancian"); *M. formosa* ("Lancian" and possibly Puercan); and the type species, *M. ambigua* (Puercan). In many local faunas species of *Mesodma* apparently were the most abundant multituberculates. The individual and taxonomic diversity of neoplagiaulacids in Paleocene and early Eocene faunas suggest that they continued to radiate into a variety of niches for small, rodent-like mammals. The most recent record of the Order Multituberculata, in the Late Eocene of North America, is provided by a tenacious neoplagiaulacid.

Utilizing abundant but isolated postcranial elements from the Bug Creek Anthills locality (Chapter 2), an attempt was made to reconstruct the skeleton of one species of *Mesodma*. Unfortunately, the only published part of that study is a generalized illustration of composite skeleton (Sloan and Van

Valen, 1965). Study of the systematic relationships of the species of *Mesodma* continues to be based entirely upon dental characters, particularly those of the posterior premolars. Recently, Novacek and Clemens (1977) carried out a multivariate analysis of characters of the posterior premolars. This helped

refine the definition of some species, highlighted some possible phylogenetic relationships, but challenged a number of previously accepted interpretations of species content or ancestor-descendant relationships. They found that in taxonomic analysis, traditional reliance on characters of the posterior

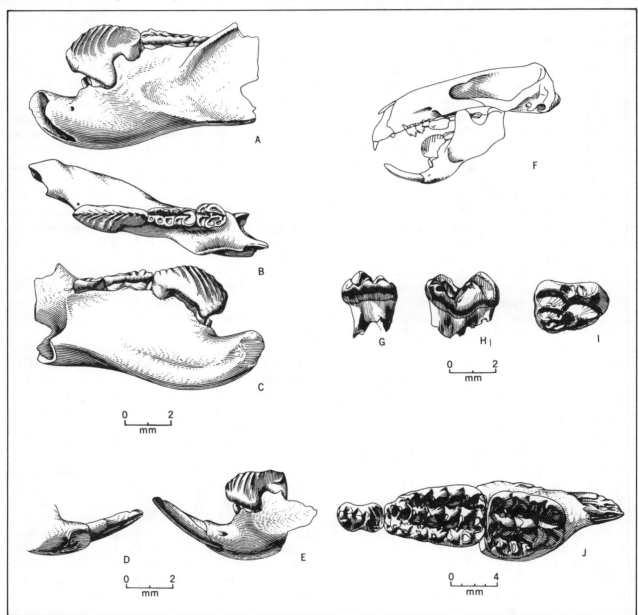

Figure 6-7.   Illustrations of various Late Cretaceous-Tertiary grade multituberculates drawn at indicated scales. *A-E, Mesodma formosa,* **left mandible with root of P**$_3$**, complete P**$_4$**, and M**$_{1-2}$ **(***A***, labial view,** *B***, occlusal view,** *C***, lingual view), and left mandible with I and P**$_{3-4}$ **(***D***, lingual view of symphyseal region,** *E***, labial view).** *F***, largely hypothetical restoration of a ptilodontid skull.** *G-I, Essonodon browni,* **isolated ?left M**$_2$ **(***G***, labial view,** *H***, posterior view,** *I***, occlusal view).** *J, Meniscoessus robustus,* **occlusal view of reconstruction of part of right upper dentition with P**^{4}**, M**$^{1-2}$**. (All drawings except** *F* **from Clemens, 1963b, copyright © 1963 by The Regents of the University of California)**

premolars is open to question. These authors neither attempted more comprehensive studies nor modified the existing taxonomy.

The upper incisors of *Mesodma* have not been positively identified, but large Lancian collections contain many small multituberculate upper incisors with bicuspid crowns that might be I^2's. The lower incisors have elongated crowns invested in enamel except for a small area immediately in front of the dorsal rim of the alveolus.

P_3 appears to be present in the dentitions of all species of *Mesodma* (Fig. 6-7). P_4 is a relatively large tooth; the P_4/M_1 ratio for the genus ranges from 1.43 to 1.80 and from 1.35 to 2.03 for other members of the family (Archibald, 1977). The serrate crest and relatively straight anterior face of P_4 do not merge to form a smooth arc but intersect at an angle. *Mesodma* and other neoplagiaulacids have from 10 to 15 serrations on this premolar. The serrate, dorsal crest of *Mesodma* P_4's varies from a symmetrical arc to an anteriorly skewed curve (Novacek and Clemens, 1977).

As far as is known, all species of *Mesodma* have four upper premolars. The P^4 cusp formula for *Mesodma* is 1-6:5-8:0-1, but for the family it can range from 0:5:0 to 6:10:1 (Archibald, 1977). On P^4 the median row of cusps tends to be dominant, although anteroexternal and posterointernal cusps can be present. A posterobasal basin behind the median row of cusps is either shallow or missing.

In both the upper and lower dentitions of *Mesodma* and probably all members of the family, the second molar is about half the length of the first. On the M^1's of *Mesodma* the internal row of cusps tends to be over half the length of the crown. Molar cusps range from conical to sub-crescentic in shape. Cusp formulae for the genus are: M_1, 5-7:4-6; M_2, 3:2; M^1, 6-8:7-10:4-7; and M^2, 1:2-4:2-4. Archibald (*ibid.*) noted the following ranges of variation for other members of the family: M_1, 6-10:4-7; M_2, 3-7:2-3; M^1, 7-12:9-13:5-10; and M^2, 1-3:3-4:3-4.

?Neoplagiaulacidae

Recent research by Kielan-Jaworowska (1974a, 1975b) and Archibald (1977) suggests that *Cimexomys* and *Gobibaatar* should at least be removed from the Neoplagiaulacidae, if not entirely from the Ptilodontoidea. In comparison with plagiaulacoids, these genera share several apomorphous traits with neoplagiaulacids and might be little-modified descendants of a common ancestral stock. However, particularly in the relatively small size of their posterior premolars and low number of cusps on the molars, *Cimexomys* and *Gobibaatar* are distinctly more primitive than any known neoplagiaulacid. To include them in this family would extraordinarily expand its scope.

As currently employed (Table 6-1), *Cimexomys* includes six named species. From his studies of these forms Archibald (1977) has concluded that the genus ought to be restricted to *C. antiquus* ("Aquilan") and the "Lancian" *C. minor, C.* sp. (Sloan and Van Valen, 1965), and a new species in the Bug Creek faunal-facies of the Hell Creek Formation, Garfield County, Montana. These species are characterized by having P_4's with only 8 to 10 serrations, of which the last two or three are separate apical cusps lacking lateral ridges. In contrast to neoplagiaulacids (*sensu stricto*), the serrate crest of P_4 does not rise above the apices of the cusps of M_1. The P_4/M_1 ratio is only 1.04-1.31. P^4 has a cusp formula of 3:5-6:2-3. The molars also differ from those of neoplagiaulacids in usually having fewer cusps per row (M_1, 5-7:4-5; M_2, 3-4:2-3; M^1, 4-5:5-6:cingulum-4; M^2, 1-5:3:1-3). The short lingual row of M^1 can be a simple cingulum or consist of only one to four cusps. In occlusal view the anterior end of the crown is tapered, the medial and external rows of cusps are almost parallel, and the crown lacks a medial constriction or waist. Molar cusps vary from subcrescentic to crescentic in shape but lack lateral ridges.

Archibald's (1977) analysis revealed that the species *Cimexomys magister* ("Aquilan"), *C. judithae,* and *C. magnus* ("Judithian"), and *C. priscus* ("Lancian") in some respects exhibit an even more primitive grade of dental evolution than the *C. minor* group of species. P_3 is present. P_4 has only 8 to 10 serrations, but the P_4/M_1 ratio (*c.* 1.46-1.67) is higher than that of the members of the *C. minor* group and overlaps that of ptilodontoids. In contrast, the molars usually have fewer cusps (M_1, 4-5:3-4; M_2, 3-4:2; M^1, 4-5:4-5:1-2; M^2, 1:3: *c.* 3-4). Also, in occlusal view, the anterior end of M^1 is truncated, not tapering. Its external and medial rows diverge anteriorly, and a distinct medial constriction or waist is present. In this group the molar cusps are not as derived as in the *C. minor* group, and vary in shape from pyramidal to subcrescentic.

Also included in the ?Neoplagiaulacidae is *Gobibaatar parvus* from Bayn Dzak (?late Santonian and/or ?early Campanian), Djadokhta Formation, Mongolia. *Gobibaatar*, known from the lower jaws and rostral region of the skull of a young animal, is the only ptilodontoid recognized in the Cretaceous record of Asia where taeniolabidoids predominate (Kielan-Jaworowska, 1969, 1974a, 1975b). In size and morphology of its cheek teeth as well as shape of the skull, *Gobibaatar* is indistinguishable from *Kryptobaatar* (Fig. 6-6). Because of the distribution of the enamel on its lower incisor and the shape of the mandible, *Kryptobaatar* is referred to the Eucosmodontidae.

"I¹" of *Gobibaatar*, probably homologous with the plagiaulacoid I^2, has a single cusp. "I²" and "DP²" (?I³ and DP³) are small teeth situated on the palate medial to its lateral margins. The crown of the lower incisor is completely covered with enamel. P_3 is present. P_4 is a relatively small tooth with a symmetrical serrate crest and short, sloping anterior face. Each of the eight serrations has lateral ridges. P_4/M_1 ratio is *c.* 1.3. Unlike neoplagiaulacids, the serrate crest of P_4 does not rise above the level of the molar cusps. Four upper premolars are present. P^4 has a cusp formula of 2:4. As is the case with *Cimexomys,* the molars of *Gobibaatar* differ from those of neoplagiaulacids in the lower number of cusps (M_1, 4:3; M_2, 3:2; M^1, 4:4:cingulum; M^2, 1:2:3).

The multituberculates included in the ?Neoplagiaulacidae are best regarded as strong testimony to our ignorance of the nature of mid-Cretaceous, multituberculate evolutionary radiations. Presently they seem to document at least three lineages of post-plagiaulacoid grade. Their early members might have been involved in the ancestry of known ptilodontoids or taeniolabidoids, but more likely they represent discrete groups.

Ptilodontidae

In his reorganization of the classification of the Multituberculata, Sloan (in Van Valen and Sloan, 1966) restricted the Ptilodontidae to include *Prochetodon* and *Ptilodus* (Tertiary genera), *Kimbetohia*, and an as yet undescribed form from the Cretaceous Judith River and/or Oldman formations. *Kimbetohia campi*, the type and only species, was typified on a maxillary fragment containing P^{2-4}. The P^4 bears two main rows of cusps and, additionally, an isolated cusp labial to the medial row. In this respect it resembles P^4's of *Ptilodus* that have as many as three cusps labial to the medial row (Simp-

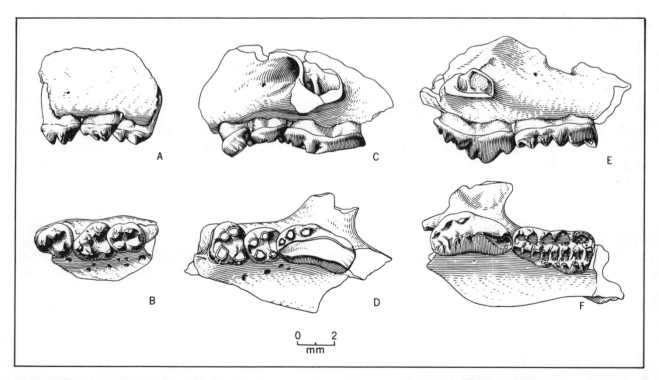

Figure 6-8. *Cimolodon nitidus*, illustrations drawn at indicated scales. *A-F*, fragments of left maxillaries containing P^{1-3} (*A*, labial view, *B*, occlusal view), P^{2-4} (*C*, labial view, *D*, occlusal view), and P^4 and M^1 (*E*, labial view, *F*, occlusal view). *G* and *H*, fragment of left mandible containing P_4 and M_1 (*G*, labial view, *H*, occlusal view). *I* and *J*, reconstruction of part of

son, 1937b). The general similarity in premolar morphology was noted by Simpson (1936), who suggested that *Kimbetohia* could have been ancestral to *Ptilodus*. This interpretation was supported by Sloan (in Van Valen and Sloan, 1966).

Clemens (1963b) described two isolated P_4's from a sample of the Lance local fauna that resembled those of *Mesodma thompsoni* and *M. ambigua* in curvature and serration count, but were significantly larger. On the basis of unpublished studies of larger samples of Puercan multituberculates, Sloan (see Clemens, 1973a) suggested reference of these Cretaceous P_4's to *Kimbetohia campi*. In addition to these teeth, Lillegraven (1969) described two isolated upper premolars from "Lancian" deposits in Alberta that might document the presence of yet another ptilodontid.

Cimolodontidae

The taxon Cimolodontidae, proposed by Marsh (1889a) but thereafter long abandoned, was revived by Sloan (in Van Valen and Sloan, 1966) to set apart a group of three genera. These are *Cimolodon* from the Cretaceous, and the Tertiary *Anconodon* and *Liotomus*. The Cretaceous record begins with two "Aquilan" species (*Cimolodon electus* and *C. similis*), distinguished primarily on differences in size. A fragment of a P_4 of *Cimolodon* sp. from the Judith River Formation was reported by Sahni (1972), and Fox (1971) noted the presence of *Cimolodon*-like multituberculates in the Oldman Formation. The oldest record of *Cimolodon nitidus* is an isolated M_2 from the St. Mary River Formation (Sloan and Russell, 1974). *Cimolodon* might also be represented in the Hunter Wash local fauna of New Mexico (Clemens, 1973b). The species *C. nitidus* is a common member of "Lancian" local faunas of the Western Interior.

Members of the species of *Cimolodon* usually fall near the middle of the range of variation in size of contemporaneous multituberculates (Fig. 6-8). The pre-"Lancian" records of *Cimolodon* are all isolated teeth. Fragments of maxillae and mandibles

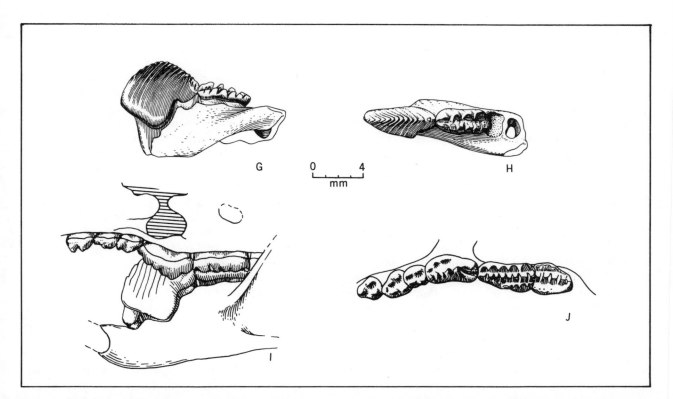

left dentition (*I*, dentitions in occlusion, lateral view; *J*, occlusal view, left upper dentition). (All drawings from Clemens, 1963b, copyright © 1963 by The Regents of the University of California).

of *C. nitidus,* described by Clemens (1963b) and Lillegraven (1969), permit reconstruction of the cheek tooth dentition. The upper incisors are still unrecognized but Lillegraven (*ibid.*) described a specimen containing a lower incisor; it is of typical ptilodontoid morphology.

A P_3 is present. In lateral view the arcuate profile of P_4 is nearly symmetrical and becomes relatively higher in later species. The length of the anterior edge of the crown (measured from the top of the anterobasal concavity to the apex of the first serration) is usually more than one-third the total length of the crown. The number of serrations varies from 12 to 15.

Four upper premolars are present. Szalay (1965) described a specimen of *Cimolodon nitidus* containing P^1, P^2, and DP^2. P^4 is a bulky tooth. The middle row of cusps gradually increases in height posteriorly, its labially convex curvature increases from the "Aquilan" to the "Lancian" species, and a distinct posterior basal depression is usually present. The composite P^4 cusp formula for the genus is 1-6:5-9:0-2. Slopes of the cusps of the "Aquilan" species are distinctly striated, while those of "Lancian" species are smooth. A similar trend in morphological simplification is seen in the reduction in fluting of the molar cusps.

Composite molar cusp formulae are: M_1, 4-8:4-6; M_2, 4-6:2-3; M^1, 5-7:7-8:3-7; and M^2, 1-5:3-6:4-6. On some molars, the number of cusps per row increases slightly from "Aquilan" to "Lancian." Individual cusps vary from conical to crescentic in shape, showing a tendency for simplification of the lateral fluting in later species. Considerable variation in the length of the lingual row of M^1 has been observed.

Studies of samples of *Cimolodon nitidus* from the Lance (Clemens, 1963b, 1973a) and Hell Creek (Archibald, 1977) formations reveal considerable variation in size of the teeth, distinctly suggesting the possibility of the presence of two species in the samples. In contrast, the dimensions of the sample of *C. nitidus* from the Scollard Formation (Lillegraven, 1969) cluster at the large ends of the ranges of variation for the samples from the Hell Creek and Lance formations.

Clemens (1963b, 1973a) reviewed the evidence supporting the possibility of ancestor-descendant relationship between *Cimolodon nitidus* and the Paleocene *Anconodon.* Archibald (1977) has dis-

covered a P_4 in the Hell Creek Formation, Montana, that helps bridge the morphological gap separating P_4's typical of *C. nitidus* and *A. gidleyi.*

Taeniolabidoidea

Taeniolabidoidea is the second subordinal taxon established by Sloan and Van Valen (1965). Their study of fossils from the latest Cretaceous Bug Creek Anthills locality, Montana, suggested that members of the Taeniolabididae and Eucosmodontidae are more closely related to each other than either is to the members of the Ptilodontoidea. In this suborder they also included *Cimolomys* and *Meniscoessus,* which were united in the Cimolomyidae, a family named but not diagnosed by Marsh (1889b). Sloan and Van Valen (1965, p. 222) defined the Taeniolabidoidea as ". . . including multituberculates in which the enamel of the lower incisor is restricted to the ventro-lateral surface of the tooth, producing a self-sharpening tooth, similar to that of rodents. The shearing premolars are reduced in proportion to the molars in all included genera except *Eucosmodon.*"

Here, we have removed the Cimolomyidae from the Taenolabidoidea; research by Archibald (1977) supports this view. Cimolomyid lower incisors are not taeniolabidid-like but are enamel capped. Although P_4's of cimolomyids are relatively small, this might reflect a primitive condition. If the multituberculates provisionally grouped in the ?Neoplagiaulacidae are representative of a primitive grade in post-plagiaulacoid evolution, it appears reasonable to hypothesize that in the Ptilodontidae (*sensu stricto*) selection emphasized enlargement of P_4^4 relative to the molars. In the Cimolomyidae, the reverse (*i.e.,* emphasis on molar enlargement) could have been the case (Archibald, 1977). We conclude that inclusion of the Cimolomyidae in the Taeniolabidoidea is not warranted by the data at hand and classify the family as suborder *incertae sedis.*

Removal of the Cimolomyidae may not be sufficiently radical surgery. To paraphrase her conclusions in the context of the classification adopted here, Kielan-Jaworowska (1974a) noted similarities of *Bulganbaatar* and, especially, *Kryptobaatar* (the oldest genera of eucosmodontids) to the ?neoplagiaulacid *Gobibaatar.* She suggested a close phylogenetic relationship of these taxa. In contrast, contemporaneous taeniolabidids, *Catopsalis* and

Kamptobaatar, as well as the sloanbaatarid *Sloanbaatar* already were distinguishable by presumably apomorphous traits. Quite possibly the Taeniolabidoidea, even as utilized here, is a polyphyletic taxon including lineages that were independently derived from a ?neoplagiaulacid or other ancestry.

The Taeniolabidoidea, including the Taeniolabididae, Chulsanbaataridae, Sloanbaataridae, and Eucosmodontidae, can be distinguished by the following traits. Restriction of the enamel on the lower incisor to a ventro-labial band is the diagnostic character usually given greatest weight. The lower incisors are at least hypsodont, and in some genera might have been ever-growing, hypselodont. Two pairs of upper incisors, the larger I^2 and smaller I^3, appear to have been retained in most taxa. Either one or two lower premolars are present. In all families, excepting the derived members of the Taeniolabididae, P_4 is a blade-like tooth. In the Taeniolabididae P_4 was reduced to a small tooth whose crown, in lateral view, is triangular with a few apical cusps (remnants of the serrations). The number of serrations varies from a low of 3 in taeniolabidids to a high of 15 in eucosmodontids. The number of upper premolars varies from four to one (greatly reduced in size in taeniolabidids). Within the Eucosmodontidae, P^{1-3} of some genera are single-rooted. Relative to the premolars, the molars tend to be large. The ratio of length of P_4/M_1 ranges from 0.50 to 1.70. The internal row of cusps on M^1 tends to be at least half the length of the crown and, in taeniolabidids, can be as long as the other rows. Molar cusps vary from conical to subcrescentic.

Taeniolabididae

The family was established by Granger and Simpson (1929) for four genera, *Taeniolabis* and *Catopsalis* (then known only from North American, Paleocene sites) as well as *Prionessus* and *Sphenopsalis* (from the Paleocene, Gashato local fauna of Asia). Reference of only one new genus, *Kamptobaatar*, to the family since 1928 is not a valid index of the increase in knowledge. The family is now known from species encompassing extensive geographic (North America and Asia) and temporal (Late Cretaceous into the Paleocene on both continents) ranges. The morphological diversity represented also is extensive. For example, the family includes both the largest known multituberculate,

Taeniolabis, which had a skull length of about 180 mm, and diminutive forms such as *Kamptobaatar* with a skull length of about 19 mm.

Records of the genera *Prionessus, Sphenopsalis,* and *Taeniolabis* have not been greatly modified since 1928. Additional material of *Taeniolabis* has been found in three Puercan deposits in eastern Montana (*e.g.*, see Van Valen and Sloan, 1965) extending its documented range northward from New Mexico. Also the geographic range of *Prionessus* is now known (Kielan-Jaworowska and Dovchin, 1968) to include the late Paleocene (Szalay and McKenna, 1971) locality at Naran Bulak.

The concept of the genus *Catopsalis*, however, is to be greatly modified. Kielan-Jaworowska and Sloan (*in press*, also see Gradziński and others, 1977) propose reference of the species of *Djadochtatherium* (*D. matthewi* and *D. catopsaloides*) to *Catopsalis*. Although probably not exactly documenting the lineage, they point out that the seven recognized species of *Catopsalis* can be organized into the following sequence illustrating increasingly apomorphous grades of evolution: *C. matthewi* and *C. catopsaloides* from the Late Cretaceous of Asia; *C. joyneri*, "Lancian" of North America; and then the North American, Paleocene species, *C. foliatus* (possibly also present in the Late Cretaceous, Archibald, 1977), *C. utahensis, C. fissidens,* and *C. calgariensis*. Kielan-Jaworowska (1974b) suggested that the family originated in Asia and later dispersed into North America.

The skulls of taeniolabidids appear to be characterized by relatively short, blunt snouts (Fig. 6-6). Also, when viewed dorsally, the anterior part of the zygomatic arch leaves the snout at a pronounced angle and then bends abruptly posteriad toward the glenoid fossa. This gives the arch a "squared" or "boxy" appearance. There is a trend for reduction in size of the frontals that, in *Taeniolabis*, taper posteriorly to a pointed end and do not contribute to the margin of the orbit. In lateral view the skull has a low, almost flat, profile. Palatal vacuities are lacking.

In all known members of the family, enamel is limited to an anteroventral band on the lower incisors and in many genera to an anterodorsal band on I^2. I^2 of *Catopsalis joyneri* exemplifies a more plesiomorphous condition in being bifid and enamel-capped. I^3 can be present and situated on the palate at its margin (*Taeniolabis*) or more medially (*Kamptobaatar*, Fig.

6-6, and *Catopsalis*). The lower incisors have a rodent-like, gliriform hypsodonty but are not known to be ever-growing. However, in *Taeniolabis* the lower incisor continued to erupt after closure of its roots (see Granger and Simpson, 1929, Fig. 1).

The primitive *Kamptobaatar, Catopsalis matthewi*, and *C. catopsaloides* have a peg-like P_3 and a small, blade-like P_4 with from three to seven serrations. Ratios of length of P_4/M_1 vary from 0.5 to 1.3. The species have four, or three, upper premolars that are broadly similar in morphology to those of ptilodontoids. P^2 is lost from the dentition of *C. catopsaloides*. Cusp formulae for P^4's of these species are 3:5-6 (*Kamptobaatar*) and 5:1 (*C. catopsaloides*). In more advanced taeniolabidids P_3 is lost and P_4 reduced to a small, two-rooted tooth. In lateral view the crown of P_4 is usually triangular carrying three or four cusps on its anterior slope. Additionally, P^{1-3} are lost. There is no indication that these upper premolars became single-rooted prior to their loss. P^4 was reduced to a tooth resembling P_4, but usually is distinguishable by a slightly more bulbous shape and presence of lateral basal cusps or cingula.

Coupled with the loss of premolars was a trend for increase in numbers of molar cusps and, in later forms, irregular addition of accessory cusps. In the plesiomorphous *Kamptobaatar* and *Catopsalis catopsaloides* the molar cusp formulae are: M^1, 5:5:cingulum to 4; M^2, 1-2:2-3:3; M_1, 4:3-4; and M_2, 2:2. At the other extreme, in *Taeniolabis* the formulae are M^1, 8:9:10 (plus as many as three or four additional cusps per row); M^2, 1:3-5:4-6; M_1, 7-8:6-7; and M_2, 5-6:3-6 (see Granger and Simpson, 1929). The lingual row of cusps on M^1 is over half the length of the crown and in *Taeniolabis* is as long as the other rows.

Molar cusps usually are either conical or pyramidal in shape but not crescentic. The striking exception to this generalization are cusps of the molars of *Sphenopsalis*. More derived taeniolabidids exhibit a change in pattern of wear of the molars. During early wear, abrasion of the cusps tended to maintain the cusp row and intervening groove topography. However, very quickly during life the cusps were truncated, and a single plane of wear developed.

Eucosmodontidae

Like the taeniolabidids, the eucosmodontids are currently thought (Kielan-Jaworowska, 1974b) to have originated in Asia during the Late Cretaceous and dispersed into North America in the latest Cretaceous ("Lancian"). Paralleling the taeniolabidids, eucosmodontids evolved a rodent-like, gliriform incisor on which the enamel was limited to an anterior band. In contrast, the premolar dentition was maintained as an effective shearing unit and the molars did not become the preeminent members of the cheek tooth dentition.

Jepsen (1940) was the first to set *Eucosmodon* apart from the typical ptilodont multituberculates through establishment of two subfamilies within the Ptilodontidae. Sloan and Van Valen (1965) elevated these subfamilies to family status. Sloan (in Van Valen and Sloan, 1966) included the following genera within the restricted Eucosmodontidae: *Neoliotomus* (Paleocene and Eocene); *Eucosmodon, Microcosmodon*, and *Pentacosmodon* (Paleocene); *Stygimys* ("Lancian" and Paleocene); an unnamed "Lancian" genus; and *Djadochtatherium matthewi*. Following the research of Kielan-Jaworowska (1974a), *Djadochtatherium* (a synonym of *Catopsalis*, see Kielan-Jaworowska and Sloan, *in press*) is referred to the Taeniolabididae. Five Mongolian, Late Cretaceous genera described after 1966 are added to the family: *Kryptobaatar* and *Bulganbaatar* from the Djadokhta Formation, *Tugrigbaatar* from Toogreeg beds, *Nemegtbaatar* from the Barun Goyot Formation, and *Buginbaatar* from Bugeen Tsav beds. The age of *Buginbaatar* is uncertain, and might be either Late Cretaceous or early Paleocene.

The possibility that the family had even greater temporal and geographic ranges is indicated by the records of fragmentary remains of eucosmodontids, possibly representing new genera and species, from the early Late Cretaceous (Cenomanian) Woodbine Formation, Texas (McNulty and Slaughter, 1968); as well as in the Late Cretaceous, Djadokhta Formation, Mongolia (Kielan-Jaworowska, 1975b); "El Gallo Formation," Baja California (referred to ?*Stygimys* sp., by Lillegraven, 1972); Fruitland and Kirtland formations, New Mexico (Clemens, 1973b); and Hell Creek Formation, Montana (Archibald, 1977).

Following Holtzman and Wolberg (1977), we relegate *Microcosmodon* and *Pentacosmodon* to a distinct subfamily, the Microcosmodontinae. A Late Cretaceous multituberculate from Montana, discovered by Archibald (1977), might be referable to this group. These genera exhibit primitive characters in the restriction of the enamel on greatly enlarged incisors and a simple molar cusp structure. The apomorphic characters of the small size of their dentitions, relatively small size of P_4, presence of accessory roots on the molars, and large pterygoid fossae set them apart from other eucosmodontids that Holtzman and Wolberg (*ibid.*) place in the Subfamily Eucosmodontinae. Even with the removal of *Microcosmodon* and *Pentacosmodon* the Eucosmodontinae might remain a taxonomically heterogeneous unit (see Kielan-Jaworowska and Dashzeveg, 1978).

The following summary of morphological variation is drawn from the Cretaceous, Mongolian genera and the two species of *Stygimys* (*S. kuszmauli* and *S. gratus*) known in "Lancian" faunas. Unless indicated otherwise, the Tertiary species are not considered.

In the majority of eucosmodontids in which the skull is known, the snout is short and bluntly pointed. In dorsal view, the zygomatic arches form smooth curves away from the sides of the skull. No eucosmodontid is known in which the "squared" arches typical of taeniolabidids are developed. A pair of palatal vacuities is present in some genera but absent in others (*Kryptobaatar* and *Tugrigbaatar*).

Two upper incisors are present. I^2 can either be a bifid, enamel-covered tooth or have a gliriform morphology with restriction of the enamel to an anterior band. I^3 is present in all Cretaceous eucosmodontids and is situated medial to the margin of the palate. The lower incisor is gliriform. Four upper premolars are present in the Cretaceous species. In *Nemegtbaatar*, *Bulganbaatar*, *Kryptobaatar*, *Tugrigbaatar*, and possibly *Neoliotomus*, all these premolars are two-rooted. The upper premolars of *Buginbaatar* are unknown. In *Stygimys*, P^{1-3} and *Eucosmodon* P^{2-3} (P^1 is lost) are supported by single roots. The cusp formulae of P^4 vary from the simple premolar of *Kryptobaatar*, 2:5, to the complex teeth of the Cretaceous species of *Stygimys* with the formula of 4:6-10:1. At least P^1 and P^3 are known to be diphyodont.

P_3 is missing from the dentition of *Stygimys*, but is present in other Cretaceous eucosmodontids. The lower dentition of *Bulganbaatar* is unknown. The lateral profile of P_4 varies from arcuate (but not as highly arched as in some ptilodontoids) to the almost horizontal crest of *Stygimys*. In no known species does the top of the crest of P_4 rise above the tops of the molar cusps. The number of serrations on P_4 varies from 6 to 11, and the ratio of lengths of P_4/M_1 varies from 1.1 to 1.7.

There is also considerable variation in cusp for-

mulae of the molars. The following summaries do not include data for the samples of *Stygimys kuszmauli* from Bug Creek Anthills or the smaller Cretaceous sample of *S. gratus*. J. D. Archibald has provided data included below, on the "Lancian" multituberculate he identified as *S.* aff. *S. gratus*. Cusp formulae of M^1 range from 4:4:cingulum (*Kryptobaatar* and *Tugrigbaatar*) to 7:7:2-3 (*Stygimys*) and 7:8:6 (*Buginbaatar*). The lingual cingulum or lingual row is at least half the length of the crown. Ranges of cusp formulae for the other molars are M^2, 1:2:2 (*Bulganbaatar*) to 1-3:3:3 (*Stygimys*); M_1, 4:3 (*Kryptobaatar* and *Tugrigbaatar*) to 7:5 (*Stygimys*) and M_2, 3:2 (*Kryptobaatar* and *Nemegtbaatar*) to 4:2 (*Tugrigbaatar*) and 3:3 (*Buginbaatar*).

Chulsanbaataridae

This family presently includes but one species, *Chulsanbaatar vulgaris*; it is the most common mammal known from the Nemegt and Khulsan sites in the Barun Goyot Formation and approximately correlative sites at Khermeen Tsav. These are thought to be of approximately middle Campanian age. Kielan-Jaworowska (1974a) reported that the sample then included 36 specimens, mostly complete or nearly complete skulls with associated dentaries (some with associated postcranial elements).

Chulsanbaatar vulgaris, a small taeniolabidoid (skull length varies from 17 to 24 mm) was described by Kielan-Jaworowska (1974a). In dorsal view, the snout anterior to the zygomatic arches is approximately rectangular in outline. The zygomatic arches are moderately divergent so that the point of maximum width of the skull is anterior to the glenoid fossae. Resembling taeniolabidids, *Chulsanbaatar* lacks palatal vacuities. In lateral view, the occipital plane and the occlusal plane of the cheek teeth intersect at approximately a right angle. The condyle of the dentary is set distinctly higher than the occlusal plane. The anteroposterior axis of the lower cheek teeth, as seen in occlusal view, is oriented obliquely to the long axis of the horizontal ramus of the dentary.

The enamel of the lower incisors is thin and limited to a band along the anteroventral surface. P_3 is present. The low, arcuate dorsal crest of P_4 carries 6 serrations, each with lateral ridges. Ratio of lengths of P_4/M_1 is 1.0. Of the four upper premolars, P^{2-3} are known to be diphyodont. P^{1-3} of *Chulsanbaatar* are plesiomorphic in that the crown of each is supported by two roots. The dental formula of P^4 is 2-3:5-6 and ratio of lengths of P^4/M^1 is 0.75. Molar cusps are basically of conical shape. The lingual row of M^1 is only about one-half the length of the crown. Cusp formulae are: M^1, 4:5:1; M^2, 1:2:2; M_1, 4:3; and M_2, 2-3:2.

Sloanbaataridae

This is a second monotypic family of small (skull length about 20 to 25 mm), Asian taeniolabidoids. *Sloanbaatar mirabilis*, known from material discovered at Bayn Dzak, is thought to be of approximately ?late Santonian and/or ?early Campanian age. Its skull has a highly specialized shape (Kielan-Jaworowska, 1970b). The braincase is highly vaulted, and the top of the occipital plate is tipped caudally so that it intersects the occlusal plane of the molars at an angle of about 115°. In dorsal view, the snout has a rectangular outline. The zygomatic arches are strongly divergent, so that the maximum width of the skull is anterior to the glenoid fossae. Two pairs of palatal vacuities are present (Fig. 6-6). The condyle of the dentary is set relatively high above the occlusal plane.

The lower incisors do not have the apomorphous, diagnostic morphology of taeniolabidoids fully developed. The enamel is not restricted to a clearly delimited, anteroventral band. Instead, the enamel is thickest in this region, thins posterodorsally, and is either thin or absent along the concave, dorsal side of the crown. Two upper incisors are present. The apex of I^2 has a single cusp. I^3, known only from the alveoli, is medial to the margin of the palate. P_3 is present. The arcuate crown of P_4 bears eight serrations, and does not rise above the level of the molar cusps. Among taeniolabidoids, the P_4 of *Sloanbaatar* is relatively large; the ratio of lengths of P_4/M_1 is 1.6. All four upper premolars are supported by two roots. Cusp formula of P^4 is 2:5. The lower molars have a primitive, relatively low number of cusps. Molar cusp formulae are: M^1, 4:4:cingulum; M^2, 1:2:3; M_1, 4:3; and M_2, 2:2.

Suborder *incertae sedis*

Cimolomyidae

Marsh (1889b, p. 177) casually proposed this family, whose name he spelled Cimolomidae, in the second of a series of papers composed of descriptions of mammalian teeth from the Lance Formation, Wyoming. About seventy-five years later, Cimolomyidae was revitalized by Sloan and Van Valen (1965) to group two genera, *Cimolomys* and *Meniscoessus*, within the Taeniolabidoidea. Sahni (1972) provided the first diagnosis of the family. Sloan and Russell (1974) and Archibald (1977) subsequently considered its membership and phylogenetic relationships.

Meniscoessus was the largest of the known "Lancian," western North American multituberculates and, probably because of its size, is well represented in current collections. Three Lancian species have been recognized. *M. conquistus* usually is limited to the small animal represented by the lectotype. Larger individuals have been allocated to two species, *M. robustus* and *M. borealis*; the latter is probably a synonym of the former (Archibald, 1977). The sample of *M. robustus* now includes the rostral region of a skull, several fragmentary dentulous mandibles and maxillae, and many isolated teeth. On the basis of their small size, three teeth from the St. Mary River Formation ("Edmontonian") were referred by Sloan and Russell (1974) to *M. conquistus*. Although these teeth are of smaller size than those characteristic of *M. robustus* (Archibald, 1977), they might represent a species other than *M. conquistus*. *M. major* and the older *M. intermedius* are interpreted as representing "Judithian" grades in the lineage (see Sahni, 1972, and Fox, 1976). The oldest ("Aquilan") species is *M. ferox* from the Milk River Formation (Fox, 1971) and could have been ancestral to *M. intermedius*.

Cimolomys is another relatively large, Late Cretaceous multituberculate. Unlike *Meniscoessus*, it is known only from isolated teeth. As currently recognized, the genus includes two "Lancian" species, *C. gracilis* and the larger, *C. trochuus*. Sahni (1972) described the "Judithian" *C. clarki* and Fox (1971) added records of two "Aquilan" species, designated ?*C.* sp. A and ?*C.* sp. B. *Essonodon* (see below) might be more closely related to *Cimolomys* and *Meniscoessus* than to any other known, Late Cretaceous multituberculate.

The only positively identified upper incisors of a cimolomyid are the heavily worn I^3's preserved in a skull of *Meniscoessus robustus* from the Hell Creek Formation. I^3 is situated medial to the palatal margin. Archibald (1977) suggested that bicuspid teeth such as the one illustrated by Osborn (1893, Pl. VII, Fig. 9) could be I^3's of *M. robustus*. Isolated I^2's, thought to be referable to *M. robustus,* have two or three apical cusps followed by a much more dorsally placed heel or posterior cusp (Clemens, 1963b, Fig. 45). The crown is fully enamel covered. The lower incisor of cimolomyids also is known only in *M. robustus*. In comparison with those of plagiaulacoids it is highly specialized. It differs from those of most ptilodontoids in being of heavier build, in the presence of apical serrations, and in development of a more complex series of lateral grooves and ridges. In contrast to taeniolabidoids, its crown is enamel covered with no indication of restriction of the enamel to an anteroventral band nor modification toward a gliriform morphology.

P_3 is present in *Meniscoessus robustus* and, possibly, *Cimolomys gracilis*, but absent in *Cimolomys trochuus*. Its development in other species is unknown. The lateral profile of P_4 varies from low and flat to relatively highly arcuate, but does not rise above the cusps of M_1. Serrations, numbering 8-11, can be rather coarse in appearance and not all have lateral ridges. The ratio of length P_4/M_1 varies from 0.68 to 1.19. In lateral view P^4's of *Cimolomys* are relatively low and long (cusp formula, 1-2:4-6:0-3), while in *Meniscoessus* they are high and short (cusp formula, 0-2:3-4:1-3). Striations or crenulations of the enamel are common.

Molar cusps vary from conical to crescentic in shape (Fig. 6-7). Basal grooves or crenulations are common. Combined cusp formulae for the molars of *Cimolomys* and *Meniscoessus* are M^1, 5-8:6-10:4-7; M^2, 2-6: 3-4:4-7; M_1, 6-8:4-7; and M_2, 4-6:2-3.

Following Archibald (1977), we remove the Cimolomyidae from the Taeniolabidoidea in recognition of the uniquely derived lower incisors of *Meniscoessus robustus*, which give no hint of the gliriform morphology of those of taeniolabidoids. In contrast to ptilodontoids, the P_4's are small relative to the molars. Perhaps this difference could result from retention of plesiomorphously small but still fully functional P_4's coupled with apomorphous enlargement of the molars. Although the number of molar cusps of *Meniscoessus* approaches that characteristic of *Taeniolabis*, the cusps are of distinctly different shape and the molars show different patterns of wear.

Essonodon

The only published reports of this highly distinctive multituberculate are descriptions of two isolated M_2's, one from the Hell Creek Formation, Montana (Simpson, 1927); the other from the Lance Forma-

tion, Wyoming (Clemens, 1963b). However, R. E. Sloan (pers. comm. to Clemens, 1977) and J. D. Archibald (1977) have been studying additional material from both Hell Creek and Bug Creek faunal-facies localities in the Hell Creek Formation. Archibald has kindly provided data on a small sample of the genus from a Hell Creek faunal-facies site in Garfield County, Montana, and another tooth from the Lance Formation, Wyoming.

Incisors and premolars of *Essonodon browni* are unknown, or unrecognized. The morphological pattern of the molars is dominated by the large intercusp basins; the cusps tend to be widely separated and merge into high ridges complicated by irregular reticula of minor crests (Fig. 6-7). Crowns of the molars are relatively low and broad. The lingual row of cusps of M^1 appears to exceed half the length of the crown. On M^2, however, there are only two distinct rows of cusps; a labial cusp row is missing or represented only by a small ridge. These are regarded as derived characters. Cusp formulae are M^1, est. 7: est. 7:4 (complete specimens are unknown); M^2, 0 to ridge:2:3-4; M_1, 7:6 plus 3 to 4 posterolabial cuspules; and M_2, 3:2.

Archibald (1977) suggested that the relatively great breadth of the molars and high cusp formula might be indicative of relationship to the cimolomyids or taeniolabidids. However, until more is known of this curious multituberculate, *incertae sedis* is the appropriate classification.

Viridomys

Viridomys orbatus is based on one complete and one fragmentary P^4 from the Milk River Formation, which were studied by Fox (1971). The crown is dominated by a high, laterally compressed blade with five serrations arranged along its nearly horizontal crest. Strong anterolabial and weaker antero- and posterolingual lobes are present. A groove on the posterior slope of the crown ends in a weak, bicuspid heel. Fox (*ibid.*) noted that the P^4's of *Viridomys* and *Buginbaatar* (the latter now classified as a eucosmodontid) are similar in the presence of a high, five-cusped median ridge. However, the P^4 of *Buginbaatar* differs in its relatively lower profile, larger cusps on the heel, and presence of three anterolabial cusps.

New Family

Kielan-Jaworowska (1975b) announced the presence of a new genus and species of multituberculate from the Djadokhta Formation, Mongolia. The dentition of this form is poorly known, but its skull structure is very different from those of other Mongolian genera. Probably it should be assigned to a new family.

PHYLOGENY
Plagiaulacid Grade

The oldest specimens certainly referable to the Multituberculata are from the Guimarota local fauna of Portugal (Fig. 6-9). They demonstrate that, by the Kimmeridgian, multituberculates already had lost certain reptilian traits still characteristic of some of their mammalian contemporaries, and stood apart as a phylogenetically isolated group. The occurrence of only paulchoffatiids in the Kimmeridgian Guimarota local fauna, only plagiaulacids at younger Late Jurassic sites in the Morrison Formation in North America, and their joint occurrence in Late Jurassic and Early Cretaceous sites in England suggests that well before the end of the Jurassic geographic provincialism already characterized their evolution. These lines of evidence, in addition to the taxonomic diversity attained as early as the Kimmeridgian, indicate that multituberculates had a much more ancient origin.

Until very recently, it was the opinion of most students of Mesozoic mammals that, early in the evolution of the Mammalia (if not among their reptilian ancestors), a dichotomy separated the class into two major lineages, the "prototherians" (or nontherians) and the therians. These could be distinguished on the basis of both dental and cranial features. On both of the prime diagnostic criteria (*i.e.*, linear organization of cusps of their cheek teeth, and formation of a greater part of the orbitotemporal region of the braincase by a large ascending lamina of the petrosal with a relatively minor contribution from the alisphenoid), multituberculates have been considered nontherian mammals. As was pointed out above and in Chapter 4, this neat picture of a simple dichotomy has been marred by the discovery of triconodonts (nontherians) that possess some apomorphic therian traits. Nevertheless, no material of any multituberculate has yet been found that demonstrates the presence of what have been taken to be diagnostic therian specializations.

Dental specializations of a single pair of procumbent lower incisors, blade-like lower premolars, multicusped molars, and evolution of a pattern of mastication involving orthal and propalinal but not transverse mandibular motion speak to the unity of the order. These characters also unambiguously isolate multituberculates from other nontherians.

Haramiyids frequently have been proposed (and frequently rejected) as possible ancestors of multituberculates. The hypothesis of close phylogenetic relationship between these groups, though not necessarily an ancestor-descendant relationship, currently seems to be favored. This reflects the discovery of several haramiyid-like characters in teeth of paulchoffatiid multituberculates (see Hahn, 1973 and 1977a). Also, functional analyses of haramiyid teeth by P. M. Butler and G. T. MacIntyre (pers. comm. to Clemens, 1977) have brought forth evidence of both upward and diagonally backward motions of haramiyid mandibles during mastication; a similarly specialized pattern of mandibular motion also is found in definitive multituberculates.

Crompton (1974) pointed out some morphological similarities between haramiyid molariform teeth and those of morganucodontids, especially *Megazostrodon*. He suggested that the three cusps of "Row A" of teeth of *Haramiya moorei* might be homologous with the principal cusps (*A, B, C*) of the upper molars of *Megazostrodon*. The similarity ". . . at the most suggests that haramiyid molars could have derived from a form ancestral to the Morganucodontidae by enlargement and modification of cingular cusps" (*ibid.*, p. 430). Mills (1971) discussed how multituberculate molars might have evolved from those characteristic of *Morganucodon watsoni*. This was done in the spirit of what Mills termed an exercise in "philosophical odontology," and he clearly regarded the hypothesis of morganucodontid origins as "non-proven."

An assessment of these analyses and other, admittedly tenuous, suggestions of phylogenetic interrelationships of morganucodontids, haramiyids, and paulchoffatiids indicates that considerable reliance has been placed upon retention of plesiomorphous characters in the purported descendants. A significant exception is the evidence of an incipient propalinal pattern of mastication in haramiyids. Although Hahn (1973) marshalled several points of similarity in developing his argument of special phylogenetic relationship between haramiyids and multituberculates, we conclude that probably it is

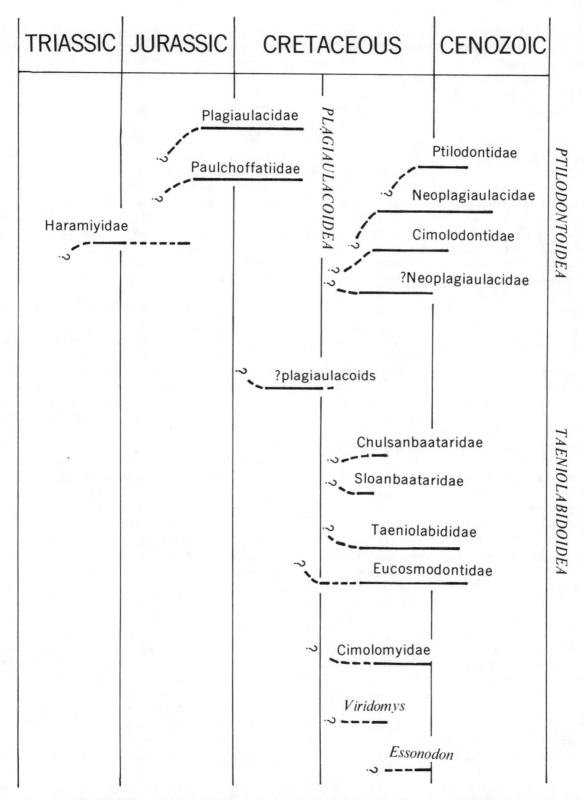

Figure 6-9. Possible phylogenetic relationships of the families and some genera of multituberculates and the Haramiyidae.

premature to classify the haramiyids as a suborder (Haramiyoidea) within the Multituberculata. The meager data available certainly do not disprove Hahn's hypothesis, but classification of haramiyids as ''?Multituberculata, *incertae sedis*'' appears to be a more realistic expression of current knowledge.

Stressing that the unity of the prototherian (or nontherian) assemblage of mammals has been challenged by recent discoveries, we place the multituberculates in this group to recognize their phylogenetic isolation from the therian mammals. Further, the Multituberculata is isolated within the Subclass Allotheria. They might share a close common ancestry with morganucodontids (classified here in the Subclass Eotheria), but differences in dental morphology of these groups are extreme, and too little of the evolutionary history of either is known to warrant additional speculation.

Turning to the plagiaulacoids of the Late Jurassic and Early Cretaceous, Hahn (1969, 1971) argued that, although more primitive in several respects, the known paulchoffatiids represent discrete side branches and not the stock ancestral to plagiaulacids or other described multituberculates. His conclusions, based primarily on the morphology of I^3 and M_2, were the subject of a review by Van Valen (1976), who concluded that the available data did not appear to rule paulchoffatiids out of the ancestry of the plagiaulacids. Hahn (1977a) has responded to Van Valen's critique.

The data and analyses pertinent to this discussion include recognition that the crown of M_2 of paulchoffatiids is basined with one dominant cusp on the rims. In the absence of two, well-organized rows of cusps separated by a clear median valley, these teeth are haramiyid-like, but not identical to any known specimens of haramiyids. The morphology of paulchoffatiid M_2's can be interpreted as either: (1) pleisomorphous, little modified from a haramiyid condition and certainly not barring them from plagiaulacoid ancestry (Van Valen, 1976) or (2) apomorphous in directions other than those to be expected in plagiaulacid ancestors (Hahn, 1977a). Given the degrees of freedom allowed by imperfections in our knowledge of the fossil record, neither argument is particularly compelling. Likewise we feel too little is known of the variation in morphology of I^3 to conclude that the presence of three or four cusps rules paulchoffatiids out of the ancestry of plagiaulacids (which have but two cusps on I^3). The latter and other relatively minor distinguishing features

of M^1 and the upper premolars (*e.g.*, the infrequent occurrence of a third row of cusps) cited by Hahn might prove merely to be minor variants when the full range of morphological variation in paulchoffatiids is known.

Of much greater phylogenetic significance is the paulchoffatiine pattern of dental occlusion as reconstructed by Hahn. He has argued that, in contrast to all other multituberculates, *Paulchoffatia* and *Pseudobolodon* are characterized by: (1) alignment of M^2 directly behind M^1; and (2) the parallel orientation of the anteroposterior axes of the lower molars and the body of the mandible. Placement of the lower cheek teeth in the mandible is clearly documented (Hahn, 1969, Text-figs. 7-8). However, review of Hahn's papers (1969, 1971, 1977a) indicates that the reconstruction of the position of M^2 is justified partially on information drawn from one fragmentary skull of *Paulchoffatia delgadoi*. The M^2's of this skull were not found in place in the maxillaries. Hahn (1969, p. 22) noted that the impression of the left M^2 is preserved. The alveolus of the right M^2 (its roots were at least partially fused) is preserved in the maxilla. Study of the illustrations of this specimen (*ibid.*, Text-fig. 9 and Plate 8, Fig. 25) suggests to us that the M^2 could have been in the normal multituberculate position (*i.e.*, offset lingually relative to M^1 so that the lingual row of cusps of M^1 was directly in front of the labial row of M^2).

The other line of evidence utilized by Hahn came from study of the isolated M^2's found at the Guimarota coal mine. These teeth are divisible into two categories on the basis of the morphology of their anterior margins. On some M^2's the anterolabial corner of the crown is indented where M^2 abutted tightly against the posterolingual corner of M^1. This is a common feature of the M^2's of more recent multituberculates in which the disposition of the molars is well documented. The anterior margins of other M^2's from Guimarota are straight and lack the anterolabial indentation. Hahn interpreted this as an indication of alignment of M^2 directly posterior to M^1. We cannot falsify this interpretation, but the lack of an indentation might also indicate that the molars of *Paulchoffatia*, although offset, were not as tightly packed or appressed as in other multituberculates. This could simply be an index of a more primitive grade in evolution of multituberculate dentitions.

Finally, noting the disposition of the lower cheek teeth in the mandible of *Paulchoffatia* and utilizing the genus as a structural model of a primitive multituberculate, Hahn (1971, p. 10) suggested, ". . . in order to compensate for the inward shift of the lower molars, in the Plagiaulacoidea the second upper molar was also shifted inward in respect to the m^1, whereas in the Ptilodontoidea and Taeniolabidoidea the upper molars become broadened by a third row of cusps, in this way compensating for the modified position of the lower and upper molars." We do not agree.

One of the principles that has emerged from recent studies of mammalian dentitions (note Chapter 9) is the stability of the functional, occlusal relationships of cusps, ridges, and basins. Thus, though the tribosphenic dentition has undergone manifold modifications, as long as the protocone remains a functional cone it is received in the basin of the talonid. Likewise, stability of occlusal relationships has been documented in therians of pretribosphenic grade and several groups of prototherians (see Crompton, 1971, 1974, and references cited therein). Members of the Morganucodontidae illustrate the most primitive known mammalian patterns of occlusion. In these forms the slopes of occluding cusps initially did not match perfectly and required wear before cutting crests were fully efficacious. There was slight individual variation in occlusal pattern involving differences in the exact point of contact of cusps and crests. However, there is no evidence of variation in the basic pattern of occlusion; for example, the labial sides of the crests of lower molars always sheared against the lingual sides of the crests of the uppers.

Hahn's hypothesis of molar evolution in multituberculates requires that in *Paulchoffatia* the central grooves of M^{1-2} received the labial rows of cusps of M_{1-2}. The presumed lingual shift of M^2 would require basic modification of the occlusal relationships of M_2^2, with a shift of the central groove of M^2 to receive the lingual row of cusps of M_2.

We feel that the available evidence warrants the suggestion that, like other nontherian mammals, the multituberculate lineage traces back to reptilian ancestors in which the crowns of the cheek teeth consisted of an anteroposteriorly aligned row of cusps. In the course of evolution from this basal stock the dentition was modified so that the labial sides of the lower cheek teeth came to occlude with the lingual sides of the uppers. Judging from their high frequency of occurrence in advanced mammal-like reptiles and early mammals, it seems likely that both labial and lingual basal cingula could have been present on the cheek teeth of a hypothetical multituberculate ancestor. Further, we assume that multituberculate molars gained their second rows of cusps through enlargement of these cingula. Thus, if the principle of stability of occlusal relationships can be applied to evolution of multituberculate dentitions, and we feel that it can, the different occlusal patterns of M_1^1 and M_2^2 were established at this evolutionary grade through the formation of second rows of cusps from different cingula.

Should future discoveries validate Hahn's reconstruction of the occlusal pattern of the paulchoffatiine dentition, we would argue that its difference from the occlusal pattern of all other multituberculates is of great phylogenetic significance. First, it would clearly bar paulchoffatiines from the ancestry of any other multituberculates. Also, it would indicate that the common ancestry of paulchoffatiines and other multituberculates would have been at the evolutionary grade at which the second rows of cusps were just being added to the molars. If this is true, a tremendous amount of parallelism followed in the evolution of the dentitions of these two lineages.

Should it be shown that the M^2's of paulchoffatiines (as in other multituberculates) were situated lingual to the M^1's, differences in orientation of the lower cheek teeth that distinguish them from other multituberculates would not necessarily have great phylogenetic significance. That is, shifting the positions of the lower cheek teeth relative to the axis of the mandible could have been accomplished through concomitant modification of the disposition of the upper cheek teeth in the skull without disruption of the basic occlusal pattern.

To return to the question posed initially, could paulchoffatiids have been ancestral to plagiaulacids? If Hahn's reconstruction of the paulchoffatiine dentition with M^2 aligned directly behind M^1 proves to be correct, then these multituberculates certainly would not have been suitable ancestors of plagiaulacids. Further, the differences in molar occlusal pattern would be so basic and ancient that they would warrant separation of the paulchoffatiines from all other multituberculates, possibly at the subordinal level.

The other subfamily of paulchoffatiids, Kuehneodontinae, includes multituberculates known to have a typical pattern of M_2^2 occlusion. They differ from plagiaulacids in characters of I^3, upper premolars, M^1, and M_2, reviewed above. Although none of the known kuehneodontines appears to be directly ancestral to a known plagiaulacid, the possibility of close phylogenetic relationships between these groups cannot be excluded.

Of the presently known species of Kimmeridgian multituberculates, only one, a kuehneodontine, appears to have had a direct descendant in the available samples of latest Jurassic faunas. This is *Kuehneodon dietrichi*, which Hahn (1971) concluded might have been ancestral to *Plioprion minor*. It is of interest to note that, according to Hahn's reconstruction of phylogenetic relationships, the loss of the crushing or grinding function of the premolars occurred independently within the kuehneodontine paulchoffatiids and the plagiaulacids.

Not enough is known even to begin to speculate about specific phylogenetic relationships among Late Jurassic and Late Cretaceous multituberculates. No material has been found that falsifies the hypothesis that the multituberculates of the Late Cretaceous were derived from a plagiaulacoid ancestry. Functional interpretations of the dentitions of Late Cretaceous species support the speculation that during the Cretaceous multituberculates, coevolving with the angiosperms and terrestrial invertebrates, began to occupy a rodent-like spectrum of ecological niches.

The preliminary report on the Early Cretaceous Khovboor local fauna demonstrates that multituberculates were part of the Asian fauna. Isolated teeth from England (see Butler and Ford, 1977), and other material from continental Europe, document the presence of plagiaulacoids during the Neocomian and possibly Aptian. Multituberculates were probably members of North American faunas throughout the Early Cretaceous. Some isolated teeth of multituberculates were found in samples of the Greenwood Canyon and Paluxy local faunas and were provisionally identified as representing plagiaulacid multituberculates (see Patterson, 1956). However, both R. C. Fox and B. H. Slaughter (pers. comms. to Clemens, 1976, 1977) suggest they are the teeth of more derived multituberculates.

These are the meager records of what must have been a period of great evolutionary diversification of multituberculates during the Cretaceous. To be sure, the diversification was abetted by fragmentation of the continental areas (see Chapter 14); by the end of the Cretaceous there is clear evidence of biogeographic provincialism. Probably of greater import

was the coevolution of multituberculates as members of increasingly complex angiosperm-based terrestrial biotas. However, only in faunas thought to be of Santonian or Campanian age do we begin to get a reasonable record of the products of the radiation.

Late Cretaceous-Tertiary Grade

Late Jurassic and Early Cretaceous records of multituberculate evolution come primarily from sites in Europe and North America, with a few specimens from Asia. The Late Cretaceous fossil record has a different geographic bias. The one available "sample" of mammals from the Late Cretaceous of Europe (a single tooth) does not demonstrate the presence of multituberculates, nor can it be interpreted as suggesting their absence. In comparison with geologically older records, much larger samples are known from the Late Cretaceous of western North America and central Asia. These provide the primary basis for research on the last, pre-Tertiary phase of evolution of the multituberculates.

Fox (1968) evaluated the adequacy of the fossil record of western North America for purposes of determination of changes in multituberculate diversity. Although additional discoveries have been made in the following years, the record continues to be drawn almost completely from faunas that inhabited the eastern coastal lowlands of western North America between the latitudes of what are now Wyoming and Alberta (Chapter 2). The apparent increase in taxonomic diversity of multituberculates from the "Aquilan" to "Lancian" probably is still in large part an artifact of the bias in the collections.

The Late Cretaceous multituberculate faunas of Mongolia and western North America are of very different composition. Only one genus, *Catopsalis*, is known from both continents, and most families now appear to be restricted to one continent or the other. Geological studies of Beringia (see Chapter 14) suggest that the marine connections linking the Arctic Sea with the North Pacific through much of the Late Cretaceous might have been interrupted by land toward the end of the period. Rather than supporting the hypothesis of a dry land connection between Asia and North America, biogeographic analyses by Kielan-Jaworowska (1974b) suggest the presence of a marine barrier to dispersal of terrestrial vertebrates that was breached by only a few organisms, and always in an eastward direction. Kielan-Jaworowska (*ibid.*) suggested that this dispersal pattern could reflect the direction of Late Cretaceous marine circulation carrying natural rafts from Asia to North America, but not in the opposite direction across the oceanic barrier.

The conflict between the biogeographic and geologic interpretations of the nature of Beringia might be more apparent than real, and be attributable to differences in ancient ecological settings of the areas now sampled. As discussed further in Chapters 2 and 12, known Mongolian, Late Cretaceous faunas come from sites thought to have been well removed from the ancient coastlines and characterized by inland continental environments. Nothing is known of the Late Cretaceous coastal faunas of Asia. In contrast, western North American, Late Cretaceous mammals are known from coastal faunas, and vertebrates of the interior of the continent are essentially unknown. Finally, at this time the Beringian region was close to the earth's north rotational pole. Though fossil floras (see Lillegraven, 1974, p. 275-276) suggest that the climate of Beringia was not frigid, it probably was colder and less equable than that of the eastern coastal lowlands of western North America, which were farther south and bordered by a large epicontinental sea.

Thus another set of working hypotheses suggests the presence of at least intermittent dry land connections between western North America and Asia during the latest Cretaceous. Terrestrial vertebrates of the eastern coastal lowlands of western North America were either ecologically barred from dispersal through Beringia, or upon reaching Asia were restricted to as yet unsampled coastal faunas. In contrast, some members of the Late Cretaceous continental faunas of Asia were able to tolerate the environments of Beringia and disperse into western North America. Some then moved into coastal lowland areas. Much more information will be needed before these hypotheses can be tested.

It must be stressed that the suprageneric classification of Late Cretaceous multituberculates is still in a state of flux. Information on postcranial anatomy is so limited that it has yet to play an effective part in current studies of systematic relationships. Nondental, cranial characters are known for an increasing number of multituberculates and are beginning to be utilized in comparative analyses.

However, the majority of systematic studies are based upon dental characters, with special emphasis on the morphology of the incisors and posterior premolars. Novacek and Clemens (1977) pointed out some of the limitations stemming from reliance upon the characters of P^4_4; Archibald (1977) has illuminated the systematic relationships of several forms through adding analyses of molar morphology.

Among known, Late Cretaceous multituberculates the most primitive appear to be the Asian *Gobibaatar* and the two species groups of the North American *Cimexomys* (see Archibald, 1977), which are temporarily classified as ?Neoplagiaulacidae. In comparison with plagiaulacoids these multituberculates are specialized in their slenderer, more elongate incisors, which remain enamel capped. In *Gobibaatar,* and possibly *Cimexomys,* the number of premolars is reduced to no more than four above and two below. M_1 is slightly enlarged relative to P_4 and M_2. The number of serrations on P_4 is somewhat greater than in plagiaulacoids, but primitively the serrate crest of P_4 does not rise above the level of the cusps of the lower molars. M^{1-2} carry the beginnings of a third row of cusps; in some species they are no more than a cingulum or a single cusp. No shared derived characters have yet been discovered suggesting that *Cimexomys* and *Gobibaatar* are particularly closely related. More likely they are relicts of a primitive grade of post-plagiaulacoid evolution whose earlier members were ancestral to derived ptilodontoids and, perhaps, other multituberculates.

Derived ptilodontoid lineages are known from Late Cretaceous, North American faunas. All members of the Ptilodontoidea share the apomorphous character of an elongated lower incisor. Though their proportions vary, ptilodontoid lower incisors are not as heavily built, nor as morphologically complex as those of the cimolomyid, *Meniscoessus.* In ptilodontoids and cimolomyids, except for a small area on the dorsal surface of its base, the crown of the lower incisor is fully enamel covered. Archibald's (1977) analysis shows that the three North American, Late Cretaceous ptilodontoid families can be ordered according to different directions and grades of dental evolution.

The Cimolodontidae is represented by "Aquilan" through "Lancian" species of *Cimolodon.* The Paleocene *Anconodon* appears to be a direct descendant of *Cimolodon.* In this family P_4 tended to evolve a distinctive high, arcuate, serrate crest. The length of P_4 (relative to M_1) and number of serrations increased, but not to the degree characteristic of members of other families, especially the ptilodontids.

The second lineage, the neoplagiaulacids (*sensu stricto*), includes the abundant Late Cretaceous multituberculate, *Mesodma.* This genus ranges from the ''Aquilan'' into the Puercan, and is known to have undergone considerable diversification during the Late Cretaceous. *Neoplagiaulax* appears in rocks of latest Cretaceous age in Montana and is known to have undergone an extensive evolutionary radiation during the Paleocene. Resembling the cimolodontids, neoplagiaulacid evolution was characterized by enlargement of P_4. In neoplagiaulacids, however, P_4 characteristically has an almost vertical face at the anterior end of the lower, flatter arch of the serrate crest. Also resembling the cimolodontids the height of the posterior end of the crown of P^4 increased. In neoplagiaulacids increase in the number of serrations on P_4 was greater than in cimolodontids. Also, increase in length of P_4 relative to M_1, as well as M_1 relative to M_2, exceeded that in cimolodontids.

Finally, the latest Cretaceous and early Paleocene *Kimbetohia* is the oldest known member of the Ptilodontidae. Ptilodontids are distinguishable from cimolodontids and neoplagiaulacids by the great emphasis on enlargement of P_4 relative to M_1. Also, the crown of P^4 did not increase in height posteriorly, and a third row of cusps was added to the anteroexternal corner of the crown.

As currently known, the North American Late Cretaceous ptilodontoids appear to represent a group of related lineages characterized by: (1) elongation of the lower incisors; (2) retention of two-rooted P^{1-3}; and (3) enlargement of P_4 relative to M_1 and M_1 relative to M_2. All known genera appear to have had Paleocene descendants. Ptilodontids might have been derived from neoplagiaulacids between ''Aquilan'' and ''Lancian'' times. Cimolodontids share many apomorphous features, though not to the same extremes, with neoplagiaulacids and ptilodontids. However, cimolodontids are distinguishable by the distinctive morphology of the serrate crest of P_4. Common ancestry of cimolodontids and neoplagiaulacids must be sought among pre-''Aquilan'' ptilodontoids.

Members of the Taeniolabidoidea are diagnosed by the presence of specialized, gliriform lower incisors, which are assumed to have evolved but once among the Multituberculata. The oldest records of taeniolabidoid multituberculates are Asian. Two monotypic families, Chulsanbaataridae and Sloanbaataridae, appear to exhibit primitive grades of taeniolabidoid evolution. In both genera, evolution of a gliriform lower incisor was incomplete; full limitation of the enamel to an anteroventral band was not achieved. The P_4 of *Sloanbaatar,* from the Djadokhta Formation, is enlarged relative to M_1. Length of M_2 is 1.1-1.2 mm. In the younger *Chulsanbaatar,* from the Barun Goyot Formation and Khermeen Tsav locality (Chapter 2), P_4 and M_1 are of similar length (a plesiomorphous condition), but M_2 is about half the length of M_1. In both genera counts of the serrations on P_4 and cusps on the molars are primitively low. The oldest members of the Taeniolabididae and Eucosmodontidae are also from the Djadokhta Formation. The occurrences in Mongolia of records of both the earliest primitive taeniolabidoids and their oldest documented evolutionary radiation suggest an Asian center of origin for the taeniolabidoids (Kielan-Jaworowska, 1974b).

Taeniolabidoids are not represented in the present samples of ''Aquilan'' through ''Edmontonian'' local faunas of western North America. They are also unknown in the extensive samples of local faunas from the ''Lancian,'' Hell Creek faunal facies (Chapter 2). The Asian taeniolabidid *Catopsalis* appears, however, in ''Lancian,'' Bug Creek faunal facies, as does the eucosmodontid *Stygimys,* which Kielan-Jaworowska (1974a) suggested was a derivative of *Nemegtbaatar.* Both *Stygimys* and *Catopsalis* have descendants in Puercan faunas.

This evidence suggests that taeniolabidoids dispersed from Asia to western North America just prior to the close of the Cretaceous. Cautionary notes are sounded by two discoveries. McNulty and Slaughter (1968) recorded the presence of a eucosmodontid in strata of Cenomanian age in the Woodbine Formation of Texas. This record is based on a gliriform incisor showing some resemblances to those of much later eucosmodontids. If substantiated, it demonstrates the presence of eucosmodontids in North America long before deposition of the Djadokhta Formation. More likely, this fossil could document parallel acquisition of gliriform incisors in an otherwise unknown lineage of multituberculates. Second, Lillegraven (1972) recorded the presence of a multituberculate, possibly a eucosmodontid tentatively identified as ?*Stygimys*, in strata of Campanian age in Baja California. Earlier occurrence of eucosmodontids in Baja California preceding their "Lancian" appearance on the eastern seaboard of western North America is in accord with, but does not particularly strengthen, the hypothesis of Asian origin of the family.

Kielan-Jaworowska and Sloan (*in press*) develop a strong case in their study of *Catopsalis* (including *Djadochtatherium*) for origin of the lineage in Asia and its dispersal into western North America. Several fragmentary skulls show that taeniolabidids were characterized by a reduction in length of the snout. In dorsal view the zygomatic arches extend laterally from the sides of the skull and then abruptly turn posteriorly. These angulations of the arches give the skull a "box-like" appearance. Members of the family show trends toward loss of the anterior upper premolars, then loss of shearing function and reduction in size of P_4^4. The number of cusps on the molars increased greatly.

Although the snout is shortened, in dorsal view the zygomatic arches of skulls of eucosmodontids are not angulated but sweep in a smooth curve away from the skull. Within the eucosmodontids there was a trend for modification of the anterior upper premolars from support by two roots to support by a single, large root. The number of upper premolars remained four, except in *Eucosmodon*, which lost P^1. P_4^4 retained their shearing function and tended to become enlarged relative to M_1^1.

As was pointed out previously, research by Archibald and Kielan-Jaworowska indicates that the strictly North American Cimolomyidae should be removed from the Taeniolabidoidea. The lower incisor is known only in *Meniscoessus*. Although derived in comparison with those of plagiaulacoids, it differs in proportions and morphological complexity from the lower incisors of ptilodontoids; it is similar, however, in retaining an almost complete enamel covering. During their "Aquilan" through "Lancian" history cimolomyids maintained a post-plagiaulacoid grade of enlargement of P_4, and the number of serrations increased. Archibald (1977) found evidence suggesting that M_1 increased in length relative to P_4 and, uniquely, M_2 increased in length relative to M_1.

Finally, the highly derived *Essonodon*, found at but a few "Lancian" sites, and the "Aquilan" *Viridomys* cannot confidently be referred to any currently recognized family. They are additional witnesses to the limitations of our knowledge of the diversity of Late Cretaceous multituberculates.

ECOLOGY

Paleontologists of the nineteenth and early twentieth centuries, including Falconer, Owen, Cope, Abel, and others (see Simpson, 1926, for resumé) argued over the nature of the diets of multituberculates. Some viewed most of them as predaceous carnivores or insectivores, while others thought they made their livings as herbivores or omnivores. Since its description by Cope, the constant exception in this debate was, and continues to be, *Taeniolabis* ($= Polymastodon$). Its massive skull, gliriform incisors, reduced premolar dentition, and large complex molars strongly suggest that this multituberculate was a rodent-like herbivore. Dispute focused on the diets of those multituberculates lacking gliriform incisors but possessing blade-like, plagiaulacoid premolars.

For the past several decades interpretations of the paleoecology of multituberculates with plagiaulacoid premolars have been based on Simpson's (*ibid.*) analysis of multituberculates as living animals. In this work he drew most of his information from *Ctenacodon*, *Ptilodus*, *Catopsalis* ($= Djadochtatherium$), and *Taeniolabis* (the genera then represented by fragmentary crania and, in some instances, elements of the postcranial skeleton). Over a dozen suites of characters were considered following patterns of analysis developed by Dollo and Abel. Simpson's principal conclusions were that the jaw musculature of multituberculates consisted of strong masseter and pterygoid, but relatively weak temporalis muscles. The condyle and glenoid fossa did not solely limit the jaw to orthal motion, but allowed horizontal excursions as well. The incisors were not caniniform, and only in the dentition of an herbivore could a function logically be ascribed to the persistent anterior upper premolars. Contrary to some earlier interpretations, the plagiaulacoid premolars were shown to be shearing mechanisms. Finally, the modifications of the molars for crushing and grinding were interpreted as being most appropriate for animals with largely herbivorous diets.

Turning to comparisons with living mammals, Simpson (1926) placed considerable emphasis on the multituberculate-like features of *Bettongia,* a marsupial rat-kangaroo. The source of data on the diet of *Bettongia* cited was Owen's (1871) report that this rat-kangaroo fed on tough, dry vegetable substances. Derived features of multituberculates analogous to those of modern rodents also were considered, and it was noted that ". . . small rodents do not live exclusively on vegetable substances, although their dentition is a specialized herbivorous one" (*ibid.*, p. 241). The weight of the evidence led Simpson to the conclusion that all multituberculates with plagiaulacoid premolars known to him were herbivores.

In a later paper on the plagiaulacoid type of dentition, Simpson (1933) maintained his basic assessment of multituberculates as herbivores. His suite of modern marsupials with analogous dental specializations was expanded to include *Bettongia, Hypsiprymnodon,* and *Aepyprymnus.* Simpson (*ibid.*, p. 105) ". . . concluded that the dentition of the rat-kangaroos is adapted to an exclusively vegetable diet and to one in which woody or other coarse fibers, bark, roots, grass, and the like predominate."

Subsequently, analogies were drawn frequently between multituberculates and herbivorous rodents. The hypothesis that the origin and adaptive radiation of the Rodentia in the Paleocene and Eocene was the cause of the extinction of multituberculates has been discussed by a number of authors. Van Valen and Sloan (1966, see for citations of earlier papers on multituberculate extinction) attributed extinction of multituberculates to competition with eutherian herbivores—first condylarths, then primates, and finally rodents. They assumed that all the later multituberculates were at least largely herbivorous. Adding to this hypothesis, Hopson (1967) argued that the competitive inferiority of multituberculates resulted from their lower grade of biological advancement in comparison with those of eutherian herbivores. He suggested that multituberculates were probably at a lower grade of evolution in a broad spectrum of features contributing to biological efficiency, for example, thermoregulation, reproduction, behavior, and locomotion.

A common scenario of the evolution of multituberculates can be summarized as follows. They entered an adaptive zone for small vertebrate herbivores at an early stage in their evolution, possibly prior to the Jurassic. Competition with small reptilian herbivores (including young dinosaurs) might have been minimized by their smaller size and utiliza-

tion of different food resources. Predation by reptilian carnivores might have been lessened by activity during different times of the diurnal circle. Presumably endothermic multituberculates fed in the cooler evening hours. With the appearance, diversification, and spread of angiosperm-dominated floras during the middle of the Cretaceous, the herbivorous multituberculates underwent a major evolutionary radiation. Although some lineages became extinct at the close of the Cretaceous, most survived and appear to have diversified. By the middle of the Paleocene, multituberculates achieved their greatest known taxonomic diversity. Their extinction was the result of competition with eutherian herbivores.

Three general lines of argument usually are invoked to substantiate this scenario. The first is based on functional analysis of the dentition, and Simpson (1926) covered most of the major points. Later discoveries and studies have added details, but not significantly modified the conclusions that the incisors were specialized for piercing, grasping, and, in some species, gnawing. The plagiaulacoid premolars and functionally related anterior upper premolars provided a shearing mechanism. The molars crushed and ground the food. As yet there is no basis for evaluating the possible degree to which food was manipulated by the forefeet. We can only assume that food items might have been torn, shredded, or dismembered prior to being stuffed into the mouth. From a functional viewpoint, multituberculates with plagiaulacoid premolars had dentitions capable of providing the range of functions appropriate for a mammal that was an obligate herbivore, generally herbivorous, or omnivorous.

Several workers have argued that the relatively great abundance of multituberculates in Mesozoic mammalian faunas demonstrates their herbivory. This is based on the unsubstantiated assumption that the mammalian assemblages can be treated as ecological units isolated from the rest of the terrestrial fauna.

Finally, to some extent, interpretations of herbivorous diets of multituberculates rested on analogies drawn with rat-kangaroos and rodents. These interpretations can be retested in light of current and greater knowledge of the diets of these extant mammals. The dietary preferences of rat-kangaroos have not been the subject of a thorough study. *Bettongia* was long considered to have a diet consisting entirely of fibrous plant material. However, Ride (1970, p.

64) noted that "bettongs are partly carnivorous and in captivity are avid meat eaters; they also gnaw bones." Troughton (1962) reported that *B. lesueur* is an omnivorous scavenger living on the shores of the islands of Shark Bay. As far as is known, *Aepyprymnus* is an herbivore (Walker, 1964), but *Hypsiprymnodon* is an omnivore including plants, insects, and worms in its natural diet (Collins, 1973). See author's note at the end of the chapter, added in proof.

Burramys, a phalangeroid marsupial with plagiaulacoid premolars that was first described from Pleistocene fossils, was discovered in 1966 living in mountainous areas of southeastern Australia. Dimpel and Calaby (1972) provided a fascinating resumé of the diet and feeding behavior of this "living fossil" containing a wealth of information applicable to our interpretations of multituberculates. Their summary of observations (*ibid.*, p. 104) is well worth repeating here:

> Food is picked up with the incisors then transferred to and manipulated with the forepaws while the animal squats on its hindquarters. The food may be held in one or both forepaws. The soft flesh of fruits is bitten off with the incisors and chewed with the molars. The skins are not eaten and *Burramys* have been observed holding pieces of apple and grape and removing the last fragment of flesh by pulling the skin with their forepaws against the lower incisors. Soft bodied insects such as moths are usually dealt with by the incisors. With insects having a hard cuticle such as mealworm larvae the animal may begin biting with the incisors but usually the insect is held in the forepaws at the side of the mouth and chopped up with the sectorial premolars. Hard-shelled seeds such as sunflowers are invariably held at the side of the mouth and bitten with the premolars. Usually the seed case is opened with a single bite. Peanuts are mostly nibbled

with the incisors but the premolars are used also to break up fragments.

Although the dietary preferences of captive animals might inaccurately reflect their natural diets, this report documents a point that should not escape the attention of any student of the functions of mammalian dentitions. Simply put, note the *utilization of the forepaws* during mastication. How many of the interpretations of dental function and diet of extinct mammals will require revision when the forelimbs of these animals are discovered and the possibility of manipulation of the food by the forepaws assessed?

Morphological similarities with rodents also have been used as a basis for suggesting that multituberculates were herbivores. However, Landry (1970) argued that the extraordinary adaptive radiation of the Rodentia is not a product of a complex of specializations limiting their diets to vegetable matter, but is rather one of the adaptations that provided flexibility in coping with a wide variety of foods. A survey of modern rodents shows examples of parallel evolution of carnivorous, insectivorous, and even piscivorous species.

We agree with the assessment that some multituberculates (*e.g.*, *Taeniolabis* and other derived taeniolabidids) probably were dominantly herbivorous. What little is known of the natural diets of modern, wild marsupials with plagiaulacoid premolars suggests that most multituberculates were not highly specialized herbivores but rather were omnivorous. The Mesozoic success of multituberculates, measured in terms of their great diversity and long history, could be attributable to their filling a broad spectrum of ecological niches available to mammals not restricted to animal prey but able to feed on a wider variety of foods.

REFERENCES CITED

Ameghino, F., 1890, Los plagiaulacideos argentinos y sus relaciones zoológicas, geológicas y geograficas: Bol. Instituto Geografico Argentino, v. 9, p. 143-201. Reprinted in Torcelli, A. J., ed., Obras Completa y Correspondencia de Florentino Ameghino: La Plata, v. 1-24, 1913-1924 (citation of Neoplagiaulacidae, v. 11, p. 56).

Archibald, J. D., 1977, Fossil Mammalia and testudines of the Hell Creek Formation, and the geology of the Tullock and Hell Creek formations, Garfield County, Montana [Ph.D. thesis]: Berkeley, California, Univ. California.

Beliajeva, E. I., Trofimov, B. A., and Reshetov, V. J., 1974, General stages in evolution of late Mesozoic and early Tertiary mammalian fauna in Central Asia, *in*

Kramarenko, N. N., and others, eds., Mesozoic and Cenozoic faunas and biostratigraphy of Mongolia: Moscow, Joint Soviet-Mongol. Paleont. Exped. (Trans., v. 1), p. 19-45 (in Russian with English summary).

Broom, R., 1914, On the structure and affinities of the Multituberculata: Amer. Mus. Nat. Hist. Bull., v. 33, p. 115-134.

Butler, P. M., and Ford, R., 1977, Discovery of Cretaceous mammals on the Isle of Wight: Isle of Wight Nat. Hist. and Arch. Soc. Proc. for 1975, p. 662-663.

Cheng, C.-C., 1955, The development of the shoulder region of the opossum, *Didelphis virginiana*, with special reference to musculature: Jour. Morph., v. 97, p. 415-471.

Clemens, W. A., 1963a, Wealden mammalian fossils: Palaeontology, v. 6, p. 55-69.

———1963b, Fossil mammals of the type Lance Formation, Wyoming. Part I. Introduction and Multituberculata: Univ. California Publs. Geol. Sci., v. 48, *vi* + 105 p.

———1973a, Fossil mammals of the type Lance Formation, Wyoming. Part III. Eutheria and summary: *ibid.*, v. 94, *vi* + 102 p.

———1973b, The roles of fossil vertebrates in interpretation of Late Cretaceous stratigraphy of the San Juan Basin, New Mexico: Four Corners Geol. Soc. Memoir Book, 1973, p. 154-167.

Collins, L. R., 1973, Monotremes and marsupials, a reference for zoological institutions: Smithson. Inst. Publ., no. 4888, *v* + 323 p.

Cope, E. D., 1882, *Mammalia* in the Laramie Formation: Amer. Natural., v. 16, p. 830-831.

———1884, The Tertiary *Marsupialia*: *ibid.*, v. 18, p. 686-697.

Crompton, A. W., 1971, The origin of the tribosphenic molar, *in* Kermack, D. M., and Kermack, K. A., eds., Early mammals: Linn. Soc. Zool. Jour., v. 50, suppl. 1, p. 65-87.

———1974, The dentitions and relationships of the southern African Triassic mammals, *Erythrotherium parringtoni* and *Megazostrodon rudnerae*: Brit. Mus. (Nat. Hist.) Bull. (Geol.), v. 24, p. 397-437.

Crusafont, M., and Gibert, J., 1976, Los primeros Multituberculados de España: Nota preliminar: Acta Geologica Hispanica, Año 11, p. 57-64.

Crusafont-Pairó, M., and Adrover, R., 1965, El primer mamifero del Mesozoico Español: Fossilia, Publnes Cat. Paleont. Univ. Barcelona, nos. 5-6, p. 28-33.

Dimpel, H., and Calaby, J. H., 1972, Further Observations on the Mountain Pigmy Possum (*Burramys parvus*): Victorian Naturalist, v. 89, p. 101-106.

Every, R. G., 1970, Sharpness of teeth in man and other primates: Postilla (Yale Univ.), no. 143, 30 p.

Falconer, H., 1857, Description of two species of the fossil mammalian genus *Plagiaulax* from Purbeck: Geol. Soc. London Quart. Jour., v. 13, p. 261-282.

Fox, R. C., 1968, Studies of Late Cretaceous vertebrates.

II. Generic diversity among multituberculates: Syst. Zool., v. 17, p. 339-342.

———1971, Early Campanian multituberculates (Mammalia: Allotheria) from the Upper Milk River Formation, Alberta: Canad. Jour. Earth Sci., v. 8, p. 916-938.

———1976, Cretaceous mammals (*Meniscoessus intermedius*, new species, and *Alphadon* sp.) from the lowermost Oldman Formation, Alberta: *ibid.*, v. 13, p. 1216-1222.

Freeman, E. F., 1976, A mammalian fossil from the Forest Marble (Middle Jurassic) of Dorset: Geol. Assoc. Proc., v. 87, p. 231-235.

Gidley, J. W., 1909, Notes on the fossil mammalian genus *Ptilodus* with descriptions of new species: U. S. Natl. Mus. Proc., v. 36, p. 611-626.

Gill, T. N., 1872, Arrangement of the families of mammals and synoptical tables of characters of the subdivisions of mammals: Smithson. Misc. Coll., no. 230, *vi* + 98 p.

Gradziński, R., Kielan-Jaworowska, Z., and Maryańska, T., 1977, Upper Cretaceous Djadokhta, Barun Goyot and Nemegt formations of Mongolia, including remarks on previous subdivisions: Acta Geol. Polonica, v. 27, p. 281-318.

Granger, W., and Simpson, G. G., 1929, A revision of the Tertiary Multituberculata: Amer. Mus. Nat. Hist. Bull., v. 56, p. 601-676.

Gregory, W. K., and Simpson, G. G., 1926, Cretaceous mammal skulls from Mongolia: Amer. Mus. Novitates, no. 225, 20 p.

Hahn, G., 1969, Beiträge zur Fauna der Grube Guimarota Nr. 3, die Multituberculata: Palaeontographica, Abt. A, v. 133, p. 1-100.

———1971, The dentition of the Paulchoffatiidae (Multituberculata, Upper Jurassic): Memória 17 (N. S.) dos Serviços Geológicos de Portugal, Lisboa, p. 1-39.

———1973, Neue Zähne von Haramiyiden aus der deutschen Ober-Trias und ihre Beziehungen zu den Multituberculaten: Palaeontographica, Abt. A, v. 142, p. 1-15.

———1977a, Neue Schädel-Reste von Multituberculaten aus dem Malm Portugals: Geologica et Palaeontologica, v. 11, p. 161-186.

———1977b, Das Coronoid der Paulchoffatiidae (Multituberculata; Ober-Jura): Paläont. Zeit., v. 51, p. 234-245.

———1978, Milch-Bezähnungen von Paulchoffatiidae (Multituberculata; Ober-Jura): N. Jahrb. Geol. Paläont. Monatsh., 1978, no. 1, p. 25-34 (see "Author's Note" for reference to Hahn, 1978b and 1978c).

Holtzman, R. C., and Wolberg, D. L., 1977, The Microcosmodontinae and *Microcosmodon woodi*, new Multituberculata taxa (Mammalia) from the Late Paleocene of North America: Sci. Mus. Minnesota Sci. Publ., n.s., v. 4, p. 1-13.

Hopson, J. A., 1967, Comments on the competitive inferiority of the multituberculates: Syst. Zool., v. 16, p. 352-355.

———1970, The classification of nontherian mammals:

Jour. Mammal., v. 51, p. 1-9.

Hopson, J. A., and Crompton, A. W., 1969, Origin of mammals, *in* Dobzhansky, T., Hecht, M. K., and Steere, W. C., eds., Evolutionary biology: New York, Appleton-Century-Crofts, v. 3, p. 15-72.

Jenkins, F. A., Jr., 1973, The functional anatomy and evolution of the mammalian humero-ulnar articulation: Amer. Jour. Anat., v. 137, p. 281-297.

Jenkins, F. A., Jr., and Parrington, F. R., 1976, The postcranial skeletons of the Triassic mammals *Eozostrodon, Megazostrodon* and *Erythrotherium*: Roy. Soc. London Phil. Trans., B (Biol. Sci.), v. 273, p. 387-431.

Jepsen, G. L., 1940, Paleocene faunas of the Polecat Bench formation, Park County, Wyoming: Amer. Philos. Soc. Proc., v. 83, p. 217-340.

Kermack, K. A., 1963, The cranial structure of the triconodonts: Roy. Soc. London, Phil. Trans., B (Biol. Sci.), v. 246, p. 83-103.

_____1967, The interrelations of early mammals: Linn. Soc. Zool. Jour., v. 47, p. 241-249.

Kermack, K. A., and Kielan-Jaworowska, Z., 1971, Therian and non-therian mammals, *in* Kermack, D. M., and Kermack, K. A., eds., Early mammals: *ibid.*, v. 50, suppl. 1, p. 103-115.

Kielan-Jaworowska, Z., 1969, Discovery of a multituberculate marsupial bone: Nature, v. 222, p. 1091-1092.

_____1970a, Unknown structures in multituberculate skull: *ibid.*, v. 226, p. 974-976.

_____1970b, New Upper Cretaceous multituberculate genera from Bayn Dzak, Gobi Desert, *in* Kielan-Jaworowska, Z., ed., Results Polish-Mongol. Palaeont. Expeds., pt. II: Palaeontologia Polonica, no. 21, p. 35-49.

_____1971, Skull structure and affinities of the Multituberculata, *in ibid.*, pt. III: *ibid.*, no. 25, p. 5-41.

_____1974a, Multituberculate succession in the Late Cretaceous of the Gobi Desert (Mongolia), *in ibid.*, pt. V: *ibid.*, no. 30, p. 23-44.

_____1974b, Migrations of the Multituberculata and the Late Cretaceous connections between Asia and North America: So. African Mus. Ann., v. 64, p. 231-243.

_____1975a, Possible occurrence of marsupial bones in Cretaceous eutherian mammals: Nature, v. 255, p. 698-699.

_____1975b, Evolution and migrations of the Late Cretaceous Asian mammals, *in* Lehman, J. P., ed., Problèmes Actuels de Paléontologie-Evolution des Vertébrés: Paris, Colloque Internat., C.N.R.S., no. 218, p. 573-584.

Kielan-Jaworowska, Z., and Dashzeveg, D., 1978, New Late Cretaceous mammal locality in Mongolia and a description of a new multituberculate: Acta Palaeont. Polonica, v. 23, p. 115-130.

Kielan-Jaworowska, Z., and Dovchin, N., 1968, Narrative of the Polish-Mongolian Palaeontological Expeditions 1963-1965, *in* Kielan-Jaworowska, Z., ed., Results

Polish-Mongol. Palaeont. Expeds., pt. I: Palaeontologia Polonica, no. 19, p. 7-32.

Kielan-Jaworowska, Z., and Sloan, R. E., 1978, *Catopsalis* (Multituberculata) from Asia and North America and the problem of taeniolabidid dispersal in the Late Cretaceous: Acta Palaeont. Polonica, v. 24.

Kielan-Jaworowska, Z., and Sochava, A. V., 1969, The first multituberculate from the uppermost Cretaceous of the Gobi Desert (Mongolia): *ibid.*, v. 14, p. 355-367.

Kühne, W., 1956, The Liassic therapsid *Oligokyphus*: London, Trustees Brit. Mus., x + 149 p.

_____1961, Une faune de mammiferes lusitaniens (Rapport provisoire): Com. Serv. Geol. Portugal, v. 45, p. 211-221.

Kühne, W. G., and Crusafont-Pairó, M., 1968, Mamíferos del Wealdiense de Uña, cerca de Cuenca: Acta Geológica Hispánica, v. 3, p. 133-134.

Lambe, L. M., 1902, On Vertebrata of the Mid-Cretaceous of the Northwestern Territory. 2: New genera and species from the Belly River series (Mid-Cretaceous): Canad. Paleont. Contribs., v. 3, p. 25-81.

Landry, S. O., Jr., 1970, The Rodentia as omnivores: Quart. Rev. Biol., v. 45, p. 351-372.

Lemoine, V., 1880, Sur les ossements fossiles des terrains tertiaires inférieurs des environs de Reims: Assoc. française Avanc. Sci. C. R., v. 8, p. 585-594.

Lillegraven, J. A., 1969, Latest Cretaceous mammals of upper part of Edmonton Formation of Alberta, Canada, and review of marsupial-placental dichotomy in mammalian evolution: Univ. Kansas Paleont. Contribs., Art. 50 (Vertebrata 12), 122 p.

_____1972, Preliminary report on Late Cretaceous mammals from the El Gallo Formation, Baja California del Norte, Mexico: Nat. Hist. Mus. Los Angeles Co. Contribs. Sci., no. 232, 11 p.

_____1974, Biogeographical considerations of the marsupial-placental dichotomy: Ann. Rev. Ecol. Syst., v. 5, p. 263-283.

McKenna, M. C., 1961, On the shoulder girdle of the mammalian Subclass Allotheria: Amer. Mus. Novitates, no. 2066, 27 p.

_____1969, The origin and early differentiation of therian mammals: New York Acad. Sci. Ann., v. 167, p. 217-240.

McNulty, C. L., Jr., and Slaughter, B. H., 1968, Stratigraphy of the Woodbine Formation, Tarrant County, Texas (Locality 3): Field Trip Guidebook, 2nd Ann. Meet. South-Central Sec. Geol. Soc. America, p. 68-72.

Marsh, O. C., 1879, Notice of new Jurassic mammals: Amer. Jour. Sci., ser. 3, v. 18, p. 396-398.

_____1880, Notice of Jurassic mammals representing two new orders: *ibid.*, ser. 3, v. 20, p. 235-239.

_____1881, New Jurassic mammals: *ibid.*, ser. 3, v. 21, p. 511-513.

_____1887, American Jurassic mammals: *ibid.*, ser. 3, v. 33, p. 326-348.

_____1889a, Discovery of Cretaceous Mammalia: *ibid.*, ser. 3, v. 38, p. 81-92.

_____1889b, Discovery of Cretaceous Mammalia, part ii: *ibid.*, ser. 3, v. 38, p. 177-180.

Mills, J. R. E., 1971, The dentition of *Morganucodon, in* Kermack, D. M., and Kermack, K. A., eds., Early mammals: Linn. Soc. Zool. Jour., v. 50, suppl. 1, p. 29-63.

Novacek, M. J., and Clemens, W. A., 1977, Aspects of intrageneric variation and evolution of *Mesodma* (Multituberculata, Mammalia): Jour. Paleont., v. 51, p. 701-717.

Osborn, H. F., 1893, Fossil mammals in the upper Cretaceous beds. I: The multituberculates. II: The trituberculates. III: Faunal relations of the Laramie mammals: Amer. Mus. Nat. Hist. Bull., v. 5, p. 311-330.

Owen, R., 1871, Monograph of the fossil Mammalia of the Mesozoic formations: Palaeontogr. Soc. Monog. 24, 115 p.

Parrington, F. R., 1947, On a collection of Rhaetic mammalian teeth: Zool. Soc. London Proc., v. 116, p. 707-728.

Patterson, B., 1956, Early Cretaceous mammals and the evolution of mammalian molar teeth: Fieldiana (Geol.), v. 13, p. 1-105.

Peyer, B., 1956, Über Zähne von Haramiyden [*sic*], von Triconodonten und von wahrscheinlich synapsiden Reptilien aus dem Rhät von Hallau, Kt. Schaffhausen, Schweiz: Schweiz. Paläont. Abh., v. 72, p. 1-72.

Pleininger, W. H. T., von, 1847, Zähne aus der oberen Grensbreccie des Keupers bei Degerloch und Steinenbronn: Verh. Naturk. Württemburg Jahresh., p. 164-167.

Poche, F., 1908, Einige notwendige Änderungen in der mammalogischen Nomenclatur: Zool. Annalen, v. 2, p. 269-272.

Ride, W. D. L., 1957, The affinities of *Plagiaulax* (Multituberculata): Zool. Soc. London Proc., v. 128, p. 397-402.

_____1959, Mastication and taxonomy in the macropodine skull: Syst. Assoc. Publ., no. 3, p. 33-59.

_____1970, A guide to the native mammals of Australia: Oxford, Oxford Univ. Press, *ix* + 249 p.

Russell, L. S., 1937, New and interesting mammalian fossils from western Canada: Roy. Soc. Canada Trans., ser. 3, v. 30, p. 75-80.

Sahni, A., 1972, The vertebrate fauna of the Judith River Formation, Montana: Amer. Mus. Nat. Hist. Bull., v. 147, p. 321-412.

Shortbridge, G. C., 1910, Account of the geographical distribution of the marsupials and monotremes of southwest Australia, having special reference to the specimens collected during the Balston Expedition of 1904-1907: Zool. Soc. London Proc. 1909, p. 803-948.

Simpson, G. G., 1925, A Mesozoic mammal skull from Mongolia: Amer. Mus. Novitates, no. 201, 11 p.

_____1926, Mesozoic Mammalia. IV. The multitubercu-

lates as living animals: Amer. Jour. Sci., ser. 5, v. 11, p. 228-250.

_____1927, Mammalian fauna of the Hell Creek Formation of Montana: Amer. Mus. Novitates, no. 267, 7 p.

_____1928a, A catalogue of the Mesozoic Mammalia in the Geological Department of The British Museum: London, Oxford Univ. Press, x + 215 p.

_____1928b, Further notes on Mongolian Cretaceous mammals: Amer. Mus. Novitates, no. 329, 14 p.

_____1929, American Mesozoic Mammalia: Peabody Mus. (Yale Univ.) Mem., v. 3, pt. 1, Yale Univ. Press, *xv* + 171 p.

_____1933, The "plagiaulacoid" type of mammalian dentition: Jour. Mammal., v. 14, p. 97-107.

_____1936, Additions to the Puerco fauna, Lower Paleocene: Amer. Mus. Novitates, no. 849, 9 p.

_____1937a, Skull structure of the Multituberculata: Amer. Mus. Nat. Hist. Bull., v. 73, p. 727-763.

_____1937b, The Fort Union of the Crazy Mountain Field, Montana, and its mammalian faunas: U.S. Natl. Mus. Bull., v. 169, x + 289 p.

_____1945, The principles of classification and a classification of mammals: Amer. Mus. Nat. Hist. Bull., v. 85, *xvi* + 350 p.

_____1947, *Haramiya*, new name, replacing *Microcleptes* Simpson, 1928: Jour. Paleont., v. 21, p. 497.

Simpson, G. G., and Elftman, O. H., 1928, Hind limb musculature and habits of a Paleocene multituberculate: Amer. Mus. Novitates, no. 333, 19 p.

Sloan, R. E., and Russell, L. S., 1974, Mammals from the St. Mary River Formation (Cretaceous) of southwestern Alberta: Roy. Ontario Mus. Life Sci. Contribs., v. 95, p. 1-21.

Sloan, R. E., and Van Valen, L., 1965, Cretaceous mammals from Montana: Science, v. 148, p. 220-227.

Szalay, F. S., 1965, First evidence of tooth replacement in the Subclass Allotheria (Mammalia): Amer. Mus. Novitates, no. 2226, 12 p.

Szalay, F. S., and McKenna, M. C., 1971, Beginning of the age of mammals in Asia: the late Paleocene Gashato fauna, Mongolia: Amer. Mus. Nat. Hist. Bull., v. 144, p. 269-318.

Troughton, E., 1962, Furred animals of Australia: Sydney, Angus and Robertson, *ix* + 376 p.

Van Valen, L., 1976, Note on the origin of multituberculates (Mammalia): Jour. Paleont., v. 50, p. 198-199.

Van Valen, L., and Sloan, R. E., 1965, The earliest primates: Science, v. 150, p. 743-745.

_____1966, The extinction of the multituberculates: Syst. Zool., v. 15, p. 261-278.

Walker, E. P., 1964, Mammals of the world: Baltimore, Johns Hopkins Univ. Press, v. 1-2, *vii* + 1500 p.

Watson, D. M. S., 1916, The monotreme skull: a contribution to mammalian morphogenesis: Roy. Soc. London Philos. Trans., v. 207, p. 311-374.

Woodward, A. S., 1891, On a mammalian tooth from the

Wealden Formation of Hastings: Zool. Soc. London Proc., p. 585-586.
_____1911, On some mammalian teeth of the Wealden of Hastings: Geol. Soc. London Quart. Jour., v. 67, p. 278-281.

AUTHOR'S NOTE

J. H. Calaby (C.S.I.R.O., Lyneham, Australia) was kind enough to review the manuscript for the section immediately above on marsupial food habits. In his comments, he stressed that interpretations of food habits in wild marsupials as based upon dietary preferences of captive animals should be considered highly suspect. Quite a number of "herbivorous" Australian marsupials in captivity will eat virtually anything made available, including meat pies, fish and chips, and hot-dogs (see Edwards and Ealey, 1975). Also, gnawing of bone by marsupials, rodents, and, apparently, multituberculates, might be attributable to mineral deficiencies and should not necessarily be interpreted as an indication of need for animal protein.

In addition to the paper cited above, Finlayson (1958) and Ride and Tyndale-Biscoe (1962) provide information on the diets of populations of *Bettongia lesueur* in areas of central Australia and on the Bernier and Dorre islands, Shark Bay, Western Australia. Here these marsupials are known to feed on a wide variety of species and parts of plants.

Finally, Calaby pointed out that there is little reliable information from field studies on diets of Australian marsupials having plagiaulacoid premolars. This group includes many species of phalangeroids, whose plagiaulacoid teeth exhibit a wide variety of variations in morphology, orientation in the dental arcade, and ontogeny. To what extent these variations are correlated with dietary differences or other factors remains unknown.

Two publications of G. Hahn (1978b and 1978c) were received after preparation of the text of this chapter was completed. Hahn (1978b) provides a review of the order that in content and organization parallels parts of the present chapter; he proposes a classification of multituberculates differing in a few respects from the one used here. Hahn (1978c) provides a thorough analysis of the lower jaws of the Kimmeridgian multituberculates from Portugal. The posterior parts of their mandibles show little morphological variation, and in all the articular surface

of the condyle is directed posteriorly, unlike later multituberculates in which it has a more dorsal orientation. In contrast, there is great morphological variation in the lower dentition (incisors and cheek teeth) and in the structure of the horizontal ramus and symphyseal region of the mandible.

In addition to presenting expanded diagnoses of many included taxa, the following changes were made by Hahn in the classification of plagiaulacoid multituberculates. These have not been entered into Table 6-1 of the present book. 1. Completion of preparation of the specimen identified by Hahn (1977) as *Kuehneodon*? sp. revealed that it represents a new species of *Paulchoffatia*. 2. Probability of associations of upper and lower dentitions were suggested for several taxa of paulchoffatiids that presently bear different names. 3. *Parendotherium herreroi* Crusafont-Pairó and Adrover (1965) from Galve, Spain (see Chapter 2) was recognized as a paulchoffatiid, but on the available evidence it cannot be referred to a particular subfamily. 4. The following additional new taxa were named or recognized: *Paulchoffatia* sp. A, *Pseudobolodon*? *robustus* (a new species), *Kuehneodon uniradiculatus* (a new species), and *Kuehneodon* sp. indet. 5. *Guimarotodon* was recognized as a paulchoffatiid, probably referable to the Kuehneodontinae.

William A. Clemens

ADDITIONAL REFERENCES CITED

Edwards, G. P., and Ealey, E. H. M., 1975, Aspects of the ecology of the swamp wallaby *Wallabia bicolor* (Marsupialia, Macropodidae): Austral. Mammal., v. 1, p. 307-317.

Finlayson, H. H., 1958, On central Australian mammals (with notice of related species from adjacent tracts), Part III, The Potoroinae: So. Austral. Mus. Rec., v. 13, p. 235-302.

Hahn, G., 1978b, Die Multituberculata, eine fossile Säugetier Ordnung, *in* Kraus, O., ed., 22. Phylogenetisches Symposion, Das evolutive Plateau Säugetier, Origin and early evolution of mammals: Hamburg, Sonderbd. naturwiss. Vereins Hamburg, v. 3, p. 61-95.

_____1978c, Neue Unterkiefer von Multituberculaten aus dem Malm Portugals: Geologica et Palaeontologica, v. 12, p. 177-212.

Ride, W. D. L., and Tyndale-Biscoe, C. H., 1962, Mammals, *in* Fraser, A. J., ed., The results of an expedition to Bernier and Dorre Islands, Shark Bay, Western Australia in July, 1959: Western Australia, Fisheries Dept., Fauna Bull., no. 2, p. 54-97.

CHAPTER 7

SYMMETRODONTA

Michael L. Cassiliano

William A. Clemens

CONTENTS

INTRODUCTION

In 1854 Richard Owen published the first description of *Spalacotherium*, an animal now recognized as a symmetrodont, but did not place it in a formal suprageneric classification. Seventeen years later, in 1871, he allocated *Spalacotherium* and the newly described *Peralestes* to the Marsupialia, a group then including many other Mesozoic mammals. Marsh (1887) established the Spalacotheriidae, based upon *Spalacotherium* (and including *Menacodon*, now considered a junior synonym of *Tinodon*). Also,

thinking the two genera were distinct, Marsh (*ibid.*) made *Tinodon* the name-bearer for another family, the Tinodontidae. Marsh's Tinodontidae included *Phascolotherium,* now known to be a triconodont. Thus began the confused classification of triconodonts and symmetrodonts, whose history has been fully reviewed by Simpson (1925a). The current suprageneric classification (Table 7-1) stems from Simpson's (*ibid.*) recognition of two families (Spalacotheriidae and Amphidontidae) and establishment (Simpson, 1925b) of the Order Symmetrodonta to include those forms of Mesozoic mammals with postcanine teeth characterized by an imperfectly symmetrical, triangular arrangement of the principal cusps (Fig. 7-1). Several new forms have been found since Simpson's (*ibid.*) original study of the order that have shed more light on symmetrodont origins, evolutionary history, and dental morphology. These discoveries, particularly discovery of the primitive symmetrodont *Kuehneotherium,* require revision of the ordinal diagnosis.

DIAGNOSIS

Symmetrodonts were shrew-sized mammals, known from jaw fragments and dentition. The mandible is slender and long, consisting of a large dentary and, probably, (1) a full complement of reptilian jaw bones in the Rhaeto-Liassic form; (2) a

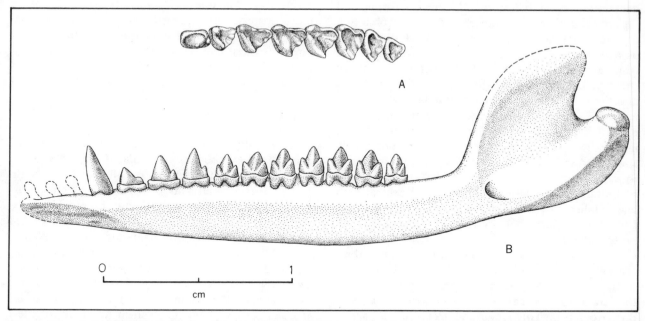

Figure 7-1. Schematic restorations of parts of the dentitions of *Peralestes* and *Spalacotherium* (probably these are synonymous taxa). *A*, occlusal view of left P³ and M¹⁻⁷ of *Peralestes longirostris*. *B*, lingual view of right mandible with three incisors (restored), canine, P₁₋₃, and M₁₋₇ of *Spalacotherium tricuspidens*. (Redrawn from Simpson, 1928, and Clemens, 1963, and notes)

TABLE 7-1 CLASSIFICATION OF SYMMETRODONTA

Infraclass Pantotheria (Marsh, 1880)
  Order Symmetrodonta Simpson, 1925b
    Family Kuehneotheriidae Kermack, Kermack, and
      Mussett, 1968
     Kuhneon Kretzoi, 1960
      K. duchyense Kretzoi, 1960 (?*nomen vanum*)
     Kuehneotherium Kermack, Kermack, and Mus-
      sett, 1968
      K. praecursoris Kermack, Kermack, and Mus-
       sett, 1968
     unnamed genus and species, Kermack, Kermack,
      and Mussett, 1968
    Family Amphidontidae Simpson, 1925a
     Amphidon Simpson, 1925a
      A. superstes Simpson, 1925a
     Manchurodon Yabe and Shikama, 1938
      M. simplicidens Yabe and Shikama, 1938
    Family Spalacotheriidae Marsh, 1887
     Spalacotherium Owen, 1854

      S. tricuspidens Owen, 1854
      S. taylori Clemens and Lees, 1971
     Peralestes Owen, 1871
      P. longirostris Owen, 1871 (probably a syn-
       onym of *Spalacotherium*)
     Spalacotheroides Patterson, 1955
      S. bridwelli Patterson, 1955
     Symmetrodontoides Fox, 1976
      S. canadensis Fox, 1976
    Family ?Spalacotheriidae *incertae sedis*
     Tinodon Marsh, 1879a
      T. bellus Marsh, 1879a
      T. lepidus Marsh, 1879b
     Eurylambda Simpson, 1929
      E. aequicrurius (Simpson, 1925a)
    unnamed genus and species, Freeman, 1976
  Symmetrodonta indet.
    unnamed genus and species, pers. comm. from D.
     Dashzeveg to Z. Kielan-Jaworowska, 1977

dentary and possibly a splenial in Jurassic forms; and (3) only a dentary in Cretaceous forms. Probably a double articulation (dentary-squamosal plus articular-quadrate) is present in the Kuehneotheriidae, while a single articulation of the dentary-squamosal characterizes the Spalacotheriidae, Amphidontidae, and the other lineage. The mandibular symphysis is long, the articular condyle is placed slightly above the molar level, and an angular process is lacking. Lower incisors are styliform, canine is small or moderately sized, and the number of postcanine teeth is known to vary from 7 to possibly as many as 11. Lower premolars have a laterally compressed central cusp and smaller anterior and posterior accessory cusps. Lower molars are characterized by a triangular, imperfectly symmetrical cusp arrangement. The central external cusp (protoconid, *a*) is the highest, and there are smaller anterior (paraconid, *b*) and posterior (metaconid, *c*) internal cusps. The basal cingulum of the lower molars carries an anterior and a large posterior cusp. This cingulum is continuous across the lingual side of the crown and can bear cuspules; it can be incomplete or continuous across the labial side of the crown. Primitive forms possess a blade-like talonid, which is lost in specialized members of the order. Upper molars have a tall internal cusp (par-

acone, *A*). An anterior (stylocone, *B*) and one or more posterior (including "metacone," *C*) external cusps can be present. The external cingulum is well developed and can bear cusps. Except in *Kuehneotherium,* an internal cingulum is missing.

ANATOMY

Virtually the entire available fossil record of symmetrodonts consists of isolated teeth and some tooth-bearing fragments of maxillaries and mandibles. Other cranial and postcranial elements, particularly of *Kuehneotherium,* may be present in existing collections, but they have yet to be identified and/or described (see Kermack and others, 1968).

Molar crowns of symmetrodonts are dominated by three principal cusps arranged in a triangular pattern (Fig. 7-1). On upper molars the apex of the triangle is on the lingual side of the tooth; on lowers it is on the labial side. The shearing blades of these teeth are aligned along the sides, but not the base, of each triangle. These shearing blades occlude in a zigzag pattern when upper and lower teeth are brought together. The phrase "reverse triangles" has been used to describe this type of dentition and shearing

TABLE 7-2   AGE AND OCCURRENCE OF GENERA OF SYMMETRODONTA

GENUS	OCCURRENCE	AGE OR STAGE
Kuehneotherium	Pont Alun Quarry, Bridgend, Wales	Rhaeto-Liassic
Kuhneon	Duchy Quarry, Bridgend, Wales	Rhaeto-Liassic
unnamed genus and species	Ewenny Quarry, Bridgend, Wales (Kermack and others, 1968)	Rhaeto-Liassic
unnamed genus and species	Forest Marble, Oxfordshire, England (Freeman, 1976)	late Bathonian
Amphidon	Morrison Fm., Como Bluff, Wyoming, U.S.A.	Late Jurassic
Eurylambda	Morrison Fm., Como Bluff, Wyoming, U.S.A.	Late Jurassic
Tinodon	Morrison Fm., Como Bluff, Wyoming, U.S.A.	Late Jurassic
Peralestes	Lulworth Beds, Durlston Bay, England	Volgian
Spalacotherium	Lulworth Beds, Durlston Bay, England;	Volgian
	Hastings Beds, Paddockhurst Park, England	Valanginian or Hauterivian
Manchurodon	Sakusiyo Coal Field, Chiatzuyao, People's Republic of China (Manchuria)	?Early Cretaceous
unnamed genus and species	Fm.? Khovboor, near Guchin Us, province (aymak) of Arvaykher, Mongolian People's Republic	?Aptian or ?Albian
Spalacotheroides	Paluxy (= Antlers Fm.) Fm., Texas, U.S.A.	"Paluxian"
Symmetrodontoides	upper part of Milk River Fm., Alberta, Canada	"Aquilan"

pattern. Functionally, it serves to increase the total length of the shearing blades without requiring equivalent lengthening of the dentition.

To adequately discuss the phylogenetic and evolutionary relationships of the Symmetrodonta, it is necessary to review the terminology applied to the cusps of the postcanine teeth. A problem in description of molar morphology (on which most studies of the Symmetrodonta are based) stems from the connotations of homology implied by the conventional terms such as protocone, metacone, and paracone. These designations have their etymological origins, and largely derive their phylogenetic significance from the Cope-Osborn theory of dental evolution and its derivatives (see Chapter 9). Attempts have been made to devise nomenclatures that would avoid suggestions of homology and eliminate cumbersome descriptive names such as "antero-external cingular cuspule." Simpson (1961) and Crompton and Jenkins (1968), for example, proposed different systems of notations that gave no implications of homology

(Fig. 7-2). One drawback of this kind of system is its initial unfamiliarity. Numerical or alphabetical designations do not immediately convey the concept of a cusp's relative position to those readers familiar with Cope-Osborn terminology but untutored in the jargon of students of the earliest mammals. The system of notations developed by Crompton and Jenkins (*ibid.*) is being employed in much of the new, primary literature. Because there is a reasonable probability that most of the Cope-Osborn cusp designations traditionally applied to teeth of symmetrodonts correctly indicate homologies with cusps of tribosphenic molars, we employ this older terminology, adding, in parentheses, the Crompton-Jenkins designations. Data on the microstructure of the enamel are presented in Chapter 11.

SYSTEMATICS

The fossil record of symmetrodonts is meager (Table 7-2). Most of the family-level groups (Kuehneotheriidae, Amphidontidae, and ?Spalacotheriidae *incertae sedis*) are based upon one or two genera. Considering the great chronological duration (Rhaeto-Liassic into Late Cretaceous) and morphological diversity of known symmetrodonts, it is clear that the known fossil record inadequately documents the evolutionary history of the order.

Kuehneotheriidae

The kuehneotheriids were symmetrodonts possessing tritubercular molars (Fig. 7-3) on which the two crests linking the apices of the three main cusps are aligned nearly anteroposteriorly or form an obtuse angle (Kermack and others, 1968, Parrington, 1971). The highest cusp of the upper molars is the paracone (*A*). Anterolabially, a crest links it with the stylocone (*B*), which in turn is linked to the parastyle (*E*). Along the crest extending posterolabiad from the paracone are the "metacone" (*C*) and metastyle (*D*). The homology of the "metacone" (*C*) of symmetrodonts with the metacone of tribosphenic molars is a debated point (see Chapter 9). Usually the basal cingulum is nearly complete around the crown of the upper molars, being interrupted only on the lingual side.

On the lower molars the principal cusps of the trigonid (paraconid, *b*; protoconid, *a*; and meta-

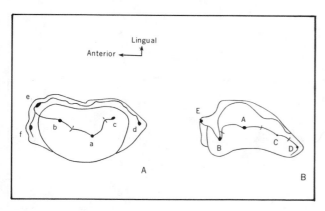

Upper molars	
After Kermack and others, 1968	After Crompton and Jenkins, 1968
paracone	*A*
metacone	*C*
stylocone	*B*
parastyle	*E*
metastyle	*D*
Lower molars	
protoconid	*a*
paraconid	*b*
metaconid	*c*
hypoconulid	*d*
mesial cuspule	*e*
—	*f*

Figure 7-2.   Comparison of two dental terminologies used for symmetrodonts. Schematic occlusal outlines of molars of *Kuehneotherium*. *A*, left lower molar. *B*, left upper molar. (Redrawn from Kermack and others, 1968)

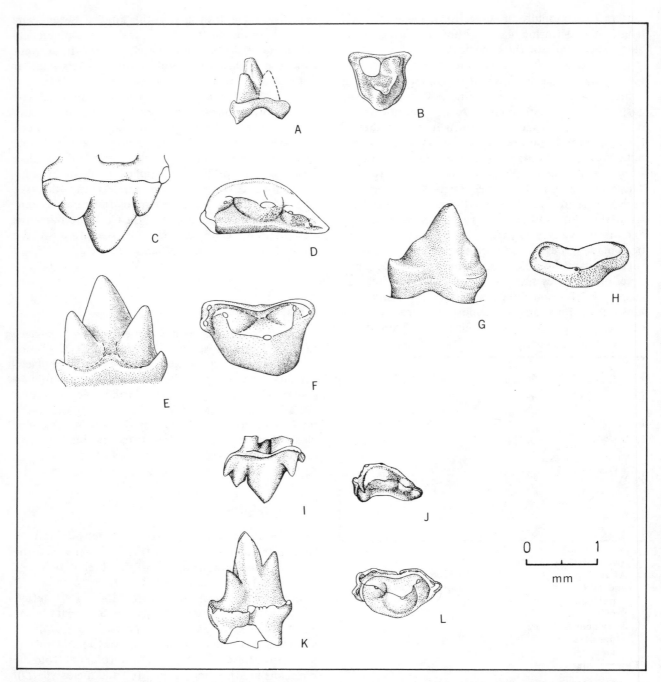

Figure 7-3. Schematic drawings to a common scale of upper and lower molars of selected symmetrodonts. (Conventions of orientation: Lower molars—first view, lingual, anterior to the right; second view, occlusal, anterior to the left, lingual side upward. Upper molars—first view, labial, anterior to the right; second view, occlusal, anterior to the left, lingual side upward.) *A* and *B*, left lower molar of *Spalacotheroides bridwelli* (redrawn from Patterson, 1955): *A*, lingual; and *B*, occlusal views. *C* and *D*, right upper molar of *Eurylambda aequicrurus* (redrawn from Simpson, 1929, and Crompton and Jenkins, 1967): *C*, labial; and *D*, occlusal views. *E* and *F*, left lower molar of *Tinodon bellus* (redrawn from Crompton and Jenkins, 1967): *E*, lingual; and *F*, occlusal views. *G* and *H*, left lower molar of *Amphidon superstes* (redrawn from Simpson, 1929): *G*, lingual; and *H*, occlusal views. *I* and *J*, right upper molar of *Kuehneotherium praecursoris*: *I*, labial; and *J*, occlusal views. *K* and *L*, left lower molar of *K. praecursoris*: *K*, lingual; and *L*, occlusal views (*I* through *L* redrawn from Kermack and others, 1968).

conid, *c*) are relatively taller than those of the uppers. A complete lingual cingulum is present, but the labial cingulum is usually restricted to mesial and distal segments. The blade-like talonid terminates in a large hypoconulid (*d*). Mandibular fragments containing all the postcanine teeth or their alveoli have yet to be discovered. Using smaller fragments, Kermack and others (1968) reconstructed the lower dentition with at least nine but no more than eleven postcanine teeth. Gill (1974), utilizing more complete material, determined a dental formula of $I_{4?}C_1P_6M_{4-5}$. The first four lower premolars are single-rooted or have incompletely divided roots. The most distal premolars, P_5 and P_6, are double-rooted, as are the molars. Crowns of premolars were lost through osteoclastic cutting of the necks of the roots. The parts of the roots remaining in the alveoli were then resorbed and replaced by spongy bone. Loss of premolars in this way occurred in *Morganucodon watsoni* (see Mills, 1971, and Parrington, 1971) but in no other known mammals.

There is no angular process on the long, slender dentary. The full reptilian array of lower jaw bones was probably present, though greatly reduced in size. The type of the family is *Kuehneotherium praecursoris* Kermack and others (1968), based on specimens from the Pontalun Quarry, Wales. *Kuhneon duchyense* Kretzoi (1960) is also placed in the Kuehneotheriidae.

The first symmetrodont from Wales was made known through the discovery of a molariform tooth by Walter Kühne (1950), which he dubbed "Duchy 33" in reference to the discovery locality. Kretzoi (1960), following Kühne, identified the tooth as a lower molar and designated it the type of *Kuhneon duchyense*. No more material of this symmetrodont has been recovered at Duchy Quarry. In their paper on *Kuehneotherium*, Kermack and others (1968) argued that the general morphology and presence of a basal cingulum encircling the entire crown indicates that the type specimen of *Kuhneon duchyense* is probably an upper molar. If this identification is correct, they point out that the type differs from typical upper molars of *Kuehneotherium* in its relatively higher paracone and absence of parastyle and metastyle. The absence of a parastyle could be the result of postmortem abrasion. This assertion cannot be checked, because the type specimen cannot be found (*fide* Kermack and others, 1968). Kühne's illustration (1950, Fig. 1) shows what might be a low, abraded base of a metastyle. In short, Kermack and others (*ibid.*) recognized three groups of animals: (1)

Kuehneotherium praecursoris, known only from Pontalun Quarry; (2) *Kuhneon duchyense*, known only from Duchy Quarry and regarded as a *nomen vanum*; and (3) a new form from another quarry in Wales that is generically distinct.

Amphidontidae

When the teeth of the "obtuse-angled" symmetrodonts (*Amphidon* and, probably, *Manchurodon*) are seen in occlusal view, the principal cusps are arranged in a triangular pattern with an obtuse angle at its apex. Lower molars of *Amphidon* have been characterized as being functionally monocuspid, with paraconid (*b*) and metaconid (*c*) being little more than breaks in the contour of the slope of the crown (Simpson, 1929). Subsequently, after additional preparation of the type and only specimen, it became clear that the teeth are heavily worn (Crompton and Jenkins, 1968). To what extent the small size of the accessory cusps or the following features are products of attrition remains unknown. Lingual anterior and posterior cingular shelves are present but not connected. The labial surface of the crown has yet to be described. The most posterior cusp shows a talonid-like expansion on at least some molars. Separated from the canine by a diastema are four premolars and four molars.

The type of *Manchurodon* (a fragmentary lower jaw and part of a scapula) was lost during World War II, and the only source of data is the paper by Yabe and Shikama (1938). They state that the molars were functionally monocuspid. The authors mentioned the presence of a posterior cuspule (? = metaconid, *c*), but not a paraconid (*b*). Molars lack a talonid, but the posterior basal cingular cusp is large. A labial basal cingulum is present; the lingual surface of the crown is unknown. A diastema separated the canine from P_1. Yabe and Shikama (1938) reported the dental formula as three premolars and five molars, but Patterson (1956, p. 29), noting a difference in size between the first four and the remaining teeth, suggested that the dentition was made up of four premolars and four molars. If cognizance is taken of the many uncertainties, for example, the complete lack of information about the morphology of the upper dentition, the similarity in the few available characters of molar morphology and dental formulae warrant provisional allocation of *Manchurodon* to the Amphidontidae.

Even though they are morphologically "obtuse-angled'' symmetrodonts, a large number of differences indicate that *Tinodon* and *Eurylambda* represent another lineage, and temporarily can best be classified as ''?Spalacotheriidae *incertae sedis*'' (Patterson, 1956, p. 87). A specimen of what was originally thought to be an amphidontid symmetrodont from the Khovboor local fauna, Mongolia, was named *Gobiodon infinitus* by Trofimov (*in* Beliajeva and others, 1974). The fossil was neither figured nor described, and the taxon must be regarded as a *nomen nudum*. According to a personal communication from B. A. Trofimov to M. C. McKenna and Z. Kielan-Jaworowska (pers. comm., 1974), he no longer allocates this fossil to the Symmetrodonta. However, D. Dashzeveg (pers. comm. to Z. Kielan-Jaworowska, 1977) has recovered material of a symmetrodont from the Khovboor locality.

Spalacotheriidae

Spalacotheriids are the ''acute-angled'' symmetrodonts. On the central upper molars, the crest extending anterolabiad from the high paracone (*A*) frequently carries a small cusp midway between it and the small, labial stylocone (*B*). Near its midpoint the crest extending posterolabiad bears a larger cusp thought to be the ''metacone'' (*C*). This crest terminates labially in a low cusp. The main crests meet at an acute angle and partially enclose a shallow basin. Upper molars lack a lingual cingulum and, differing from those of other symmetrodonts, might have been supported by three roots. On the central lower molars the crests linking protoconid (*a*) with paraconid (*b*) and metaconid (*c*) also intersect at an acute angle. Their crowns are nearly or completely encircled by a basal cingulum that carries a small anterior and slightly larger posterior cusp. As far as is known, the dental formula of spalacotheriids is $I_{3+}^? C_1^1 P_3^3 M_7^7$ (Clemens, 1963).

The only described species of *Peralestes*, *P. longirostris*, is known from fragmentary maxillaries; *Spalacotherium tricuspidens* is represented by several mandibles. Both species are members of the Purbeck local fauna. Though spalacotheriids have the most symmetrical molars among the symmetrodonts, their slight asymmetry was an important consideration in Simpson's (1928) argument that *Peralestes* and *Spalacotherium tricuspidens* are in reality based upon upper and lower molars of the same species. This interpretation has been widely accepted and has not yet been proven false. The final step of formally proposing synonymy, however, has yet to be taken. *Spalacotherium* is the older name.

In terms of degree of morphological modification from a putative kuehneotheriid ancestry, the Spalacotheriidae contain the most advanced forms of the symmetrodonts. In addition to their Late Jurassic records, spalacotheriids are known in three Cretaceous local faunas. *Spalacotherium taylori*, probably of the Valanginian stage, documents the continuation of this generic lineage into the Early Cretaceous of England. *Spalacotheroides* is present in the Greenwood Canyon local fauna, ''Paluxian'' of Texas, and might have been a descendant of *Spalacotherium*. *Symmetrodontoides*, from the local fauna of the Milk River Formation, ''Aquilan,'' of Alberta, Canada, is a highly modified spalacotheriid. It is distinguishable from other genera by the increasingly acute crest arrangement and higher trigonid cusps in passing from M_3 to M_6. Fox (1976) also allocated a mandibular fragment containing an obtuse-angled lower molar, thought to be an M_1, to this species.

?Spalacotheriidae, *incertae sedis*

Eurylambda, based on a single upper molar, and *Tinodon*, known from lower dentitions, are ''obtuse-angled'' symmetrodonts. These mammals were recently studied by Crompton and Jenkins (1967) who, going farther than did Simpson (1925a, 1929), strongly suggested that the two genera are based on elements of the upper and lower dentitions of the same species. On the lower molars, the paraconid (*b*) and metaconid (*c*) were distinct functional cusps. The valley between two anterior cingular cusps (*e* and *f*) received the elongated, talonid-like hypoconulid (*d*) of the preceding molar. A prominent lingual cingulum is present. On the labial side, a small anterior cingulum is developed on M_1, but not on the other molars. Paracone (*A*), stylocone (*B*), and ''metacone'' (*C*) are relatively shorter than principal cusps of the lowers. Small crenulations are present in the parastylar (*E*) and metastylar (*D*) regions. A lingual cingulum is lacking. The labial cingulum is prominent and crenulated, but narrows and is lost toward the posterior end of the crown. Three or four lower premolars are present. Of the four molars, M_4 is the smallest.

Freeman (1976) described a fragmentary symmetrodont molar found in the Bathonian Forest Marble formation at Kirtlington Quarry, England. This fossil shows resemblances to teeth of *Kuehneotherium* and amphilestids. It might represent a symmetrodont in, or related to, the *Tinodon-Eurylambda* lineage.

PHYLOGENY

In comparison with vast samples of *Morganucodon watsoni* from the Rhaeto-Liassic fissure fillings of Wales, *Kuehneotherium* is a rare and poorly represented mammal. Study of its phylogenetic relationships is essentially an exercise in dental anatomy.

A current hypothesis (see Chapter 3) suggests that the molars of *Kuehneotherium* could have been derived from those of a *Thrinaxodon*-like therapsid. The last common ancestor of prototherian and therian mammals is thought to have been an as yet undiscovered morganucodontid in which the main cusps of the upper and lower molars were arranged in straight lines, nearly parallel to the long axes of the jaws. The next grade in dental evolution was achieved by the lingual displacement of the anterior and posterior accessory cusps on the lower molars. A similar but labial displacement of the accessory cusps occurred on the upper molars. The result was a pattern of "reversed triangles" formed by the shearing blades of the molars, a diagnostic feature of primitive therians.

The kuehneotheriids also possess a talonid with a hypoconulid, which fits between two small anterior cingular cusps (*e* and *f*) of the following molar. This interlocking served to prevent food from becoming impacted between the teeth and gums. The interlocking also acted to align the teeth, probably a necessary step in the evolution of precise patterns of occlusion.

Crompton and Jenkins (1967, 1968) and Parrington (1971) stressed that the evolution of the kuehneotheriids from a hypothetical morganucodontid (Fig. 7-4) involved changes in cusp arrangement and shape that maximized length and efficiency of shearing crests and minimized attrition of the teeth. This was not simply a matter of the evolution of the "reversed triangle" pattern of shearing crests by shifting the positions of cusps. In *Morganucodon*, and presumably in the hypothetical morganucodontid common ancestor as well, occluding crests were not precisely matched and the teeth wore quickly.

The occluding crests of the molars of *Kuehneotherium*, like those of later therians, appear to have been formed under much more rigorous genetic control. The fossils do not show the extensive wear found on molars of *Morganucodon*.

Among the other known groups of symmetrodonts, *Tinodon* and *Eurylambda* appear to be most closely related to *Kuehneotherium*. Again stressing the limited knowledge of even the dentitions of these animals, Crompton and Jenkins (1967) cited only a few differences separating the two genera from *Kuehneotherium*. A homologue of the short, anterolabial cingulum of the lower molars of *Kuehneotherium* is present only on M_1 of *Tinodon*. Unlike *Kuehneotherium*, the lingual cingulum of the upper molar of *Eurylambda* is not extensive or well developed. Also, the stylocone (*B*) of *Eurylambda* is smaller and shifted to a more medial position. Finally, the postcanine dentition of *Tinodon* was reduced to P_{3-4}, M_4; the dental formula of *Eurylambda* is unknown. To these points Kermack and others (1968) added the reduction in size of the talonid and "metacone" (*C*).

Patterson (1956) suggested that *Tinodon* and *Eurylambda* be classified as ?Spalacotheriidae *incertae sedis*, and his proposal is adopted here. Subsequent investigation by Crompton and Jenkins (1967) strengthens the interpretation that these animals represent a discrete lineage in which there was little modification of the dentition from the morphology characteristic of *Kuehneotherium*. Considering how little is known of *Tinodon* and *Eurylambda* and their distinctly younger age, recognition of a separate family for these two genera possibly is warranted. However, as McKenna (pers. comm. to Clemens, 1977) has pointed out, on the basis of the limited available data, the morphological differences between these Late Jurassic symmetrodonts and *Kuehneotherium* are not great. They easily could be classified in the same family, for which the name Tinodontidae, Marsh, 1879, is available.

The amphidontids, *Amphidon* and *Manchurodon*, can be interpreted as members of a second lineage. They retain the primitive "obtuse-angled" arrangement of the principal molar cusps. Possibly in parallel with the *Tinodon-Eurylambda* lineage, the number of postcanine teeth was reduced to P_4, M_4. The apparently unique, derived character of the amphidontids is the small size or absence of the paraconid (*b*) and metaconid (*c*). Their small size might be a product of wear on the type and only specimen. On the other hand, if reduction of these cusps occurred during evolution from a kuehneotheriid ancestor, this was a reversal of the general trend among mammals for addition of cusps to the single cusp of the teeth of their primitive reptilian ancestors. Considering the number of instances of dental simplification recorded in Cenozoic evolutionary radiations of mammals, it is not unlikely that a similar path was followed during the Jurassic as well.

Spalacotheriids are regarded as the most derived (advanced) of the symmetrodonts. The total number of postcanine teeth was reduced only slightly, if at all; kuehneotheriids had ten or eleven postcanines while spalacotheriids had ten. However, in *Kuehneotherium* there were but four or five molars while *Spalacotherium* and *Peralestes* possessed seven. Fur-

thermore, spalacotheriid molars were reduced in anteroposterior length and concomitantly developed the acute angle formed by the molar crests. Functionally, they were refined to a simple pair of shearing crests.

Although we have attempted to analyse the interrelationships of these three groups of kuehneotheriid descendants, the data are few and conclusions can easily be skewed by weighting of characters. At present, it appears that the *Tinodon-Eurylambda* lineage was most closely related to the kuehneotheriids, while the amphidontids and spalacotheriids were more specialized groups.

It is possible to postulate evolutionary derivation of the occlusal pattern of the Eupantotheria (Chapter 8), and ultimately those of the Metatheria (Chapter 11) and Eutheria (Chapter 12), from that of

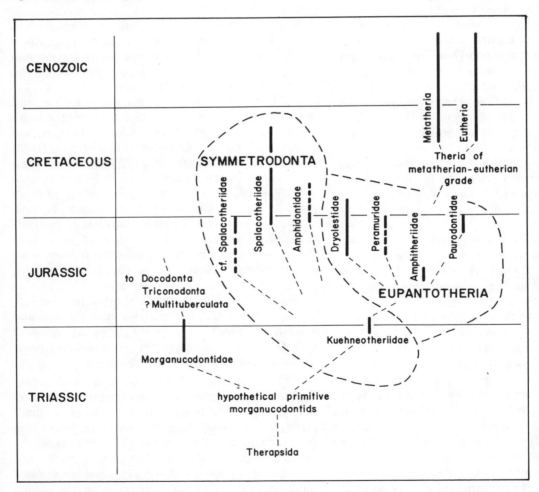

Figure 7-4.   Possible phylogenetic relationships of families of symmetrodonts and eupantotheres.

Kuehneotherium. The eupantotheres are united and distinguished from symmetrodonts by the apomorphic character of an angular process on the mandible. Subsequently, evolution of the dryolestid eupantothere dentiton involved a shifting of the stylocone (*B*) and "metacone" (*C*) of the upper molars and paraconid (*b*) and metaconid (*c*) of the lowers to form a pattern of acute, "reversed triangles," presumably paralleling the evolution of the dentition in spalacotheriids. The talonid was reduced in anteroposterior length, but, in many species, was proportionally broadened transversely. Upper molars were divested of lingual cingula. Dental evolution of the eupantotherian Amphitheriidae and Peramuridae was characterized by enlargement and addition of cusps to the talonid. The upper molars were modified by addition of a metacone and by remodeling of the lingual cingulum. Finally, in paurodont eupantotheres, the length of the molar crowns relative to width was retained or increased. The cusps became lower and frequently are poorly differentiated. In some paurodonts the dental formula is reduced to P_4 M_4 or less.

The basal family of the Symmetrodonta, the Kuehneotheriidae, includes the oldest known therian mammals. Because of their pivotal position with respect to the evolution of the therians, their exact taxonomic assignment has been a matter of discussion. Following Kühne's (1950) description of "Duchy 33" (the type of *Kuhneon*), many paleontologists informally referred to this form as the "Rhaetic symmetrodont." In their study of *Kuehneotherium,* Kermack and others (1968) argued that the evolutionary relationships of the Kuehneotheriidae could best be expressed by classification in the Infraclass Pantotheria that contained but one order, the Eupantotheria. In turn, the Eupantotheria were divided into three suborders, Amphitheria (including Kuehneotheriidae), Dryolestoidea, and Symmetrodonta. Certain characters of *Kuehneotherium* (such as the presence of a talonid and an antero-external cingulum on the lower molars and development of the lingual cingulum, parastyle, and stylocone on the upper molars) were interpreted as attributes primitive to the Eupantotheria, and thus the therians as a whole. They argued (*ibid.*) that these features were modified along different lines in the descendant families of amphitherians, dryolestoids, and symmetrodonts. Their classification shifts the Kuehneotheriidae from a basal position within the Sym-

metrodonta to a similar position in a new grouping, Amphitheria, in which it is allied with three groups of derived therian mammals, the Amphitheriidae, Paurodontidae, and Peramuridae (see Chapter 8). This action has the immediate drawback, which has already caused some misunderstanding, of removing the well-known "Rhaetic symmetrodont" from the Symmetrodonta.

Following long-standing usage, Crompton and Jenkins (1967, 1968, 1973) and Parrington (1971, 1973) considered the Kuehneotheriidae to be classified as symmetrodonts. They emphasized the many points of similarity between the Kuehneotheriidae and symmetrodonts. These similarities appear to be the result of retention or slight modification of the morphology characteristic of *Kuehneotherium*. They also noted the absence of an angular process on the mandibles of *Kuehneotherium* and later symmetrodonts. *Amphitherium* and later eupantotheres (as we use the taxon) possess this process.

The case for reference of the Kuehneotheriidae to the Symmetrodonta is founded on three lines of argument. First is the great morphological similarity between teeth of *Kuehneotherium* and those of later symmetrodonts, especially *Tinodon* and *Eurylambda*. These points of resemblance all appear to be the result of the retention of plesiomorphic features. Secondly, *Kuehneotherium* lacks apomorphic (derived) characters taken as diagnostic of the eupantotheres. For example, *Kuehneotherium* lacks an angular process on the dentary. It also lacks derived features characteristic of the later symmetrodonts. Finally, reference of the Kuehneotheriidae to the Symmetrodonta can be justified on the grounds that it gives stability to the nomenclature and thereby promotes communication.

The classification employed here utilizes the name Eupantotheria to remove the confusing double meaning of Pantotheria employed in earlier classifications (Simpson, 1945). We feel that Romer's (1966) attempt to deal with this problem by use of an Infraclass Trituberculata invokes too many allusions to other meanings. Simpson's (1971) Infraorder Patriotheria adds yet another name to an already confused nomenclatorial problem. We recognize but two orders, Symmetrodonta and Eupantotheria, within the Infraclass Pantotheria.

Following Simpson (1971), the Kuehneotheriidae are provisionally referred to the Symmetrodonta. It must be stressed that this action is not based upon the presence of unique shared derived characters. Currently, the Kuehneotheriidae is based on a single, monotypic genus. As the fossil record of the Late Triassic and Jurassic becomes better known, we suspect that it will document an evolutionary radiation of mammals soon after the origin of the precise, "reversed triangles" pattern of tooth occlusion, which possibly was but one aspect of major physiological and ecological changes (Chapter 3). If this speculation eventually proves true, the earliest radiation of therians (the members of which lack the specializations characteristic of eupantotheres and most symmetrodonts) will warrant classification as a separate order. On strictly cladistic principles McKenna (1975) has already proposed a classification separating the Kuehneotheriidae from the later symmetrodonts and eupantotheres by placing the family in its own Superlegion, Kuehneotheria. This classification is not utilized here.

ECOLOGY

Anatomical data on the Symmetrodonta are essentially limited to information about their dentitions and mandible. Admittedly, one scapula has provisionally been identified as part of the skeleton of *Manchurodon*, but this is hardly basis for a restoration of these early mammals. What can be said is that they were small animals, not as large as the "giant" triconodonts. Their dentitions were adapted to slicing and breaking prey, probably not mastication of vegetable matter. Most likely they were insectivorous.

REFERENCES CITED

Beliajeva, E. I., Trofimov, B. A., and Reshetov, V. J., 1974, General stages in evolution of late Mesozoic and early Tertiary mammalian fauna in central Asia, *in* Kramarenko, N. N., and others, eds., Mesozoic and Cenozoic faunas and biostratigraphy of Mongolia: Moscow, Joint Soviet-Mongol. Paleont. Exped. (Trans., v. 1), p. 19-45 (in Russian with English summary).

Clemens, W. A., 1963, Late Jurassic mammalian fossils in the Sedgwick Museum, Cambridge: Palaeontology, v. 6, p. 373-377.

Clemens, W. A., and Lees, P. M., 1971, A review of English Early Cretaceous mammals, *in* Kermack, D. M., and Kermack, K. A., eds., Early mammals: Linn. Soc. Zool. Jour., v. 50, suppl. 1, p. 117-130.

Crompton, A. W., and Jenkins, F. A., Jr., 1967, American Jurassic symmetrodonts and Rhaetic "pantotheres": Science, v. 155, p. 1006-1009.

———1968, Molar occlusion in Late Triassic mammals: Biol. Rev., v. 43, p. 427-458.

———1973, Mammals from reptiles: A review of mammalian origins: Ann. Rev. Ecol. Syst., v. 4, p. 131-155.

Fox, R. C., 1976, Additions to the mammalian local fauna from the Upper Milk River Formation (Upper Cretaceous), Alberta: Canad. Jour. Earth Sci., v. 13, p. 1105-1118.

Freeman, E. F., 1976, Mammal teeth from the Forest Marble (Middle Jurassic) of Oxfordshire, England: Science, v. 194, p. 1053-1055.

Gill, P., 1974, Resorption of premolars in the early mammal *Kuehneotherium praecursoris*: Arch. Oral Biol., v. 19, p. 327-328.

Kermack, D. M., Kermack, K. A., and Mussett, F., 1968, The Welsh pantothere *Kuehneotherium praecursoris*: Linn. Soc. Zool. Jour., v. 47, p. 407-423.

Kretzoi, M., 1960, Zur Benennung des ältesten Symmetrodonten: Vertebr. Hungarici, v. 2, p. 307-309.

Kühne, W. G., 1950, A symmetrodont tooth from the Rhaeto-Lias: Nature, v. 166, p. 696-697.

McKenna, M. C., 1975, Toward a phylogenetic classification of the Mammalia, *in* Luckett, W. P., and Szalay, F. S., eds., Phylogeny of the primates: New York, Plenum Press, p. 21-46.

Marsh, O. C., 1879a, Additional remains of Jurassic mammals: Amer. Jour. Sci., ser. 3, v. 18, p. 215-216.

———1879b, Notice of new Jurassic mammals: *ibid.*, ser. 3, v. 18, p. 396-398.

———1880, Notice of Jurassic mammals representing two new orders: *ibid.*, ser. 3, v. 20, p. 235-239.

———1887, American Jurassic mammals: *ibid.*, ser. 3, v. 33, p. 326-348.

Mills, J. R. E., 1971, The dentition of *Morganucodon, in* Kermack, D. M., and Kermack, K. A., eds., Early mammals: Linn. Soc. Zool. Jour., v. 50, suppl. 1, p. 29-63.

Owen, R., 1854, On some fossil reptilian and mammalian remains from the Purbecks: Geol. Soc. London Quart. Jour., v. 10, p. 420-433.

_____1871, Monograph of the fossil Mammalia of the Mesozoic formations: Paleontogr. Soc., Monog. 24, 115 p.

Parrington, F. R., 1971, On the Upper Triassic mammals: Roy. Soc. London Philos. Trans., B (Biol. Sci.), v. 261, p. 231-272.

_____1973, The dentitions of the earliest mammals: Linn. Soc. Zool. Jour., v. 52, p. 85-95.

Patterson, B., 1955, A symmetrodont from the Early Cretaceous of northern Texas: Fieldiana (Zool.), v. 37, p. 689-693.

_____1956, Early Cretaceous mammals and the evolution of mammalian molar teeth: Fieldiana (Geol.), v. 13, p. 1-105.

Romer, A. S., 1966, Vertebrate paleontology (3rd ed.): Chicago, Univ. Chicago Press, _ix_ + 468 p.

Simpson, G. G., 1925a, Mesozoic Mammalia II: _Tinodon_ and its allies: Amer. Jour. Sci., ser. 5, v. 10, p. 451-470.

_____1925b, Mesozoic Mammalia III: Preliminary comparison of Jurassic mammals except multituberculates: _ibid._, ser. 5, v. 10, p. 559-569.

_____1928, A catalogue of the Mesozoic Mammalia in the Geological Department of The British Museum: London, Oxford Univ. Press, _x_ + 215 p.

_____1929, American Mesozoic Mammalia: Peabody Mus. (Yale Univ.) Mem., v. 3, pt. 1, Yale Univ. Press, _xv_ + 171 p.

_____1945, The principles of classification and a classification of mammals: Amer. Mus. Nat. Hist. Bull., v. 85, _xvi_ + 350 p.

_____1961, Evolution of Mesozoic mammals, _in_ Vandebroek, G., ed., International colloquium on the evolution of lower and non specialized mammals: Brussels, Kon. Vlaamse Acad. Wetensch., Lett. Schone Kunsten Belgie, pt. 1, p. 57-95.

_____1971, Concluding remarks: Mesozoic mammals revisited, _in_ Kermack, D. M., and Kermack, K. A., eds., Early mammals: Linn. Soc. Zool. Jour., v. 50, suppl. 1, p. 181-198.

Yabe, H., and Shikama, T., 1938, A new Jurassic Mammalia from South Manchuria: Imp. Acad. Tokyo, Proc., v. 14, p. 353-357.

CHAPTER 8

EUPANTOTHERIA

Mary J. Kraus

INTRODUCTION

The Order Eupantotheria is a poorly understood group of small mammals, currently recognized in the fossil record, except for one specimen, only by lower jaws, maxillae, and isolated teeth. The exceptional specimen mentioned above is a nearly complete but as yet undescribed skeleton (see Henkel and Krebs, 1977). The earliest known occurrence of eupantotheres is from Middle Jurassic strata of England, which have produced *Amphitherium, Palaeoxonodon*, and teeth of a dryolestid. Recent discoveries in England, Spain, and Asia have shown that the order survived into the Early Cretaceous. The eupan-

totheres are closely related to the Symmetrodonta and are probably descendants of kuehneotheriid symmetrodonts (but not *Kuehneotherium praecursoris*). The Eupantotheria may well be the most important group of Jurassic mammals from an anthropomorphic point of view, because it is generally agreed that the more advanced therians (*i.e.*, therians of metatherian-eutherian grade, marsupials, and placentals) had their origins within the order.

Because of the nature of the existing fossil record, the general characteristics of the order and of the families are based upon the dentition. Although recent work has added greatly to the knowledge of the Eupantotheria, the following descriptive material, except where stated otherwise, has been gleaned from Simpson's major works on Mesozoic mammals of 1928 and 1929.

DIAGNOSIS

The eupantotheres, with the exception of the paurodontids, have long, slender mandibles, and all members possess an angular process, a character not seen in the symmetrodonts. Simpson (1961) observed that the incisors, premolars, and canine are not distinguishing features, and resemble those of primitive metatherians and eutherians. Incisors are known from very few specimens, and in these they are small and unspecialized; the general formula is possibly four upper and four lower incisors. The piercing and trenchant premolars are simple and never molariform; they usually consist of one main cusp followed posteriorly by a small heel. The upper molars have two anterior roots and a single posterior root. Two principal cusps are present, a lingually positioned paracone and a stylocone on the buccal portion of the tooth (see Chapter 9). Although the general pattern includes two or more additional cusps, a protocone is absent from all known upper molars. The upper molars are much wider than the lowers, quite unlike the condition in symmetrodonts in which they are equivalent in width. The double-rooted lower molars, except for those of *Peramus*, have four main cusps. The trigonid is usually asymmetrical, and is separated from the talonid by a crest joining the protoconid to the metaconid. The simple talonid is not fully basined and has but one cusp, the hypoconulid. Epipubic ("marsupial") bones are present on the only known skeleton.

SYSTEMATICS

The Order Pantotheria was named and described by Marsh in 1880. Simpson, in his 1945 classification, grouped the orders Pantotheria and Symmetrodonta under Infraclass Pantotheria. Although he regretted the repetitive use of the name "Pantotheria," Simpson felt it to be the most suitable term for the infraclass (for full discussion, see Simpson, 1945). To alleviate the ensuing confusion, Kermack and Mussett (1958) proposed retain-

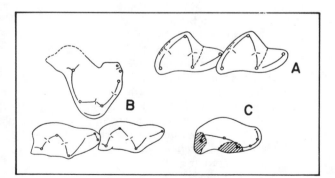

Figure 8-1. Schematic occlusal views of eupantotherian dentitions (not to common scales): *A*, two right lower molars of *Amphitherium prevostii*; *B*, molars of *Peramus tenuirostris*, left M² (above), right M₃₋₄ (below); and *C*, the Porto Pinheiro lower molariform tooth (anterior to left, labial up). (Reproduced, with permission, from Clemens, "Mesozoic mammalian evolution," **Annual Review of Ecology and Systematics, Volume 1. Copyright © 1970 by Annual Reviews Inc. All rights reserved)**

ing the Infraclass Pantotheria and substituted Eupantotheria as the ordinal name. Simpson (1971) later suggested the adoption of Infraclass Patriotheria and retention of the Order Pantotheria. Confusion still exists in the literature (*e.g.*, Crompton and Jenkins, 1967, refer to "the so called 'pantotheres' "). However, the use of Order Eupantotheria and Infraclass Pantotheria has become widespread and will be followed in the present chapter.

The following classification (Table 8-1), with one exception, is that of Butler and others (1967). The "unnamed Rhaetic material" that they tentatively assigned to the Eupantotheria has since been described as *Kuehneotherium* by Kermack and others (1968), and was classified as a symmetrodont by Crompton and Jenkins (1968; see Chapter 7).

Amphitheriidae

The Amphitheriidae are represented by a single genus, *Amphitherium*, which is known only from lower jaws and lower teeth (see Mills, 1964, and Fig. 8-1). *Amphitherium* possessed at least eleven postcanine teeth, five of which are considered to be premolars (W. A. Clemens, pers. comm., 1977). The last premolar is nearly equal in crown height to the first molar. The protoconid is the most prominent molar cusp and, together with the metaconid and the paraconid, forms a nearly equilateral triangle. The unicuspid talonid is fairly elongate, more so than that of *Kuehneotherium*. The two molar roots are about equal in anteroposterior diameter.

Paurodontidae

The Paurodontidae share several dental characteristics with *Amphitherium*. The roots of the lower molars are nearly equal in anteroposterior diameter, the trigonid is elongate, and the most prominent cusp is the protoconid. Kühne (1968) suggested, however, that paurodontids may be distinguished from other eupantotheres on the basis of tooth morphology. They have a stout and short lower jaw and long talonid. The talonid is shorter anteroposteriorly than that seen in *Amphitherium*, but is more elongate than those of either dryolestids or symmetrodonts. The feature that had traditionally been considered characteristic of paurodontids is the possession of no more than eight postcanine teeth (characteristic, for example, of the paurodontids from the Morrison Formation). Kühne (1968), however, reported the discovery of older specimens from Guimarota, Portugal, that have paurodont-like teeth, but as many as ten postcanine teeth and no fewer than eight. Clemens (1970) suggested that one trend in the evolutionary history of the Paurodontidae was reduction through time of the number of cheek teeth. These new finds from Portugal strongly suggest that the diversity of paurodontids in par-ticular and eupantotheres in general was considerably greater than expected from study of the Morrison-Purbeck samples, and that the family-level systematics is in great need of revision.

Peramuridae

Peramus had been classified for many years as a paurodontid. Results of further study (Kretzoi, 1960,

TABLE 8-1   CLASSIFICATION OF EUPANTOTHERIA

Infraclass Pantotheria Simpson, 1929
  Order Eupantotheria Kermack and Mussett, 1958
    Family Amphitheriidae Owen, 1846
      Amphitherium de Blainville, 1838
        A. prevostii (von Meyer, 1832)
    Family Peramuridae Kretzoi, 1960
      Peramus Owen, 1871
        P. tenuirostris Owen, 1871
      cf. *Peramus* Kühne, 1968
    Family ?Peramuridae
      Brancatherulum Dietrich, 1927
        B. tendagurense Dietrich, 1927
      Palaeoxonodon Freeman, 1976
        P. ooliticus Freeman, 1976
      undescribed new genus and species (pers. comm.
        to Z. Kielan-Jaworowska from D. Dashzeveg,
        1977)
    Family Paurodontidae Marsh, 1887
      Paurodon Marsh, 1887
        P. valens Marsh, 1887
      Archaeotrigon Simpson, 1927a
        A. brevimaxillus Simpson, 1927a
        A. distagmus Simpson, 1929
      Tathiodon Simpson, 1927b
        T. agilis (Simpson, 1927a)
      Araeodon Simpson, 1937
        A. intermissus Simpson, 1937
    Family Dryolestidae Marsh, 1879b
      Dryolestes Marsh, 1878
        D. priscus Marsh, 1878
      Amblotherium Owen, 1871
        A. nanum (Owen, 1871)
        A. pusillum (Owen, 1871)
        A. gracilis (Marsh, 1879a)
        A. debilis Simpson, 1927a
      Peraspalax Owen, 1871
        P. talpoides Owen, 1871
      Phascolestes Owen, 1871

        P. mustelula (Owen, 1871)
      Kurtodon Osborn, 1887
        K. pusillus Osborn, 1888
      Melanodon Simpson, 1927a
        M. oweni Simpson, 1927a
        M. goodrichi Simpson, 1929
        M. cf. *goodrichi* Simpson, 1929
        M. hodsoni Clemens and Lees, 1971
      Euthlastus Simpson, 1927a
        E. cordiformis Simpson, 1927a
      Herpetairus Simpson, 1927a
        H. arcuatus (Marsh, 1879b)
        ?*H. humilis* Simpson, 1929
      Herpetairus or *Melanodon* Simpson, 1929
      Kepolestes Simpson, 1927a
        K. coloradensis Simpson, 1927a
      Laolestes Simpson, 1927a
        L. eminens Simpson, 1927a
        L. grandis Simpson, 1929
        ?*Laolestes* sp. indet. Simpson, 1929
      Malthacolestes Simpson, 1927a
        M. osborni Simpson, 1927a
      Miccylotyrans Simpson, 1927a
        M. minimus Simpson, 1927a
      Pelicopsis Simpson, 1927a
        P. dubius Simpson, 1927a
      Crusafontia Henkel and Krebs, 1969
        C. cuencana Henkel and Krebs, 1969
      two lower molars, unnamed; Freeman, 1976
    Eupantotheria, *incertae sedis*
      Butlerigale Kühne, 1968
        B. sp. Kühne, 1968
      Guimarota Kühne, 1968
        G. freyi Kühne, 1968
      Simpsonodon Kühne, 1968
        S. splendens Kühne, 1968
      lower molar, unnamed; Krusat, 1969
      upper molar, unnamed; Freeman, 1976

Clemens and Mills, 1971), however, supplied adequate justification to place the genus in a separate family, the Peramuridae. Clemens and Mills (1971) demonstrated that *Peramus* has several characters that set it apart from all other eupantotheres (Figs. 8-1 and 8-2). The talonids of M₂ and M₃ have both a hypoconid and an entoconid, and the talonids are incipiently basined. The last upper and lower premolars have a markedly greater crown height than the preceding premolars and the first molars. Both the upper and the lower first molars are noticeably different morphologically from the other molars in that: (1) cusps of the trigon and the trigonid are either reduced or missing; (2) the talonid is simple and unicuspid; and (3) M¹ has only two roots. M² and M³ of *Peramus* possess a broad stylar shelf, and a small stylocone joined to the paracone by a paracrista. Three additional cusps are placed on the labial portions of these molars. Clemens and Mills (1971) regarded the cusp distal to the paracone as a metacone and suggested that it is a neomorph added to the molar pattern typical of *Kuehneotherium*. Crompton (1971) considered the cusp posterolabial to the metacone as cusp "*c*," homologous with the similarly designated cusp in *Kuehneotherium*. He also considered the disto-buccal cusp a metastylid. The postcanine formula given by Clemens and Mills (1971) is P⁴M⁴ (but see Chapter 9 for alternate interpretation).

In addition to the material described and reviewed by Clemens and Mills are several specimens from Guimarota that Kühne (1968) identified as "cf. *Peramus*." The identification was based in part upon the presence of a ventrally deflected (docodont-like) angular process, a feature found in common to *Brancatherulum, Peramus*, cf. *Peramus, Archaeotrigon*, and *Amphitherium* (see Kühne, 1968). Kühne believed this to be a feature characteristic of the Peramuridae and Amphitheriidae that is not seen in the Dryolestidae (see below). Clemens and Mills (1971) concluded that although cf. *Peramus* bears some similarity to *Peramus* and was found in older strata, the evidence did not necessarily indicate that cf. *Peramus* was ancestral to *Peramus*.

Recent work by Freeman (1976) on fossils from the Middle Jurassic of England has uncovered new material provisionally assigned to the Peramuridae. He described a new genus (*Palaeoxonodon*) on the basis of a lower molar. Other specimens referred to the genus include a second partial lower molar and several upper molars. The upper molars possess a prominent paracone, a smaller metacone, and a cusp that Freeman believed to correspond with cusp "*c*" of Crompton (1971). Also present is a stylocone, larger than that seen in *Peramus*. The protoconid of the lower molar is tall. The lower molar of *Palaeoxonodon* is of special interest because its talonid is incipiently basined. Two very small protuberances lie on the disto-lingual margin of the talonid, and Freeman suggested that these may represent an incipient hypoconulid and entoconid. Freeman found the talonid structure to be intermediate between the simple, unicuspid talonid of *Amphitherium* and the tricuspid, incipiently basined condition seen in *Peramus*.

A second genus tentatively referred to the Peramuridae is *Brancatherulum* (see Dietrich, 1927), represented by a single edentulous jaw from Tendaguru in Tanzania. Simpson (1929) felt that this jaw bore similarities to *Peramus*, and originally classified *Brancatherulum*, with *Peramus*, as a paurodontid. A lower jaw of a mammal showing some similarities to *Peramus* and *Amphitherium* was discovered at the Early Cretaceous fossil locality near Khovboor, Mongolia, and is being studied by D. Dashzeveg (see below).

Dryolestidae

The most diverse group, and the only eupantotherian family known to have survived into the Early Cretaceous, is the Dryolestidae. The dryolestid mandible is similar to that of *Amphitherium* in having an angular process, but its shape and the construction of the molars are quite different (Fig. 8-3). The two lower molar roots are unequal in diameter (the anterior is larger) and the talonid is reduced in comparison with that of *Amphitherium*. The metaconid is equal or nearly equal in height with the protoconid, and the trigonid has been compressed anteroposteriorly with a resultant sharpening of the labial angle. Dryolestid upper molars are much broader than long. The paracone is the most prominent cusp, but a distinct stylocone as well as two other stylar cusps are present. Data on the microstructure of enamel are presented in Chapter 11.

Henkel and Krebs (1969) observed that Jurassic species tended to reduce and lose the lingual cingulum of the lower molars. This cingulum reappears in Cretaceous dryolestids, but it is unclear whether this represents evolutionary reacquisition or

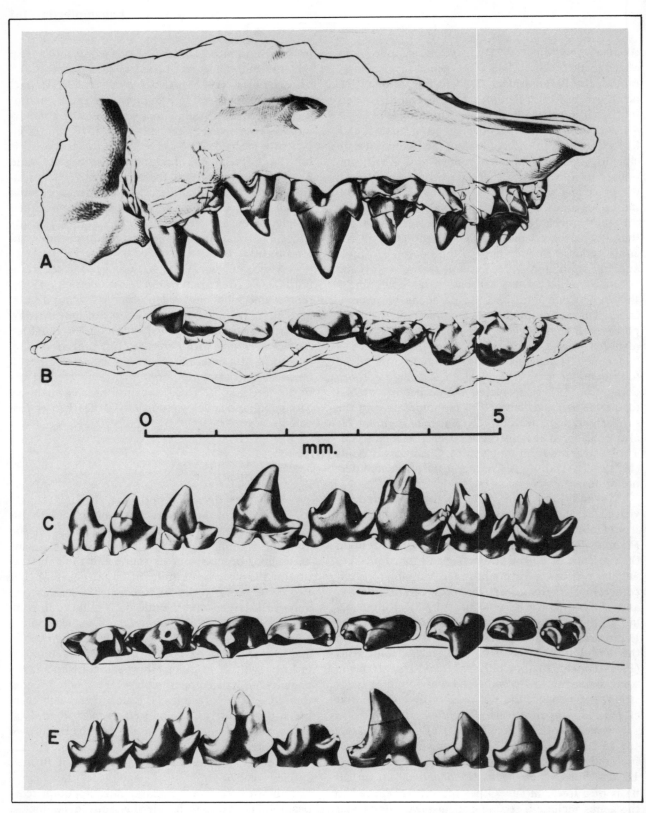

Figure 8-2. Dentition of *Peramus tenuirostris*: *A* and *B*, left maxilla containing P^{1-4} and M^{1-4} (*A*, labial view, *B*, occlusal view); *C-E*, left mandible with P_{1-4} and M_{1-4} (*C*, labial view, *D*, occlusal view, *E*, lingual view). (From Clemens and Mills, 1971; reproduced with permission of Trustees, British Museum [Natural History])

an accident of sampling of lineages in which a plesiomorphic trait had been retained. Simpson (1928, 1929) noted that there are usually twelve upper and lower postcanine teeth in the dryolestids. Krebs (1971), in his comparison of the Kimmeridgian dryolestids with the Early Cretaceous *Crusafontia*, found that eight molars were seen in the Late Jurassic species and were retained in *Crusafontia*. He viewed this ". . . as a primitive feature inherited from the therapsids of the Triassic" (1971, p. 89).

Several additional features possessed by the dryolestids have been described by Krebs (1971). Examination of the Guimarota (Kimmeridgian) dryolestids revealed what he judged to be evidence for the presence into adulthood of coronoid and splenial bones, as well as a Meckelian cartilage. Krebs did not, however, find evidence that they possessed a reptilian type of jaw articulation. He found no traces of these features in the Early Cretaceous genus *Crusafontia*. Krebs also observed that the dryolestids paralleled more advanced therians in their development and refinement of the process of thegosis.

The Porto Pinheiro Molar

One final and interesting eupantothere is represented by a single lower molariform tooth from Kimmeridgian rocks of Porto Pinheiro, Portugal, described by Krusat (1969). This tooth has a trigonid resembling that of *Amphitherium* and *Peramus*, and a large talonid with three cusps (Fig. 8-1). The talonid basin is deep and well developed and, until the discovery of *Palaeoxonodon* by Freeman, was thought to represent the earliest occurrence of a distinctly basined talonid.

The incipient basin of the talonid of *Peramus* (Fig. 8-1) is placed lingual to the cristid obliqua and probably functioned to drain food into the mouth, to protect the gums from the upper teeth, or both. The

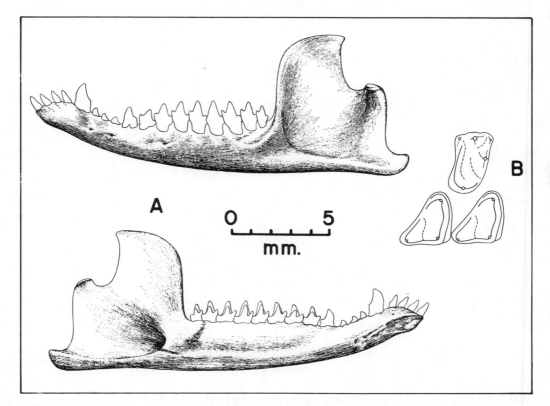

Figure 8-3.   Dryolestidae: *A*, **restoration of left mandible of** *Crusafontia cuencana*, **labial view above, lingual view below (from Krebs, 1971; reproduced with permission of the Linnean Society, Academic Press Inc. [London] Limited); and** *B*, **schematic occlusal view of molars of a "typical" dryolestid (anterior to left, labial up), upper left molar above, two right lower molars below (reproduced, with permission, from Clemens, "Mesozoic mammalian evolution," Annual Review of Ecology and Systematics, Volume 1. Copyright © 1970 by Annual Reviews Inc. All rights reserved). Scale applies only to** *A* **.**

basin of the Porto Pinheiro molar, however, is labial to the cristid obliqua and probably accommodated a very large paracone.

PHYLOGENY

Because of the small number of eupantotheres known (Table 8-2), it is difficult to elucidate phylogenetic relationships within the group. Most authors seem to agree that eupantotheres could have been derived from Rhaeto-Liassic symmetrodonts of the Kuehneotheriidae. Relationships among the var-

ious eupantothere families and genera, however, are far from clear.

Amphitherium is the earliest known eupantothere, but it seems probable that the genus was ancestral to no other known family. Henkel and Krebs (1969) concluded on the basis of dental differences that *Amphitherium* was not ancestral to the dryolestids. Furthermore, the discovery by Freeman (1976) of two dryolestid molars from upper Bathonian strata indicates that the dryolestids were practically contemporaneous with *Amphitherium*. Crompton and Jenkins (1968) suggested that the dryolestids and the amphitheriids had separate

TABLE 8-2   AGE AND OCCURRENCE OF GENERA OF EUPANTOTHERIA

GENUS	OCCURRENCE	AGE OR STAGE
Amphitherium	Stonesfield Slate, Oxfordshire, England	Bathonian
Palaeoxonodon	Forest Marble, Oxfordshire, England	late Bathonian
unnamed dryolestid and eupantothere	Forest Marble, Oxfordshire, England (Freeman, 1976)	late Bathonian
Guimarota	Guimarota coal pits, Guimarota, Portugal	?early Kimmeridgian
Simpsonodon	Guimarota coal pits, Guimarota, Portugal	?early Kimmeridgian
cf. *Peramus*	Guimarota coal pits, Guimarota, Portugal	?early Kimmeridgian
unnamed genus	Guimarota coal pits, Guimarota, Portugal (Henkel and Krebs, 1977)	?early Kimmeridgian
unnamed genus	Porto Pinheiro, Lourinhã, Portugal (Krusat, 1969)	?late Kimmeridgian
Amblotherium	Morrison Fm., Como Bluff, Wyoming, U.S.A.	Late Jurassic
	Lulworth Beds, Durlston Bay, England	Volgian
Araeodon	Morrison Fm., Como Bluff, Wyoming, U.S.A.	Late Jurassic
Archaeotrigon	Morrison Fm., Como Bluff, Wyoming, U.S.A.	Late Jurassic
Brancatherulum	Tendaguru Beds, Tanzania, Africa	late Kimmeridgian
Dryolestes	Morrison Fm., Como Bluff, Wyoming, U.S.A.	Late Jurassic
Euthlastus	Morrison Fm., Como Bluff, Wyoming, U.S.A.	Late Jurassic
Herpetairus	Morrison Fm., Como Bluff, Wyoming, U.S.A.	Late Jurassic
Kepolestes	Morrison Fm., Garden Park, Colorado, U.S.A.	Late Jurassic
Kurtodon	Lulworth Beds, Durlston Bay, England	Volgian
Laolestes	Morrison Fm., Como Bluff, Wyoming, U.S.A.	Late Jurassic
Malthacolestes	Morrison Fm., Como Bluff, Wyoming, U.S.A.	Late Jurassic
Miccylotyrans	Morrison Fm., Como Bluff, Wyoming, U.S.A.	Late Jurassic
Paurodon	Morrison Fm., Como Bluff, Wyoming, U.S.A.	Late Jurassic
Pelicopsis	Morrison Fm., Como Bluff, Wyoming, U.S.A.	Late Jurassic
Peramus	Lulworth Beds, Durlston Bay, England	Volgian
Peraspalax	Lulworth Beds, Durlston Bay, England	Volgian
Phascolestes	Lulworth Beds, Durlston Bay, England	Volgian
Tathiodon	Morrison Fm., Como Bluff, Wyoming, U.S.A.	Late Jurassic
Melanodon	Morrison Fm., Como Bluff, Wyoming, U.S.A.	Late Jurassic
	Wadhurst Clay, Hastings, England	Valanginian
Crusafontia	Uña lignite mine, Uña, Spain	Early Cretaceous
unnamed ?peramurid	Fm.?, Khovboor, near Guchin Us, province (aymak) of Arvaykher, Mongolian People's Republic	?Aptian or ?Albian

origins from the Kuehneotheriidae, and demonstrated that the morphology of lower molars both of *Amphitherium* and of typical dryolestids could independently have been derived from that of *Kuehneotherium* (see Chapter 7). *Amphitherium* has an enlarged talonid. The dryolestids, although possessing a small and simple talonid, show specializations of it beyond the condition seen in *Kuehneotherium* in significant transverse widening and anteroposterior shortening.

Clemens and Mills (1971) also excluded *Amphitherium* from the likelihood of ancestry to *Peramus*. Their conclusion was based upon differences in size and morphology of lower premolars and molars. The cusps of the first molar of *Peramus* are markedly lower than either the towering principal cusp of the preceding premolar or the cusps of the second molar. Clemens and Mills hypothesized that the greater height of the principal cusp of the last premolar, relative to the cusps of the first molar, probably was a primitive trait. The cusps of the first molar of *Amphitherium* are slightly taller than those of the preceding premolar, a specialization probably ruling it out of the ancestry of *Peramus*. Clemens and Mills also thought that the unusual first molar of *Peramus* could more easily have been derived from *Kuehneotherium*-like molars than from those of *Amphitherium*. Freeman (1976) argued that the presence

of the ?peramurid *Palaeoxonodon* in Middle Jurassic rocks eliminates the likelihood of *Amphitherium* from the ancestry of the Peramuridae. Such an argument rests upon the actual nature and affinities of *Palaeoxonodon*. That is, was it truly a peramurid, or not? It would also assume that *Amphitherium* could not have been a relict descendant of a more primitive stock. It is possible, however, that an earlier, as yet undiscovered amphitheriid was ancestral to the peramurids. It is also possible that the amphitheriids were ancestral to the paurodontids. Such a relationship was suggested as early as 1928 by Simpson, based upon dental similarities between the two groups. I visualize the relationships seen in Figure 8-4 among the eupantotherian families. The system agrees in most respects with the ideas of Hopson and Crompton (1969).

The relationships of the eupantotheres to later mammals are as unclear as those within the group. It is generally agreed that more advanced therians had their origins somewhere within the Eupantotheria. Which group was actually ancestral to marsupials and placentals, however, is a difficult question. Patterson (1956) presumed the dryolestids to be the group most probably ancestral to more advanced therians, but most authors now believe this highly unlikely. Krebs (1971) concluded that specializations within the dryolestid lines (*e.g.*, anteroposterior com-

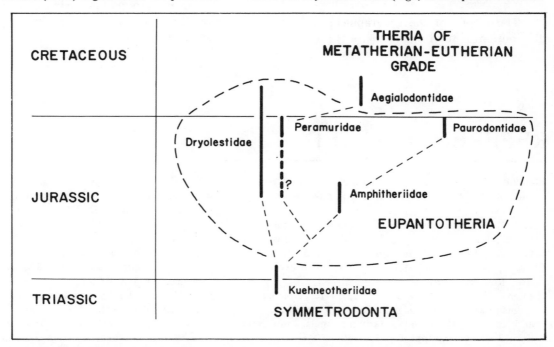

Figure 8-4.   Possible phylogenetic relationships among eupantotherian families.

pression of the molars, sharpening of the labial angle of the trigonid, and the small, unicuspid talonid) disqualify them as possible ancestors. The paurodontids also appear unrelated to more advanced therians. Patterson (1956) judged the trigonids of paurodontids to be too long and narrow to have given rise to the animals represented by the "Trinity therian molars" (see Chapter 10). Furthermore, the paurodontid talonid shows no great elongation.

Clemens and Mills (1971) suggested that *Peramus* gave rise neither to *Aegialodon* nor to the more advanced therians. *Peramus* is disqualified as a probable ancestor on the basis of the small size of the stylocone and parastyle, which appear to be apomorphic features. The development of the talonid seen in *Peramus*, however, is a logical forerunner of that seen in *Aegialodon* and later therians (see Chapter 10). Kermack and others (1965) have indicated that the actual ancestor of *Aegialodon* doubtlessly showed similarity to *Peramus*. Clemens and Mills (1971) concluded that Cretaceous advanced therians probably did arise from some sort of peramurid. *Peramus* itself may not have been in the direct line to metatherians and eutherians, but it does provide clues to the probable appearance of such an ancestor.

ECOLOGY

The record of the geographical and temporal distribution of the Eupantotheria is poor, and even less is known about their general appearance and habits. All were small animals; many were shrew-sized, others slightly larger. Their shearing teeth suggest a carnivorous or omnivorous diet. Simpson (1933) suggested that eupantotheres subsisted primarily on invertebrates, as do many living mammals. The only known skeleton shows the animal to have had well-developed claws and a strong tail, suggesting the possibility of an arboreal existence (Henkel and Krebs, 1977). Beyond that, however, it would be mere speculation at present to say anything concerning eupantotherian locomotion, mode of reproduction, and life habits.

EDITORS' NOTE:

After M. J. Kraus prepared the manuscript of this chapter the editors learned of an important discovery of a new genus of eupantothere. The fossil, a lower jaw containing P_2 through M_2, was found by Demberlyin Dashzeveg (pers. comm. to Z. Kielan-Jaworowska, 1977) at Khovboor (Chapter 2), a Mongolian locality thought to be of Aptian or Albian age. This new eupantothere is neither a paurodont nor a dryolestid but shows some significant similarities to *Peramus* and *Amphitherium*. Possibly it documents another lineage in a eupantotherian radiation that produced the first mammals with tribosphenic dentitions.

REFERENCES CITED

Blainville, H. H., de, 1838, Doutes sur le pretendu Didelphe de Stonesfield: Acad. Sci. Paris C. R., v. 7, p. 402-418.

Butler, P. M., and others, 1967, Mammalia, *in* Harland, W. B., and others, eds., The fossil record: London, Geol. Soc. London, Burlington House, p. 763-787.

Clemens, W. A., 1970, Mesozoic mammalian evolution: Ann. Rev. Ecol. Syst., v. 1, p. 357-390.

Clemens, W. A., and Lees, P. M., 1971, A review of English Early Cretaceous mammals, *in* Kermack, D. M., and Kermack, K. A., eds., Early mammals: Linn. Soc. Zool. Jour., v. 50, suppl. 1, p. 117-130.

Clemens, W. A., and Mills, J. R. E., 1971, Review of *Peramus tenuirostris* Owen (Eupantotheria, Mammalia):

Brit. Mus. Nat. Hist. Bull. (Geol.), v. 20, p. 87-113.

Crompton, A. W., 1971, The origin of the tribosphenic molar, *in* Kermack, D. M., and Kermack, K. A., eds., Early mammals: Linn. Soc. Zool. Jour., v. 50, suppl. 1, p. 65-87.

Crompton, A. W., and Jenkins, F. A., Jr., 1967, American Jurassic symmetrodonts and Rhaetic "pantotheres": Science, v. 155, p. 1006-1009.

———1968, Molar occlusion in Late Triassic mammals: Biol. Rev., v. 43, p. 427-458.

Dietrich, W. O., 1927, *Brancatherulum* n. g., ein Proplacentalier aus dem obersten Jura des Tendaguru in Deutsch-Ostafrika: Zbl. Min. Geol. Paläont. (B), 1927, p. 423-426.

Freeman, E. F., 1976, Mammal teeth from the Forest Marble (Middle Jurassic) of Oxfordshire, England: Science, v. 194, p. 1053-1055.

Henkel, S., and Krebs, B., 1969, Zwei Säugetier-Unterkiefer aus der Unteren Kreide von Uña (Prov. Cuenca, Spanien): N. Jahrb. Geol. Paläont. Monatsh., 1969, p. 449-463.

———1977, Der erste Fund eines Säugetier-Skelettes aus der Jura-Zeit: Umschau in Wissenschaft und Technik 77, p. 217-218.

Hopson, J. A., and Crompton, A. W., 1969, Origin of mammals, in Dobzhansky, T., Hecht, M. K., and Steere, W. C., eds., Evolutionary biology: New York, Appleton-Century-Crofts, v. 3, p. 15-72.

Kermack, D. M., Kermack, K. A., and Mussett, F., 1968, The Welsh pantothere, *Kuehneotherium praecursoris*: Linn. Soc. Zool. Jour., v. 47, p. 407-423.

Kermack, K. A., and Mussett, F., 1958, The jaw articulation of the Docodonta and the classification of Mesozoic mammals: Roy. Soc. London Proc., B (Biol.), v. 149, p. 204-215.

Kermack, K. A., Lees, P. M., and Mussett, F., 1965, *Aegialodon dawsoni*, a new trituberculosectorial tooth from the lower Wealden: *ibid.*, v. 162, p. 535-554.

Krebs, B., 1971, Evolution of the mandible and lower dentition in dryolestids (Pantotheria, Mammalia), in Kermack, D. M., and Kermack, K. A., eds., Early mammals: Linn. Soc. Zool. Jour., v. 50, suppl.,1, p. 89-102.

Kretzoi, M., 1960, Zur Benennung des ältesten Symmetrodonten: Vertebr. Hungarici, v. 2, p. 307-309.

Krusat, G., 1969, Ein Pantotheria-Molar mit dreispitzigem Talonid aus dem Kimmeridge von Portugal: Paläont. Zeit., v. 43, p. 52-56.

Kühne, W. G., 1968, Kimeridge [sic] mammals and their bearing on the phylogeny of the Mammalia, in Drake, E. T., ed., Evolution and environment: New Haven, Yale Univ. Press, p. 109-123.

Marsh, O. C., 1878, Fossil mammal from the Jurassic of the Rocky Mountains: Amer. Jour. Sci., ser. 3, v. 15, p. 459.

———1879a, Notice of a new Jurassic mammal: *ibid.*, ser. 3, v. 18, p. 60-61.

———1879b, Notice of new Jurassic mammals: *ibid.*, ser. 3, v. 18, p. 396-398.

———1880, Notice of Jurassic mammals representing two new orders: *ibid.*, ser. 3, v. 20, p. 235-239.

———1887, American Jurassic mammals: *ibid.*, ser. 3, v. 33, p. 326-348.

Meyer, H., von, 1832, Palaeologica, zur Geschichte der Erde und ihrer Geschöpfe: Frankfurt, a.M., *xi* + 560 p.

Mills, J. R. E., 1964, The dentitions of *Peramus* and *Amphitherium*: Linn. Soc. London Proc., v. 175, p. 117-133.

Osborn, H. F., 1887, On the structure and classification of the Mesozoic Mammalia: Acad. Nat. Sci. Philadelphia Proc., 1887, p. 282-292.

———1888, On the structure and classification of the Mesozoic Mammalia: Acad. Nat. Sci. Philadelphia Jour., v. 9, p. 186-264.

Owen, R., 1846, A history of British fossil mammals and birds: London, *xlvi* + 560 p.

———1871, Monograph of the fossil Mammalia of the Mesozoic formations: Paleontogr. Soc. Monog. 24, 115 p.

Patterson, B., 1956, Early Cretaceous mammals and the evolution of mammalian molar teeth: Fieldiana (Geol.), v. 13, p. 1-105.

Simpson, G. G., 1927a, Mesozoic Mammalia. VI: Genera of Morrison pantotheres: Amer. Jour. Sci., ser. 5, v. 13, p. 409-416.

———1927b, *Tathiodon*, new genus, to replace *Tanaodon* Simpson non Kirk: *ibid.*, ser. 5, v. 14, p. 71.

———1928, A catalogue of the Mesozoic Mammalia in the Geological Department of The British Museum: London, Oxford Univ. Press, *x* + 215 p.

———1929, American Mesozoic Mammalia: Peabody Mus. (Yale Univ.) Mem., v. 3, pt. 1, Yale Univ. Press, *xv* + 171 p.

———1933, Paleobiology of Jurassic mammals: Palaeobiologica, v. 5, p. 127-158.

———1937, A new Jurassic mammal: Amer. Mus. Novitates, no. 943, 6 p.

———1945, The principles of classification and a classification of mammals: Amer. Mus. Nat. Hist. Bull., v. 85, *xvi* + 350 p.

———1961, Evolution of Mesozoic mammals, in Vandebroek, G., ed., International colloquium on the evolution of lower and non specialized mammals: Brussels, Kon. Vlaamse Acad. Wetensch., Lett. Schone Kunsten Belgie, pt. 1, p. 57-95.

———1971, Concluding remarks: Mesozoic mammals revisited, in Kermack, D. M., and Kermack, K. A., eds., Early mammals: Linn. Soc. Zool. Jour., v. 50, suppl. 1, p. 181-198.

CHAPTER 9

ORIGIN OF THE TRIBOSPHENIC MOLAR AND METATHERIAN AND EUTHERIAN DENTAL FORMULAE

Thomas M. Bown

Mary J. Kraus

INTRODUCTION

The first mammals were probably derived from dentally and skeletally advanced mammal-like reptiles (cynodont therapsids) in the Late Triassic, about 200 million years before present. Romer (1961) believed that the persistent development of complex "molar" crowns in cynodonts suggests that the dental structure and evolution in this group of reptiles is most compatible with that expected for reptilian forerunners of the Mammalia.

Advanced cynodonts typically possessed a heterodont dentition that was differentiated into "incisor," "canine," and postcanine elements. The incisor count was characteristically 4/3-4, the canines one or two, and the postcanine teeth never exceeded fourteen in number. Rarely, some cynodonts possessed one or two precanine teeth in the maxillary bone. The cynodonts and bauriomorphs were the only advanced therapsids known to develop a variety of crown forms on the postcanine teeth (see Romer, 1961, Figs. 16-18). Crown patterns on the cheek teeth of the bauriomorphs, however, were rapidly worn away during the lives of these animals, whereas those developed on the cheek teeth of the cynodonts were commonly retained into advanced stages of wear. The crown patterns of certain advanced cynodonts were, moreover, developed along convergent lines with those of some later mammals. For example, certain of the narrow, shearing postcanine teeth of the aberrant cynodonts *Dromatherium, Tricuspes,* and *Microconodon* resemble cheek teeth of certain triconodonts.

Upper and lower postcanine teeth in cynodonts did not occlude, but instead formed batteries of crushing or shearing teeth that held and partially pulverized food, or cut food placed obliquely between them. Although the upper and lower postcanine teeth in the earliest known mammals did occlude, they had not yet developed the complex of cusps and cristae that typify the tribosphenic molars of the earliest metatherian and eutherian mammals.

As noted by Hiiemäe (1976), the fully-formed tribosphenic molar probably required an additional 100 million years to develop.

The earliest mammals therefore probably evolved from some hierarchy of cynodont reptiles. Because those cynodonts which are dentally closest to early mammals (*e.g.*, *Thrinaxodon*) possessed more than seven loci for postcanine teeth, it is clear that considerable tooth loss occurred at one or several points in the reptile-to-mammal transition. Although part of this loss certainly occurred in the evolution of early mammal lineages, fossil evidence is not yet sufficient to infer when and within which groups most tooth reduction took place. It therefore

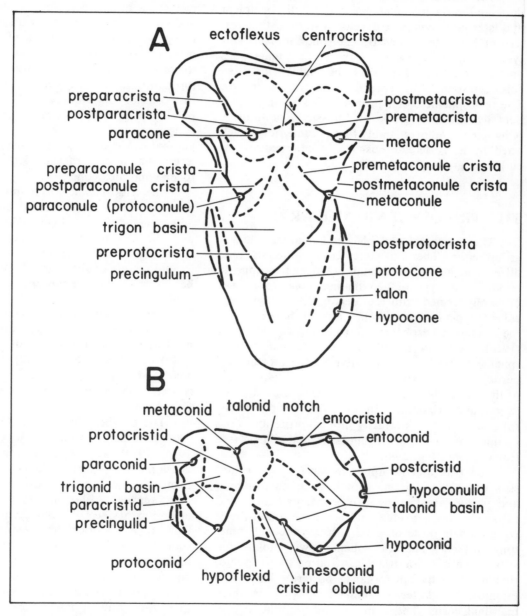

Figure 9-1.   Important terminology used for generalized tribosphenic (tuberculosectorial) molar teeth, as seen in occlusal view. *A*, **upper, and** *B*, **lower, both from left side. Anterior to left of page. Based upon** *Gypsonictops hypoconus*, **a North American Late Cretaceous eutherian (redrawn from Kay and Hiiemäe, 1974;** *A* **is reversed).**

remains doubtful to what extent postcanine teeth are homologous among prototherian, metatherian, and eutherian mammals and, considering recently discovered fossil evidence pertaining to the earliest eutherians, even to what extent tooth homologies are correctly inferred within the Eutheria.

Concomitant with tooth loss in advanced cynodont and early mammal lineages was the incipient and later more complete development of a standardized molar pattern (the "tribosphenic" molar). This type of molar characterizes the earliest marsupials and eutherians and persists, in slightly modified forms, in some living representatives of these groups. The tribosphenic molar probably had its origin in a dentally advanced group of Jurassic eupantotheres (Chapter 8) and presumably first became fully developed in Early Cretaceous Theria of metatherian-eutherian grade (Chapter 10).

THE TRIBOSPHENIC MOLAR

The marsupial and placental mammals and a group termed Theria of metatherian-eutherian grade differ from all other mammals in having tribosphenic molars. This type of mammalian molar tooth was originally termed "tuberculosectorial," or "tritubercular." Most recent workers, however, have adopted the name tribosphenic, introduced by Simpson (1936). He (1936, p. 797) intended the name tribosphenic to be ". . . suggestive of the mortar and pestle, opposing action of protocone and talonid and of the wedge-like, alternating and shearing action of trigon and trigonid." In occlusion, upper tribosphenic molars are normally situated posterior to the midline of their lower molar counterparts (see Romer, 1966, Fig. 298).

The tribosphenic upper molar (Fig. 9-1) consists of a large trigon, with lingual, anterolabial, and posterolabial cusps (protocone, paracone, and metacone, respectively), and a smaller talon (heel) with a single posterolingual cusp (hypocone) sometimes present. The tribosphenic lower molar consists of an anterior triangle of cusps (the trigonid) that is normally taller than a posterior basin (the talonid); the latter is flanked by two or three marginal cusps. The cusps of the trigonid form a triangle in occlusal view that has its apex directed labially. In contrast, the triangle of the trigon of the upper molars has its apex directed lingually. The labial cusp of the trigonid is the protoconid, the

anterolingual cusp the paraconid, and the posterolingual cusp the metaconid. The talonid is bordered lingually by the entoconid and labially by the hypoconid. A posteromedial cusp, the hypoconulid, is often present.

A number of accessory cusps often occur on tribosphenic upper molars. The para-, meso-, and metastyles are situated on the anterolabial, mesial, and posterolabial margins of the stylar shelf, respectively. Some generalized marsupials may have one or more accessory stylar cusps on the stylar shelves of the upper molars. These cusps are designated A through E, in order of their occurrence from anterior to posterior on the stylar shelf (Chapter 11). A paraconule is commonly present on the anteromedial margin of the trigon, between the protocone and paracone, and a metaconule may occur on the posteromedial margin of the trigon, between the protocone and metacone.

The tribosphenic lower molar rarely possesses accessory cusps. A mesoconid, however, may occur anteromedially to the hypoconid, between that cusp and the elevated trigonid. An entoconulid occasionally is present between the entoconid and the lingual margin of the trigonid, and a metastylid may be developed on the posterior border of the metaconid.

The principal cusps and conules are thickenings of the crown enamel and dentine that frequently mark the confluence of two or more cristae (upper teeth) or cristids (lower teeth). Cristae and cristids consist of crests or ridges on the crowns of the teeth; several of the more important ones are illustrated in Figure 9-1.

The tritubercular theory (Osborn, 1888, 1897, 1904) and the "premolar analogy theory" (Gregory, 1916, 1934) were early attempts to explain the development of tribosphenic, multicuspate teeth from the single-cusped tooth condition common in many reptiles. Although these early concepts of the evolution of the tribosphenic molar are interesting from their historical and deductive viewpoints, it soon became clear that some of the stages of development assumed by these theories (i.e., the triconodont and symmetrodont molar morphologies) do not form a phylogenetic sequence. Moreover, it is now known that the multicuspate stage was independently achieved by several therapsid groups and that the earliest known mammals possessed cusp patterns more complex than those typical of later triconodonts or symmetrodonts.

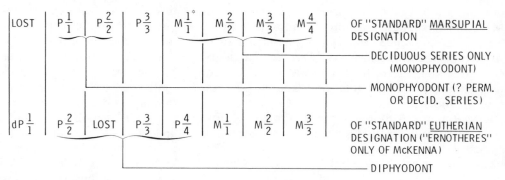

A

PERAMUS

| P$\frac{1}{1}$ | P$\frac{2}{2}$ | P$\frac{3}{3}$ | P$\frac{4}{4}$ | M$\frac{1}{1}$ | M$\frac{2}{2}$ | M$\frac{3}{3}$ | M$\frac{4}{4}$ | | OF CLEMENS & MILLS, 1971 |
| dP$\frac{1}{1}$ | P$\frac{2}{2}$ | P$\frac{3}{3}$ | P$\frac{4}{4}$ | P$\frac{5}{5}$ | M$\frac{1}{1}$ | M$\frac{2}{2}$ | M$\frac{3}{3}$ | | OF McKENNA, 1975 |

ULTIMATE DESCENDANTS (RE McKENNA, 1975)

| LOST | P$\frac{1}{1}$ | P$\frac{2}{2}$ | P$\frac{3}{3}$ | M$\frac{1}{1}$* | M$\frac{2}{2}$ | M$\frac{3}{3}$ | M$\frac{4}{4}$ | OF "STANDARD" MARSUPIAL DESIGNATION |

— DECIDUOUS SERIES ONLY (MONOPHYODONT)

— MONOPHYODONT (? PERM. OR DECID. SERIES)

| dP$\frac{1}{1}$ | P$\frac{2}{2}$ | LOST | P$\frac{3}{3}$ | P$\frac{4}{4}$ | M$\frac{1}{1}$ | M$\frac{2}{2}$ | M$\frac{3}{3}$ | OF "STANDARD" EUTHERIAN DESIGNATION ("ERNOTHERES" ONLY OF McKENNA) |

— DIPHYODONT

*IMPORTANT POINT—
THE TERMINAL DECIDUOUS PREMOLAR IS MOLARIFORM

B

1. ASIORYCTES	$\frac{5}{4}$	$\frac{1}{1}$	$\frac{4}{4}$	$\frac{3}{3}$	
2. KENNALESTES	$\frac{?4}{3}$	$\frac{1}{1}$	$\frac{5}{5}$	$\frac{3}{3}$	JUVENILE
	$\frac{?4}{3}$	$\frac{1}{1}$	$\frac{4}{4}$	$\frac{3}{3}$	ADULT
3. GYPSONICTOPS	$\frac{?}{2+}$	$\frac{1}{1}$	$\frac{4-5}{5}$	$\frac{3}{3}$	
4. PERAMUS	$\frac{?}{?}$	$\frac{1}{1}$	$\frac{5}{5}$	$\frac{3}{3}$	OF McKENNA (1975)
	$\frac{?}{?}$	$\frac{1}{1}$	$\frac{4}{4}$	$\frac{4}{4}$	OF CLEMENS AND MILLS (1971)
5. AMPHITHERIUM	$\frac{?}{?}$	$\frac{?}{1}$	$\frac{?}{5}$	$\frac{?}{6}$	

Figure 9-5. *A*, **Interpretations of the dental formulae in** *Peramus tenuirostris*, **and possible phyletic consequences; and** *B*, **interpretations of the dental formulae of Mongolian (1, 2) and North American (3) Late Cretaceous eutherians, and those of English Late (4) and Middle (5) Jurassic eupantotheres. (Modified from Lillegraven, unpublished diagram)**

arisen through a reduction of one premolar or one molar, respectively. This interpretation, although both possible and the most simplistic, is not documented, because intermediate evolutionary stages are unknown, as are relatively complete and serially associated dentitions of important Early Cretaceous mammals such as *Aegialodon, Kielantherium, Pappotherium, Holoclemensia,* and *Kermackia* (see Chapter 10).

Van Valen (1974) advanced the argument that the presence of seven cheek teeth, with the fourth being molariform, may have been common to the ancestry of marsupials and placentals. Under such a scheme, the teeth traditionally designated as dP4/4 or P4/4 of placentals represent the homologue of M1/1 of marsupials. This interpretation is compatible with the presumed derivation of therian mammals from eupantotheres which, like *Peramus,* possessed eight postcanine teeth. In *Peramus,* the anterior four postcanine teeth are premolariform and the posterior four are molariform.

McKenna (1975) reinterpreted the dental formula of *Peramus* (see Fig. 9-5*A*), and presented evidence that primitive eutherians in general possessed five premolars (*e.g.,* some *Gypsonictops,* following Lillegraven, 1969, and Clemens, 1973, and noting a juvenile specimen of *Kennalestes*), but only three molars. In McKenna's view, the proper cheek tooth formula of *Peramus* is $P_5^5 M_3^3$; marsupials, as well as primitive eutherians, obtained their first "molar" (traditional designation of M_1^1) by the paedomorphic retention of a molariform (molar-like) deciduous P_5^5. Eutherian ancestors thereafter lost the last molar. This resulted in the establishment of the three "molars" (actually, in McKenna's view, dP5M1-2) that characterize modern representatives of the Eutheria.

The possession of five premolars by a eutherian as dentally advanced as Late Cretaceous *Gypsonictops* indicates that the retention of eight postcanine teeth can be expected in several other of the earliest eutherians. *Deltatheridium,* a mammal that was apparently undergoing the loss of the most posterior postcanine tooth (Butler and Kielan-Jaworowska, 1973), occurs later than the first undoubted eutherians (see Chapter 12) and could not itself have played a part in the evolution of that group. Nevertheless, it is possible that parallel trends took place in the line leading to eutherians. The loss of a fourth (and ultimate) molariform postcanine tooth may have occurred considerably earlier in the eutherian line, and the eutherian formula became standardized by the loss of the first premolariform postcanine tooth (Fig. 9-5*A* and *B*). McKenna's theory implies that diphyodont teeth characterized metatherian and eutherian ancestors. Although this is an interesting and, indeed, probable assumption, critical fossil evidence is lacking. Further interpretation will have to await the discovery of additional Jurassic and Early Cretaceous therian fossils that possess relatively complete and serially associated dentitions. Thus even the most basic questions concerning the origins of dental formulae characteristic of advanced therian mammals remain unanswered. Additional details concerning marsupial dental formulae are provided in Chapter 11 (see, especially, the new interpretation by Archer, 1978).

REFERENCES CITED

Archer, M., 1978, The nature of the molar-premolar boundary in marsupials and a reinterpretation of the homology of marsupial cheekteeth: Queensland Mus. Mem., v. 18, p. 157-164.

Butler, P. M., 1961, Relationships between upper and lower molar patterns, *in* Vandebroek, G., ed., International colloquium on the evolution of lower and non specialized mammals: Brussels, Kon. Vlaamse Acad. Wetensch., Lett. Schone Kunsten Belgie, pt. 1, p. 117-126.

Butler, P. M., and Kielan-Jaworowska, Z., 1973, Is *Deltatheridium* a marsupial?: Nature, v. 245, p. 105-106.

Clemens, W. A., 1973, Fossil mammals of the type Lance Formation, Wyoming. Part III. Eutheria and summary: Univ. California Publs. Geol. Sci., v. 94, *vi* + 102 p.

Clemens, W. A., and Mills, J. R. E., 1971, Review of *Peramus tenuirostris* Owen (Eupantotheria, Mammalia): Brit. Mus. Nat. Hist. Bull. (Geol.), v. 20, p. 87-113.

Crompton, A. W., 1971, The origin of the tribosphenic molar, *in* Kermack, D. M., and Kermack, K. A., eds., Early mammals: Linn. Soc. Zool. Jour., v. 50, suppl. 1, p. 65-87.

Crompton, A. W., and Hiiemäe, K. M., 1969a, Functional occlusion in tribosphenic molars: Nature, v. 222, p. 678-679.

———1969b, How mammalian molar teeth work: Discovery, New Haven, Yale, v. 5, p. 23-34.

———1970, Molar occlusion and mandibular movements during occlusion in the American opossum, *Didelphis marsupialis*, L.: Linn. Soc. Zool. Jour., v. 49, p. 21-47.

Crompton, A. W., and Kielan-Jaworowska, Z., 1978, Molar structure and occlusion in Cretaceous therian mammals, *in* Butler, P. M., and Joysey, K. A., eds., Studies in the development, function and evolution of teeth: London and New York, Academic Press, p. 249-287.

Crompton, A. W., and Sita-Lumsden, A., 1970, Functional significance of the therian molar pattern: Nature, v. 227, p. 197-199.

Every, R. G., 1970, Sharpness of teeth in man and other primates: Postilla (Yale Univ.), no. 143, 30 p.

Fox, R. C., 1975, Molar structure and function in the Early Cretaceous mammal *Pappotherium*: evolutionary implications for Mesozoic Theria: Canad. Jour. Earth Sci., v. 12, p. 412-442.

Gregory, W. K., 1916, Studies on the evolution of the Primates. Part I: The Cope-Osborn "Theory of Trituberculy" and the ancestral molar patterns of the Primates: Amer. Mus. Nat. Hist. Bull., v. 35, p. 239-257.

———1934, A half century of trituberculy: the Cope-Osborn theory of dental evolution, with a revised summary of molar evolution from fish to man: Amer. Philos. Soc. Proc., v. 73, p. 169-317.

Hiiemäe, K. M., 1976, Masticatory movements in primitive mammals, *in* Anderson, D., and Matthews, B., eds., Mastication: Bristol, John Wright and Son, p. 105-117.

Kay, R. F., and Hiiemäe, K. M., 1974, Jaw movement and tooth use in recent and fossil primates: Amer. Jour. Phys. Anthro., v. 40, p. 227-256.

Kermack, D. M., Kermack, K. A., and Mussett, F., 1968, The Welsh pantothere, *Kuehneotherium praecursoris*: Linn. Soc. Zool. Jour., v. 47, p. 407-423.

Krusat, G., 1969, Ein Pantotheria-Molar mit dreispitzigem Talonid aus dem Kimmeridge von Portugal: Paläont. Zeit., v. 43, p. 52-56.

Lillegraven, J. A., 1969, Latest Cretaceous mammals of upper part of Edmonton Formation of Alberta, Canada, and review of marsupial-placental dichotomy in mammalian evolution: Univ. Kansas Paleont. Contribs., Art. 50 (Vertebrata 12), 122 p.

McKenna, M. C., 1975, Toward a phylogenetic classification of the Mammalia, *in* Luckett, W. P., and Szalay, F.

S., eds., Phylogeny of the primates: New York, Plenum Press, p. 21-46.

Mills, J. R. E., 1955, Ideal dental occlusion in the Primates: Dental Practnr. and Dent. Rec., v. 6, p. 47-61.

———1966, The functional occlusion of the teeth of Insectivora: Linn. Soc. Zool. Jour., v. 47, p. 1-25.

Osborn, H. F., 1888, The evolution of mammalian molars to and from the tritubercular type: Amer. Nat., v. 22, p. 1067-1079.

———1897, Trituberculy: a review dedicated to the late Professor Cope: *ibid.*, v. 31, p. 993-1016.

———1904, Palaeontological evidence for the original tritubercular theory: Amer. Jour. Sci., v. 17, p. 321-323.

Patterson, B., 1956, Early Cretaceous mammals and the evolution of mammalian molar teeth: Fieldiana (Geol.), v. 13, p. 1-105.

Romer, A. S., 1961, Synapsid evolution and dentition, *in* Vandebroek, G., ed., International colloquium on the evolution of lower and non specialized mammals: Brussels, Kon. Vlaamse Acad. Wetensch., Lett. Schone Kunsten Belgie, pt. 1, p. 9-56.

———1966, Vertebrate paleontology (3rd ed.): Chicago, Univ. Chicago Press, *ix* + 468 p.

Schwartz, J. H., 1975, Dental development, homologies and the ancestral primate stock (abstract): Amer. Jour. Phys. Anthrop., v. 42, p. 328.

Simpson, G. G., 1936, Studies of the earliest mammalian dentitions: Dental Cosmos, 1936 (Aug.-Sept.), p. 1-24.

———1961, Evolution of Mesozoic mammals, *in* Vandebroek, G., ed., International colloquium on the evolution of lower and non specialized mammals: Brussels, Kon. Vlaamse Acad. Wetensch., Lett. Schone Kunsten Belgie, pt. 1, p. 57-95.

Turnbull, W. D., 1971, The Trinity therians: their bearing on evolution in marsupials and other therians, *in* Dahlberg, A. A., ed., Dental morphology and evolution: Chicago, Univ. Chicago Press, p. 151-179.

Vandebroek, G., 1961, The comparative anatomy of the teeth of lower and non specialized mammals, *in* Vandebroek, G., ed., International colloquium on the evolution of lower and non specialized mammals: Brussels, Kon. Vlaamse Acad. Wetensch., Lett. Schone Kunsten Belgie, pt. 1, p. 215-320.

Van Valen, L., 1974, *Deltatheridium* and marsupials: Nature, v. 248, p. 165-166.

CHAPTER 10

THERIA OF METATHERIAN-EUTHERIAN GRADE

Zofia Kielan-Jaworowska

Jeffrey G. Eaton

Thomas M. Bown

CONTENTS

INTRODUCTION AND DIAGNOSIS

The term "Theria of metatherian-eutherian grade" was introduced by Patterson (1956) for certain of the Early Cretaceous ("Paluxian") Greenwood Canyon mammals from Texas. Several kinds of Early and Late Cretaceous mammals from Holarctic continents have since been referred by different authors to this group, a heterogeneous and informal unit. The Theria of metatherian-eutherian grade (Table 10-1) is best defined as a "wastebasket" category. It includes therians that possess a rudimentary tribosphenic dentition, advanced beyond the condition in the Jurassic eupantotheres in having upper molars with a well-developed protocone and lower molars with a strongly basined talonid. Theria of metatherian-eutherian grade are not, however, sufficiently specialized (or adequately known) to be confidently assigned either to definite marsupial (metatherian) or placental (eutherian) groups. Such a concept could imply an ancestral condition for later therian mammals. Also included in this informal rank, however, are taxa such as the Deltatheridiidae, mammals that possess peculiar specializations and probably were not ancestral to any known later mammals. As such, the therians of metatherian-eutherian grade encompass the basal stock ancestral both to marsupials and placentals, as well as to more specialized forms that diverged from the "main stem" of Cretaceous therian evolution. Theria of metatherian-eutherian grade are, therefore, united for purposes of convenience of discussion by what they are *not*, rather than necessarily by commonality of close morphological characters or phylogenetic relationships.

Turnbull (1971) introduced the term "Tribosphena" to include, for the most part, mammals of metatherian-eutherian grade. This taxon is not employed here, however, because it seems premature to erect a formal taxonomic category for such a diverse group that does not constitute a closely-knit assemblage either in a phylogenetic or in a morphologic sense.

ANATOMY, SYSTEMATICS, AND PHYLOGENY

Aegialodontidae

The oldest known mammal of metatherian-eutherian grade (Table 10-2) is *Aegialodon dawsoni* from the Valanginian Cliff End bonebed in England (Kermack and others, 1965). The only known specimen of *Aegialodon* is a lower molar having a well-developed talonid with wear indicating that a protocone probably was present on the occluding upper molar. Crompton (1971) reconstructed a hypothetical occluding upper molar of *Aegialodon*. The status of *Aegialodon* as a therian of metatherian-eutherian grade is firmly established in the literature, and it has been considered to represent a reasonable

structural ancestor of practically every subsequent group of advanced therians.

Kielantherium gobiensis, from ?Aptian or ?Albian rocks of Khovboor in Mongolia, is also known from but a single lower molar (Fig. 10-1). The well-preserved specimen was placed in the Aegialodontidae by Dashzeveg (1975). He believed the tooth to be nearly identical with those of *Aegialodon* from Cliff End and *Kermackia* from rocks of Early Cretaceous age in Texas. Fox (1976) argued that *Kielantherium* should be considered a junior synonym of *Aegialodon*. Because Dashzeveg made no attempt to distinguish *Kielantherium* on morphological criteria either from *Aegialodon* or *Kermackia*, it appears that he proposed the new generic name primarily on the basis of the disparate geographic occurrence and different ages of the specimens. In the present state of limited knowledge of the three genera, we consider it premature to synonymize any of them (also see Chapter 2 for discussion). It should be stressed that the lower molar of *Kielantherium* (better preserved than the type specimen of *Aegialodon*) also shows similarities with certain deltatheridiids (see below). The type of *Aegialodon*, however, is distinctly smaller. The structure of the trigonid and the placement of the talonid

---

TABLE 10-1   CLASSIFICATION OF THERIA OF METATHERIAN-EUTHERIAN GRADE

Family Aegialodontidae Kermack, Lees, and Mussett, 1965

  Aegialodon Kermack, Lees, and Mussett, 1965

    A. dawsoni Kermack, Lees, and Mussett, 1965

  Kermackia Slaughter, 1971[1]

    K. texana Slaughter, 1971

  Kielantherium Dashzeveg, 1975

    K. gobiensis Dashzeveg, 1975

Family Deltatheridiidae Gregory and Simpson, 1926

  Deltatheridium Gregory and Simpson, 1926

    D. pretrituberculare pretrituberculare Gregory and Simpson, 1926

    D. pretrituberculare tardum Kielan-Jaworowska, 1975b

  Deltatheroides Gregory and Simpson, 1926

    D. cretacicus Gregory and Simpson, 1926

    D. sp. Fox, 1974

Family ?Deltatheridiidae Gregory and Simpson, 1926

  Hyotheridium Gregory and Simpson, 1926

    H. dobsoni Gregory and Simpson, 1926

Family Pappotheriidae Slaughter, 1965[1]

  Pappotherium Slaughter, 1965

    P. pattersoni Slaughter, 1965

Family uncertain[1]

  Holoclemensia Slaughter, 1968b and 1968c

    H. texana Slaughter, 1968b and 1968c

  Potamotelses Fox, 1972

    P. aquilensis Fox, 1972

  Beleutinus Bashanov, 1972

    B. orlovi Bashanov, 1972

1. Several isolated molars and premolars of Trinity therians were described and figured by Patterson (1956) and were simply referred to as Trinity therians. Slaughter (1965, 1968a, 1968b, 1971) referred to these by "Trinity therian type numbers" or as *Holoclemensia texana*, *Pappotherium pattersoni*, or *Kermackia texana*. Turnbull (1971) variously referred particular teeth to *Pappotherium pattersoni*, *P.* cf. *pattersoni*, *P.* sp., *Holoclemensia texana*, *H.* cf. *texana*, or *H.* sp. As there is great uncertainty in the allocation of these teeth to particular species or even genera, we do not cite them in Table 10-1.

behind the lingual part of the trigonid are identical in both groups. The only recognizable differences are that the talonid is relatively smaller in *Kielantherium* and it possesses no entoconid, a cusp present in the known Deltatheridiidae. It is questionable whether the upper molars of *Kielantherium* possessed a fully differentiated protocone.

Possibly aegialodontids and deltatheridiids will eventually be shown to have been related at the family level. *Kielantherium gobiensis* occurs in faunal association with undoubted eutherians. Thus, if the Eutheria is considered a monophyletic group, *K. gobiensis* itself lived too late to have been an ancestral eutherian.

Deltatheridiidae

The Deltatheridiidae were named by Gregory and Simpson (1926) to include *Deltatheridium* (Figs. 10-2 and 10-3), *Deltatheroides*, and, more tentatively, *Hyotheridium*. These genera are from the Djadokhta Formation of Mongolia, the age of which has been estimated as ?late Santonian and/or ?early Campanian by Gradziński and others (1977).

Deltatheridium is also known from the Barun Goyot Formation (?middle Campanian) of Mongolia (Kielan-Jaworowska, 1975a). All were originally compared with *Didelphodus* (a North American Eocene proteutherian) and the "Creodonta," a diverse group of mainly carnivorous Cenozoic mammals. The upper postcanine teeth of *Deltatheridium* were interpreted by Gregory and Simpson as representing three premolars plus three molars and, in *Deltatheroides*, as four premolars and three molars. They regarded the deltatheridiids as undoubted eutherians, an approach also followed by many subsequent authors (*e.g.,* Van Valen, 1966; Szalay and McKenna, 1971; and McKenna and others, 1971). Butler and Kielan-Jaworowska (1973) demonstrated that deltatheridiids possessed a dental formula similar to that of marsupials, but with a tendency, unusual for marsupials, for the loss of M^4. Because of this and other differences from typical marsupials, they did not classify the Deltatheridiidae in the Marsupialia, but rather as Theria of metatherian-eutherian grade. The same approach was followed by Kielan-Jaworowska (1975a) and Crompton and Kielan-Jaworowska (1978). Kielan-Jaworowska (1975a) assigned only two Asian genera to the Delta-

TABLE 10-2   AGE AND OCCURRENCE OF GENERA OF THERIA OF METATHERIAN-EUTHERIAN GRADE

GENUS	OCCURRENCE	AGE OR STAGE
Aegialodon	Wadhurst Clay, Cliff End, England	Valanginian
Kielantherium	Fm.?, Khovboor, near Guchin Us, province (aymak) of Arvaykher, Mongolian People's Republic	?Aptian or ?Albian
Kermackia	Paluxy (= Antlers Fm.) Fm., Texas, U.S.A.	"Paluxian"
Pappotherium	Paluxy (= Antlers Fm.) Fm., Texas, U.S.A.	"Paluxian"
Holoclemensia	Paluxy (= Antlers Fm.) Fm., Texas, U.S.A.	"Paluxian"
Beleutinus	Beleutinskaya Svita, Kazakhstan, U.S.S.R.	?Coniacian
Potamotelses	upper part of Milk River Fm., Alberta, Canada	"Aquilan"
Deltatheroides-like mammal	Oldman Fm., Alberta, Canada	"Judithian"
	Scollard Fm., Alberta, Canada	"Lancian"
	Lance Fm., Wyoming, U.S.A.	"Lancian"
Deltatheridium	Djadokhta Fm., Bayn Dzak (Shabarakh-Usu), Mongolian People's Republic	?late Santonian and/or ?early Campanian
	Barun Goyot Fm., Nemegt Basin; beds of Khermeen Tsav, Khermeen Tsav, Mongolian People's Republic	?middle Campanian
Deltatheroides	Djadokhta Fm., Bayn Dzak (Shabarakh-Usu), Mongolian People's Republic	?late Santonian and/or ?early Campanian
Hyotheridium	Djadokhta Fm., Bayn Dzak (Shabarakh-Usu), Mongolian People's Republic	?late Santonian and/or ?early Campanian

theridiidae: *Deltatheridium* and *Deltatheroides*. She did suggest, however, that *Hyotheridium*, with its short snout and single-rooted canines, is much more reminiscent of the Deltatheridiidae than of faunally associated eutherian mammals. *Hyotheridium* is known only from a single, badly damaged specimen. Because of its poor condition, it cannot confidently be identified to the family level; the fossil is here only tentatively assigned to the Deltatheridiidae.

Fox (1974) described the upper and lower molars

of deltatheridiid-like mammals from rocks of Late Cretaceous age of North America. As the dental formulae or any other anatomical features of these animals are not known, the presence of the Deltatheridiidae in North America remains uncertain (Kielan-Jaworowska, 1975a).

The Asiatic Deltatheridiidae (see Kielan-Jaworowska, 1975a) were medium-sized (length of skull about 4 cm) mammals with a shortened snout. The nasals are strongly expanded posteriorly and

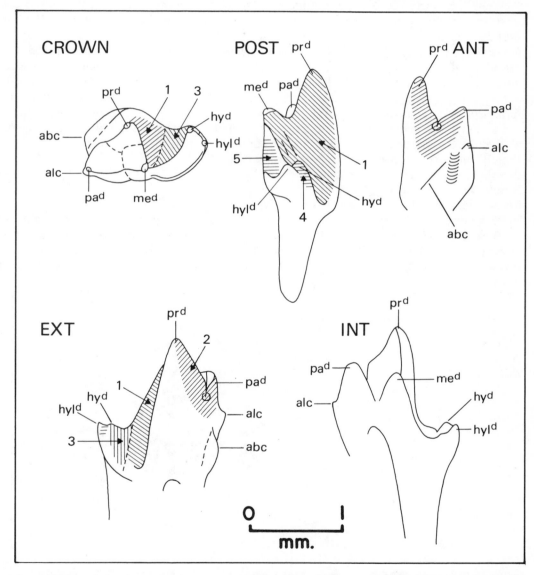

Figure 10-1. *Kielantherium gobiensis*, **right lower molar in five views: upper left, occlusal; upper center, posterior; upper right, anterior wall of trigonid; lower left, labial; and lower right, lingual. Hatched areas (*1-5*) denote shearing surfaces;** *abc*, **anterior buccal cuspule (cingulum);** *alc*, **antero-lingual cuspule;** *hy^d*, **hypoconid;** *hyl^d*, **hypoconulid;** *me^d*, **metaconid;** *pa^d*, **paraconid; and** *pr^d*, **pro-toconid. (Modified from Crompton and Kielan-Jaworowska, 1977)**

contact the lacrimals. The lacrimals have a large facial wing and a large lacrimal foramen. The jugal is deep and long, and palatine fenestrations are lacking. The canine is very large and single-rooted. There are three nonmolariform premolars and three to four molars with wide stylar shelves. The lower molars have metaconids smaller than paraconids, and small talonids. The dental formula is $I_{1-2}^{?4}C_{1}^{1}P_{3}^{3}M_{4}^{3-4}$.

The upper molars of *Deltatheridium* (Fig. 10-3) are roughly triangular, and slightly longer than wide. They are symmetrical in occlusal outline because of the strong development of the metastylar region. The ectoflexus is deep and the stylar shelf wide. The metastylar region is strongly elongated postero-laterally with a single cusp (metastyle). The parastylar region is smaller in occlusal view than the metastylar region, and possesses three styles. Paracrista and metacrista are developed as strong ridges. Paracone and metacone are situated in the middle of the tooth and, although they have approximated bases (connate), their tips are widely separated. Paracone is taller than the metacone. Conules are comparatively large, swollen cusps, and are not winged. The protocone is relatively small. There is no pre- or postcingulum.

The trigonid is markedly wider and slightly longer than the talonid. The talonid is situated rather lingually with respect to the trigonid. The protoconid is the tallest and largest of the trigonid cusps, and the metaconid the smallest. The surface of the talonid is strongly worn in all known specimens, but the entoconid, hypoconid, and hypoconulid are distinct.

Among the forms informally classified within the Theria of metatherian-eutherian grade, only the Asiatic Deltatheridiidae are known from almost complete dentitions and skulls. These were comparatively large mammals for Late Cretaceous times (see scales in Figs. 10-2 and 10-3), and probably were of carnivorous habits. This best-known group was ancestral neither to metatherians nor eutherians, and probably represented yet a third evolutionary experiment. Descendants of the Deltatheridiidae are unknown or remain unrecognized. It is regrettable that all other therians of metatherian-eutherian grade are known only from isolated teeth or small bits of jaws; the specimens help little in determining the anatomy, general appearance, or habits of the animals they represent.

Beleutinus

Bashanov (1972) assigned an incomplete mandible with damaged dentition from Upper Cretaceous beds (?Coniacian) of Kazakhstan to a new genus, *Beleutinus* (see comments on its description in

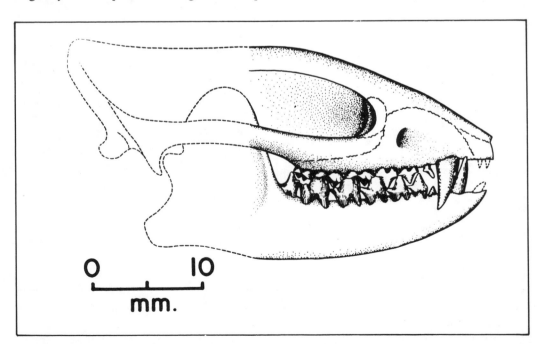

Figure 10-2. *Deltatheridium pretrituberculare tardum*, reconstruction by Kielan-Jaworowska of right side of skull and mandible.

Chapter 2). The specimen is poorly preserved, and its taxonomic affinities cannot be recognized; by default, we place it with the Theria of metatherian-eutherian grade.

"Trinity Therians"

Patterson (1956) described tribosphenic teeth from the Paluxy Formation (referring to it as the Trinity Sandstone; "Paluxian") of Greenwood Canyon in Texas. He did not name new genera, but classified all the specimens as Theria of metatherian-eutherian grade. Slaughter (1965, 1968a, 1968b, 1971) described additional material from the same formation at Butler Farm, naming three new genera and species. Two were based upon upper molars (*Pappotherium pattersoni* and *Holoclemensia texana*), while the third (*Kermackia texana*) is known

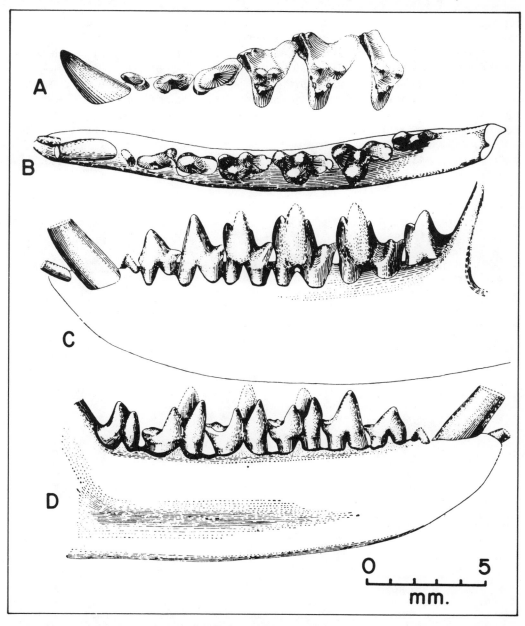

Figure 10-3. Reconstructions of dentition of *Deltatheridium pretrituberculare tardum*: *A*, left upper canine and cheek teeth in occlusal view; and *B-D*, left lower dentition in occlusal (*B*), labial (*C*), and lingual (*D*) views. (From Kielan-Jaworowska, 1975b)

only from a lower molar. Data on the microstructure of the enamel are presented in Chapter 11.

Upper molars of *Holoclemensia* and *Pappotherium* are of essentially similar morphological pattern (Fig. 10-4), and differ principally in the arrangement of the stylar cusps. *Holoclemensia* has a large median stylar cusp "*C*," whereas that cusp in *Pappotherium* is lacking, and the stylocone (cusp "*B*") is extremely tall. The upper molars of both genera have large stylar shelves and no cingula. The metacone in *Holoclemensia* appears to be relatively smaller than that of *Pappotherium*. *Holoclemensia* was assigned to the Metatheria by Slaughter because of the large cusp *C* placed in the middle of the ectoflexus. Slaughter (1971) pointed out that although many primitive eutherians possess stylar cusps on the upper molars, none yet known have them so strongly developed in the *C* position.

Isolated lower molars were identified by Slaughter (1968b, p. 254) as *Holoclemensia* ". . . on the basis of size and ease of occlusion." Turnbull (1971) assigned two different types of lower molars to *Holoclemensia*, but Kielan-Jaworowska (1975a) demonstrated that these were not from congeneric forms.

Pappotherium was identified as an early eutherian by Slaughter, as based upon evidence gleaned both from upper (mentioned above) and lower teeth. In addition to the partial upper jaw designated as the type specimen of *Pappotherium pattersoni*, a series of lower teeth, which have variously been referred to the genus, occurs in the same beds. For example, Slaughter (1971) tentatively identified a fragment of a lower jaw with four teeth as *Pappotherium*. The anterior two teeth are premolariform and are associated with well-worn molariform teeth. The most anterior tooth is not fully erupted, suggesting that it had recently replaced a deciduous counterpart. The sequence of eruption, which differs from that of Late Cretaceous and Cenozoic marsupials, led Slaughter to consider the

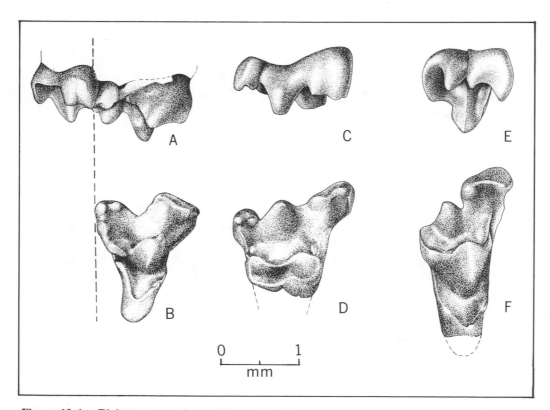

Figure 10-4.   Right upper molars of *Pappotherium pattersoni*: *A*, **labial view of ultimate and penultimate molars; and** *B*, **occlusal view of penultimate molar (dashed line designates distal end of penultimate molar in the two views). Right upper molars of** *Holoclemensia texana*: *C*, **labial view of nonultimate molar;** *D*, **occlusal view of** *C*; *E*, **labial view of ultimate molar; and** *F*, **occlusal view of** *E*. **(Redrawn from Slaughter, 1971 and casts of fossils)**

jaw to be from a eutherian. In this respect, he was followed by Fox (1975). Slaughter's (1971, p. 136) reason for referring the specimen to *Pappotherium* was ''. . . size and probable occlusal relationships.'' As the lower jaw in question was not found in occlusion with upper molars, attribution to *Pappotherium* must remain in doubt. Crompton (1971), on similar bases, tentatively identified a different type of lower molar from the Trinity collection as *Pappotherium.* Turnbull (1971), in addition to the tooth identified by Crompton, assigned still different lower molars (of quite different structure) to this genus.

The attribution of unassociated lower molars from the collections of Trinity therians to upper teeth supposedly representing congeneric forms is most difficult. It is not yet possible to demonstrate unequivocal congeneric relationships between any two upper and lower teeth from that collection.

Two other factors are involved in the recognition of the existence of placentals among the Trinity therians. First, in the collection described by Slaughter (1968a), there occur isolated semimolariform lower premolars. Although semimolariform premolars are common among eutherians, they are unknown in primitive marsupials. Second, Fox (1975) speculated that *Pappotherium* possessed three molars. As only two upper molars of *Pappotherium* are known, Fox based his argument upon comparisons of crown shapes with Deltatheridiidae, *Holoclemensia*, and *Potamotelses* (see below).

The systematic positions of *Pappotherium* and *Holoclemensia* have been discussed by many students of Mesozoic mammals. Slaughter's (1968a) allocation of *Holoclemensia texana* to the Marsupialia has been accepted by several authors (*e.g.,* Sigé, 1972; Fox, 1975; and Crompton and Kielan-Jaworowska, 1978), but Turnbull (1971), Tedford (1974), and Clemens (*in prep.*) questioned this placement. Slaughter's (1968b, 1971) identification of *Pappotherium* as a eutherian was followed by McKenna (1969), Clemens (1971), Fox (1975), and others. Hopson and Crompton (1969), Turnbull (1971), Cox (1973), Crompton and Kielan-Jaworowska (1977) have, alternatively, felt that *Pappotherium* might more logically be retained in the Theria of metatherian-eutherian grade. An additional argument for such classification was given by Kielan-Jaworowska (1975a), who compared the upper molars of *Pappotherium* and *Deltatheridium* and demonstrated a close similarity between teeth of the two genera. The

only significant difference is the presence of a cusp on the metacrista of *Pappotherium* at the spot, in *Deltatheridium,* at which a carnassial notch occurs.

Because of the general lack of basic information from the fossils, and the resultant high degree of uncertainty with respect to the affinities of *Holoclemensia, Pappotherium,* and *Kermackia*, we prefer to take a conservative approach and classify them all as therians of metatherian-eutherian grade.

Familial assignments of the Trinity therians also pose difficulties. We assign *Kermackia*, which is known only from a lower molar, to the Aegialodontidae because of its basic similarity with molars of *Aegialodon* and *Kielantherium*. We agree with Slaughter's (1965) assignment of *Pappotherium* to the monotypic family Pappotheriidae. On the other hand, we give *Holoclemensia*, which was placed by Slaughter (1968b) in the Didelphidae, a ''family uncertain'' status.

As a miscellaneous point, the ''Trinity therians'' have recently been studied by P. M. Butler (*in prep.*), who will describe two new genera on the basis of lower teeth. These are not discussed further in the book.

Potamotelses

Fox (1972) described *Potamotelses* from ''Aquilan'' (roughly early Campanian) rocks of Alberta, Canada, classifying it as a therian of metatherian-eutherian grade. *Potamotelses aquilensis* is based upon isolated upper and lower molars. Fox felt that teeth of *Potamotelses* were structurally more primitive than those of any other known Late Cretaceous nonsymmetrodont therians in the retention of a poorly developed protocone. Furthermore, the teeth are more generalized than those of contemporary metatherians in the possession of small stylar cusps between the stylocone (cusp *B*) and the metastylar area, and in the possession of a small and more labially placed metacone. The referred lower molars have well-developed cristids obliqua and talonids, and seem to be fully tribosphenic (Fox, 1974). Fox suggested that *Potamotelses* represented a late-surviving relict, less advanced than either *Pappotherium* or *Holoclemensia*. Fox (1975) furthermore regarded *Aegialodon* and *Potamotelses* to be relatively primitive within the grade of mammals having tribosphenic teeth, and felt that both genera shared a level of development with that of the Late

Cretaceous Deltatheridiidae of Asia. He concluded that *Aegialodon, Potamotelses*, and the Deltatheridiidae could be united within a higher level taxonomic category that could have included the common ancestors of the Metatheria and Eutheria.

Kielan-Jaworowska (1975a) compared *Potamotelses* with *Deltatheridium* and advocated that there were strong differences between the two taxa. Crompton and Kielan-Jaworowska (1978) suggested that *Potamotelses* might have been a marsupial, and Russell (1975) believed that it may have been a eutherian. In this book we follow Fox (1972) in classifying *Potamotelses* as a therian of metatherian-eutherian grade.

ECOLOGY

Little knowledge of life habits of the Theria of metatherian-eutherian grade is obtainable from known occurrences. The North American forms lived in nearshore environments, along the borders of the great Western Interior Seaway (see Chapter 14). Asiatic species, however, are known from the continental interior, where the sediments indicate that they lived in arid or even desert habitats (Gradziński and Jerzykiewicz, 1974). It is therefore probable that the Theria of metatherian-eutherian grade lived in a wide range of environments.

It is inferred from dentitions that these animals were insectivorous, although the comparatively large *Deltatheridium*, with its strong canine development, was probably carnivorous.

MISCELLANEOUS COMMENTS

The Theria of metatherian-eutherian grade include a number of mammals that are in some respects intermediate in dental morphology between the eupantotheres and the marsupials and placentals. The known record of this significant group, however, is poor both in temporal and geographic terms (see Fig. 12-22), and the proposal of lineages among the described genera would now be quite premature. The potential is great for further investigation of these interesting mammals; it is only through a study of them that understanding of the origins of the Metatheria and Eutheria will be gained.

REFERENCES CITED

Bashanov, V. S., 1972, First Mesozoic Mammalia (*Beleutinus orlovi* Bashanov) from the USSR: Teriologia, Akademiya Nauk SSSR, Sibirskoe Otdelenie, v. 1, p. 74-80 (in Russian with English summary).

Butler, P. M., and Kielan-Jaworowska, Z., 1973, Is *Deltatheridium* a marsupial?: Nature, v. 245, p. 105-106.

Clemens, W. A., 1971, Mammalian evolution in the Cretaceous, *in* Kermack, D. M., and Kermack, K. A., eds., Early mammals: Linn. Soc. Zool. Jour., v. 50, suppl. 1, p. 165-180.

Cox, C. B., 1973, Systematics and plate tectonics in the spread of marsupials, *in* Hughes, N. F., ed., Organisms and continents through time: London, Palaeont. Assoc., Syst. Assoc. Publ. 19, Spec. Paper Palaeont. 12, p. 113-119.

Crompton, A. W., 1971, The origin of the tribosphenic molar, *in* Kermack, D. M., and Kermack, K. A., eds., Early mammals: Linn. Soc. Zool. Jour., v. 50, suppl. 1, p. 65-87.

Crompton, A. W., and Kielan-Jaworowska, Z., 1978, Molar structure and occlusion in Cretaceous therian mammals, *in* Butler, P. M., and Joysey, K. A., eds.,

Studies in development, function and evolution of teeth: London and New York, Academic Press, p. 249-287.

Dashzeveg, D., 1975, New primitive therian from the Early Cretaceous of Mongolia: Nature, v. 256, p. 402-403.

Fox, R. C., 1972, A primitive therian mammal from the Upper Cretaceous of Alberta: Canad. Jour. Earth Sci., v. 9, p. 1479-1494.

———1974, *Deltatheroides*-like mammals from the Upper Cretaceous of North America: Nature, v. 249, p. 392.

———1975, Molar structure and function in the Early Cretaceous mammal *Pappotherium*: evolutionary implications for Mesozoic Theria: Canad. Jour. Earth Sci., v. 12, p. 412-442.

———1976, Additions to the mammalian local fauna from the Upper Milk River Formation (Upper Cretaceous), Alberta: *ibid.*, v. 13, p. 1105-1118.

Gradziński, R., and Jerzykiewicz, T., 1974, Sedimentation of the Barun Goyot Formation, *in* Kielan-Jaworowska, Z., ed., Results Polish-Mongol. Palaeont. Expeds., pt. V: Palaeontologia Polonica, no. 33, p. 111-146.

Gradziński, R., Kielan-Jaworowska, Z., and Maryańska, T., 1977, Upper Cretaceous Djadokhta, Barun Goyot and Nemegt formations of Mongolia, including remarks on previous subdivisions: Acta Geol. Polonica, v. 27, p. 281-318.

Gregory, W. K., and Simpson, G. G., 1926, Cretaceous mammal skulls from Mongolia: Amer. Mus. Novitates, no. 225, 20 p.

Hopson, J. H., and Crompton, A. W., 1969, Origin of mammals, *in* Dobzhansky, T., Hecht, M. K., and Steere, W. C., eds., Evolutionary biology: New York, Appleton-Century-Crofts, v. 3, p. 15-72.

Kermack, K. A., Lees, P. M., and Mussett, F., 1965, *Aegialodon dawsoni*, a new trituberculosectorial tooth from the Lower Wealden: Roy. Soc. London Proc., B (Biol. Sci.), v. 162, p. 535-554.

Kielan-Jaworowska, Z., 1975a, Evolution of the therian mammals in the Late Cretaceous of Asia. Part I. Deltatheridiidae, *in* Kielan-Jaworowska, Z., ed., Results Polish-Mongol. Palaeont. Expeds., pt. VI: Palaeontologia Polonica, no. 33, p. 103-132.

_____1975b, Evolution and migrations of the Late Cretaceous Asian mammals, *in* Lehman, J. P., ed., Problèmes Actuels de Paléontologie-Évolution des Vertébrés: Paris, Colloque Internat., C.N.R.S., no. 218, p. 573-584.

McKenna, M. C., 1969, The origin and early differentiation of therian mammals: New York Acad. Sci. Ann., v. 167, p. 217-240.

McKenna, M. C., Mellett, J. S., and Szalay, F. S., 1971, Relationships of the Cretaceous mammal *Deltatheridium*: Jour. Paleont., v. 45, p. 441-442.

Patterson, B., 1956, Early Cretaceous mammals and the evolution of mammalian molar teeth: Fieldiana (Geology), v. 13, p. 1-105.

Russell, L. S., 1975, Mammalian faunal succession in the Cretaceous system of western North America: Geol. Assoc. Canada Spec. Paper 13, p. 137-161.

Sigé, B., 1972, La faunule de mammifères du Crétacé supérieur de Laguna Umayo (Andes péruviennes): Mus. Natl. Hist. Natur. Bull., 3ᵉ sér., no. 99, Sciences de la Terre 19, p. 375-409.

Slaughter, B. H., 1965, A therian from the Lower Cretaceous (Albian) of Texas: Postilla (Yale Univ.), no. 93, 18 p.

_____1968a, Earliest known eutherian mammals and the evolution of premolar occlusion: Texas Jour. Sci., v. 20, p. 3-12.

_____1968b, Earliest known marsupials: Science, v. 162, p. 254-255.

_____1968c, *Holoclemensia* instead of *Clemensia*: *ibid.*, v. 162, p. 1306.

_____1971, Mid-Cretaceous (Albian) therians of the Butler Farm local fauna, Texas, *in* Kermack, D. M., and Kermack, K. A., eds., Early mammals: Linn. Soc. Zool. Jour., v. 50, suppl. 1, p. 131-143.

Szalay, F. S., and McKenna, M. C., 1971, Beginning of the age of mammals in Asia: the late Paleocene Gashato fauna, Mongolia: Amer. Mus. Nat. Hist. Bull., v. 144, p. 269-318.

Tedford, R. H., 1974, Marsupials and the new paleogeography, *in* Ross, C. A., ed., Paleogeographic provinces and provinciality: Tulsa, Soc. Econ. Paleont. Mineral., Spec. Publ. 21, p. 109-126.

Turnbull, W. D., 1971, The Trinity therians: their bearing on evolution in marsupials and other therians, *in* Dahlberg, A. A., ed., Dental morphology and evolution: Chicago, Univ. Chicago Press, p. 151-179.

Van Valen, L., 1966, Deltatheridia, a new order of mammals: Amer. Mus. Nat. Hist. Bull., v. 132, p. 1-126.

CHAPTER 11

MARSUPIALIA

William A. Clemens

INTRODUCTION

Marsupials (often referred to as "metatherians") were common members of most North American, Late Cretaceous ("Aquilan" through "Lancian") local faunas. For example, five of the twelve mammalian species currently recognized in the Judith River local fauna of Montana are marsupials (Chapter 2). In "Lancian" local faunas, other than those of the Bug Creek faunal-facies, their tax-

onomic diversity ranges from 46 percent of the mammalian species represented in the Lance local fauna of Wyoming to 33 percent in the Trochu local fauna of Alberta (Archibald, 1977). The individual abundance of marsupials, though yet to be accurately determined in most of these local faunas, appears equally high. Even though the taxonomic diversity of marsupials remains high, the abundance of individuals is much lower in Bug Creek faunal-facies localities. For example, in the Bug Creek Anthills local fauna of Montana 47 percent of the mammalian species represented are marsupials, but in a sample of 6000 mammalian fossils from this locality only slightly more than 1 percent are elements of marsupials (Sloan and Van Valen, 1965). Most of these Cretaceous lineages became extinct before the beginning of the Paleocene, so that in Puercan (North American, early Paleocene) local faunas, only two species of the didelphid *Peradectes* are represented.

The fossil record of Mesozoic marsupials is an odontologist's delight. Almost all the known specimens are isolated teeth or, at most, dentulous fragments of maxillae and dentaries. Aspects of the evolution of the marsupial dentition already have been considered by T. M. Bown and M. J. Kraus (Chapter 9). Small fragments of skulls of *Eodelphis* and *Didelphodon* have been discovered and described, but are not extensive enough to serve as the basis of a restoration of the entire skull. Likewise, elements of postcranial skeletons have been tentatively identified, but, to the best of my knowledge, restoration of an entire skeleton or even a limb has yet to be attempted.

If overall size of the dentition is an accurate index of total body size, the largest of the "Lancian" mammals was the stagodontid *Didelphodon vorax*, which probably was not much larger than an adult *Didelphis virginiana*. *Didelphodon* might well have been in the same size range as the "giant" Early Cretaceous triconodont from the Cloverly Forma-

tion (Chapter 4). The smallest species of *Alphadon* and *Pediomys* had dentitions similar in size to those of smaller modern species of *Marmosa*. Molars of all the known Cretaceous marsupials are of basic tribosphenic pattern. The most extreme modifications are found in forms such as *Glasbius* whose broadly basined, low cusped molars exhibit some dental specializations also characterizing many kinds of early primates. At another extreme, *Didel-*

TABLE 11-1   CLASSIFICATION OF MESOZOIC MARSUPIALIA

Infraclass Metatheria Huxley, 1880
  Order Marsupialia Illiger, 1811
    Superfamily Didelphoidea (Gray, 1821)
      Family Didelphidae Gray, 1821
        Subfamily Didelphinae (Gray, 1821)
          Alphadon Simpson, 1927b
            A. austrinum Sigé, 1971
            A. creber Fox, 1971
            A. halleyi Sahni, 1972
            A. lulli Clemens, 1966
            A. marshi Simpson, 1927b
            A. cf. *A. marshi* (*fide* Clemens, 1973b)
            A. cf. *A. marshi* (*fide* Clemens, Chapter 2, "Dumbbell Hill")
            A. praesagus Russell, 1952
            A. rhaister Clemens, 1966
            A. cf. *A. rhaister* (*fide* Clemens, 1966)
            A. cf. *A. rhaister* (*fide* Sahni, 1972)
            A. wilsoni Lillegraven, 1969
            A. sp. Fox, 1971
            A. sp. Fox, 1976
            ?*A.* sp. Clemens, 1973b
          Peradectes Matthew and Granger, 1921
            P. cf. *P. pusillus* (*fide* Archibald, 1977)
         Subfamily Glasbiinae Clemens, 1966
          Glasbius Clemens, 1966
            G. intricatus Clemens, 1966
            G. new species Archibald, 1977
        Didelphidae, genus and species indet. of Sigé, 1971
        ?Didelphidae *incertae sedis*
          Albertatherium Fox, 1971
            A. primus Fox, 1971
        Family Pediomyidae (Simpson, 1927a)
          Pediomys Marsh, 1889a
            P. clemensi Sahni, 1972
            P. cooki Clemens, 1966
            P. cf. *P. cooki* (*fide* Sloan and Russell, 1974)

            P. cf. *P. cooki* (*fide* Clemens, 1973b)
            P. cf. *P. cooki* (*fide* Archibald, 1977)
            P. elegans Marsh, 1889a
            P. exiguus Fox, 1971
            P. florencae Clemens, 1966
            P. cf. *P. florencae* (*fide* Archibald, Chapter 2, Powder River Basin)
            P. hatcheri Osborn, 1898
            P. cf. *P. hatcheri* (*fide* Archibald, Chapter 2, Powder River Basin)
            P. krejcii Clemens, 1966
            P. cf. *P. krejcii* (*fide* Sloan and Russell, 1974)
            P. sp. Lillegraven, 1972
            cf. *P.* sp. (*fide* J. H. Ostrom, pers. comm. to Lillegraven, 1976, see Waage, 1968, p. 127)
      ?Pediomyidae (*fide* Sahni, 1972)
      ?Pediomyidae indet. (*fide* Sigé, 1971)
      ?Pediomyidae *incertae sedis*
        Aquiladelphis Fox, 1971
         A. incus Fox, 1971
         A. minor Fox, 1971
      Family Stagodontidae Marsh, 1889b
        Didelphodon Marsh, 1889a
         D. padanicus Cope, 1892
         D. vorax Marsh, 1889a
         D.? sp. Sloan and Russell, 1974
        Eodelphis Matthew, 1916
         E. browni Matthew, 1916
         E. cutleri Woodward, 1916
         E. sp. Fox, 1971
         E. ? sp. (*fide* Sloan and Russell, 1974)
      ?Stagodontidae
        Boreodon Lambe, 1902 (probably a *nomen dubium*)
         B. matutinus Lambe, 1902 (probably a *nomen dubium*)

phodon, the most derived stagodontid, has molars in which the postvallum-prevallid shearing crests are relatively large, producing an oxyaenoid-like set of multiple carnassials. Anterior to the molars were greatly enlarged, bulbous premolars.

As utilized here the Cretaceous membership of the Marsupialia differs from that recognized by several recent workers. *Holoclemensia* is regarded as a therian of metatherian-eutherian grade (see Chapter 10). Thus, except for their occurrence in a South American local fauna possibly of Late Cretaceous age (Laguna Umayo, Chapter 2), the entire Mesozoic fossil record of marsupials comes from North American, Late Cretaceous local faunas. Finally, as will be discussed below, the question of whether marsupials should be classified in one or several orders is being debated again. Taxonomists in favor of the use of several orders continue to increase in number. However, under either classificatory scheme, all known Cretaceous marsupials probably would be allocated to one superfamily. The question of choice of the appropriate ordinal level units hinges on interpretation of the Cenozoic evolutionary radiation of marsupials. At the moment promotion of communication concerning Mesozoic marsupials appears best served through use of a single order.

The subjects of the origin of marsupials and their phylogenetic relationships to eutherian mammals have been considered in a variety of studies. Although all usually take a broad range of data into account (including what little information can be gleaned from the fossil record), there currently appear to be two major areas of emphasis in these works. Some recent workers have stressed comparative analyses of the anatomy, physiology, embryology, and other characters of modern mammals. Elsewhere in this book J. A. Lillegraven (Chapter 13) considers the evolutionary significance of the differences in reproductive patterns of monotremes, marsupials, and eutherians. He correlates the greater success of eutherians in diversification, dispersal, and dominance to adaptive advantages conferred by the relatively precocial development of their neonates. This pattern of development appears to be linked in part to the functions of the eutherian trophoblast.

The second current area of emphasis is illustrated by papers presenting syntheses of research on the changing patterns of distribution of continents, the physical evolution of their topography and climates, routes of dispersal or instances of vicariant disruption of their terrestrial faunas, and analysis of the membership of these faunas. Farther

TABLE 11-2   AGE AND OCCURRENCE OF GENERA OF MESOZOIC MARSUPIALIA

GENUS	OCCURRENCE	AGE OR STAGE
Alphadon	upper part of Milk River Fm., Oldman Fm., and Scollard Fm., Alberta, Canada; Judith River Fm. and Hell Creek Fm., Montana; Lance Fm., Wyoming; Fruitland Fm. and Kirtland Fm., New Mexico, U.S.A.; Vilquechico Fm. (or equivalent), Peru	"Aquilan" through "Lancian" or Paleocene
Peradectes	Hell Creek Fm., Montana, U.S.A.	"Lancian"
Glasbius	Hell Creek Fm., Montana; Lance Fm., Wyoming, U.S.A.	"Lancian"
Albertatherium	upper part of Milk River Fm., Alberta, Canada	"Aquilan"
Pediomys	upper part of Milk River Fm., St. Mary River Fm., and Scollard Fm., Alberta, Canada; Judith River Fm. and Hell Creek Fm., Montana; Lance Fm., Wyoming; Fox Hills Fm., South Dakota; Fruitland Fm. and Kirtland Fm., New Mexico, U.S.A.; "El Gallo Fm.," Baja California, Mexico	"Aquilan" through "Lancian"
Aquiladelphis	upper part of Milk River Fm., Alberta, Canada	"Aquilan"
Didelphodon	St. Mary River Fm. and Scollard Fm., Alberta, Canada; Hell Creek Fm., Montana and South Dakota; Lance Fm., Wyoming, U.S.A.	"Edmontonian" through "Lancian"
Eodelphis	upper part of Milk River Fm., Oldman Fm., and St. Mary River Fm., Alberta, Canada; Judith River Fm., Montana, U.S.A.	"Aquilan" through "Judithian"
Boreodon	Oldman Fm., Alberta, Canada	"Judithian"

on in this book (Chapter 14) J. A. Lillegraven, M. J. Kraus, and T. M. Bown provide a summary of the changing paleogeography of the Mesozoic world. Particularly in relation to the following discussion of marsupial phylogeny, reference should be made to their maps depicting Cretaceous paleogeography (Figs. 14-4 and 14-5).

DIAGNOSIS

Marsupials are therian mammals characterized by the following derived (apomorphic) traits. A pseudovaginal canal is developed in females. The neonates, born when many organ systems are only slightly developed, are carried externally and initially are linked to nipples. Pouches surrounding the mammary area are present in females of many species. Dental replacement is reduced so that only the last premolars, here designated P_3^3, are diphyodont. Primitively, the postcanine dentition consists of three premolars and four molars. The alisphenoid contribution to the ossified bulla is relatively large. The jugal reaches the glenoid fossa and contributes to formation of a preglenoid crest.

Many other characters have been cited as diagnostic of marsupials. For the most part they appear to be primitive features probably characterizing the common ancestors of marsupials and eutherians but lost in Cenozoic eutherians. Even some of those characters listed in the preceding paragraph are suspect or require qualification.

Morphology of the reproductive organs of marsupials and their patterns of reproduction are analyzed in considerable detail in Chapter 13. In brief, this study shows that most of the differences in mode of reproduction distinguishing modern marsupials from eutherians appear to be the result of retention of primitive (plesiomorphic) therian features in marsupials. Evolution of the pseudovaginal canal in female marsupials is one of the few clearly derived traits. Patterns of care of marsupial neonates usually distinguish them from eutherians. However, in some eutherians the neonate is briefly attached to a nipple (Chapter 13), suggesting that such ephemeral postnatal linkages might have been characteristic of early therians and that an increase in their duration is the marsupial specialization. Some modern female marsupials lack a pouch. This structure might well have evolved independently in several marsupial lineages as well as in the echidnas (see Kirsch, 1977b).

The following are other traits of the "soft" anatomy or physiology of marsupials that appear to distinguish Recent marsupials and eutherians. They are all characters not directly documented in the fossil record, and many are interpreted as essentially retentions, with little modification, of the characters of primitive therian mammals: (1) marsupials lack a hypertrophied embryonic trophoblast (both in its relative development and functions the trophoblast is a unique feature of eutherians); (2) metanephric ducts (presumptive ureters) are situated medial to derivatives of the Müllerian ducts; (3) the duration of active embryogenesis is always significantly shorter than the estrous cycle characteristic of the species (however, the duration of pregnancy can be slightly longer than the cycle); (4) most marsupial embryos have a choriovitelline placenta (in only a few species is a chorioallantoic placenta functional); (5) erosion of the uterine wall by extraembryonic membranes of the developing young is an infrequent specialization; (6) the young are altricial and born at stages of anatomical and physiological development characteristic of eutherian embryos; (7) in comparison with eutherians, marsupials have a low number of chromosomes ($2n = 10$ to 32; see Kirsch, 1977b, for discussion); (8) in general marsupials maintain a lower body temperature and have lower metabolic rates than eutherians; and (9) the lack of a corpus callosum in the brains of marsupials is probably a primitive character (see Johnson, 1977, for a discussion of the differences distinguishing marsupial and eutherian brains).

Turning to the dentition, currently there is no evidence contradicting the hypothesis that, in comparison with their reptilian ancestors, reduction in frequency of replacement of teeth is a mammalian specialization. Among therians the frequency of replacement is least in marsupials. Only the posterior premolars (P_3^3) are known to be replaced. In contrast, eutherians retain diphyodonty of the incisors, canines, and at least some premolars.

Usually the presence of three premolars and four molars is also considered a diagnostic character of primitive marsupials. This rests on the far from substantiated hypothesis that the ancestors of eutherians and metatherians had more than eight postcanine teeth, and the primitive dental formulas of eutherians and metatherians evolved through different patterns of reduction of the postcanine dentition. Although yet to be shown false, substantiating data are meager (see Chapter 9 and below).

In animals now judged to be the most primitive marsupials, morphological differences clearly distinguish the posterior premolars from the anterior molars. The crowns of the posterior premolars are not molariform, or even submolariform, but have a simple, usually trenchant morphology. Though the posterior premolars of some of their descendants evolved complex crowns, for example those of kangaroos (Macropodidae), they did not become molariform but retained a distinctive morphology. In most eutherians now considered to have primitive dentitions, the posterior premolars are somewhat molariform, producing a more gradual morphological transition between premolar and molar regions of the dentition. The question of whether the lack of molariform premolars in marsupials is a primitive characteristic or a specialization is moot and awaits discovery of dentitions of members of the last common ancestral stock of the marsupials and eutherians.

The structure of the cranium provides two characters apparently diagnostic of metatherian relationships. One is the posterior extension of the jugal to reach the glenoid fossa where it participates in formation of the preglenoid crest. In a few eutherians, for example, *Asioryctes* (pers. comm. from Kielan-Jaworowska) and *Moeritherium*, the jugal reaches the glenoid but does not form a preglenoid crest. So little is known of the evolution of the zygomatic arch in therian mammals that this criterion cannot be given much weight. The second character of cranial morphology that usually distinguishes marsupials from eutherians is the structure of the auditory bulla. Although the alisphenoid is known to make small contributions to the ossified auditory bullae of some eutherians, in none of them is it as extensive as in most marsupials.

Finally, modern species, probably most if not all Cenozoic forms, and possibly many Late Cretaceous marsupials can be distinguished from their eutherian contemporaries by the following osteological characters. Many of these features probably also characterize the last common ancestors of marsupials and eutherians: (1) epipubic bones are present in members of both sexes (they are lost in a few derived species, *e.g., Thylacinus*); (2) baculum or os clitoridis is lacking; (3) in comparison with most eutherians the braincase is relatively small (primitively, the cerebellar fossa is entirely behind and the olfactory fossa entirely in front of the cerebral fossa); (4) usually a postorbital bar is not present; (5) primi-

tively, the internal carotid artery enters the skull via a foramen in the basisphenoid (see Archer, 1976a, and Marshall, 1976 and 1978); (6) the angular process of the dentary is inflected medially or lost, as in *Tarsipes* (the angular processes of most known Cretaceous eutherians have a similar inflection [Chapter 12]); (7) the enamel is perforated by extensions of the dentinal tubules; (8) primitively, more than three pairs of incisors are present in both the upper and lower dentitions (the maximum number documented to date is five upper and four lower; the presence of more than three pairs of incisors has been demonstrated in the dentition of one Cretaceous eutherian, *Asioryctes* [Chapter 12]); (9) molars of Cretaceous and primitive Cenozoic marsupials tend to retain a stylar shelf and a large stylar cusp *B* (presence of a large stylar cusp *C* probably is not a diagnostic character of the earliest marsupials); (10) among Cretaceous therians the crowns of the upper molars of marsupials usually are not as transversely broad (relative to anteroposterior length) as are those of contemporaneous eutherians, and usually lack antero- and posterolingual cingula; (11) the conules of the upper molars of Cretaceous marsupials frequently are smaller than those of eutherians and commonly lack distinct, wing-like subsidiary crests; (12) on the lower molars of Cretaceous marsupials the metaconid is usually distinctly lower than the protoconid and approximates the paraconid in height; (13) hypoconulid and entoconid are closely approximated, "twinned," and well separated from the hypoconid; and (14) antero- and posterolabial cingula of lower molars of Cretaceous marsupials are usually smaller than those of contemporaneous eutherians (the molars of *Glasbius* provide the known exception).

ANATOMY

Introduction

This section will be limited to consideration of those aspects of marsupial anatomy now documented in their Mesozoic fossil record. Thus it is restricted to the anatomy of the dentition, the dentary and tooth-bearing region of the maxillary, and parts of the zygomatic arch and ventrolateral region of the skull (specifically the ventral margin of the squamosal, the petrosal, and associated elements of the basicranial region).

Dental Microstructure

Since much of this book is devoted to the macroscopic forms and functions of mammalian dentitions, it is appropriate to pause here and consider the evolutionary histology of the tissues forming mammalian teeth, especially the dentin and enamel. This digression is particularly suitable for inclusion in a discussion of the Marsupialia, for one of the first systematic studies of dental histology revealed the presence of tubules in the enamel of the teeth of most marsupials and their absence from the enamel of many eutherians (J. Tomes, 1849). Subsequently, some authors have uncritically repeated the citation of the presence of enamel tubules as a diagnostic character of the Marsupialia. Now, after more than a century of research, one may ask to what extent can histological characters of teeth be used in the preparation of diagnoses of mammalian taxa?

Without doing extreme injustice to the facts, the early phylogenetic history of the histology of vertebrate dentitions can be condensed by first noting that teeth are currently thought to have originated through modification of elements (odontodes) of the dermal skeletons of early fishes. Primitive vertebrate teeth consist of a core, usually of conical shape and made up of some form of dentin; a basal unit or attachment to other skeletal elements; and usually a capping of some kind of hard, enameloid material. Many variations on this basic structural pattern are found in fishes and amphibians (see Ørvig, 1967, and Poole, 1967b). In some amphibians, and in most reptiles and mammals, the harder material capping the teeth is formed largely of calcium phosphate, in the form of hydroxyapatite, containing small but important amounts of other inorganic and organic components. This tissue, enamel, is deposited by cells of ectodermal derivation dubbed ameloblasts. Of course the shape and disposition of the enamel cap of primitive conical teeth was highly modified with extreme change in dental morphology, for example, the evolution of the hypsodont cheek teeth of rodents and horses among eutherians and wombats among the marsupials.

The enamel of the teeth of a wide range of reptiles and "toothed" birds studied (see Poole, *ibid.*) conforms to a surprisingly constant structural pattern, which differs from that characteristic of most mammals. When the crown of a reptilian tooth is viewed in longitudinal (mesial-distal) cross-section a series of incremental "lines" in the enamel parallel the junction of the enamel and dentin. These are particularly apparent in teeth that are not fully formed. Second, in most reptiles the enamel appears to be "amorphous," "continuous," or "non-prismatic," *i.e.*, the crystallites are not arranged in regular, columnar prisms or rods. The enamel of at least some mammal-like reptiles is traversed by tubules (Moss, 1969). Finally, in general the enamel layer capping the crowns of reptilian teeth usually is significantly thinner than that of mammalian teeth of similar size.

Before going farther, pertinent aspects of the dental histology of *Homo sapiens* need to be summarized, for they are used as the basic frame of reference in most recent comparative studies. At an early stage in the ontogeny of the tooth bud in *H. sapiens*, and all other eutherians and marsupials yet investigated, a membrane, the membrana preformativa, is formed. This ephemeral layer marks the future site of the dentin-enamel junction. In both reptiles and mammals, unlike many other vertebrates, deposition of dentin is initiated prior to the formation of the enamel. Starting in the areas that will be the topographic highs of the crown (apices of cusps or crests of ridges), the odontoblasts are organized along the membrana preformativa. A gel-like substance (predentin) is formed around the odontoblasts, and then apatite is deposited in the predentin. As this process continues the bodies of the odontoblasts retreat and are not incorporated in the newly formed dentin. In *H. sapiens* each odontoblast maintains contact with the membrana preformativa or, later, the enamel-dentin junction by a single but branching process enclosed within a tubule in the dentin.

In all mammals formation of the enamel begins only after a dentin substrate is deposited, and like the ontogeny of dentin, deposition of enamel begins at the apices of cusps and crests. The crystallites of enamel usually are organized into structures that resemble rods or prisms, which extend from the enamel-dentin junction to near the surface of the crown. There has and continues to be considerable discussion about the nature of these prisms. In some mammals the boundaries of the individual prisms probably are zones of abrupt change in the orientation of the c-axes of the enamel crystallites. In others, a layer of interprismatic substance appears to separate the prisms (see Moss, *ibid.*, and Kraus and others, 1969). The cross-sectional outlines of prisms vary from hexagonal or polygonal, to horseshoe-shaped, to, in *Homo sapiens*, a complex, keyhole-like outline. Within any tooth there is considerable variation in prism outline, but one pattern usually dominates. Studies (*e.g.*, Shobusawa, 1952, and Boyde, 1971) suggest that dominant patterns of cross-sectional outlines might serve as diagnostic characters of mammalian orders, families, or possibly smaller taxonomic units.

Whatever their exact nature, enamel prisms are growth tracks recording the secretory and organizing functions of the ameloblasts. In most mammals the course of a prism from the enamel-dentin junction toward the surface of the crown usually is slightly sinuous and parallels its neighbors. Locally, particularly toward the crown's surface, the prisms can intertwine, forming what has been termed a gnarled enamel. Near the surface of the crown the prismatic structure is lost and a thin layer of surficial enamel is continuous in structure. As a last step in its ontogeny, the enamel undergoes a maturation process involving further deposition of salts and withdrawal of water (for further details see Kraus and others, 1969, and Copenhaver and others, 1971).

Correlation of evolution of prismatic structure and greater thickness of the enamel of mammalian teeth with changes in their macroscopic form, ontogeny, and function has only begun to be explored. Poole (1956, 1967b) studied the microstructure of the enamel in several Triassic synapsids, and Moss (1969) considered others. They found that in some of the synapsids studied the enamel was thicker than average for reptiles and in all there was the beginning of a regular pattern of organization of the crystallites. They are not organized into recognizable prisms, but the orientation of their c-axes varies in a regular fashion, producing what is called a pseudoprismatic pattern (see Moss, *ibid.*).

Moss and Kermack (1967) analyzed the enamel structure of teeth of *Morganucodon* (probably *M. watsoni*) and "an unnamed Pantothere" (probably *Kuehneotherium praecursoris*), respectively, among the earliest nontherian and therian mammals. In both the teeth are capped with an enamel of pseudoprismatic pattern. The pattern of variation in orientation of the c-axes of the crystallites, however, is slightly different from that found in the synapsids studied so far. Thus it appears that major modifications in coronal morphology and function of early mammalian teeth, which distinguish them from those of most synapsids, occurred prior to significant change in the histology of the enamel or dentine.

The histology of the teeth of a surprisingly wide variety of nontherian mammals has been investigated. Excluding multituberculates, Moss (1969) studied teeth of *Docodon*, sp. indet. from the Morrison Formation, Wyoming, an otherwise unidentified triconodont from the same area, *Astroconodon denisoni* from the Paluxy Formation, Texas, and the modern *Ornithorhynchus*. The enamel of all these animals was found to be continuous, and only that of the ephemeral teeth of the platypus, *Ornithorhynchus*, showed tubular structure.

Histological data are available for teeth of the following multituberculates (taxa are ordered according to the classification in Chapter 6; unless noted, data are from Moss, 1969): (1) Plagiaulacidae, genus and species indet., Late Jurassic, Morrison Formation, Wyoming; (2) ?Plagiaulacidae, gen. and sp. indet., "Paluxian," Paluxy Formation, Texas; (3) Neoplagiaulacidae, *Ectypodus* sp., Early Eocene, Wasatch Formation, Wyoming; (4) Cimolodontidae, *Cimolodon* sp., "Lancian," Scollard Formation, Alberta; (5) Taeniolabididae, *Taeniolabis taoensis*, Early Paleocene, Nacimiento Formation, New Mexico; (6) Cimolomyidae, *Meniscoessus*, probably *M. robustus*, "Lancian," Lance Formation, Wyoming; and (7) Multituberculata, family, genus, and species indet. (*a*, "Judithian," Mesa Verde Formation, Wyoming; *b*, middle Paleocene; *c*, "Lancian," Bug Creek Anthills locality, Hell Creek Formation, Montana [Fosse and others, 1973]; and *d*, multituberculate [Poole, 1967a]).

On the basis of his analysis of a large number of multituberculate teeth, Moss (1969) concluded that the enamel of multituberculates, like that of other nontherians, was continuous and showed the development of pseudoprisms. In contrast, Fosse and others (1973) found that the enamel of six multituberculate teeth from the Bug Creek Anthills locality " . . . was discontinuous, sharply-defined crystallite orientations demarcating prisms, interprismatic enamel and sometimes crystallitic prismsheaths" (*ibid.*, p. 146). They also note that the prisms of the enamel of these multituberculates are very large relative to those of other mammals. At the moment it cannot be determined if the apparently contradictory results of these studies simply point out specializations of the otherwise unspecified Bug Creek multituberculates or have some other basis.

The enamel of most multituberculates can be distinguished from that of other nontherians by the presence of tubular structures, possibly of the same ontogenetic origin as those of marsupial enamel (*ibid.*). The abundance, distribution, and length of the enamel tubules varies between species, but in all they follow spiral or zig-zag courses. In the species examined by Moss (1969) tubules are abundant in the enamel of most but are rare in the enamel of *Cimolodon* and were absent from the one fragment of enamel of *Taeniolabis taoensis* examined. Obviously much more work needs to be done before the variation in histology of the enamel of multituberculates, an order that existed for more than 100 million years and underwent several evolutionary radiations, is understood.

Turning to therian lineages, the enamel of the earliest known genus, *Kuehneotherium*, is reported to be pseudoprismatic (Moss and Kermack, 1967). Although listing a dryolestid tooth from the Late Jurassic Morrison Formation, Wyoming, among his materials, Moss (1969) did not describe its histology. Also, he did not cite the abstract prepared by Poole (1967a; also see 1971) in which the enamel of another unspecified dryolestid was found to consist of a basal prismatic layer capped by a thinner but substantial layer of continuous enamel. The earliest incidence of prismatic enamel reported by Moss (1969) was found in two teeth from the Early Cretaceous, Paluxy Formation, Texas. One of these teeth was identified as a lower molar of Trinity Type 5 and allocated to the Pappotheriidae; the other was simply designated a therian tooth. Resembling the enamel of the dryolestid described by Poole (see 1971), the prismatic layer is covered by a distinct layer of continuous enamel.

On the basis of his findings, Moss (1969) argued that prismatic enamel had evolved only in the dentitions of therian mammals and that this occurred during the Cretaceous well after the origin of the group. Poole's (1967a) discovery of prismatic enamel in a Late Jurassic dryolestid pushes back the time of origin of this pattern of crystallite organization in mammalian evolution. Also, the discovery of prismatic enamel on the teeth of an agamid lizard, *Uromastix* (see Poole and Cooper, 1971), demonstrates that it is not a unique therian tissue. Perhaps the findings of Fosse and others (1973) document independent evolution of prismatic enamel in the Multituberculata.

J. Tomes (1849) noted that the enamel of the teeth of most marsupials was distinguishable from that of many eutherians by the presence of structures called enamel tubules. The nature of these structures has been debated. Moss and Applebaum (1963) ar-

gued that they were actually areas of uncalcified enamel matrix and their formation reflected the rapid rate of amelogenesis in marsupials. Others (see Boyde, 1971) supported the view of Tomes that enamel tubules were continuations of the dentinal tubules. Risnes and Fosse (1974) argued that during the ontogeny of the teeth of marsupials odontoblastic processes penetrate the developing enamel ahead of the mineralizing front.

The taxonomic distribution of enamel with tubules is intriguing. Moss (1969) noted the presence of tubules in the enamel of the four synapsid reptiles he examined (the question of the homology of these tubules with those of mammals remains unanswered). The enamel of almost all multituberculates yet examined is tubular, as is that of the teeth of *Ornithorhynchus*. However, the enamel of other nontherians (*Morganucodon*, a Late Jurassic triconodont, and a docodont) apparently lacks tubules. Turning to therians, tubules are unknown in the few Jurassic and Early Cretaceous forms examined. Among Cenozoic marsupials tubular enamel has been found in all of the large number of species examined except wombats, the only marsupials known to have evolved hypsodont cheek teeth. Among Cenozoic eutherians, *Homo sapiens* and many others have enamel lacking tubules. But tubular enamel does occur in a curious collection of forms, ". . . certain members of the orders Rodentia (*e.g.*, the jerboa), Insectivora (*e.g.*, hedgehog, mole, shrew), Lemuroidea, and Chiroptera" (Boyde, 1971, p. 81). The enamel of hyraxes also is reported to have tubules (C. S. Tomes, 1904).

Moss (1969) examined the enamel of one Cretaceous therian, the proteutherian *Gypsonictops* from the "Lancian," Lance Formation, Wyoming. Other than having a relatively thick external layer of continuous enamel, it does not differ significantly from nontubular prismatic eutherian enamel. Also Moss (*ibid.*) analyzed the enamel of Late Cretaceous marsupials. Three were marsupials of Lancian age (a didelphid, *Alphadon* sp. and *Pediomys* sp.). All have prismatic enamel and enamel tubules. The fourth specimen, identified as "Marsupial, gen. et sp. indet.," was derived from a "Judithian" locality in the Mesa Verde Formation, Wyoming. Like the other three, the enamel is prismatic; Moss (*ibid.*), however, noted that the density of tubules is relatively low.

In summary, this survey of the histology of dentin and enamel of Mesozoic mammals suggests that further work could provide characters of considerable utility in systematic analysis. The possibility of establishing phylogenetic affinity on the basis of enamel histology is particularly inviting. However, such analyses must await the completion of much more descriptive and analytical research.

Dental Macrostructure

Turning to the macrostructure of marsupial molars, one of the unifying characters of the upper molars of Cretaceous marsupials, excepting only the pediomyids, is retention of a primitively broad labial shelf or cingulum bearing several stylar cusps (see

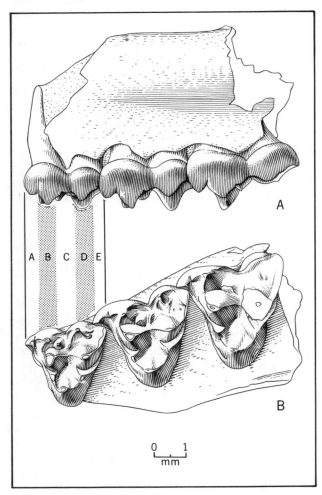

Figure 11-1. *Alphadon rhaister*, **fragment of left maxillary containing M**[1-3] **(lines and shaded areas illustrate method of assigning alphabetic designations to stylar cusps, see text for explanation):** *A*, **labial view; and** *B*, **occlusal view. (Illustrations from Clemens, 1966, copyright © by The Regents of the University of California, emended)**

Chapters 9 and 12 and Fig. 11-1). A broad, cuspidate stylar shelf is found also on molars of the Cenozoic members of the Didelphidae and Dasyuridae. The various nomenclatures coined to designate cusps of the stylar shelf stem in large part from the work of Bensley (1903, 1906), who was influenced by Winge's theory of dental evolution that focused attention on this part of the crown. Bensley (*ibid.*) thought the presence of three main stylar cusps and three subsidiary cusps (all represented on the molars of *Peratherium* that he studied) characterized the upper molars of primitive marsupials. Simpson (1929) reached a slightly different conclusion and argued that there were five primary styles. This interpretation probably is correct for the common ancestor of Cenozoic marsupials, a species of *Alphadon* or dentally similar species of Cretaceous didelphid (Clemens, 1968a and research in progress). However, the presence of five stylar cusps might not characterize the molars of the earliest Cretaceous marsupials. Before launching into a discussion of the evolution of the stylar region, which is presented in the section on phylogeny, nomenclatorial problems must be resolved.

Clemens (1966) stressed the need to distinguish between nomenclatorial systems that were strictly descriptive and those that carried implications of homology. The Bensley-Simpson system for designation of stylar cusps was redefined as a descriptive system. Alphabetic designations were assigned solely on the basis of position on the stylar shelf. Thus, in brief, a stylar cusp anterior to the paracone is designated cusp *A*. A cusp labial to the paracone is designated cusp *B*. Cusp *C* is one situated posterior to the paracone but anterior to the metacone, while cusp *D* is located labial to the metacone. A stylar cusp posterior to the metacone is designated cusp *E*. Obviously, problems did arise in the application of this nomenclature. However, it was hoped that the difficulties of assigning alphabetic designations to cusps in intermediate positions would remind the author and reader that the defining criteria were to be strictly topographic. This system had limited success. For cusps *A, B,* and *E,* the names parastyle, stylocone, and metastyle, respectively, were available and were used in place of the alphabetic designations when homology was to be implied. In contrast, no alternative names for cusps in the *C* and *D* positions were developed to designate cusps thought to be homologous. Thus, as used in recent literature, the terms stylar cusp *C* and stylar cusp *D* can designate cusps in similar topographic position, or cusps thought to be homologous, or both.

The functions of the stylar cusps are far from fully understood. Cusps in the *A* and *E* positions, when developed, appear to be involved in both the interlocking of adjacent molars and the provision of a protective arch over the gums. Stylar cusp *B* of primitive marsupials is thought to be homologous with the stylocone of therians of metatherian-eutherian grade. The crest linking stylocone and paracone, the paracrista, carries shear surface *1* (see Chapter 9). Although maintained in the *Alphadon* lineage, in others the paracrista and surface *1* were de-emphasized as functional units. In stagodontids the paracrista and paracone were reduced in size while a large stylar cusp *B* was maintained. In contrast, in pediomyids cusp *B* and the paracrista were reduced while the paracone was not greatly modified.

The functions of cusps in the *C* and *D* positions are probably as diverse as their size and morphology. This interspecific variation in morphology probably does not reflect the lack of genetic constraints on their development. Except where they are minute, intraspecific variation in the development of cusps in the *C* and *D* positions is not exceptionally greater than that of other elements of the crown. Most likely, stylar cusps in these positions are not functionless embellishments. One general hypothesis of the functions of cusps in the *C* and *D* positions suggests they help form a fence along the margin of the upper dentition, reducing the possibility of food slipping labially. Also, the stylar cusps would aid in puncturing food during the initial phase of mastication prior to the occlusion of the shearing blades. In some species stylar cusp *C* is situated on or near the crest between paracone and metacone, and might be involved as a labial block or guide for the hypocone as it moved linguad into the trigonid basin. This brief list certainly does not exhaust the possibilities.

The functions of the dentition of the North American or Virginian opossum, *Didelphis virginiana* (see Gardner, 1973, for systematic review), have been the object of study by Crompton, Hiiemäe, and their colleagues. Crompton and Hiiemäe (1970) presented an analysis especially pertinent to consideration of the functions of individual cusps and crests. The bibliography in Crompton and others (1977) provides citations to many of the papers reporting the results of their wide-ranging studies.

Although in some species small basal, lingual cingula occur as occasional variants on the anterior and posterior slopes of the protocone, in none are they constant features of the crown. Interestingly, *Glasbius* is a member of the only Late Cretaceous marsupial lineage known to have undergone selection for reduction of height of the trigonid and closure of the embrasures between the upper molars. Enlargement of the posterolingual corner of the crown was accomplished not by evolution of a basal cingulum or a hypocone, but by a shift in the position of the metaconule.

Comparison of the lower molars of therians of metatherian-eutherian grade with those of latest Cretaceous marsupials reveals a number of differences, but, in most cases, determination of the patterns and directions of evolutionary change remain goals for future research. Obviously, the evolution of the primitive marsupial dentition involved enlargement of the talonid relative to the trigonid and probably some reduction in the relative height of the trigonid. The paraconid, metaconid, and entoconid of latest Cretaceous marsupial molars usually are aligned. This might be a marsupial apomorphy, for in most Early Cretaceous tribosphenic molars the paraconid is situated labial to a line connecting apices of metaconid and entoconid. Primitive proportions of the trigonid cusps of tribosphenic molars remain to be determined. There is every reason to suspect that the protoconid was the highest and largest cusp. Primitively, in therians the paraconid probably exceeded the metaconid in height (note *Kuehneotherium* and *Peramus*, for example). However, among the earliest tribosphenic molars there is considerable variation in the relative heights of these cusps (see Slaughter, 1971, and Turnbull, 1971). For latest Cretaceous marsupials the primitive pattern appears to be one in which the metaconid is distinctly smaller than the protoconid. In turn, the paraconid varies from distinctly lower and smaller, on M_1, to approximately the same size as the metaconid on posterior molars. The morphology of stagodontid trigonids, which have a large paraconid and small metaconid, is most likely a specialization.

In both total width and area of its basin, the talonids of Late Cretaceous marsupial molars are larger than those of primitive tribosphenic molars. Lower molars of Late Cretaceous marsupials and eutherians usually can be distinguished easily by the morphology of the talonid cusps. In both the entoconid has evolved relatively larger size than is typical of early tribosphenic molars. On marsupial molars the entoconid and hypoconulid are closely approximated, "twinned," and distinctly separated from the hypoconid. On eutherian molars the hypoconulid is in a more central position on the back of the talonid with the hypoconid and entoconid situated at approximately equal distances on either side of it. These differences probably are the results of different patterns of talonid enlargement in marsupials and placentals (Clemens, 1966).

Dental Formulae

Bown and Kraus devote a major part of Chapter 9 to consideration of the evolution of metatherian and eutherian dental formulae. They conclude, ". . . even the most basic questions concerning the origins of dental formulae characteristic of advanced therian mammals remain unanswered." The answers will not be found here. The following paragraphs are devoted to a resumé of details of marsupial dental formulae.

Until the discovery of *Asioryctes* it could be and was stated that primitive eutherians had only three pairs of upper and lower incisors, while primitive marsupials had as many as five upper and four lower. Although the presence of five pairs of upper and four pairs of lower incisors in *Asioryctes* and possibly four pairs of upper incisors in *Kennalestes* (Chapter 12) required revision of this almost axiomatic criterion, it has done little toward elucidating the evolution of therian incisors. Known, advanced cynodonts most frequently have an incisor formula of $\frac{4}{3\text{-}4}$; rarely there are one or two precanine teeth socketed in the maxillary (Chapter 9). Probably the known morganucodontids were derived from an ancestral stock with a formula of I_4^4 (Chapter 4). One symmetrodont is known to have had at least three pairs of lower incisors (Chapter 7), while I_4^4 appears to be the primitive dental formula of eupantotheres (Chapter 8). The incisor count of only one group of therians of metatherian-eutherian grade is known, and it is the formula ($I_{1\text{-}2}^{?4}$) of the derived Asian deltatheridiids (Chapter 10).

Almost all didelphids have an incisor formula of I_4^5, and there is embryological evidence that the primitive formula of the Marsupialia could have been as great as I_5^6 (Ride, 1962, 1964). Thus, as in so many other features, it appears likely that primitive marsupials tend to maintain a primitively large number of incisors, or possibly in the course of their evolution even increased their number. In contrast, in eutherian lineages during the Late Cretaceous the number appears to have been quickly reduced to three pairs of upper and lower incisors.

Almost nothing can be said about the morphology of the incisors of Cretaceous marsupials, for, at best, they are known only from their alveoli. These few data, and what can be obtained from Cenozoic species (see Archer, 1976b), suggest that, primitively, the incisors were single rooted and of approximately equal size.

The canines of primitive marsupials appear to have been single rooted. No occurrences of double-rooted canines are known in Cretaceous species.

Several nomenclatorial systems have been devised for designating individual premolars. The one used here is strictly descriptive. Premolars are simply numbered from anterior (P1) to posterior (P3). The tooth displaced when P3 erupts is designated DP3. An exception to these simple criteria is provided by the highly modified dental ontogeny of kangaroos (Macropodidae) in which P3 displaces both DP3 and P2. This nomenclature is adopted because its defining criteria exclude considerations of homology between eutherian and metatherian dentitions. Also, currently it is the nomenclatorial system used in the primary literature on Cretaceous and most Cenozoic American marsupials.

Another nomenclatorial system now used for the most part by Australian workers designates the three premolars P1, P3, and P4. The tooth replaced during dental ontogeny is designated DP4. This terminology traces back to the researches of Thomas (1887). As used by many workers (*e.g.*, Ride, 1964), it reflects the view that the common ancestor of marsupials and eutherians had four premolars, and differentiation of marsupials involved loss of P2. The data cited in support of this viewpoint are the frequent occurrences of a diastema between the first and second premolars. Also, the rare development of a tooth between these premolars has been interpreted as an atavistic trait. Archer (1974a, 1975b) found no embryological evidence of the former development of a tooth between what are termed here P1 and P2 of marsupials, and cast considerable doubt on the interpretation of teratologic occurrences of additional premolars as atavistic traits.

Ziegler (1971), in a general review of the evolution of mammalian dental formulas and replacement patterns, argued that the common ancestor of marsupials and eutherians had four premolars and that P1 is lost from marsupial dentitions. Again, data are not available from the fossil record to properly evaluate this hypothesis. Also, Archer (1974a) could not find embryological evidence supporting the hypothesis of loss of a premolar from this position in marsupial dentitions.

Another tack in investigations of the embryology of marsupial dentitions has been consideration of the homologies of the last premolar and its deciduous precursor. One of the hypotheses coming out of this work suggests that the "permanent" premolars (P1-3) belonged to one dental series while the DP3 belonged to another. There is argument over whether the molars were part of the DP3 or the P1-3 series (see Berkovitz, 1966, for review). Some workers favoring membership of DP3 in the same dental series as the molars also suggested that the teeth designated M1 in marsupials are homologous with the DP4 of eutherians. By this hypothesis the P4 of the common ancestral stock was lost in marsupials. Another hypothesis suggests that DP3 and P3 belong to the same dental series (Berkovitz, *ibid.*). In a series of papers, based in part on his studies of the modern dasyurid *Antechinus flavipes*, Archer (1974a, 1974b, 1975a, 1975b) hypothesizes that DP3 and P3 (his designations are DP4 and P4) belong to different dental series but that they develop in a manner distinctly different from that thought to be typical of diphyodont teeth of eutherians. More recently, Archer (1978, p. 157) suggested that ". . . all systems of homology [of marsupial teeth] in current use are incorrect, in part because all are based on the evidently erroneous assumption that true postcanine tooth replacement occurs in marsupials." His reinterpretation, based upon detailed study of marsupial tooth development and dental abnormalities, is that these animals primitively have two cheek tooth series including: (1) three premolars (P1-3); and (2) five molars (a deciduous first molar, M1, plus four permanent molars, M2-5). Under this interpretation, Archer's "M1" is homologous with the marsupial tooth designated elsewhere in the present chapter as DP3; similarly, Archer's "M2-5" are homologous with M1-4 of more traditional usage. Thus, if Archer's (1978) hypothesis is correct, marsupials have three premolars, five molars, and lack true postcanine milk teeth. Clearly, with the present state of knowledge, it would be premature to adopt any system of designation of premolars and molars carrying implications of homologies of eutherian and metatherian cheek teeth.

As far as is known, all Cretaceous species of marsupials have four molars. Only in *Glasbius* are M_4^4 strikingly smaller than the preceding molars.

Nearly complete dentaries of several Cretaceous species have been discovered. They have inflected angular processes and show no significant departures from the morphology characteristic of Cenozoic didelphids. The much rarer fragments of maxillaries, which typically have lost most if not all of their palatal and rostral processes, also do not significantly differ from homologous parts of Cenozoic didelphids.

Three fragments of Cretaceous marsupial skulls have been discovered and analyzed. One is a small part of the ventrolateral corner of a skull of *Eodelphis browni*, a "Judithian" stagodontid described by Matthew (1916). The second is a petrosal and parts of some of the adjacent bones of a skull of the "Lancian" *Didelphodon vorax* (see Clemens, 1966). The third is a smaller fragment of the otic region of *D. vorax* (*ibid.*). The two larger specimens show that, like most Cenozoic didelphoids, the jugal of *Eodelphis* and *Didelphodon* was elongated posteriorly to the anterior margin of the glenoid fossa. This prolongation of the jugal and its participation in formation of a preglenoid crest might be a diagnostic character of primitive marsupials. So little is known of the Cretaceous evolutionary history of the zygomatic arch of therians that assignment of diagnostic value to the structure of the jugal probably is, at best, a speculation allowed by ignorance. In contrast, the presence of large squamosal epitympanic sinuses sets both stagodontid genera apart from most members of the Didelphidae (see Archer, 1976a). Also, unlike most didelphids, the petrosal of *Didelphodon vorax* appears to have made some contribution to an ossified bulla.

SYSTEMATICS

Didelphidae

This family includes a variety of American and Cenozoic European marsupials united primarily by the retention or relatively slight modification of primitive marsupial characters. Particularly in regard to nondental morphology the following characterization is based largely on information drawn from recent members of the family. Many characters cited (*e.g.*, the morphology of the auditory region) are known in but a few prehistoric species. To the best of my knowledge, these data from the fossil record are in accord with the generalizations.

The didelphid dental formula is $I_4^5 C_1^1 P_3^3 M_4^4$ or not greatly reduced from this primitive number. The deciduous premolars (DP_3^3) are relatively large, approximating the size of the molars. Molars are of little modified, tribosphenic patterns (Figs. 11-1 and 11-2). On upper molars the stylar shelf usually is wide, and bears a large stylar cusp B, thought to be homologous with the stylocone of earlier therians. Primitively, stylar cusp D is present and slightly smaller than B; stylar cusp C is absent or small. In advanced species the paracone is reduced in size and the metacone enlarged. The protoconule tends to be reduced or lost. A hypocone is not known to be present, though the metaconule can be shifted to the posterolingual corner of the crown. Lingual cingula are rare. They usually occur as individual variations and are not known to be a constant feature of the molars of any species. Paraconid, metaconid, and entoconid commonly are aligned anteroposteriorly, and the hypoconulid is situated closer to the entoconid than the hypoconid ("entoconid-hypoconulid twinning"). Paraconid is usually slightly smaller

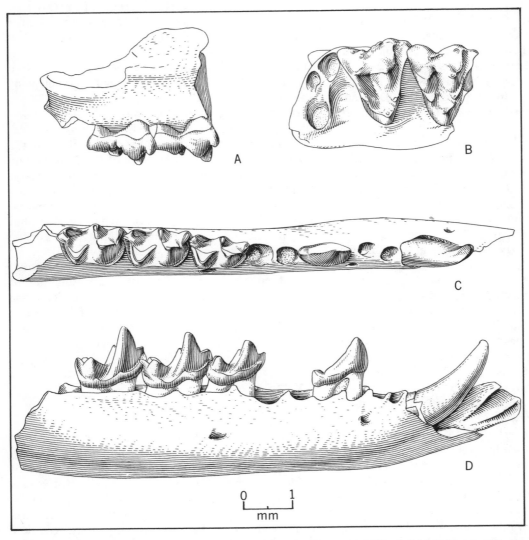

Figure 11-2. *A*-*B*, *Alphadon lulli*, **fragment of right maxillary with M$^{2\text{-}3}$:** *A*, **labial view; and** *B*, **occlusal view.** *C*-*D*, *A. ?lulli*, **fragment of right mandible with canine, P$_2$, and M$_{1\text{-}3}$:** *C*, **occlusal view; and** *D*, **labial view. (Illustrations from Clemens, 1966, copyright © by The Regents of the University of California)**

or the same size as the metaconid, which is distinctly smaller and lower than the protoconid.

Snout tends to be long and pointed. Nasal does not contact lacrimal. Frontal lacks postorbital process. Palate is usually fenestrated. In most species the ossified auditory bulla is formed by a process of the alisphenoid and is incomplete posteroventrally. However, in microbiotheres it is complete and composed of processes of both the alisphenoid and petrosal. Five toes are present on each foot; the hallux is opposable.

The classification of members of the Didelphidae utilized here recognizes at least five subfamilies; the Didelphinae (which contains the most primitive didelphids), Caluromyinae, Glasbiinae, Caroloameghiniinae, Sparassocyninae, and, possibly, the microbiotheres. Caluromyinae was established by Kirsch (1977a) for *Caluromys* and several allied, Recent, South American didelphids. Sparassocyninae includes some highly modified marsupials, apparently small carnivores of the late Tertiary, South American steppes (see Reig and Simpson, 1972). They are characterized by a short, triangular face and wide zygomatic arches on the sides of a broad cranium. The bulla is well ossified and encloses both hypo- and epitympanic sinuses.

The microbiotheres are a group of South American, Cenozoic marsupials with at least one modern representative, *Dromiciops* (see Reig, 1955). Until recently they have been classified as members of a subfamily of the Didelphidae, but Kirsch (1977a) elevated the group to full family status. Microbiotheriids are distinguishable dentally by the great reduction of the stylar cusps and shelf of the upper molars. Also, both conules are greatly reduced or lost. The talonid of M_4 is greatly reduced and unicuspid. Canines can be reduced to teeth only slightly larger than the incisors. At least in *Dromiciops* the auditory bulla, formed of contributions of both the alisphenoid and petrosal, is completely ossified.

Caroloameghiniinae includes one extinct genus composed of two species found in South American, early Eocene deposits. The entire sample consists of a few isolated teeth and fragmentary mandibles documenting the presence of very small marsupials with somewhat bunodont molar cusps. The molars exhibit several specializations also found in the North American, later Cretaceous glasbiines, which might be taken as suggesting an ancestor-descendant relationship. However, the M_4 of *Caroloameghinia* is not as reduced as that of *Glasbius,* and the lower molars lack the pronounced labial cingulum characteristic of the latter genus. Most likely the similarities between the members of these two subfamilies are the result of convergent evolution.

Both of the remaining subfamilies, Didelphinae and Glasbiinae, are represented in Late Cretaceous local faunas; the latter is restricted to latest Cretaceous "Lancian" local faunas of North America. *Glasbius,* the only genus allocated to the subfamily, was a small marsupial with low, bunodont molar cusps (Fig. 11-3). Its upper molars have broad stylar shelves; cusps B and D are large, C is smaller or absent. On some molars small cusps are developed labial to the principal stylar cusps. The metacone is larger than the paracone. The large metaconule is situated nearly posterior to the protocone, thus tending to give the tooth a rectangular occlusal outline. Lower molars are most easily distinguished by their low, anteroposteriorly compressed trigonids. Reduction of the trigonid was functionally correlated with enlargement of the metaconules. The talonid basin is large. All lower molars have a prominent labial, basal cingulum. On some teeth it carries distinct cingular cusps on the slopes of both the talonid and trigonid.

Finally, members of the Didelphinae are most easily diagnosed by the absence of any of the derived features of members of the other subfamilies. The premolars usually are of trenchant morphology but in some species are slightly inflated. Stylar cusps B and D are present in most species; C is frequently present. Paracone and conules are relatively large in primitive species but tend to be reduced in their descendants.

The trigonid is higher than the talonid. In primitive species the cristid obliqua contacts the back of the trigonid below the notch separating protoconid and metaconid. In derived forms, with enlargement of the talonid basin, the cristid obliqua runs forward to the base of the protoconid.

Of the three didelphine genera recognized in the Late Cretaceous, *Alphadon* is by far the most abundant, taxonomically diverse, and geographically widespread (Figs. 11-1 and 11-2). The oldest known species, *A. creber,* is part of an "Aquilan" local fauna of the Milk River Formation of Canada. Three species are present in the "Judithian," Judith River Formation fauna. At least four species are present in most "Lancian" local faunas. The number of species is most likely greater because many large teeth of

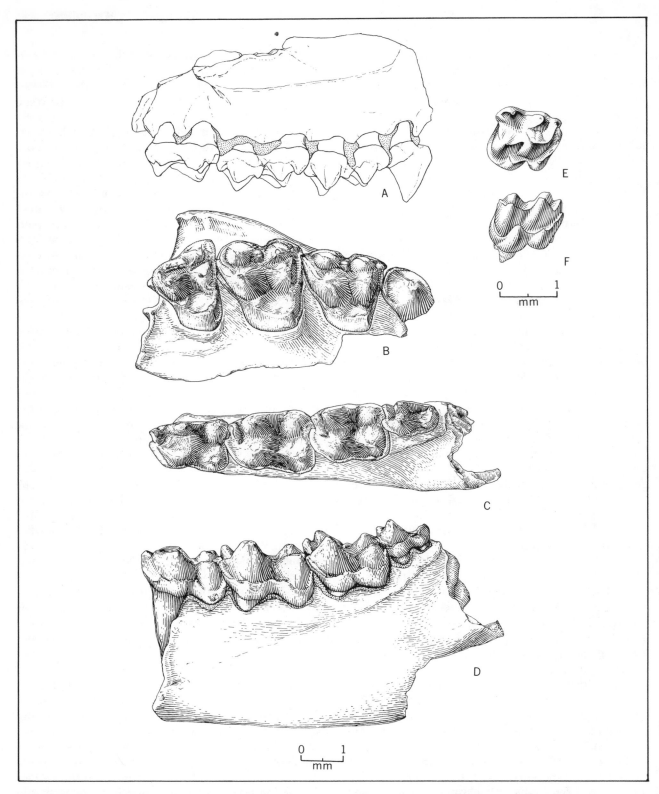

Figure 11-3. *Glasbius intricatus. A-B*, fragment of right maxillary with P³, M¹⁻³: *A*, labial view; and *B*, occlusal view. *C-D*, fragment of left mandible with M₁₋₄: *C*, occlusal view; and *D*, labial view. *E-F*, isolated right M₃, illustrating maximum known development of labial cingulum: *E*, occlusal view; and *F*, labial view. (Illustrations from Clemens, 1966, copyright © by The Regents of the University of California)

Alphadon-like morphology have been lumped into the category *A.* cf. *A. rhaister*. Probably most of these isolated teeth fall outside the range of variation of *A. rhaister* and represent new species.

Alphadon austrinum is the only species known from outside North America and is currently represented by a few fragments of teeth. Sigé (1972) included only three fragments of upper molars in the hypodigm and referred an upper premolar. The age of the site near Laguna Umayo in Peru that produced these fossils is open to question, but it is probably either Late Cretaceous or early Paleocene (see Chapter 2). *A. austrinum* is a small didelphine. Resembling the molars of other species, stylar cusps *B* and *D* are present. On two molar fragments a cusp *C* is present and smaller than *B*; cusp *C* is not present on the third specimen. Reference of this species to *Alphadon* is appropriate so long as it is remembered that the morphological similarities are all the result of shared, primitive didelphid characters. Sigé (*ibid.*) also noted the discovery of a fragment of an upper molar too small to be referable to *A. austrinum* and possibly documenting the presence of another didelphid. [Note added in proof: J.-Y. Crochet (pers. comm., 1978, and see 1977b) suggested that the relatively small size of the stylar cusps of *Alphadon austrinum*, the slightly smaller size of its paracone relative to the metacone, and other possibly apomorphic characters of its upper molars (which resemble those of *Peradectes*) require the removal of the species *austrinum* from the genus *Alphadon*.]

Until recently *Peradectes* (including *Thylacodon*) was known only from North American Paleocene deposits. Crochet (1977a, 1977b) now recognizes its presence in Europe in the Eocene, and Archibald (1977) records the occurrence of another species in North American, "Lancian" local faunas of Bug Creek faunal-facies. Finally, Fox (1971) described *Albertatherium primus* from the "Aquilan" Verdigris Coulee local fauna of the Milk River Formation. His hypodigm included four isolated upper molars, and five isolated lower molars were referred. If a didelphine, the relatively large size of the stylar cusp *C* of *Albertatherium* could be a specialization ruling it out of the ancestry of *Alphadon*.

Pediomyidae

This grouping of marsupials was established by Simpson (1927a) as a subfamily of the Didelphidae, an allocation he maintained in later classifications

(*e.g.*, Simpson, 1935 and 1945). However, the taxonomic diversity of pediomyids, the degree of their morphological distinction from didelphids, and their biostratigraphic duration suggest that this complex of lineages ought to be set apart in a separate family (see Clemens, 1973a, and Simpson, 1970, for discussion of different viewpoints).

Pediomyids are known only from fossil localities of Late Cretaceous age. They are represented entirely by isolated teeth and dentulous fragments of mandibles and maxillaries. Nothing is known of either the remainder of the skull or the postcranial skeleton, although probably some of these skeletal elements are present in large collections from Late Cretaceous localities but currently cannot be identified. Pediomyid dentitions are characterized by a small series of specializations distinguishing them from the dentitions of didelphids. First, the stylar shelf of the upper molars is greatly reduced, particularly anteriorly, so that cusp *B* usually is lost, and the shelf is not continuous across the labial side of the paracone (Fig. 11-4). A stylar cusp *C* is present in a few species, and cusp *D* is developed in most. Paracone and metacone tend to be maintained at subequal heights. Protoconule and metaconule are present. Reduction in size of the stylar shelf was correlated with enlargement of the trigon and talonid basins. This specialization is most easily, and least subjectively, seen in the labial shift of the cristid obliqua, which abuts against the back of the trigonid at the base of the protoconid.

The Verdigris Coulee local fauna of "Aquilan" age from the Milk River Formation of Canada includes the oldest species of *Pediomys*, *P. exiguus*. Another species, *P. clemensi*, is present in "Judithian" local faunas of Montana. Pediomyids, probably species of *Pediomys*, are represented in some of the small available samples of "Edmontonian" local faunas. Five species of *Pediomys* have been recognized in "Lancian" local faunas. These range in size from the minute *P. krejcii* to *P. florencae*, which is among the larger of the "Lancian" mammals. When more is known of the anatomy of these species, bases for allocation of some to new genera probably will emerge.

In addition to *Pediomys exiguus*, Fox (1971) described two other species of a new genus, *Aquiladelphis incus* and *A. minor*, which he allocated to the Pediomyidae. In both species the stylar shelf appears to be somewhat reduced in width, but two small stylar cusps *B* are present. Cusp *C* is the largest stylar cusp. The principal cusps of the molars are low

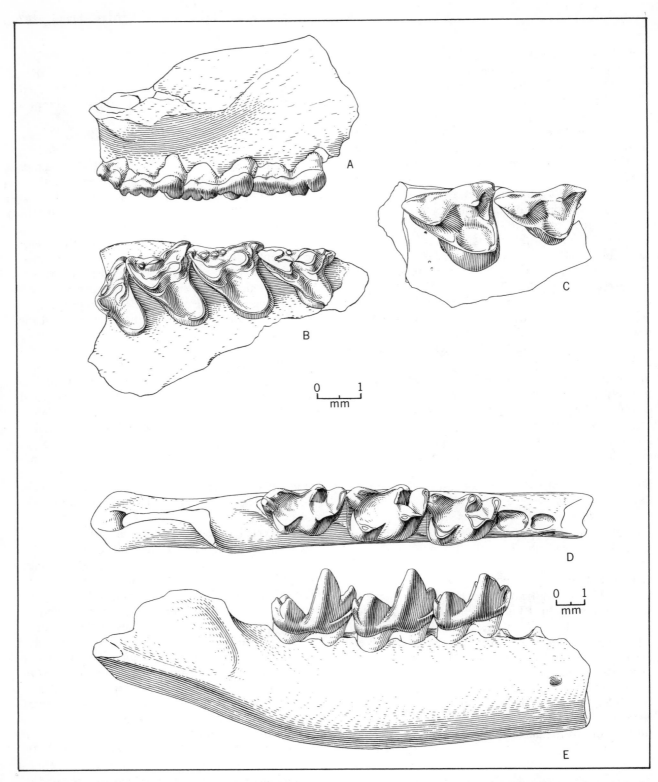

Figure 11-4. *A-B, Pediomys elegans*, fragment of right maxillary with M$^{1-4}$: *A*, labial view; and *B*, occlusal view. *C, P. hatcheri*, fragment of right maxillary with DP^3 and M^1, occlusal view. *D-E, P. ?hatcheri*, fragment of right mandible with M$_{2-4}$: *D*, occlusal view; and *E*, labial view. (Illustrations from Clemens, 1966, copyright © by The Regents of the University of California)

and somewhat bunodont. The talonid basins are broad, and the cristid obliqua reaches the talonid at the base of the protoconid. Unlike any member of *Pediomys*, stylar cusp *C* is the largest stylar cusp. This and the specializations of cusp morphology would apparently rule earlier species of *Aquiladelphis* out of the ancestry of *Pediomys*. Fox (*ibid.*, p. 159) concluded: "More probably species of *Aquiladelphis* were part of a lineage of pediomyids in which crushing specializations of the molar dentition were emphasized, to an unusual degree—in *A. incus*, at least—among Cretaceous therians." In summary, the derived characters shared by *Aquiladelphis* and *Pediomys* are few and, if not independently acquired, must reflect a dichotomy within the Pediomyidae soon after its derivation from a didelphid ancestry.

Sigé (1972) suggested that one fragment of a lower molar from Laguna Umayo might be from the dentition of a pediomyid. As far as can be determined, its talonid could have been wider than its trigonid. The labial border of the tooth is straight, and the cristid obliqua contacts the distal slope of the protoconid. If found in Late Cretaceous strata in North America, these characters of the tooth could be interpreted as being indicative of pediomyid affinities. It is possible, of course, that both pediomyids and didelphids were able to disperse throughout the Americas. However, this would place increased reliance upon the improbable events of successful overwater sweepstakes dispersal. Also, it is possible that in the few characters of the lower molar available for study, early caenolestoids paralleled the dental evolution of pediomyids. Again, more material is needed in order to test the hypothesis offered by Sigé.

Among marsupials three groups share the characters of having upper molars of essentially tribosphenic pattern but modified through reduction in width or loss of the anterior portion of the stylar shelf and cusp *B*. These are the pediomyids, the South American Tertiary borhyaenids, and the Australian Cenozoic thylacinids. It appears unlikely that pediomyids were ancestral to borhyaenids. Although there are similarities in the derived structure of their stylar shelves, the lingual portions of the molars show different patterns of modification. In pediomyids the protocone and talonid basin were enlarged. In the borhyaenids these and functionally associated structures, for example, the metaconids, were reduced or lost. Also, primitive borhyaenids, such as

Patene, appear to bridge the phylogenetic gap between South American didelphids and borhyaenids. The evolutionary relationships of thylacinids and borhyaenids are being investigated by Archer (1976a, 1976b) and Marshall (1977, 1978). However this question is resolved, it now appears most likely that pediomyids were not part of the ancestry of either family.

Stagodontidae

The earliest known stagodontids are members of the "Aquilan," Verdigris Coulee local fauna and contemporaries of the earliest known didelphids and pediomyids. Judging from dental dimensions, here as in more recent, well-sampled North American, Late Cretaceous local faunas, stagodontids are among the larger if not the largest marsupials. Anatomically, the fossil record of stagodontids is almost as limited as that of pediomyids, although three specimens provide some information about the morphology of the zygomatic arch and a small portion of the basicranial region.

Stagodontids are distinguishable from contemporaneous marsupials by modifications of the molars related to emphasis on postvallum-prevallid shear (Fig. 11-5). This is most clearly indicated by relative reduction in size of the metaconid, enlargement of the paraconid, and remodeling of the protocristid with the evolution of a carnassial notch. Initially, the larger size of the paraconid, relative to the metaconid, might have been a primitive metatherian trait, but within the stagodontids the difference has been emphasized and correlated with a pronounced anteroposterior shortening of the trigonid. Anatomical details of the auditory region have already been summarized, but it should be reemphasized that both *Eodelphis browni* and *Didelphodon vorax* have large squamosal epitympanic sinuses. These sinuses are not well developed in Cenozoic didelphids (Archer, 1976a), and their development in stagodontids is interpreted as a derived character of the family.

The oldest known stagodontid is of "Aquilan" age and was identified as *Eodelphis* sp. (see Fox, 1971). Probably two or more species of stagodontids are represented in the "Judithian" local faunas of the Judith River and Oldman formations. Currently, their taxonomy and nomenclature are in a state of flux. Three species, assigned to two genera, are involved. *Boreodon matutinus* Lambe, 1902, is typified on an isolated lower molar found in the Oldman Formation near Steveville, Alberta, Canada. Descriptions of *Cimolestes cutleri* Woodward, 1916, and *Eodelphis browni* Matthew, 1916, were published within a few weeks of each other (May 30 and July 24, respectively, *fide* Simpson, 1928). Simpson (*ibid.*) concluded these two species are referable to the same genus for which the name *Eodelphis* is appropriate. The type of *E. cutleri* is a fragmentary mandible containing P_3 and M_{2-3} as well as the alveoli for the outer cheek teeth, the canine, and at least some of the incisors. It was collected from the Oldman Formation near Little Sandhill ("Sand") Creek, southeast of Steveville, Alberta (Russell, 1952). *E. browni* is

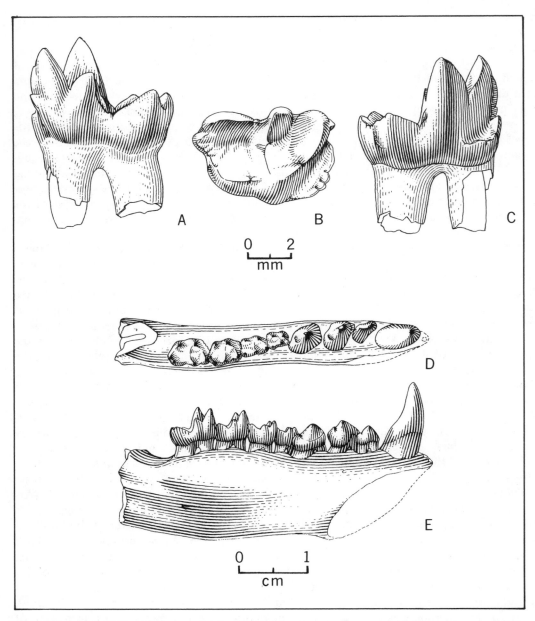

Figure 11-5. *Didelphodon vorax. A-C*, isolated right M_4: *A*, lingual view; *B*, occlusal view; and *C*, labial view. *D-E*, partial restoration of left mandible with canine, P_{1-3}, and M_{1-4}: *D*, occlusal view; and *E*, lingual view. **(Illustration *A-C* from Clemens, 1966, copyright © by The Regents of the University of California. *D-E* redrawn from Clemens, 1968b)**

typified on a fragmentary mandible and a small part of a skull also found in the vicinity of Little Sandhill Creek (*ibid.*).

Simpson (1928, 1929) thought *E. browni* was a junior synonym of *E. cutleri*. He remarked that the type of *Boreodon* ". . . is probably the premolar of a didelphid, but is indeterminate" (1929, p. 34). Clemens (1966) pointed out that the premolars of *E. browni* are trenchant, uncrowded teeth while those of the type of *E. cutleri* are relatively larger and closely approximated like those of the "Lancian" *Didelphodon vorax*. Recognition of two species appears warranted. Russell (1952) suggested that the type of *Boreodon* might be a premolar of *Eodelphis*. However, it could equally well be a premolar of a large didelphid or pediomyid, and the genus is considered indeterminate (Clemens, 1966).

The most recent nomenclatorial changes were authored by Sahni (1972). He argued that the species *cutleri* and *browni* ought to be placed in separate genera and considered *Eodelphis cutleri* to be a junior synonym of *Boreodon matutinus*. Sahni

(*ibid.*) allocated two complete and two fragmentary upper cheek teeth from the Judith River fauna to *Boreodon matutinus*. Second, noting that some of the "Judithian" isolated teeth he allocated to *Alphadon* cf. *A. rhaister* might prove to be parts of the dentition of *E. browni*, he removed this species from the Stagodontidae, but did not formally synonymize the "Judithian" *A.* cf. *A. rhaister* with *E. browni*.

Although readily agreeing with Sahni that much more material is needed before the interrelationships of these taxa can be understood, I cannot find compelling reasons to accept his changes in the classification, but see advantages in maintaining the earlier assignments (Clemens, 1966; also see Clemens and Marshall, 1976). The type of *Boreodon matutinus* remains an indeterminate specimen, and these nomina should be treated as *nomina dubia*. *Eodelphis browni* and *E. cutleri* appear to be closely related species; note, for example, that criteria for distinguishing their lower molars have yet to be found. Mandibles of the two can be distinguished only when there are

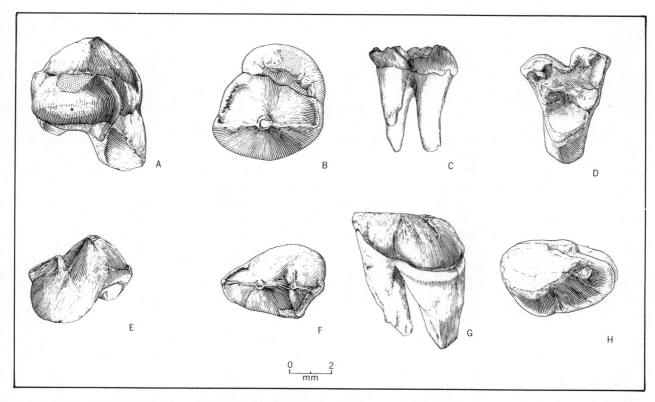

Figure 11-6. *Didelphodon vorax*, isolated cheek teeth. *A-B*, ?right P³: *A*, lingual view; and *B*, occlusal view. *C-D*, left M²: *C*, labial view; and *D*, occlusal view. *E-F*, left P₂: *E*, lingual view; and *F*, occlusal view. *G-H*, worn right P₃: *G*, lingual view; and *H*, occlusal view. (Illustrations from Clemens, 1966, copyright © by The Regents of the University of California)

data on premolar morphology. Also, shifting *E. browni* from the Stagodontidae to the Didelphidae implies the hypothesis that squamosal epitympanic sinuses evolved more than once in the diversification of Cretaceous marsupials, a possibility but not the most parsimonious hypothesis.

Didelphodon is known primarily from "Lancian" local faunas, but an isolated fragmentary tooth from the St. Mary River Formation was tentatively allocated to the genus (Sloan and Russell, 1974). These authors refer another tooth from the same locality to *Eodelphis*? sp. The dentition of *Didelphodon* (Figs. 11-5 and 11-6) is represented by dentulous fragments of maxillaries and mandibles, and many isolated teeth (see Simpson, 1929, and Clemens, 1966, 1968b, and 1973a). Two "Lancian" species, *D. vorax* and *D. padanicus*, are recognized. As is the case with *Eodelphis*, these species are diagnosed on the basis of differences in premolar morphology.

Discussion of Systematics

At family and lower taxonomic levels, the classification of Mesozoic marsupials utilized here (see Table 11-1) does not differ greatly from those presented in other recent publications. Simpson (1970) suggested that the Pediomyidae and Stagodontidae should be treated as subfamilies of the Didelphidae, but this ranking has not been adopted by other workers. In fact, the current trend in revisions of the classification of didelphoid marsupials is one of subdivision of taxa. For example, Kirsch (1977a) suggested removing the microbiotheres to a separate family, including several extinct genera and the Recent *Dromiciops*. He also grouped *Caluromys* and allied Recent genera in a separate didelphid subfamily, Caluromyinae. In Kirsch's classification, Caroloameghiniinae and Glasbiinae were maintained as subfamilies of the Didelphidae. Although leading to restructuring of the grouping of its contents, recent research has not undermined the concept of the basic phylogenetic unity of the Didelphoidea.

An increasing number of systematists are adopting changes in the higher levels of classification and recognizing several orders within a Superorder or Subclass Marsupialia. Ride (1964) suggested a fourfold division of a Superorder Marsupialia into the orders Marsupicarnivora, Paucituberculata, Peramelina, and Diprotodonta. This action was justified

on three lines of argument. First, in comparison with classifications of eutherian mammals, utilization of but one order for the marsupials stringently limits expression of their diversity and carries an inaccurate implication of homogeneity. In addition to qualitative data, Ride (*ibid.*) presented comparative statistics on the numbers of genera of marsupials and placentals then recognized, and argued that knowledge of prehistoric evolutionary radiations of marsupials, particularly the Australian radiation, was more rudimentary than knowledge of eutherian radiations. Thus the heirarchy should be expanded in expectation of the discovery of a greater diversity of prehistoric marsupials. Subsequent discoveries, particularly in Australia (see Tedford and others, 1975), are living up to these expectations. Second, Ride (1964) argued that use of a single order was an historical artifact reflecting the great significance earlier generations of mammalogists attached to the unique pattern of reproduction of marsupials. He felt that unification of all marsupials in one order simply to recognize this common character appeared to be too heavy a weighting. Finally, the great and probably essentially equal antiquity of eutherians and marsupials could warrant recognition of additional orders of marsupials. In his classification Ride (*ibid.*) included all Mesozoic marsupials in the Superfamily Didelphoidea of the Order Marsupicarnivora. Subsequently Kirsch (1968, 1977a) offered alternative classifications. In the latter, three orders of marsupials were recognized: Polyprotodonta, Paucituberculata, and Diprotodonta. Mesozoic mammals were united in the Didelphoidea of the Polyprotodonta.

Although having maintained the conservative position of utilization of a single Order Marsupialia, recent discoveries and reviews of South American and Australian Tertiary marsupials documenting greater diversity are compelling arguments for raising the Marsupialia to superordinal rank. Simpson (1931, 1945) and most subsequent systematists have recognized the close phylogenetic interrelationships of didelphoid, borhyaenoid, and dasyuroid marsupials. Those who have argued for a multiordinal classification appear to be agreed in the inclusion of these superfamilies in one order. However, the difference between Kirsch's Polyprotodonta and Ride's Marsupicarnivora is not one of simple terminology, but reflects differences in opinion on whether the peramelids ought to be included in the same order with the "marsupicarnivorans." Until this issue is resolved, use of a single Order Marsupialia will promote communication.

EVOLUTION

The available record of Mesozoic marsupials is listed in Chapter 2 and summarized in Table 11-2. Almost all the fossils come from deposits formed on coastal lowlands along the western shores of the Cretaceous Western Interior Sea (Fig. 14-5). The only site outside western North America where fossil marsupials possibly of Late Cretaceous age have been found is Laguna Umayo, Peru (Sigé, 1972). The age of these fossils has not been firmly established, but the diversity of late Paleocene, South American marsupials suggests that members of the order probably inhabited the continent in the latest Cretaceous.

Nothing is known of the mammalian fauna of Africa during the Late Cretaceous. The oldest Tertiary faunas known from samples including microvertebrate fossils (Early Oligocene, Egypt) lack marsupials, and there are no reasons to assume they ever occupied the continent. Essentially the same holds true for Europe, which during most of the Late Cretaceous was an archipelago rather than a continent (Chapter 14). The one Late Cretaceous mammalian fossil described from Europe is a tooth of a eutherian. Late Paleocene faunas of western Europe are known from several large collections and appear to lack marsupials. In the early Eocene, *Peradectes* and *Peratherium*, probably immigrants, make their appearance (Crochet, 1977a, 1977b). Thus, the usual assumption that marsupials were not part of the European Late Cretaceous fauna is supported by its simplicity, but not by direct evidence.

[Note added in proof: Demonstration of the absence of a group of animals from a prehistoric fauna of a continent such as Africa is nearly impossible. However, it should be noted that Cappetta and others (1978) recently discovered an early Paleocene local fauna in Morocco containing mammals. This is the oldest known occurrence of mammals in the Cenozoic record of Africa (the limited Mesozoic record, almost entirely of Triassic age, is reviewed in Chapter 2). To date (*ibid.*, and pers. comm. from B. Sigé, 1978) all the identifiable mammalian fossils recovered are jaws or teeth of small eutherian mammals; no evidence of the presence of marsupials or multituberculates has yet been found.]

In contrast, several Mongolian local faunas of Late Cretaceous age are known from large collections of microvertebrates (Chapter 2). The absence of marsupials from the samples is reasonably persuasive evidence that marsupials were not part of these local faunas. However, it must be noted that all these local faunas are situated in what is thought to have been the interior of the Late Cretaceous, Asian continent. Terrestrial faunas of quite different composition might well have inhabited the Asian coastal lowlands. Finally, there is no direct evidence on the time of arrival or origin of marsupials in Australia. Geophysical evidence suggests that separation of Australia from Antarctica occurred in the Paleocene or Eocene. The documented diversity of Australian Oligocene and Miocene mammalian faunas is in accord with the hypothesis that marsupials were inhabitants of Australia prior to this separation, but does not add data refining determination of the time of their first occurrence there (see Clemens, 1977; Keast, 1977; and Martin, 1977, for reviews).

Determination of the geographic locale where differentiation of marsupials from an ancestral stock of metatherian-eutherian grade took place has occupied the attention of many systematists, but still remains an open question. The initial step in origin of the Marsupialia might have been a vicariance event in which a group of therians of metatherian-eutherian grade was isolated from their contemporaries by the sundering of continents, flooding of epicontinental seas, or some other clearly documented event in the physical evolution of the earth's surface. However, it is equally probable, if not more likely, that their differentiation began in a small, peripheral population of therians of metatherian-eutherian grade isolated by relatively minor ecologic or geographic barriers. Perhaps the exact area of origin of marsupials will never be determined, but identification of the Cretaceous continent on which marsupials originated could be within the range of possibilities afforded by the fossil record.

Assuming that marsupials are descendants of therians of metatherian-eutherian grade, the combination of the following characters probably will suggest the Cretaceous continent on which they originated: (1) the presence of a suitable ancestral stock (*i.e.*, therian mammals with primitive tribosphenic dentitions); (2) the earliest record of morphologically primitive marsupials; and (3) that the oldest evolutionary radiation should have occurred in the area of origin, assuming that their pattern of reproduction or other features of the earliest marsupials afforded them a competitive advantage over their mammalian contemporaries.

Currently, only the fossil record of marsupials on the Late Cretaceous, western North American continent meets all these specifications. However, it must be stressed that essentially nothing is known of the composition of contemporary terrestrial faunas of South America or Australia. In view of the diversity of their Tertiary marsupial faunas, there is a distinct possibility that marsupials originated on one or the other of these continents. At the moment I think the evidence in hand favors the hypothesis that marsupials originated in the Americas and probably in western North America (see Tedford, 1974, for arguments in favor of the hypothesis of South American origin). Only the discovery of additional Cretaceous local faunas in the southern continents will permit testing of these hypotheses.

Slaughter (1968) allocated the Aptian therian *Holoclemensia* to the Didelphidae. That interpretation is questioned, and here *Holoclemensia* is regarded as a therian of metatherian-eutherian grade (see Chapter 10 and below). The oldest known, unequivocal records of marsupials are provided by fossils discovered in the upper part of the Milk River Formation, Alberta, Canada. These records are based on isolated teeth in the sample of the Verdigris Coulee local fauna, which is of "Aquilan" age

(Chapter 2; and Fox, 1971). The mammals of this local fauna represent a curious mixture of relics of primitive grades of mammalian evolution and some very derived forms. The relics include the last known records of triconodonts and symmetrodonts as well as a therian of metatherian-eutherian grade. Among the Verdigris Coulee marsupials are representatives of the three families (Didelphidae, Pediomyidae, and Stagodontidae) that also include all the subsequent Late Cretaceous marsupials. Clearly the differentiation of these family lineages was a pre-"Aquilan" event (Fig. 11-7). *Albertatherium* and *Aquiladelphis*, known only from Verdigris Coulee, might be relics of early radiations within the didelphid and pediomyid lineages.

The published records of "Judithian" and "Edmontonian" local faunas are not numerous and are based on small samples. At the moment all that can be said is that evolution within the three families appears to have been limited essentially to changes best reflected at the specific level within genera present in the Verdigris Coulee local fauna. However, a specimen from the "Edmontonian," Scabby Butte local fauna, Alberta, might record the first occurrence of *Didelphodon*. Also, the "Edmontonian" local faunas of the Fruitland and Kirtland formations, New Mexico, hint at the possibility of some biogeographic provincialism at this time (Clemens, research in progress).

"Lancian" local faunas from Wyoming, South Dakota, Montana, and Alberta are known from extensive samples and provide information both on evolutionary diversification and on biogeographic provincialism. Looking at the "Lancian" local faunas as a unit, their taxonomic diversity is much greater than that recorded for older local faunas. At the moment, the degree to which this apparent increase in diversity is a product of incomplete sampling of older local faunas cannot be determined. Depending on how provisionally referred specimens are counted, at least five species of *Alphadon* and five of *Pediomys* were present in the "Lancian" local faunas (Archibald and Clemens, 1977, and *in press*). These counts probably underestimate the diversity of species. For example, a variety of large, *Alphadon*-like teeth showing some differences in morphological details have been referred to *A.* cf. *A. rhaister*. Also, when more is known of their morphology, probably some of the species of *Alphadon* and, particularly, *Pediomys* might well be allocated to other genera.

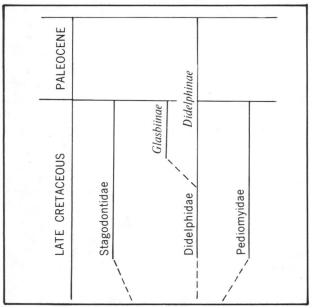

Figure 11-7.   Postulated phylogram of known families and subfamilies of Cretaceous marsupials.

The largest known species of *Pediomys, P. florencae*, is distinctly smaller than members of the species of *Didelphodon*. Finally, the appearance of *Glasbius* in "Lancian" local faunas is the first occurrence of a member of a subfamily that is not yet recorded in the only known "Aquilan" fauna.

Marsupials of the "Lancian" local faunas appear to show considerable biogeographic provincialism. It should be stressed that the temporal duration of the "Lancian" probably was in excess of several million years, and "biogeographic" differences might reflect biologically significant differences in age that are outside the resolution of current methods of correlation. In samples of the Lance local faunas, Wyoming, specimens (and probably individuals) of pediomyids are much more abundant than those of didelphids. In the stratigraphically lowest Bug Creek faunal-facies localities, most of the species found in the Lance Formation are present. Only *Alphadon lulli* and *A. rhaister* are missing; *Glasbius intricatus* is replaced by a new species of *Glasbius* (see Archibald, 1977). Similarly, the taxonomic composition of the Hell Creek faunal-facies marsupial assemblage is almost identical to that of the Lance local fauna. The only major difference is replacement of *Glasbius intricatus* by a new species of *Glasbius* (see Archibald, *ibid.*). However, relative abundances are significantly different; didelphids are abundant while pediomyids are rare. Finally, yet farther to the north in Alberta, some didelphids and pediomyids present in more southern local faunas (*Alphadon lulli, Glasbius, Pediomys cooki*, and *P. florencae*) are missing from available samples. However, the pattern of greater relative abundance of didelphids characterizing the Hell Creek faunal-facies is not modified.

Morphology of the stylar shelf is one of the features of dental morphology extensively utilized in research on the phylogenetic relationships of Late Cretaceous marsupials. As discussed in the preceding section on anatomy, a system for providing alphabetic designations to stylar cusps on the basis of their topographic positions currently is widely used (Fig. 11-1). Other names for some cusps (*e.g.*, stylocone) are sometimes employed when designation of homologous cusps is intended. Also, recent research has added support to the hypothesis that Cenozoic marsupial lineages probably share a common ancestral stock characterized by having upper molars with at least a parastyle, stylocone, cusps in the *C* and *D*

positions, and probably also in the *E* position (*i.e.*, either a species of *Alphadon* or another genus with *Alphadon*-like molars). Finally, unlike the parastyle and stylocone, the possible functions of stylar cusps in the *C* and *D* positions are not immediately apparent. Except when they are minute, the range of morphologic variation of the cusps in these positions is not exceptionally great. This limited variation suggests they have some functional significance and their degree of development is under selective control.

Slaughter (1971) based his reference of *Holoclemensia* to the Didelphidae primarily on the presence of a large stylar cusp *C* (Fig. 10-4), but mentioned two other possibly significant features. On both the type and paratype of *Holoclemensia*, the paracone appears to have been larger and higher than the metacone. In a comparison with *Pappotherium*, Slaughter noted the relatively greater size of the metacone of *Holoclemensia*. He suggested that this could reflect the beginning of the evolutionary trend that produced molars of Cenozoic didelphids in which the metacone is much larger than the reduced paracone. Slaughter's third point concerns the morphology of the talonid. The hypoconulid of the molar he referred to *Holoclemensia* is not centered on the back of the talonid but is slightly closer to the entoconid. The talonid of this molar is small and distinctly narrower than the trigonid. If these proportions were maintained as selection favored enlargement of the talonid, the result could have been evolution of the typical, marsupial talonid morphology.

To return to Slaughter's primary criterion that the presence of a large stylar cusp in the *C* position is indicative of marsupial affinities: Currently it appears most probable that all Cenozoic marsupials share a common ancestor that had stylar cusps in the *C* and *D* positions of its upper molars. To determine if this might also have been true for the common ancestor of Late Cretaceous marsupials a character analysis was carried out. It was based on the assumption that a stylar cusp was formed only once in the *C* and *D* positions, and employed the principle of commonality (*i.e.*, characters found in many members of a group probably were inherited from the common ancestral stock). The analysis of Late Cretaceous marsupials whose upper molars have been identified shows that a cusp is present in the *D* position in all species of *Alphadon, Glasbius, Didelphodon, Albertatherium,* and *Aquiladelphis.* Within the genus *Pediomys*, where selection was favoring general reduction of the stylar shelf, a cusp in the *D* position can be large (*e.g., P. elegans*), small (*e.g., P. krejcii*), or present on only some of the referred molars (*e.g., P. florencae*). On the principle of commonality, presence of a cusp in the *D* position appears to be a primitive marsupial trait.

The picture is not as clear in regard to the development of a stylar cusp in the *C* position. Presence or absence of a cusp *C* is one of the criteria used in distinguishing species of *Alphadon, Pediomys,* and *Glasbius.* At most, *Didelphodon vorax* has only minor cuspules in the *C* position. In *Aquiladelphis* and *Albertatherium* cusp *C* is the largest stylar cusp, exceeding even cusp *B* (the stylocone) in height. Strict application of the principle of commonality would suggest that presence of a stylar cusp *C* was also a primitive trait. In both *Alphadon* and *Pediomys,* the stratigraphically oldest ("Aquilan") species lack a stylar cusp in the *C* position. Thus if presence of a large stylar cusp *C* is a primitive trait, it must have been independently reduced or lost in several lineages prior to the "Aquilan."

It can be argued that the morphology of the molars of *Kuehneotherium* and *Peramus* shows that stylar cusps in the *C* and, possibly, *D* positions were not elements of the primitive therian molar, but were added later, possibly during evolution of the primitive tribosphenic dentition. Presence of a cusp *D* appears to be a primitive marsupial trait maintained in most Late Cretaceous marsupials. If it is also assumed that the presence of a large *C* cusp is both a primitive and a diagnostic feature of marsupials, then an interpretation of the phylogenetic relationships of the Mesozoic marsupials must invoke several instances of reversal of an evolutionary trend. For example, it must be argued that, in the ancestry of *Holoclemensia,* a stylar cusp *C* was not only added to the crown but selection favored increase in its size until it became the largest stylar cusp. Later this trend was reversed, and the cusp was reduced in size or lost.

Alternatively, it can be argued that the basic assumption that a stylar cusp could arise but once in the *C* position is weakened, if not falsified, by the apparently independent acquisition of mesostyles in some lineages of eutherians (*e.g.,* mixodectids and microsyopids). If cusps in the *C* position were added to the molars in several lineages of therians of metatherian-eutherian grade, then serious doubt is cast on the primary criterion for reference of

Holoclemensia to the Didelphidae or even the Marsupialia. Another working hypothesis suggests that during the early evolutionary radiation of therians of metatherian-eutherian grade stylar cusps were added to the molars in more than one lineage. In the lineage leading to *Holoclemensia* there was selection for reduction in size of the stylocone, a change probably ruling it out of the ancestry of *Alphadon.*

The affinities of the "Aquilan" *Albertatherium* and *Aquiladelphis* pose vexatious problems. The two characters speaking most strongly for metatherian affinity are the presence of several stylar cusps and the "twinning" of the entoconid-hypoconulid on the referred lower molars. In both genera the largest stylar cusp is in the *C* position. *Albertatherium* has a relatively large, blade-like cusp *B,* suggesting that the genus was not derived from *Holoclemensia.* Two small cusps are present in the *B* position on the described specimen of *Aquiladelphis.* Provisionally, *Albertatherium* has been referred to the Didelphidae, *Aquiladelphis* to the Pediomyidae. In contrast, *Alphadon creber,* a didelphine, and *Pediomys exiguus,* which are members of the same local fauna as *Albertatherium* and *Aquiladelphis,* do not differ greatly in dental morphology from "Lancian" species of *Alphadon* and *Pediomys.* The evidence suggests there were pre-"Aquilan" diversifications within both families.

After the close of the Cretaceous, marsupials were never dominant elements of North American terrestrial faunas. Research being carried on in eastern Montana (Archibald and Clemens, 1977, and *in press*) is providing the first approximation of a detailed account of the extinction of many lineages of marsupials at the close of the Cretaceous. The picture emerging suggests that in at least this area the extinction of most taxa of marsupials, dinosaurs, and other terrestrial vertebrates usually thought of as characteristic members of Late Cretaceous faunas was not an abrupt eradication. Their extinction appears to have been part of a complex modification of the fauna that took a recognizable period of time.

The research is far from complete, but the data from eastern Montana suggest that during deposition of most of the upper part of the Hell Creek Formation the composition of the Hell Creek faunal-facies (see Chapter 2) did not change greatly. These lineages of vertebrates appear to have been characterized by an evolutionary stasis. In contrast, in the stratigraphically lowest Bug Creek faunal-facies local faunas (see Sloan and Van Valen, 1965), there was a mixture of many of the Hell Creek faunal-facies vertebrates and new mammals, condylarths and multituberculates. Sequentially, in stratigraphically higher local faunas of Bug Creek faunal-facies many, but not all, of the lineages of Hell Creek faunal-facies mammals became rarer and then dropped out of the record. The first occurrence of *Peradectes*, a descendant of *Alphadon*, is in one of the stratigraphically higher Bug Creek faunal-facies local faunas. Extinction of the dinosaurs, and of marsupials such as *Pediomys*, of the Bug Creek faunal-facies appears to have occurred before their extinction in the Hell Creek faunal-facies.

ECOLOGY

With the fossil record of Mesozoic marsupials limited to fragments of their dentitions, any attempt to fathom the ecological roles of these animals stands an excellent chance of being an exercise in futility. A pertinent warning stems from the observation that systematists searching for dental characters to distinguish members of the Dasyuridae and Didelphidae found that the only consistent difference is the number of incisors present (see Archer, 1976b). However, a comparison of the adaptive ranges of the modern members of these families highlights significant differences. Modern dasyurids are largely carnivorous or insectivorous (see Ride, 1970), but modern didelphids are dominantly opportunistic feeders (Hunsaker, 1977) whose success seems to be linked to their ability to make the best of almost any situation. Perhaps there are aspects of dental morphology closely correlated with these different adaptive strategies, but they have yet to be discovered.

A survey of the dental dimensions suggests that among North American, Late Cretaceous mammals some of the smallest and probably the largest were marsupials. Almost all known Late Cretaceous marsupials come from local faunas thought, on other grounds, to have inhabited coastal lowland environments. The diversity of known taxa suggests that they evolved a significant range of adaptive strategies. Perhaps the adaptive opportunism of modern didelphids is an inheritance from their Cretaceous ancestors. Some modern dasyurids and didelphids live in semiarid to arid environments. The absence of marsupials from the Late Cretaceous, Mongolian local faunas might indicate that late Mesozoic marsupials had not evolved adaptations to areas of relatively low rainfall and continental conditions, but there are many other possible explanations for their absence.

Only two of the known genera of Late Cretaceous marsupials have dentitions that exhibit major departures from the morphology of the dentitions of modern American opossums of the genus *Marmosa*. The dentition of the largest known Cretaceous marsupial, *Didelphodon*, is characterized by great enlargement of the premolars and modifications of the molars emphasizing postvallum-prevallid shear (Clemens, 1968b). Among modern mammals the closest approximation to the specialized morphology of the premolars of *Didelphodon* is to be found in the dentition of the sea otter, *Enhydra*. Functionally, the specializations of the molars suggest emphasis on shearing but without reduction of the protocone and talonid basin, which provide both additional shearing crests and a mechanism for crushing or grinding. Its size and dental specializations suggest that *Didelphodon* was able to feed on organisms encased in hard shells: for example, freshwater or terrestrial invertebrates (clams, snails, and the like), turtles, or young ankylosaurs. The other extreme in dental modification is found in the dentition of *Glasbius*. Modifications of its molars involving the muting of shearing crests, inflation of cusps, enlargement of the trigon and talonid, and development of basal cingulae are all specializations found in modern eutherian and metatherian mammals with diets emphasizing herbivory or frugivory.

In summary, the dentitions of the species of *Alphadon* and *Marmosa* are very similar, and possibly *Alphadon* was an equally opportunistic, omnivorous marsupial. Reduction of the stylar shelf of the upper molars characteristic of species of *Pediomys* appears to be associated with emphasis on postvallum-prevallid shear. Perhaps, resembling dasyurids, *Pediomys* was a more insectivorous marsupial. *Didelphodon* and *Glasbius* are the only known Late Cretaceous marsupials with dental specializations strongly suggesting significant departures from omnivorous diets.

REFERENCES CITED

Archer, M., 1974a, The development of the cheek-teeth in *Antechinus flavipes* (Marsupialia, Dasyuridae): Roy. Soc. Western Australia Jour., v. 57, p. 54-63.

———1974b, The development of premolar and molar crowns of *Antechinus flavipes* (Marsupialia, Dasyuridae) and the significance of cusp ontogeny in mammalian teeth: *ibid.*, v. 57, p. 118-125.

———1975a, *Ningaui*, a new genus of tiny dasyurids (Marsupialia) and two new species, *N. timealeyi* and *N. ridei*, from arid Western Australia: Queensland Mus. Mem., v. 17, p. 237-249.

———1975b, Abnormal dental development and its significance in dasyurids and other marsupials: *ibid.*, v. 17, p. 251-265.

———1976a, The basicranial region of marsupicarnivores (Marsupialia), interrelationships of carnivorous marsupials, and affinities of insectivorous marsupial peramelids: Linn. Soc. Zool. Jour., v. 59, p. 217-322.

———1976b, The dasyurid dentition and its relationships to that of the didelphids, thylacinids, borhyaenids (Marsupicarnivora) and peramelids (Peramelina: Marsupialia): Austral. Jour. Zool., Suppl. Ser., no. 39, p. 1-34.

———1978, The nature of the molar-premolar boundary in marsupials and a reinterpretation of the homology of marsupial cheekteeth: Queensland Mus. Mem., v. 18, p. 157-164.

Archibald, J. D., 1977, Fossil Mammalia and testudines of the Hell Creek Formation, and the geology of the Tullock and Hell Creek formations, Garfield County, Montana [Ph.D. thesis]: Berkeley, California, Univ. California.

Archibald, J. D., and Clemens, W. A., 1977, The beginning of the age of mammals, *in* Abstracts of Papers, North American Paleontological Convention II: Jour. Paleont., v. 51, suppl. to no. 2, part III, p. 1.

———*in press*, Beginning of the age of mammals in Montana, *in* Berggren, W. A., and Van Couvering, J. A., eds., Catastrophies in earth history: the new uniformitarianism: Princeton, Princeton University Press.

Bensley, B. A., 1903, On the evolution of the Australian Marsupialia: with remarks on the relationships of the marsupials in general: Linn. Soc. London Trans., v. 9, p. 83-217.

———1906, The homologies of the stylar cusps in the upper molars of the Didelphidae: Univ. Toronto Studies (Biol. Ser.), v. 5, p. 1-13.

Berkovitz, B. K. B., 1966, Homology of the premolar teeth in *Setonix brachyurus* (Macropodidae: Marsupialia): Arch. Oral Biol., v. 11, p. 1371-1384.

Boyde, A., 1971, Comparative histology of mammalian teeth, *in* Dahlberg, A. A., ed., Dental morphology and evolution: Chicago and London, Univ. Chicago Press, p. 81-94.

Cappetta, H., Jaeger, J.-J., Sabatier, M., Sigé, B., Sudre, J., and Vianey-Liaud, M., 1978, Decouverte dans le Paleocene du Maroc des plus anciens Mammiferes eutheriens d'Afrique: Geobios, v. 11, p. 257-263.

Clemens, W. A., 1966, Fossil mammals of the type Lance Formation, Wyoming. Part II. Marsupialia: Univ. California Publs. Geol. Sci., v. 62, *vi* + 122 p.

———1968a, Origin and evolution of marsupials: Evolution, v. 22, p. 1-18.

———1968b, A mandible of *Didelphodon vorax* (Marsupialia, Mammalia): Nat. Hist. Mus. Los Angeles Co. Contribs. Sci., no. 133, 11 p.

———1973a, Fossil mammals of the type Lance Formation, Wyoming. Part III, Eutheria and summary: Univ. California Publs. Geol. Sci., v. 94, *vi* + 102 p.

———1973b, The roles of fossil vertebrates in interpretation of Late Cretaceous stratigraphy of the San Juan Basin, New Mexico: Four Corners Geol. Soc. Memoir Book, 1973, p. 154-167.

———1977, Phylogeny of the marsupials, *in* Stonehouse, B., and Gilmore, D., eds., The biology of marsupials: London, Macmillan Press Ltd., p. 51-68.

Clemens, W. A., and Marshall, L. G., 1976, American and European Marsupialia, *in* Westphal, F., ed., Fossilium catalogus, I: Animalia, Pars 123: Dr. W. Junk B. V. -'s-Gravenhage, p. 1-114.

Cope, E. D., 1892, On a new genus of *Mammalia* from the Laramie formation: Amer. Natur., v. 26, p. 758-762.

Copenhaver, W. M., Bunge, R. P., and Bunge, M. B., 1971, Bailey's textbook of histology (16th ed.): Baltimore, Williams and Williams, *v* + 745 p.

Crochet, J.-Y., 1977a, Les *Didelphidae* (Marsupicarnivora, Marsupialia) holarctiques tertiares: Acad. Sci. Paris C. R., v. 284, p. 357-360.

———1977b, Les Didelphidés paléogènes holarctiques: Historique et tendances évolutives, *in* Hartenberger, J.-L., ed., Faunes de Mammifères du Paléogène d'Eurasie: Geobios, mem. spéc., no. 1, p. 127-134.

Crompton, A. W., and Hiiemäe, K. M., 1970, Molar occlusion and mandibular movements during occlusion in the American opossum, *Didelphis marsupialis*, L.: Linn. Soc. Zool. Jour., v. 49, p. 21-47.

Crompton, A. W., Thexton, A. J., Parker, P., and Hiiemäe, K., 1977, The activity of the jaw and hyoid musculature in the Virginian opossum, *Didelphis virginiana*, *in* Stonehouse, B., and Gilmore, D., eds., The biology of marsupials: London, Macmillan Press Ltd., p. 287-305.

Fosse, G., Risnes, S., and Holmbakken, N., 1973, Prisms

and tubules in multituberculate enamel: Calc. Tiss. Res., v. 11, p. 133-150.

Fox, R. C., 1971, Marsupial mammals from the early Campanian Milk River Formation, Alberta, Canada, *in* Kermack, D. M., and Kermack, K. A., eds., Early mammals: Linn. Soc. Zool. Jour., v. 50, suppl. 1, p. 145-164.

_____1976, Cretaceous mammals (*Meniscoessus intermedius*, new species, and *Alphadon* sp.) from the lowermost Oldman Formation, Alberta: Canad. Jour. Earth Sci., v. 13, p. 1216-1222.

Gardner, A. L., 1973, The systematics of the genus *Didelphis* (Marsupialia: Didelphidae) in North and Middle America: Mus. Texas Tech. Univ. Spec. Publ., no. 4, 81 p.

Gray, J. E., 1821, On the natural arrangement of vertebrose animals: London Med. Reposit., v. 15, p. 296-310.

Hunsaker, D., II, 1977, Ecology of New World marsupials, *in* Hunsaker, D., II, ed., The biology of marsupials: New York, Academic Press, p. 95-156.

Huxley, T. H., 1880, On the application of the laws of evolution to the arrangement of the Vertebrata, and more particularly of the Mammalia: Zool. Soc. London Proc., 1880, p. 649-662.

Illiger, C., 1811, Prodromus systematis mammalium et avium additis terminis zoographicus utrindque classis: Berlin, C. Salfeld, *xviii* + 301 p.

Johnson, J. I., Jr., 1977, Central nervous system of marsupials, *in* Hunsaker, D., II, ed., The biology of marsupials: New York, Academic Press, p. 157-278.

Keast, A., 1977, Historical biogeography of the marsupials, *in* Stonehouse, B., and Gilmore, D., eds., The biology of marsupials: London, Macmillan Press Ltd., p. 69-95.

Kirsch, J. A. W., 1968, Prodromus of the comparative serology of Marsupialia: Nature, v. 217, p. 418-420.

_____1977a, The classification of marsupials, *in* Hunsaker, D., II, ed., The biology of marsupials: New York, Academic Press, p. 1-50.

_____1977b, The six-percent solution: second thoughts on the adaptedness of the Marsupialia: Amer. Sci., v. 65, p. 276-288.

Kraus, B. S., Jordan, R. E., and Abrams, L., 1969, A study of the masticatory system, dental anatomy and occlusion: Baltimore, Williams and Williams, *vii* + 317 p.

Lambe, L. M., 1902, New genera and species from the Belly River Series (mid-Cretaceous): Geol. Surv. Canada, Contribs. Canad. Palaeont., v. III, pt. II, p. 25-81.

Lillegraven, J. A., 1969, Latest Cretaceous mammals of upper part of Edmonton Formation of Alberta, Canada, and review of marsupial-placental dichotomy in mammalian evolution: Univ. Kansas Paleont. Contribs., Art. 50 (Vertebrata 12), 122 p.

_____1972, Preliminary report on Late Cretaceous mammals from the El Gallo Formation, Baja California del Norte, Mexico: Nat. Hist. Mus. Los Angeles Co. Contribs. Sci., no. 232, 11 p.

Martin, P. G., 1977, Marsupial biogeography and plate tectonics, *in* Stonehouse, B., and Gilmore, D., eds., The biology of marsupials: London, Macmillan Press Ltd., p. 97-115.

Marsh, O. C., 1889a, Discovery of Cretaceous Mammalia: Amer. Jour. Sci., ser. 3, v. 38, p. 81-92.

_____1889b, Discovery of Cretaceous Mammalia. Part II: *ibid.*, p. 174-180.

Marshall, L. G., 1976, New didelphine marsupials from the La Venta fauna (Miocene) of Colombia, South America: Jour. Paleo., v. 50, p. 402-418.

_____1977, Cladistic analysis of borhyaenid, dasyuroid, didelphoid, and thylacinid (Marsupialia: Mammalia) affinity: Syst. Zool., v. 26, p. 410-425.

_____1978, Evolution of the Borhyaenidae, extinct South American predaceous marsupials: Univ. California Publs. Geol. Sci., v. 117, *v* + 89 p.

Matthew, W. D., 1916, A marsupial from the Belly River Cretaceous. With critical observations upon the affinities of the Cretaceous mammals: Amer. Mus. Nat. Hist. Bull., v. 35, 477-500.

Matthew, W. D., and Granger, W., 1921, New genera of Paleocene mammals: Amer. Mus. Novitates, no. 13, 17 p.

Moss, M. L., 1969, Evolution of mammalian dental enamel: *ibid.*, no. 2360, 39 p.

Moss, M. L., and Applebaum, E., 1963, The fibrillar matrix of marsupial enamel: Acta Anat., v. 53, p. 289-297.

Moss, M. L., and Kermack, K. A., 1967, Enamel structure in two upper Triassic mammals: Jour. Dent. Res., v. 46, p. 745-747.

Ørvig, T., 1967, Phylogeny of tooth tissues: evolution of some calcified tissues in early vertebrates, *in* Miles, A. E. W., ed., Structural and chemical organization of teeth: New York and London, Academic Press, v. 1, p. 45-110.

Osborn, H. F., 1898, Evolution of the *Amblypoda*. Part I. *Taligrada* and *Pantodonta*: Amer. Mus. Nat. Hist. Bull., v. 10, p. 169-218.

Poole, D. F. G., 1956, The structure of the teeth of some mammal-like reptiles: Quart. Jour. Micro. Sci., v. 97, p. 303-312.

_____1967a, Enamel structure in primitive mammals: Jour. Dent. Res., v. 46, p. 124.

_____1967b, Phylogeny of tooth tissues: enameloid and enamel in recent vertebrates, with a note on the history of cementum, *in* Miles, A. E. W., ed., Structural and chemical organization of teeth: New York and London, Academic Press, v. 1, p. 111-149.

_____1971, An introduction to the phylogeny of calcified tissues, *in* Dahlberg, A. A., ed., Dental morphology and evolution: Chicago, Univ. Chicago Press, p. 65-79.

Poole, D. F. G., and Cooper, J. S., 1971, Prism structure

in the enamel of a reptile: Jour. Dent. Res., v. 50, p. 681.

Reig, O. A., 1955, Noticia preliminar sobre la presencia de microbiotherinos viventes en la fauna sudamerican: Invest. Zool. Chilenas, v. 2, p. 121-130.

Reig, O. A., and Simpson, G. G., 1972, *Sparassocynus* (Marsupialia, Didelphidae), a peculiar mammal from the late Cenozoic of Argentina: Linn. Soc. Zool. Jour., v. 167, p. 511-539.

Ride, W. D. L., 1962, On the evolution of Australian marsupials, *in* Leeper, G. W., ed., The evolution of living organisms: Melbourne, Melbourne Univ. Press, p. 281-306.

———1964, A review of Australian fossil marsupials: Roy. Soc. Western Australia Jour., v. 47, p. 97-130.

———1970, A guide to the native mammals of Australia: Oxford, Oxford Univ. Press, *ix* + 249 p.

Risnes, S., and Fosse, G., 1974, The origin of marsupial enamel tubules: Acta Anat., v. 87, p. 275-282.

Russell, L. S., 1952, Cretaceous mammals of Alberta: Nat'l. Mus. Canada, Ann. Rept. for Fiscal Year 1950-1951, Bull. 126, p. 110-119.

Sahni, A., 1972, The vertebrate fauna of the Judith River Formation, Montana: Amer. Mus. Nat. Hist. Bull., v. 147, p. 321-412.

Shobusawa, M., 1952, Vergleichende Untersuchungen über die Form der Schmelzprismen der Säugetiere: Okajimas Folia Anat. Japan., v. 24, p. 371-392.

Sigé, B., 1971, Les Didelphoides de Laguna Umayo (formation Vilquechico, Crétacé supérieur, Pérou), et le peuplement marsupial d'Amérique du Sud: Acad. Sci. Paris, C. R., v. 273, p. 2479-2481.

———1972, La faunule de mammifères du Crétacé supérieur de Laguna Umayo (Andes péruviennes): Mus. Natl. Hist. Natur. Bull., 3ᵉ ser., no. 99, Sciences de la Terre 19, p. 375-409.

Simpson, G. G., 1927a, Mammalian fauna of the Hell Creek Formation of Montana: Amer. Mus. Novitates, no. 267, 7 p.

———1927b, Mesozoic Mammalia. VIII. Genera of Lance mammals other than multituberculates: Amer. Jour. Sci., ser. 5, v. 14, p. 121-130.

———1928, A catalogue of the Mesozoic Mammalia in the Geological Department of The British Museum: London, Oxford Univ. Press, *x* + 215 p.

———1929, American Mesozoic Mammalia: Peabody Mus. (Yale Univ.) Mem., v. 3, pt. 1, Yale Univ. Press, *xv* + 171 p.

———1931, A new classification of mammals: Amer. Mus. Nat. Hist. Bull., v. 59, p. 259-293.

———1935, Note on the classification of recent and fossil opossums: Jour. Mammal., v. 16, p. 134-137.

———1945, The principles of classification and a classification of mammals: Amer. Mus. Nat. Hist. Bull., v. 85, *xvi* + 350 p.

———1970, The Argyrolagidae, extinct South American marsupials: Mus. Comp. Zool. (Harvard Univ.) Bull., v. 139, 86 p.

Slaughter, B. H., 1968, Earliest known marsupials: Science, v. 162, p. 254-255.

———1971, Mid-Cretaceous (Albian) therians of the Butler Farm local fauna, Texas, *in* Kermack, D. M., and Kermack, K. A., eds., Early mammals: Linn. Soc. Zool. Jour., v. 50, suppl. 1, p. 131-143.

Sloan, R. E., and Russell, L. S., 1974, Mammals from the St. Mary River Formation (Cretaceous) of southwestern Alberta: Roy. Ontario Mus. Life Sci. Contribs., v. 95, p. 1-21.

Sloan, R. E., and Van Valen, L., 1965, Cretaceous mammals from Montana: Science, v. 148, 220-227.

Tedford, R. H., 1974, Marsupials and the new paleogeography, *in* Ross, C. A., ed., Paleogeographic provinces and provinciality: Tulsa, Soc. Econ. Paleont. Mineral., Spec. Publ. 21, p. 109-126.

Tedford, R. H., Banks, M. R., Kemp, N. R., McDougall, I., and Sutherland, F. L., 1975, Recognition of the oldest known fossil marsupials from Australia: Nature, v. 255, p. 141-142.

Thomas, O., 1887, On the homologies and succession of the teeth in the Dasyuridae with an attempt to trace the history of the evolution of mammalian teeth in general: Roy. Soc. London Philos. Trans., v. 178, p. 443-462.

Tomes, C. S., 1904, A manual of dental anatomy (6th ed.): London, J. and A. Churchill, *vi* + 636 p.

Tomes, J., 1849, On the structure of the dental tissues of marsupial animals and more especially of the enamel: Roy. Soc. London Philos. Trans., v. 139, p. 402-412.

Turnbull, W. D., 1971, The Trinity therians: their bearing on evolution in marsupials and other therians, *in* Dahlberg, A. A., ed., Dental morphology and evolution: Chicago, Univ. Chicago Press, p. 151-179.

Waage, K. M., 1968, The type Fox Hills Formation, Cretaceous (Maestrichtian), South Dakota: Peabody Mus. Nat. Hist. (Yale Univ.) Bull. 27, 175 p.

Woodward, A. S., 1916, On a mammalian mandible (*Cimolestes cutleri*) from an Upper Cretaceous formation in Alberta, Canada: Zool. Soc. London Proc., v. 158, p. 525-528.

Ziegler, A. C., 1971, A theory of the evolution of therian dental formulas and replacement patterns: Quart. Rev. Biol., v. 46, p. 226-249.

CHAPTER 12

EUTHERIA

Zofia Kielan-Jaworowska

Thomas M. Bown

Jason A. Lillegraven

INTRODUCTION

A number of morphological and physiological characters, when used in combination, serve well to distinguish the two great groups of *living* therian mammals, the marsupials (Infraclass Metatheria) and the placentals (Infraclass Eutheria). Living representatives of the Metatheria and Eutheria differ in the following (and many other) respects, and the two lists can be used as general diagnoses.

METATHERIA	EUTHERIA
1. Postorbital bar usually lacking	Postorbital bar commonly present
2. Braincase relatively small	Braincase relatively large
3. Posterior palatal vacuities usually present	Posterior palatal vacuities developed in only a few forms

4. Usually, a poorly developed auditory bulla derived from alisphenoid

Auditory bulla commonly well developed, and of various origins

5. Angle of lower jaw usually inflected medially

Angle of lower jaw usually not inflected medially

6. Dental formula derived from $I_4^5 C_1^1 P_3^3 M_4^4$

Dental formula derived from $I_3^3 C_1^1 P_4^4 M_3^3$

7. Essentially monophyodont teeth; only third premolar is replaced

Diphyodont teeth; replacement of most antemolar teeth

8. Relatively broad stylar shelf on upper molars in most polyprotodont forms

Relatively narrow stylar shelf in most forms

9. Epipubic bones in both sexes of most forms

No epipubic bones

10. None possess baculum or os clitoridis

Baculum or os clitoridis commonly present

11. Cerebral hemispheres usually small

Cerebral hemispheres tend toward larger size

12. Ureters medial to derivatives of Müllerian ducts

Ureters lateral to derivatives of Müllerian ducts

13. Pseudovaginal canal present

No pseudovaginal canal

14. Young carried externally on nipples, and commonly enclosed within pouch

Young in uterus or nest; rarely carried on nipples, and never enclosed in true pouch

15. No true embryonic trophoblast

Embryonic trophoblast present, as distinguished from the inner cell mass

16. Erosion of uterine wall by extraembryonic membranes of developing young uncommon

Erosion common

17. Choriovitelline placenta in most forms; chorioallantoic placenta in only a few genera

"Chorioallantoic" placenta largely replaces choriovitelline placenta

18. Altricial young

Precocious young common

Because of an almost identical pattern of braincase structure, possession of tribosphenic molars, and many other similarities in anatomy and physiological functions between the two groups, there is little doubt that they had a common ancestor more recently than either had with the monotremes or, probably, any other prototherian group (see Lillegraven, 1974, 1975). Mills (1961) advocated the probability of independent origin of Metatheria and Eutheria from different stocks within the Eupantotheria. Known Late Jurassic fossils, however, do not necessarily support this view.

It follows that as one traces the fossil records of marsupial and placental mammals back in time toward their last common ancestor, preservable anatomical features should merge in form to a point at which it becomes impossible to differentiate features characteristic of marsupials from features characteristic of placentals. That, indeed, is exactly what is emerging from study of the available fossil record; characteristics of dental and skeletal anatomy of known species of Cretaceous therians are clearly shown to form a marsupial-like plus placental-like mosaic. It is the documentation of this mosaicism, and the problems incurred thereby in recognizing members of modern lineages, that form the underlying theme of the descriptive parts of this chapter.

The earliest occurrence of eutherians (Tables 12-1 and 12-2), in our opinion, is from ?Aptian or ?Albian rocks (age very questionable) of Khovboor, Mongolia (Beliajeva and others, 1974), although the specimens are not yet formally described. There is no indication from the known record of the Jurassic that differentiated marsupials and placentals had existed at that time. Therefore, the marsupial-placental dichotomy in mammalian evolution most probably occurred sometime during the Early Cretaceous; it is to that interval of geologic time that searches should be focused for the last common ancestor of the two groups. There is a general agreement in the likelihood that such an ancestor possessed molars characteristic of *Aegialodon* (see Kermack and others, 1965, and Chapters 9 and 10). Unfortunately, *Aegialodon* is known only from a single lower molar from Wealden rocks of England, and can thus reveal little about the nature of the common ancestor of marsupial and placental mammals. Existing knowledge of the cranial and postcranial anatomy of Cretaceous therian mammals (see Kielan-Jaworowska, 1975a, 1977, *in press*) and the comparison of reproductive systems of both groups (see Lillegraven, 1975, and Chapter 13) indicate that the common ancestor of marsupials and placentals was probably more generalized and didelphid marsupial-like in its anatomical and physiological features than placental-like.

Many problems exist that prevent confident recognition of Cretaceous placental mammals, even late in the period. Perhaps the single most important of these difficulties is the generally paltry nature of the known fossil record (as discussed in Chapter 2); immense geographical, chronological, paleoecological, and anatomical gaps exist. Adequate knowledge is approximated only in rocks of Late Cretaceous age, and only in limited parts of Holarctica. Second, most anatomical features of living therians that can readily be used in the differentiation of marsupials and placentals are not preservable as fossils (for example, seven of the eighteen features listed above cannot be fossilized, and several others are unlikely to be properly prepared, even if found as fossils). Molar teeth, mainly isolated or in minor fragments of jaws, have therefore been used most heavily in interpreting the Mesozoic histories of marsupials and placentals. This procedure is particularly fraught with difficulties such as these: (1) homologous teeth cannot always be compared (or, perhaps,

even recognized); and (2) extremely few diagnostic dental characters are available for use that are consistently present in homologous teeth.

Despite the aforementioned problems, evidence is now adequate to prove that considerable taxonomic and anatomical diversity of advanced therians existed in the latest Cretaceous (involving marsupials, placentals, and therians of metatherian-

TABLE 12-1   CLASSIFICATION OF MESOZOIC EUTHERIA

Infraclass Eutheria Gill, 1872
  Order Proteutheria (Romer, 1966)
    Superfamily Leptictoidea (Gill, 1872), new family
      Gypsonictops Simpson, 1927
        G. hypoconus Simpson, 1927
        G. illuminatus Lillegraven, 1969
        G. lewisi Sahni, 1972
        G. sp., probably new species, *in* Clemens, 1973b
        G. sp. Fox, 1970
      ?Leptictoidea *incertae sedis*
        Kennalestes Kielan-Jaworowska, 1969
          K. gobiensis Kielan-Jaworowska, 1969
    Superfamily Palaeoryctoidea (Winge, 1917)
      Family Palaeoryctidae Simpson, 1931
        Cimolestes Marsh, 1889
          C. incisus Marsh, 1889
          C. magnus Clemens and Russell, 1965
          C. cerberoides Lillegraven, 1969
          C. propalaeoryctes Lillegraven, 1969
          C. stirtoni Clemens, 1973a
          cf. *Cimolestes* sp., *in* Clemens, 1973b
        Batodon Marsh, 1892
          B. tenuis Marsh, 1892
        Procerberus Sloan and Van Valen, 1965
          P. formicarum Sloan and Van Valen, 1965
        Asioryctes Kielan-Jaworowska, 1975b
          A. nemegetensis Kielan-Jaworowska, 1975b
      Palaeoryctidae? *incertae sedis*
        Telacodon Marsh, 1892
          T. laevis Marsh, 1892
        "Champ-Garimond tooth" of Ledoux, Hartenberger, Michaux, Sudre, and Thaler, 1966
    Proteutheria *incertae sedis*
      Family Zalambdalestidae Gregory and Simpson, 1926
        Zalambdalestes Gregory and Simpson, 1926
          Z. lechei Gregory and Simpson, 1926
        Barunlestes Kielan-Jaworowska, 1975b
          B. butleri Kielan-Jaworowska, 1975b

  Order Condylarthra Cope, 1881
    Superfamily Arctocyonoidea Trouessart, 1885
      Family Arctocyonidae Murray, 1866
        Protungulatum Sloan and Van Valen, 1965
          P. donnae Sloan and Van Valen, 1965
          P. sp. "O" Sloan and Van Valen, 1965
          P. sp. "S" Sloan and Van Valen, 1965
          ?*P.* sp. "H" Sloan and Van Valen, 1965
          P. sp. "E" Sloan and Van Valen, 1965
        genus and species indet. of Archibald, 1977
    ?Condylarthra *incertae sedis*
      Perutherium Grambast, Martinez, Mattauer, and Thaler, 1967
        P. altiplanense Grambast, Martinez, Mattauer, and Thaler, 1967
  Order Primates Linnaeus, 1758
    Suborder Prosimii Illiger, 1811
      Infraorder Plesiadapiformes Simons and Tattersall, *in* Simons, 1972
        Family *incertae sedis*
          Purgatorius Van Valen and Sloan, 1965
            P. ceratops Van Valen and Sloan, 1965
  Eutheria *incertae sedis*
    Gallolestes Lillegraven, 1976
      G. pachymandibularis Lillegraven, 1976
  ?Eutheria *incertae sedis*
    Endotherium Shikama, 1947
      E. niinomii Shikama, 1947
    unnamed upper molar, Fox, 1974
    eutherian of uncertain ordinal affinities, Clemens, 1973b
  Nomina nuda
    Prozalambdalestes Beliajeva, Trofimov, and Reshetov, 1974
      P. simpsoni Beliajeva, Trofimov, and Reshetov, 1974
    Prokennalestes Beliajeva, Trofimov, and Reshetov, 1974
      P. kozlovi Beliajeva, Trofimov, and Reshetov, 1974

eutherian grade). This diversity presumably resulted from evolutionary radiations that occurred throughout the 70 million years of the Cretaceous. As a result, many dental features had probably already undergone, by the Late Cretaceous, extensive parallel and convergent evolution in different lineages, as occurred in Cenozoic mammalian history. Thus, respectively, similarities or differences in comparative odontology cannot unequivocally be considered the result of common inheritance or indicative of "phyletic distance." Furthermore, interrelationships of evolutionary lineages of Cretaceous eutherians among stratigraphic horizons can today, with minor exceptions, only be hypothesized. Pertinent additional complications to the interpretation of evolutionary radiations of advanced therians during the

TABLE 12-2   AGE AND OCCURRENCE OF GENERA OF MESOZOIC EUTHERIA

GENUS	OCCURRENCE	AGE OR STAGE
Endotherium	Hsinchiu (Husin) Coal Field, Fuxian, People's Republic of China (Manchuria)	?Early Cretaceous
"*Prozalambdalestes*"	Fm.?, Khovboor, near Guchin Us, province (aymak) of Arvaykher, Mongolian People's Republic	?Aptian or ?Albian
"*Prokennalestes*"	Fm.?, Khovboor, near Guchin Us, province (aymak) of Arvaykher, Mongolian People's Republic	?Aptian or ?Albian
Kennalestes	Djadokhta Fm., Bayn Dzak (Shabarakh Usu), Mongolian People's Republic	?late Santonian and/or ?early Campanian
Zalambdalestes	Djadokhta Fm., Bayn Dzak (Shabarakh Usu), Mongolian People's Republic	?late Santonian and/or ?early Campanian
"Champ-Garimond tooth"	Fm.?, near Fons, France	late Senonian (Valdo-Rogniacien)
undescribed genera A and B	upper part of Milk River Fm., Alberta, Canada, Fox (1972)	"Aquilan"
Gallolestes	"El Gallo Fm.," Baja California, Mexico	?middle to late Campanian
Asioryctes	Barun Goyot Fm., Nemegt Basin; beds of Khermeen Tsav, Khermeen Tsav, Mongolian People's Republic	?middle Campanian
Barunlestes	Barun Goyot Fm., Nemegt Basin; beds of Khermeen Tsav, Khermeen Tsav, Mongolian People's Republic	?middle Campanian
Gypsonictops	Lance Fm., Wyoming; Judith River Fm. and Hell Creek Fm., Montana; Fruitland Fm. and Kirtland Fm., New Mexico, U.S.A.; Scollard Fm. and Oldman Fm., Alberta, Canada	"Judithian"-"Lancian"
Telacodon	Lance Fm., Wyoming, U.S.A.	"Lancian"
Procerberus	Hell Creek Fm., Montana, U.S.A.	"Lancian"
	Polecat Bench Fm., Wyoming, U.S.A.	Puercan
Batodon	Lance Fm., Wyoming, U.S.A.; Scollard Fm., Alberta, Canada	"Lancian"
Perutherium	Vilquechico Fm. (or equivalent), Peru	?late Maastrichtian
Purgatorius	Hell Creek Fm., Montana, U.S.A.	"Lancian"
	Tullock Fm., Montana, U.S.A.	Puercan
Protungulatum	Hell Creek Fm., Montana, U.S.A.	"Lancian"
	Polecat Bench Fm., Wyoming, U.S.A. (under name of *Loxolophus*)	Puercan
Cimolestes	Hell Creek Fm., Montana; Lance Fm., Wyoming; Fruitland Fm. and Kirtland Fm., New Mexico, U.S.A.; Scollard Fm., Alberta, Canada	"Edmontonian"-"Lancian"
	Puerco Fm., New Mexico, U.S.A.	Puercan

Cretaceous are introduced by considerations of comparative mammalian reproduction (see Chapter 13) and world paleogeography (Chapter 14).

What, then, are the specific characters that paleontologists, so wisely, use to differentiate molar teeth of the Eutheria from those of their Cretaceous contemporaries, the Metatheria and Theria of metatherian-eutherian grade? A more complete diagnosis of the Cretaceous Eutheria is presented in a section below (in which nondental features are also cited), but the following characters of individual molars have been considered to be the most useful in recognizing Cretaceous placental mammals:

Upper molars
1. They tend to be more transversely widened than in known contemporary metatherians (M) and therians of metatherian-eutherian grade (TMEG).
2. Lingual cingula are usually present (but absent in several known species) in contrast to absence in known M and TMEG.
3. Conules are stronger and usually winged (but not very distinct in zalambdalestids) in contrast to weak, usually unwinged condition in M (but strong in *Didelphodon vorax*) and TMEG.
4. Stylar shelf is usually narrower (but is primitively wide) than in known contemporary M (but is reduced in *Pediomys*) and TMEG.
5. Stylar cusps are usually small or absent (especially cusp *C*), in contrast to strong development of *B, D*, and sometimes *C* in known TMEG and M (although reduced or absent in some M).

Lower molars
1. Paraconid is usually markedly smaller than protoconid and metaconid, in contrast to more equal proportions of the three cusps in M (except Stagodontidae, in which paraconid exceeds height of metaconid); height of paraconid relative to metaconid is highly variable in known TMEG, but in most cases the paraconid is taller.
2. Hypoconulid is nearly centrally placed between entoconid and hypoconid, and talonid is usually somewhat broader transversely (with several exceptions) than M; M with hypoconulid is approximated with entoconid and separated from hypoconulid; TMEG with centrally placed hypoconulid, but on transversely narrow talonid.
3. Antero- and posterolabial cingula are commonly (with many exceptions) stronger and more extensive than M (but very strong in *Glasbius*) and TMEG.

To the above can be added, if one is fortunate enough to have available for study a nearly complete tooth row, a few points concerning the premolar-molar differentiation. Cretaceous mammals identified as placentals usually have three molars and primitively five premolars (that tend to be reduced to four in adult stages of more advanced species). Trends toward molarization of the posterior premolars (especially the last) occurred in eutherians, such that the morphological break is usually not sharp between the premolar and molar series. Late Cretaceous marsupials, on the other hand, seem to have had four molars and three premolars, and showed no tendency toward the molarization of posterior premolars. Therefore, a sharp morphological break occurred in marsupials between the premolar and molar series, a condition also existing in the few known therians of metatherian-eutherian grade. Generalizations concerning the dental formula of the latter group cannot yet be made.

The brevity of the above listing, and the qualifications appended thereto, give one pause for contemplation when seriously considering an attempt at reconstruction of evolutionary lineages of Cretaceous advanced Theria.

The practical difficulties in identification of these animals are classically shown when one summarizes the history of interpretations of certain of the Early Cretaceous ("Paluxian") mammals from Texas (see Chapter 10). This fauna has been discussed during the past twenty years by virtually every paleontologist actively involved in the study of Mesozoic mammals; there has been unanimity only in disagreement concerning the affinities of the advanced therians in the fauna. Some students, including Slaughter (1965, 1971) and Fox (1975) recognized the presence of early representatives both of metatherian and of eutherian mammals. Others (*e.g.*, Kielan-Jaworowska, 1975c; Crompton and Kielan-Jaworowska, 1978) believed that eutherian mammals are not recognizable within this fauna. In this book we classify all the "Trinity therians" as Theria of metatherian-eutherian grade.

DIAGNOSIS OF CRETACEOUS EUTHERIAN MAMMALS

Cretaceous eutherians were small, ranging from shrew- to marmot-size. The snout was primitively narrow and elongated, but became shortened in carnivorous forms. The braincase is narrow with a postorbital constriction. The nasals, where known, are expanded posteriorly and probably contact the lacrimals. In primitive forms, the lacrimals have a large facial wing, and the zygomatic arches are slender with long jugals. Auditory bullae are not developed. The ectotympanic is ring-like, and is situated more anteriorly than in modern mammals. Entotympanic bones are absent in known skulls.

The mandible is slender and, where known, the angular process of most species is inflected medially. Known lower incisors are semiprocumbent, and the incisor count varies from 5/4 to 3/3. There are five premolars in known Early Cretaceous eutherians, but typically there are four in later Cretaceous forms. The last premolar is usually not completely molarized, and a metacone is usually absent. The upper canine is primitively double-rooted, but in a few forms is single-rooted. The molars are three in number and are tuberculosectorial with high, acute cusps. The stylar shelves of the upper molars are primitively wide, but tend toward reduction in more advanced forms. Pre- and postcingula are absent in Early Cretaceous eutherians, but are present in most Late Cretaceous forms.

A suture exists between the axial and atlantal parts of the axis vertebral body. The sacrum (known only in the Zalambdalestidae) has two vertebrae. Paired epipubic bones presumably were present. The manus, where known, has a nonopposable pollex, and the pes is primitively long, plantigrade, and has a nonopposable hallux.

CRANIAL ANATOMY AND DENTAL PATTERN

The cranial anatomy of present-day and Tertiary eutherian mammals is generally well known, and detailed descriptions of a number of species occur in standard anatomical textbooks. Complete skulls of Cretaceous eutherian mammals, on the other hand, are known only from rocks of Late Cretaceous age from Mongolia (Gregory and Simpson, 1926; Simpson, 1928; Kielan-Jaworowska, 1969, 1975a, 1975b). Most knowledge of Cretaceous eutherians from North America is from isolated teeth and fragments of jaws. In addition, however, some isolated petrosals from the Late Cretaceous Hell Creek Formation have been described by MacIntyre (1972). He demonstrated that all eutherian petrosals known from the Late Cretaceous and early Tertiary are of a similar pattern, designated by him as "trisulcate." The term is derived from the characteristic development of three grooves that carry: (1) the facial nerve; (2) the stapedial artery; and (3) the inferior petrosal vein. The description of cranial anatomy of Cretaceous eutherians that follows is based upon com-

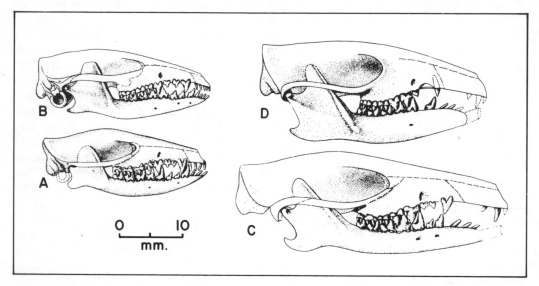

Figure 12-1.   Reconstructions of skulls, seen in right lateral view, of four Late Cretaceous genera of eutherians from Mongolia: *A*, *Kennalestes gobiensis*; *B*, *Asioryctes nemegetensis*; *C*, *Zalambdalestes lechei*; and *D*, *Barunlestes butleri*. *Kennalestes* and *Asioryctes* **are from the Djadokhta Formation and** *Asioryctes* **and** *Barunlestes* **are from the Barun Goyot Formation. (From Kielan-Jaworowska, 1975a)**

plete skulls from Asia. Features peculiar to the dentitions of non-Asiatic kinds will be discussed below, in the section entitled "Systematics and Review of Phylogenetic Interpretations."

Complete skulls for all four eutherian genera thus far known from the Late Cretaceous of Mongolia have been discovered (Figs. 12-1 and 12-2). A specimen of a juvenile *Kennalestes* (see Kielan-Jaworowska, 1975c, and Fig. 12-2) and two skulls of *Asioryctes* (see Kielan-Jaworowska, 1975a, and Fig. 12-2) are especially well preserved. *Kennalestes* and *Asioryctes* are more primitive in their cranial and postcranial anatomy than are *Zalambdalestes* or *Barunlestes* (see section entitled "Postcranial Anatomy"). Detailed descriptions of the braincases of the Mongolian genera have not yet been published. Available descriptions of other parts of the skulls, however, allow comparison of some characters of the cranial anatomy of Asiatic Cretaceous eutherian mammals with later eutherians.

The skulls of *Kennalestes* and *Asioryctes* resemble the general cranial proportions of *Tupaia* and some other generalized present-day eutherian mammals. The snout is narrow and elongate, a postorbital constriction is present, the glenoid fossa is situated anterolaterally to the petrosal, and the braincase is rather narrow and is elongated posteriorly to the rear of the glenoid fossa. The nasals are expanded posteriorly, and probably are in contact with the lacrimals.

The lacrimals have a large facial wing, but this wing is relatively smaller than in the contemporaneous Deltatheridiidae. The infraorbital foramina are large, and the zygomatic arches are slender with long jugals that extend back to the glenoid fossae. Sharp lambdoidal crests are present, but the sagittal crest is weak or absent. Entotympanic bones are apparently absent, but the ectotympanics are large and well preserved in *Asioryctes* (see Kielan-Jaworowska, 1975a) and form three-quarters of a ring that opens posterodorsally. The ectotympanic ring is inclined in an undistorted specimen at an angle of about 45 degrees from the horizontal plane. It is placed more anteriorly than in modern mammals, and has its anteromedial part concealed by the angular process of the mandible. The mandibles are slender with a large coronoid process. The angular processes in *Asioryctes* and *Kennalestes* are inflected medially.

The skulls of known Zalambdalestidae differ from those of *Asioryctes* and *Kennalestes* in having more elongated snouts, wider braincases, shorter jugals, and laterally more expanded zygomatic arches.

The incisor count differs in known Asian Cretaceous eutherians. *Asioryctes* has the "metatherian" formula of 5/4, whereas there are ?4/3 in *Kennalestes* and ?3/3 in the Zalambdalestidae. The zalambdalestids have semiprocumbent I_{2-3}, and I_1 is fully procumbent and greatly enlarged. In *Kennalestes, Asioryctes,* and *Zalambdalestes,* a strong, double-rooted tooth, situated posterior to the premaxillary-maxillary suture, is interpreted as the canine. Although *Barunlestes* has a single-rooted canine, it must have been derived from ancestors with the double-rooted condition (see Kielan-Jaworowska, 1975a).

All known Asian Late Cretaceous eutherians have a basic cheek-tooth formula typical of Cenozoic eutherians, with four premolars and three molars (one premolar is lost in *Barunlestes*). In *Kennalestes* (Fig. 12-3), *Barunlestes, Asioryctes,* and *Zalambdalestes* there is a short diastema to the rear of the canine, behind which a small P^1 occurs. The P^1 and P^2 are double-rooted and do not occlude with lower premolars. P^3, with a high, piercing paracone, is the largest tooth of the maxillary series. Only an incipient protocone is present on P^3 in *Kennalestes* and *Asioryctes,* whereas in the zalambdalestids this cusp is strongly developed. P^4 is semimolariform in all four genera.

Molars of *Kennalestes* are described below as an example of the most primitive type yet known for eutherians. They are similar to the "hypothetical primitive tribosphenic molar" reconstructed by Crompton and Kielan-Jaworowska (1978). The stylar shelf on upper molars of *Kennalestes* (Fig. 12-3) is comparatively wide at the corners and is strongly narrowed at the middle. The parastylar area in coronal view is developed as a large rounded lobe with a prominent parastyle. A stylocone is present. The metastylar area is smaller than the parastylar area, and possesses a small and sharp stylar cusp that is situated in front of the metastyle. The paracone is larger and taller than the metacone. The conules are distinct and are winged, with the metaconule situated more labially than the paraconule. The protocone is large and is placed asymmetrically toward the anterior face of the tooth, opposite the paracone. The preprotocrista and postprotocrista are sharp-edged and have a protofossa.

Upper molars of *Kennalestes* differ from the

hypothetical type mentioned above in the presence of pre- and postcingula. These structures appear first in *Kennalestes* among known eutherians. The trigonids of the lower molars are compressed anteroposteriorly, and the protoconid is the strongest cusp. The metaconid is larger than the paraconid, and the paraconid is situated centrally on the anterior moiety of the tooth. A weak anterior cingulid is present. The hypoconulid is the tallest of the talonid cusps and the hypoconid is the lowest. The talonid basin is comparatively large, rounded, and has been hollowed out by wear.

Molars of other eutherian genera known from Late Cretaceous rocks of Asia and North America have a relatively more specialized structure. They are discussed below in the section entitled "Systematics and Review of Phylogenetic Interpretations."

Four Asian Late Cretaceous eutherian genera (*Kennalestes, Asioryctes, Zalambdalestes*, and *Barunlestes*) are similar to one another in skull structure and in the general organization of their dentitions. They differ significantly, however, in molar coronal structure and in postcranial anatomy. The similarities that do exist among these forms suggest that they were all derived from a not-too-distant common ancestor. This ancestor may have had molars similar to those of the hypothetical form mentioned above.

Interesting comparisons can be made between the crania of the known Asiatic eutherians and contemporary members of the Deltatheridiidae (see Kielan-Jaworowska, 1975b, and Fig. 10-2). In contrast to the eutherians, the skulls of the deltatheridiids are shortened and have strongly developed zygomatic arches, large facial wings on the lacrimals,

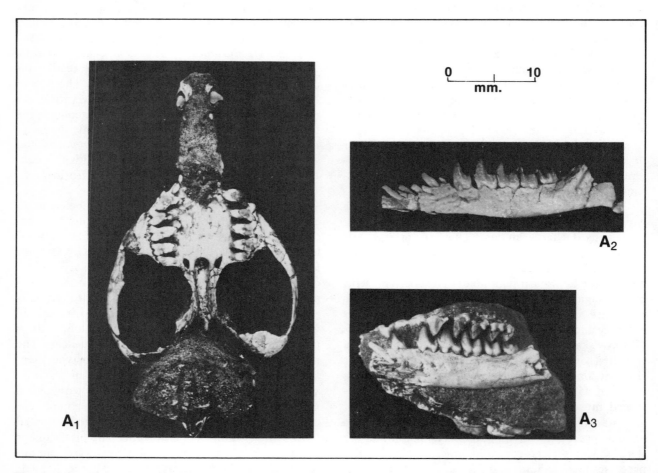

Figure 12-2.   Photographs of skulls and mandibles of Late Cretaceous eutherian mammals from the Djadokhta and Barun Goyot formations of Mongolia, to show the typical state of preservation: *A*, *Zalambdalestes lechei* (Djadokhta Fm.); *B*, *Kennalestes gobiensis* (Djadokhta Fm.); and *C*, *Asioryctes nemegetensis* (Barun Goyot Fm.). A_1, skull in palatal view; A_2, left mandible in labial view; A_3, damaged skull in oblique lateral view, not completely removed from the rock, showing upper and lower jaws with teeth in occlusion. B_1, skull of juvenile individual in dorsal view; B_2, the same, in palatal view; B_3,

and large lacrimal foramina. The number of incisors is reduced in the deltatheridiids, possibly in connection with the shortening of the skull. Deltatheridiid canines are large and single-rooted in contrast to their structure in the earliest eutherians. The postcanine dental formula and tooth structure also differ in the Deltatheridiidae, where there are three nonmolariform premolars and four molars. Deltatheridiids show a tendency to reduce the last molar.

Tooth homologies between Cretaceous Asiatic eutherians and the deltatheridiids are not clear.

Asioryctes, for example, has five incisiform upper teeth that have been interpreted as true incisors (Fig. 12-1), the last of which is situated at the premaxillary-maxillary suture. It is possible that this last tooth is actually a reduced and incisiform canine, rather than an incisor. The single-rooted canines similar to those of the deltatheridiids are also characteristic of the known triconodonts and cynodont reptiles (Parrington, 1971; Mills, 1971; Crompton, 1974). It might be argued that the large, double-rooted tooth that is situated posterior to the pre-

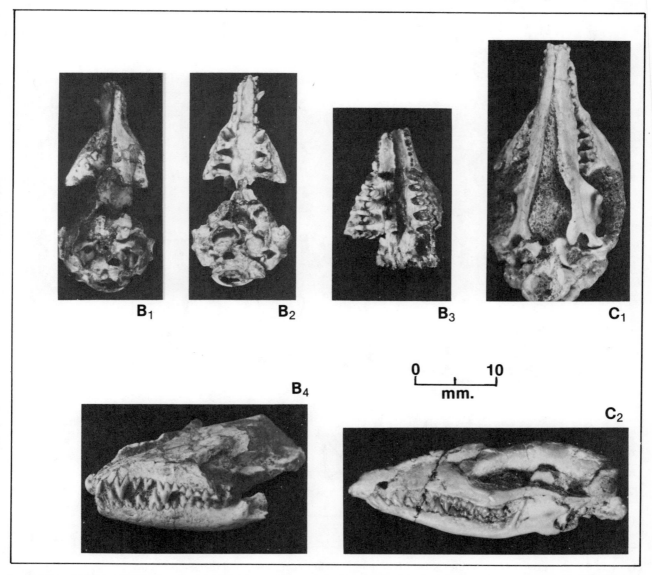

incomplete skull in palatal view; B_4, third skull specimen, with associated mandible, as seen in left lateral view before final preparation. C_1, skull of holotype specimen associated with mandibles, as seen in ventral view; C_2, skull and mandible of a second, and laterally compressed specimen, in left lateral view. (After Kielan-Jaworowska, 1969, 1975a, 1975c. A_2 reproduced here for first time) maxillary-maxillary suture in *Kennalestes, Asioryctes*, and *Zalambdalestes* is in reality the first premolar (Lillegraven, 1969). However, in various modern insectivores (*e.g., Erinaceus* and the Macroscelididae) the upper canine is situated posterior to this suture. The tooth is also double-rooted in the Macroscelididae (see Evans, 1942). Kielan-Jaworowska (1975b) argued that this double-rooted

tooth in the Asiatic Cretaceous eutherians was a canine, and she (1975a) observed that the double-rooted tooth of *Zalambdalestes* developed into a single-rooted structure in its probable descendant, *Barunlestes* (Fig. 12-1).

McKenna (1975) suggested that primitive eutherians possessed five premolars and three molars in the adult series (see Chapter 9). He referred to unfigured

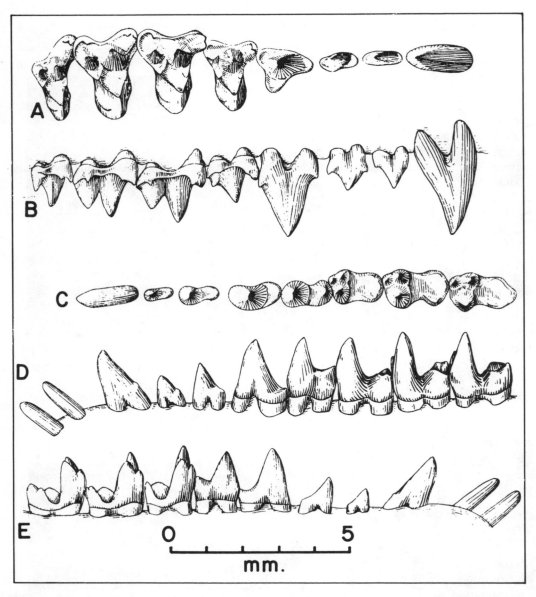

Figure 12-3.   Dentition of *Kennalestes gobiensis*. *A* and *B*, right upper canine and cheek teeth in occlusal and labial views, respectively. *C, D,* and *E,* left lower posterior incisors, the canine, and cheek teeth in occlusal, labial, and lingual views, respectively (incisors are not shown in *C*). (From Kielan-Jaworowska, 1969)

and undescribed specimens of *Prokennalestes* Trofimov (*in* Beliajeva and others, 1974) from ?Aptian or ?Albian beds of Khovboor in Mongolia. Lillegraven (1969) and Clemens (1973a) observed that some species of *Gypsonictops* possessed five premolars situated in front of three molars. The skull of an undescribed specimen of a juvenile *Kennalestes* (figured by Kielan-Jaworowska, 1975c, and Fig. 12-2) shows that the deciduous upper canine in that animal was single-rooted. Five premolariform teeth exist on the right maxilla posterior to the deciduous canine. The penultimate of these was in the process of eruption, and the last is clearly of the deciduous series. Probably all but the last tooth of this premolar series belong to an adult Zahnreihe. Adult *Kennalestes* thus probably possess only four premolars. To the rear of the five premolariform teeth in the specimen of a juvenile *Kennalestes* are two molariform teeth and a third, unerupted tooth. McKenna (1975) suggested that the dental count in juvenile *Kennalestes* supported his hypothesis of the primitive presence of five premolars in the adult dental series of ancestral eutherians.

The general organization of the dentition in known representatives of Late Cretaceous Asian eutherians is therefore very different from that of the Deltatheridiidae. It may be reasonably assumed that these two groups were derived from a relatively distant Early Cretaceous ancestor.

Eutherian mammals known from rocks of Late Cretaceous age in Asia have cranial and dental features that were lost in later stages of evolution. Some of these characters would be regarded as "metatherian" in comparison with the skulls of living representatives of the Metatheria and Eutheria. Included are the relatively small braincase, the posteriorly expanded nasals, mediad inflection of the angle of the lower jaw, relatively wide stylar shelves of upper molars, and the large numbers of incisors seen in *Asioryctes* (5/4) and *Kennalestes* (?4/3).

POSTCRANIAL ANATOMY

Introduction

The considerable taxonomic diversity of metatherian and eutherian mammals of the Cretaceous has been known for some time. However, specific information on the postcranial structure of these mammals has only recently been published (Kielan-Jaworowska, 1977; *in press*).

Cretaceous Metatheria are known only from teeth and incomplete skull fragments. Not a single bone of the postcranial skeleton of a Cretaceous metatherian has yet been described, although they probably exist in the many miscellaneous collections of mammalian limb bones. Similarly, nothing is known of the postcranial skeletons of Theria of metatherian-eutherian grade (see Kielan-Jaworowska, 1975b, and Chapter 10).

The postcranial skeletal morphology of North American Cretaceous eutherian mammals is undescribed except for a restoration (from physically unassociated parts) of the astragalo-calcaneal complexes of *Procerberus* and *Protungulatum* from the latest Cretaceous of Montana (see Szalay and Decker, 1974). These forms are apparently rather advanced, and provide little information on the foot structure of more primitive eutherians. A rich collection of isolated mammalian postcranial elements from the Hell Creek Formation exists, but is virtually undescribed (see Sloan and Van Valen, 1965).

Articulated skeletons of Asiatic Late Cretaceous mammals have recently been collected through the efforts of the Polish-Mongolian Palaeontological Expeditions. Of the four currently recognized Asiatic eutherian genera, postcranial remains are unknown only for *Kennalestes* (except for an incomplete atlas). This absence of knowledge of the postcranial anatomy of *Kennalestes* is especially regrettable because the dental morphology of this animal is the most generalized of known eutherians thus far described.

The postcranial skeleton of *Asioryctes* is represented by fragments of the vertebral column, an incomplete hand, and an incomplete hind limb; it is extremely primitive for a eutherian. The zalambdalestids *Barunlestes* and *Zalambdalestes* are represented by much better postcranial remains. In contrast to *Asioryctes*, the zalambdalestids possess a combination of primitive and advanced skeletal characters. The information below regarding the postcranial skeletons of *Asioryctes* and the zalambdalestids is based upon the descriptions by Kielan-Jaworowska (1977; *in press*).

Postcranial Skeleton of *Asioryctes*

Vertebral Column

Known elements of the vertebral column of *Asioryctes* include all cervical vertebrae and the first thoracic vertebra (Figs. 12-4 and 12-5). The cervical vertebrae of *Asioryctes* are in some respects intermediate in structure between those of known Triassic triconodonts (see Jenkins and Parrington, 1976, and Chapter 4) and those of modern eutherian mammals. In cynodont reptiles (Jenkins, 1971) and Triassic triconodonts, the atlas consists of four separate ossifications, including right and left arches, an intercentrum, and an atlas body that is synostosed to the axis body. The intercentrum is not preserved in known specimens of *Asioryctes* or *Kennalestes*, and it is possible that, as in known Triassic mammals, it was not fused to the arches. Right and left arches are preserved together and probably are synostosed. A transverse foramen in the atlas, as occurs in known Triassic triconodonts, is lacking in *Asioryctes* and *Kennalestes*. A transverse foramen is absent from the atlas in living members of the Monotremata, Marsupialia, Cetacea, Sirenia, Ruminantia (excepting Tylopoda), and Rhinocerotidae (Rüeger, 1938; Lessertisseur and Saban, 1967). This absence is probably a primitive feature only in the Monotremata and Marsupialia.

The arteria vertebralis of monotremes and marsupials, after coursing anteriad from the axis, passes by the root of the transverse process of the atlas, causing the bone to be grooved around it. A similar groove for the arteria vertebralis is present in the atlas both of *Asioryctes* and of *Kennalestes*. The lack of a transverse foramen in the atlas of modern eutherians is connected either with special adaptations of the cervical vertebrae (as in Cetacea and Sirenia) or with a different course of the arteria vertebralis. For example, in the Ruminantia the arteria vertebralis enters the vertebral canal between the third and second cervical vertebrae (Sisson and Grossman, 1953), and the transverse foramina are small or absent on the axis and absent from the atlas. It is suspected (see Kielan-Jaworowska, 1977) that the lack of a transverse foramen on the atlas of *Asioryctes* and *Kennalestes* is primitive and thus, in this respect, demonstrates a level of organization typical of that in monotremes and primitive marsupials. The transverse foramen is probably also lacking on the axis of *Asioryctes*, although there is a groove for the arteria vertebralis. Another primitive feature of the axis of *Asioryctes* is the presence, in the adult condition, of a clear suture between the atlantal and axial parts of the body; these parts are not completely synostosed. Such a joint is characteristic of the known Triassic triconodonts (Jenkins and Parrington, 1976) and is present in adult living monotremes, marsupials, and juvenile eutherians (Rüeger, 1938; Jenkins, 1969).

It is speculative whether cervical ribs (with a

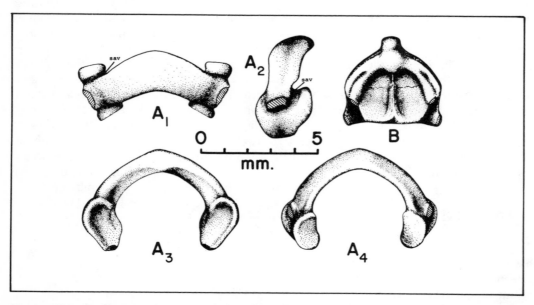

Figure 12-4.   Reconstructions of atlas, without intercentrum (*A*), and axis (*B*) of *Asioryctes nemegetensis*. Views are: A_1, dorsal; A_2, right lateral; A_3, anterior; A_4, posterior; and *B*, ventral. Hatched areas denote broken bases of transverse processes; *sav*, sulcus arteriae vertebralis. (From Kielan-Jaworowska, 1977)

distinct suture separating them from the transverse processes) were still present in the neck of *Asioryctes*. Distinct cervical ribs, characteristic of cynodont reptiles, may have been present in Triassic triconodonts (see Jenkins and Parrington, 1976). Recognizable cervical ribs are also present in living monotremes, and occur on the axis of a living marsupial, *Perameles*. The cervical ribs of the monotremes *Ornithorhynchus* and *Tachyglossus* are synostosed with the transverse processes, but visible sutures are retained into early adulthood; thereafter they may disappear. Cervical ribs also occur on the last cervical vertebra in some Cetacea and Edentata, and have been described as an anomaly in man and several domestic animals.

In the only known specimen of *Asioryctes* in which the neck is preserved, the transverse foramina on the third to sixth vertebrae are distinct (Fig. 12-5). The transverse processes of the cervical vertebrae are long and cracked in various places. However, these cracks are irregularly placed, and none is unequivocally a suture line. It was concluded by Kielan-Jaworowska (1977) that cervical ribs probably did not occur as distinct features in *Asioryctes*. The sixth cervical vertebra in living mammals is characterized by a special development of the ventral branch of the transverse process. This development causes a loss of contact with the rest of the transverse process, and the structure is arranged longitudinally as a lamella that projects strongly downward. The structure has variously been called the inferior lamella (Howell, 1926), carotid tubercle, Chassaignac's tubercle, and the transverse ventral tubercle (see Lessertisseur and Saban, 1967). The size and shape of the inferior lamella is dependent upon the relative development of the longus colli muscle that extends away from it in both directions. The inferior lamella does not occur in known Triassic triconodonts or in monotremes. A similar structure occurs in a specimen of a multituberculate from rocks of Late Cretaceous age of Mongolia, but is undescribed and does not occur in all members of the order. The inferior lamella is a constant feature of generalized marsupials and placentals, and disappears only in some specialized

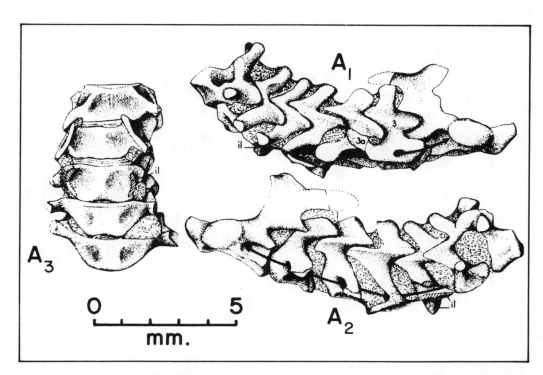

Figure 12-5.   Cervical and anterior thoracic vertebrae of *Asioryctes nemegetensis*. A_1 and A_2, second cervical to first thoracic vertebrae in right and left lateral views, respectively. A_3, fourth cervical (above) to first thoracic vertebrae of same specimen, in ventral view. *3* and *3a* denote parts of third cervical vertebra. Arrows indicate course of arteria vertebralis. Hatched areas denote broken bases of inferior lamella (*il*) of transverse process on sixth cervical vertebra. (From Kielan-Jaworowska, 1977)

forms. The structure is less prominent in *Asioryctes* than in modern therian mammals, and is only incipiently developed (see Fig. 12-5).

Neural spines are lacking on the cervical vertebrae of *Asioryctes*. In comparison, the cervical spines of *Didelphis* are enlarged and contact one another. Thus, the second to the seventh vertebrae act as a single, rigid structure. Slijper (1946) noted a correlation between the length of the cervical spines and the absolute body sizes of the animals that possess them. The absence of cervical spines in *Asioryctes* might be explained by the small size of the animal (skull length approximately 3 cm).

Forelimb

The known parts of the forelimb of *Asioryctes* consist of the distal portions of the radius and ulna, a nearly complete carpus, and the proximal elements of all metacarpals. There are probably eleven bones (including two phalanges of the praepollex) in the carpus of *Asioryctes* (Fig. 12-6). Three bones, the scaphoid (naviculare), the lunar (lunatum), and the cuneiform (triquetrum), form the proximal row. A pisiform is not preserved, but there is an articular surface for it on the ventral side of the cuneiform. The proximal row forms an arch that embraces the bones of the distal row. Wedged medially between the scaphoid and the trapezium is a praepollex that consists of two bones. The centrale, not positively identified, is small. Of the four bones of the distal row, the trapezium and the unciform (hamatum) are large, and the trapezoid and magnum (capitatum) small. The metacarpals are arranged subparallel to one another.

The carpus of *Asioryctes* is very different from

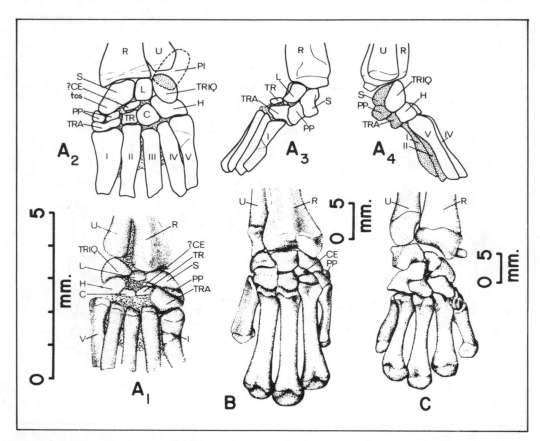

Figure 12-6. Comparison of right carpus and metacarpals of Late Cretaceous *Asioryctes nemegetensis* (*A*) with Recent *Tenrec ecaudatus* (*B*) and *Didelphis virginiana* (*C*). Views are: A_1, B, and C, dorsal; A_2, ventral; A_3, left lateral; and A_4, right lateral. Abbreviations are: C, magnum (capitatum); CE, centrale; H, unciform (hamatum); L, lunar (lunatum); PI, pisiform; PP, praepollex; R, radius; S, scaphoid; *tos*, tuber ossi scaphoidei; $TRIQ$, cuneiform (triquetrum); TR, trapezoid; TRA, trapezium; U, ulna; and I-V, metacarpals. (From Kielan-Jaworowska, 1977)

that of *Didelphis*. *Asioryctes* resembles the general pattern of the carpus of the "convergent" hands of terrestrial insectivores such as *Tenrec* (Fig. 12-6), while *Didelphis* has a structure characteristic of grasping hands (see Altner, 1971; Yalden, 1972; and below).

Hindlimb

Known parts of the hindlimb of *Asioryctes* (Fig. 12-7) consist of the distal parts of the tibia and the fibula, an almost complete tarsus, all metatarsals, and a few phalanges. The tarsus of *Asioryctes* is perhaps the most primitive known for eutherian mammals. In articulation, the proximal body of the astragalus (talus) does not override the calcaneum and is situated medial to it. The astragalus is situated medial to the calcaneum in the reptiles, but in later eutherian mammals the astragalus is supported by the calcaneum. The known Triassic triconodonts are, in this respect, at a reptilian grade of organization, and *Asioryctes* is at an intermediate stage of development. Another characteristic feature of the tarsus of *Asioryctes* is that the sustentacular facet of the astragalus is well developed, but extends beneath only two-thirds of the width of the astragalar head.

An astragalo-calcaneal complex similar to that of *Asioryctes* occurs in *Didelphis* (Fig. 12-7). The proximal body of the astragalus in *Didelphis* is inflated with a shallow groove in the middle, and the tibial trochlea is not as fully developed as in *Asioryctes*. The calcaneo-astragalar complex in *Didelphis* is more extensive than in *Asioryctes* because not only the astragalar head, but also a large part of the proximal body, is supported on the calcaneum. Thus, it seems likely that the development of an extensive overlap of the astragalus upon the calcaneum developed independently within meta-

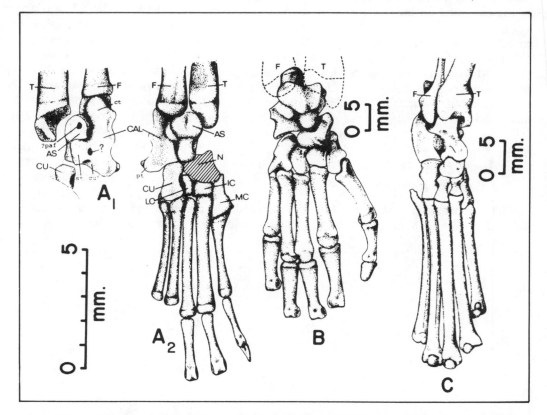

Figure 12-7. **Comparison of right tarsus and metatarsals of Late Cretaceous** *Asioryctes nemegetensis* (*A*) **with Recent** *Didelphis virginiana* (*B*) **and** *Tupaia* **sp.** (*C*). **Views are:** A_1, **ventral, as preserved in articulation;** A_2, **dorsal, reconstructed from parts of same individual found scattered in immediately adjacent rock parts; and** *B* **and** *C*, **dorsal. Abbreviations are:** *AS*, **astragalus (talus);** *CAL*, **calcaneum;** *ct*, **calcaneal tuberosity;** *CU*, **cuboid;** *cuf*, **cuboid facet;** *F*, **fibula;** *IC*, **intermedial cuneiform;** *LC*, **lateral cuneiform;** *MC*, **medial cuneiform;** *N*, **navicular;** *paf*, **?plantar astragalar foramen;** *pt*, **peroneal tubercle;** *T*, **tibia; and** *st*, **sustentacular facet. (From Kielan-Jaworowska, 1977)**

therian and eutherian mammals. The most important difference between the tarsus of *Asioryctes* and that of *Didelphis* is the joint between the mesocuneiform and first metatarsal. This joint is saddle-like in *Didelphis,* and the hallux is opposable. The joint is hinge-like in *Asioryctes*, and the hallux does not show any significant degree of opposability.

Comments on the Postcranial Skeleton of *Asioryctes*

It follows from the foregoing comparative discussion that the Late Cretaceous eutherian *Asioryctes* shares more characters with the extant metatherian *Didelphis* than with any known fossil or living eutherian mammal (see Kielan-Jaworowska, 1977). *Asioryctes* shares with *Didelphis* such primitive characters as the lack of a transverse foramen in the atlas, the presence in the adult of a joint between the atlantal and axial parts of the body of the axis, and an incomplete superposition of the astragalus on the calcaneum. It is not known whether epipubic bones were present in *Asioryctes*. Certain characters that differ in *Asioryctes* and *Didelphis*, including the presence of large cervical spines and opposable pollex and hallux in *Didelphis*, might be regarded as adaptations to specific life styles of that marsupial.

Postcranial Skeleton of the Zalambdalestidae

The postcranial skeleton of the Zalambdalestidae, although more completely known than that of *Asioryctes*, is less interesting from the phylogenetic point of view because it is so highly specialized for particular adaptive roles. Although *Zalambdalestes* has been found in beds somewhat older than those yielding *Asioryctes*, it is much more specialized. *Barunlestes*, the other known zalambdalestid, occurs in the same beds as *Asioryctes*. Zalambdalestids differ in their dental formulae and skull proportions (Kielan-Jaworowska, 1975b). It is probable that there are other differences in their post-cranial skeletons, but these are not discernible in existing collections. The reconstruction of the skeleton of *Zalambdalestes* (Fig. 12-8) is based in part upon elements of *Barunlestes*.

Vertebral Column

The atlas of known members of the Zalambdalestidae differs from that in *Asioryctes* in the presence of a transverse foramen (Fig. 12-9). The suture between the atlantal and axial parts of the body of the axis, characteristic of *Asioryctes*, is also present in the Zalambdalestidae.

The distinctive feature of the zalambdalestid neck is the unusually long spinous process of the axis, which projects posteriad above the posterior edge of the fourth cervical vertebra (see Kielan-Jaworowska, *in press*). This process (Fig. 12-10) is delicate and is aligned roughly parallel to the ventral margins of the vertebral bodies. The anterior part of the dorsal edge of the spinous process is dorso-ventrally flattened, and forms a tear-shaped area for the attachment of the rectus capitis dorsalis. A spinous process is not present on succeeding cervical vertebrae.

The inferior lamella on the sixth vertebra is not

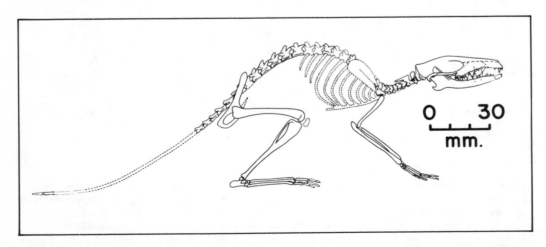

Figure 12-8.   Skeletal reconstruction of *Zalambdalestes lechei*, based in part upon the skeleton of *Barunlestes butleri*. (From Kielan-Jaworowska, *in press*)

prominent, and distinct cervical ribs do not occur. The known thoracic vertebrae are characterized by short and crescent-shaped spinous processes. The lumbar vertebrae of *Barunlestes* are similar to those of *Didelphis* in that both have very short transverse processes. Differences exist, however, in the shape of the spinous processes. In *Didelphis* these are short and straight, whereas in *Barunlestes* they are longer and bent anteriad.

The sacrum of zalambdalestids consists of two vertebrae, only the more anterior of which articulates with the ilium. In this respect, the zalambdalestids are more primitive than living eutherian mammals.

Shoulder Girdle and Forelimb

The shoulder girdle and forelimb of *Barunlestes* do not differ significantly from those of generalized extant eutherians. The clavicles have not been preserved, but the structure of the scapula suggests the presence of these bones in *Barunlestes*.

The carpus of *Barunlestes* (Fig. 12-11) is rather advanced for a Cretaceous mammal in that the scaphoid and lunar are fused into a scapholunar. These bones are not fused in the Macroscelididae (elephant shrews). The centrale of *Barunlestes* is large, but otherwise the carpus is structurally typical of convergent hands (see discussion below) seen in several present-day eutherians. The carpals of *Barunlestes* are comparatively long, and the pollex is not opposable.

Pelvic Girdle and Hindlimb

It was shown by Kielan-Jaworowska (1975d) that the pelvic girdle of *Barunlestes* has a structure unusual for eutherian mammals. A shallow triangular fossa exists on the lower part of the margin of the pubic bone that was interpreted as an articular surface for an epipubic bone. If this interpretation is correct, the Zalambdalestidae would, in this respect, be at a marsupial-monotreme level of organization.

A characteristic feature of postcranial skeletons of known zalambdalestids (see Kielan-Jaworowska, *in press*) is the great length of the hindlimbs and feet. The proportions of the hindlimb segments and the ratio of hindlimb to forelimb resemble those in living elephant shrews. The tibia and fibula are strongly fused along their distal halves in a manner similar to that characteristic of modern macroscelidids, leporids, tarsiids, and dipodids (see McKenzie, 1911, and Barnett and Napier, 1953). The lower half of the

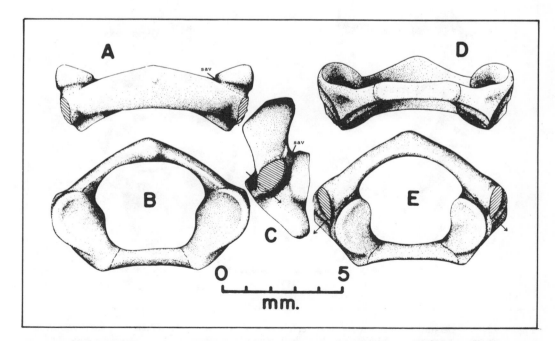

Figure 12-9.   Reconstruction of atlas of *Barunlestes butleri*. Views are: *A*, dorsal; *B*, anterior; *C*, right lateral; *D*, ventral; and *E*, posterior. Hatched areas denote broken bases of transverse processes. Arrows indicate course of transverse canal. *sav*, sulcus arteriae vertebralis. (From Kielan-Jaworowska, *in press*)

fibular shaft cannot be distinguished in known zalambdalestids.

The tarsus of *Zalambdalestes* (Fig. 12-11) differs from that of *Asioryctes* in the possession of an astragalus that is supported by the calcaneum, as in present-day eutherian mammals, and in that the trochlea of the astragalus is deep. The calcaneal fibular facet is wanting in the zalambdalestid tarsus, a specialized feature. The mesocuneiform protrudes distally beyond the level of other cuneiforms, and the joint between it and the first metatarsal is of a hinge type. The hallux is not opposable. The metatarsals

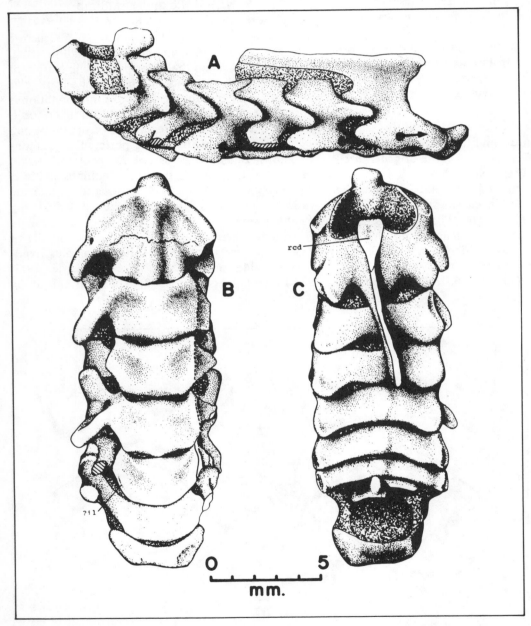

Figure 12-10.   Second to seventh cervical vertebrae and first thoracic vertebra of *Zalambdalestes lechei*, **drawn as preserved. Views are:** *A*, **right lateral;** *B*, **ventral; and** *C*, **dorsal. Arrow denotes course of arteria vertebralis. Transverse processes are preserved on right sides of axis,** C_3, **and** C_5. *?il*, **incipient inferior lamella on** C_6. *rcd*, **attachment area for rectus capitis dorsalis muscle. (From Kielan-Jaworowska,** *in press*)

are very long, relatively longer than in the Leporidae, and are similar to the proportions characteristic of the Macroscelididae (see Evans, 1942, and Kielan-Jaworowska, *in press*).

Comments on Postcranial Skeleton of Zalambdalestidae

The structure of the spinous process of the axis indicates that the anterior part of the neck was immobile and that a ligamentum nuchae was probably absent in *Zalambdalestes*. The short spinous processes of the thoracic vertebrae also suggest the lack of a ligamentum nuchae. An immobile neck region is characteristic of mammals of various habits, including aquatic (not appropriate for comparison with zalambdalestids), fossorial, and ricochetal adaptations (see Lessertisseur and Saban, 1967, and Hatt, 1931). It is improbable that the known zalambdalestids were habitually fossorial, because the limb structure shows no appropriate adaptations. It seems likely that they lived under the cover of vegetation or among the rocks, as do modern macroscelidids. The neck of the known zalambdalestids is not greatly shortened, and thus differs from the common condition in small, ricochetal mammals. Nevertheless, it seems possible (Kielan-Jaworowska, *in press*) that the partial immobility of the anterior part of the neck in *Zalambdalestes* is indicative of a tendency toward richochetal behavior.

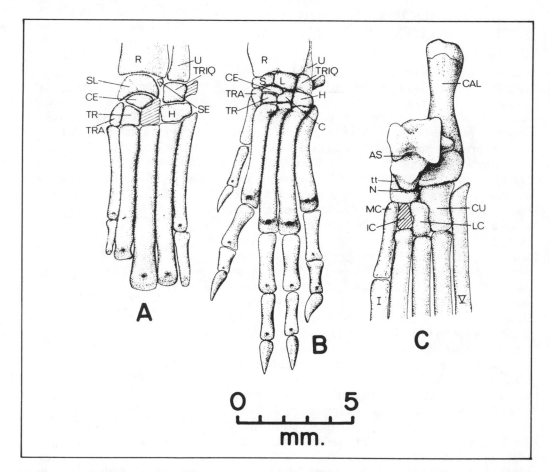

Figure 12-11. Pedal elements. Comparison of left hands in dorsal view of Late Cretaceous *Barunlestes butleri* **(A) with Recent** *Elephantulus myurus* **(B). C, reconstruction of tarsus of** *Zalambdalestes lechei*. **Abbreviations are:** *AS*, **astragalus;** *C*, **magnum (capitatum);** *CAL*, **calcaneum;** *CE*, **centrale;** *CU*, **cuboideum;** *H*, **unciform (hamatum);** *IC*, **intermedial cuneiform;** *L*, **lunar;** *LC*, **lateral cuneiform;** *MC*, **medial cuneiform;** *N*, **navicular;** *R*, **radius;** *S*, **scaphoid;** *SE*, **sesamoid bone;** *SL*, **scapholunar;** *TR*, **trapezium;** *TRA*, **trapezoid;** *TRIQ*, **cuneiform (triquetrum);** *tt*, **tuber tibialis; and** *U*, **ulna. (After Kielan-Jaworowska,** *in press*)

The relative proportions of the forelimbs to the hindlimbs in known zalambdalestids resemble those characteristic of living macroscelidids. Brown (1964) and Brown and Yalden (1973) observed that, in contrast to widespread belief, the macroscelidids (commonly called "jumping shrews") are not completely bipedal in locomotion; their usual form of progression is quadrupedal. It seems likely that the locomotion of the known zalambdalestids was rather similar to that of elephant shrews. Although the similarities in the skeleton of zalambdalestids and macroscelidids suggest similarities in mode of life, they do not necessarily imply phylogenetic relationship.

TERRESTRIAL OR ARBOREAL ANCESTRY OF EUTHERIAN MAMMALS

It has long been speculated that marsupial and placental mammals both had arboreal origins. Huxley (1880) was the first to argue specifically for an arboreal ancestry of marsupials. He observed that members of most families of living marsupials possess a prehensile pes with an opposable hallux. This theory was subsequently accepted and developed further by Dollo (1899) and Bensley (1901a, 1901b). Matthew (1904, 1909, 1937), using paleontological evidence from Tertiary sequences, argued that placental mammals were also of arboreal heritage, and since that time the presumed arboreal ancestry of all modern therians has repeatedly been discussed. Among modern authors, the idea has been supported by Lewis (1964), Steiner (1965), and Martin (1968). Gidley (1919), Haines (1958), and Szalay and Decker (1974) have been the main opponents. Discussions by Napier (1961) and Altner (1971) also speak against the likelihood of arboreal origins of modern therian mammals.

Until recently, this discussion was mainly in the nature of speculation; there was little relevant information from fossils concerning the postcranial structure of ancient therians. The newly-described skeletal remains of *Asioryctes* and zalambdalestids from Cretaceous rocks of Mongolia (Kielan-Jaworowska, 1977; *in press*) now provide pertinent and sorely-needed evidence. Although the zalambdalestids represent the oldest known skeletons of eutherian mammals, they are relatively progressive in specialization and therefore are not as useful as *Asioryctes* in interpreting the locomotory-ecological habits of ancestral

eutherians. Therefore, *Asioryctes*, the most generalized eutherian for which postcranial remains are known, is most relevant to the discussion.

Two structural types of carpus have been recognized among generalized therian mammals (Fig. 12-12). The "convergent hand," discussed by Haines (1958) and Napier (1961), corresponds more or less with the "Spreizhand" defined by Altner (1971). The second type is commonly known as the "grasping hand," and corresponds to the "Greifhand" discussed by Altner. Altner (1971) and Yalden (1972) studied the carpus of arboreal mammals, and independently observed that they are capable of large deviational movements at the wrist that are associated with a special arrangement of the carpal bones. Features of the wrists of convergent (Spreizhand) and grasping (Greifhand) hands were discussed by Altner (1971). The following represents a summarization by us of the key points from his writings (refer to Fig. 12-12):

1. Convergent hand. The proximal row of the carpal bones is concave distally, and embraces the distal row. The centrale may be incorporated either in the proximal row (in Insectivora), or in the distal row (in Rodentia). The trapezoid and magnum (capitatum) are small in comparison with the trapezium and unciform (hamatum). The fifth digit projects

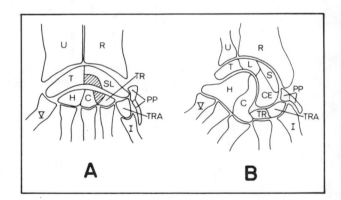

Figure 12-12. Diagrammatic illustrations of arrangement of carpus as seen in dorsal view in a mammalian "convergent" hand (*A*) and "grasping" hand (*B*). Abbreviations are: *C*, magnum (capitatum); *CE*, centrale; *H*, unciform (hamatum); *L*, lunar; *S*, scaphoid; *SL*, scapholunar; *T*, cuneiform (triquetrum); *TR*, trapezoid; and *TRA*, trapezium. Hatched areas denote the centrale, which may be incorporated into either the proximal row (Insectivora) or the distal row (Rodentia) of carpals. (Modified and redrawn from Altner, 1971)

laterally beyond the unciform, and may contact the cuneiform (triquetrum). The trapezium is longitudinally elongated, and projects distally beyond the distal margin of the remaining carpal bones. The carpo-metacarpal joint of the pollex is of a hinge type, and the pollex is not opposable.

2. Grasping hand. The three bones of the proximal row plus the centrale form a crescent-shaped structure. The distal margin of the proximal row is strongly sigmoid, and its greatest concavity faces obliquely with respect to the longitudinal axis of the hand; the concavity embraces the enlarged unciform and magnum. The magnum and unciform together form a bell-shaped structure. The trapezium and the trapezoid are small in comparison with the magnum and unciform. The trapezium is transverse, and does not protrude beyond the distal margin of the remaining carpal bones. The carpo-metacarpal joint of the pollex is of a saddle-type, and the pollex is not opposable.

The carpus of *Asioryctes* is very different from those characteristic of grasping hands as developed, for example, in arboreal primates and *Didelphis*; it corresponds in a general way with the development of a convergent hand of primitive insectivores (see Fig. 12-6) in having a nonopposable hallux.

The structure and habits of *Tupaia* have played an important part in the history of discussions of terrestrialism versus arborealism in the ancestors of eutherian mammals. Jenkins (1974) studied the locomotion of *Tupaia glis* and concluded that terrestrialism and arborealism in small, generalized mammals are not discrete phenomena. Most tree-shrews, for example, move freely across the ground and through the trees.

Altner (1971) studied the morphogenesis of the hand of *Tupaia* and compared its structure with hands of semiarboreal (*Sciurus*) and terrestrial (*Xerus*) rodents and terrestrial insectivores (*Erinaceus* and *Microgale*). He observed that all of these forms, despite their different modes of life, have hands of essentially similar structure. Thus it is impossible, on the basis of hand structure alone, to conclude confidently that an extinct small mammal was a tree-runner, was adapted to semiarboreal life, or was exclusively terrestrial. As shown by Altner (1971), the hand of the tree-runner *Tupaia* has a structure somewhat intermediate between the "Spreizhand" and the "Greifhand," but other arboreal forms such as *Sciurus* possess a wrist structure

indistinguishable from exclusively terrestrial sciurids. The study of the pes of small modern mammals of different habits has led to similarly inconclusive results.

The question arises whether *Asioryctes* was a tree-runner adapted to a semiarboreal life, or was principally terrestrial. Although such a conclusion apparently cannot be drawn on anatomical criteria alone, additional evidence is obtainable from studies of the environment of deposition of the rocks from which the skeletons of *Asioryctes* were recovered. Sedimentological investigations of the Djadokhta and Barun Goyot formations (Lefeld, 1971; Gradziński and Jerzykiewicz, 1974) demonstrate that both rock units are composed of sand-dune deposits that interdigitate with less extensive strata of fluviatile and lacustrine origin. No indications of the presence of trees were seen. The sedimentological evidence strongly suggests that the known Late Cretaceous mammals from Mongolia lived in a semidesert environment; the animals were probably not primarily adapted to life in trees.

It could be argued that *Asioryctes* was only secondarily adapted to life in a xeric setting and was derived from ancestors possessing an opposable pollex and hallux. This seems improbable, however, because all known Early Cretaceous therian mammals were of the small size range characteristic of *Asioryctes*, and probably had no "need" for opposable hands or feet. As stated by Napier (1961, p. 130) for the primates:

> Below a critical size, clawed, convergent hands offer little or no disadvantage, but once the ratio of average branch diameter to the size of animal has reached a critical point, clawed and convergent extremities are no longer adequate to maintain stability in an arboreal environment, and some form of grasping mechanism is required.

It is virtually certain that hand and foot opposability evolved independently in several groups of eutherian mammals during the Cenozoic from ancestors that lacked pedal opposability. No paleontological data are available to suggest when pedal opposability developed among the marsupials.

It is probable that semiarboreal eutherian mammals existed as contemporaries with *Asioryctes* in forest habitats. These probably did not have grasping extremities, but rather were small tree-runners with convergent hands (see Kielan-Jaworowska, 1977).

SYSTEMATICS AND REVIEW OF PHYLOGENETIC INTERPRETATIONS

In the following section we mention those few Asiatic eutherian taxa not covered above and discuss the remainder of eutherian genera known from other continents. Some anatomical features of particular taxa are summarized. The section is also designed to review previous opinions with respect to the phylogenetic significance of these particular organisms. Our personal interpretations are summarized in the succeeding section entitled "Phylogeny."

Eutheria *incertae sedis*

This noncommital category includes poorly known mammals from Europe, Asia, and North America. The grouping of these forms is not meant to imply special relatedness.

"*Prokennalestes*" and "*Prozalambdalestes*" were named, but neither was described or figured, by Trofimov (*in* Beliajeva and others, 1974); hence they are *nomina nuda*. The material is interesting because of its probable antiquity, and it is hoped that it will soon be described. Trofimov believed these taxa to have been in or near the ancestries of *Kennalestes* and *Zalambdalestes*, respectively. From personal communications of B. A. Trofimov to M. C. McKenna (see McKenna, 1975) and Z. Kielan-Jaworowska (see Crompton and Kielan-Jaworowska, 1978), it appears that "*Prokennalestes*" has five lower premolar loci, and its upper molars lack pre- and postcingula. Both genera are reported from a single locality at Khovboor in Mongolia. The age, assumed to be Albian by Trofimov (*in* Beliajeva and others, 1974) and ?Aptian by Dashzeveg (1975), is uncertain.

Gallolestes pachymandibularis (see Lillegraven, 1972a and 1976) is known from four fragmentary specimens from the "El Gallo Formation" of northern Baja California, Mexico (middle to late Campanian). The specimens were assigned to the Eutheria on the basis of: (1) a small and labially situated paraconid; and (2) a strongly developed hypoconulid that is medially situated on the talonid. The affinities of *Gallolestes* are unknown. Lillegraven (1972a), however, indicated that the specimens suggest somewhat greater similarities with molars of Late Cretaceous palaeoryctids than with other known groups of equivalent antiquity.

Endotherium niinomii was described by Shi-

kama (1947) on the basis of two lower jaws from the Hsinchiu Coal Field of southern "Manchuria," People's Republic of China. Shikama accorded the specimens a Middle Jurassic age, but Patterson (1956) and Kermack and others (1965) suggested a later, possibly Aptian or Albian age. The genus was placed in the Eutheria by Shikama (1947), and the published figures suggest that *Endotherium* had tribosphenic lower molars characteristic of later placentals. Unfortunately, the type and referred specimens of *Endotherium* have been lost.

Parendotherium herreroi Crusafont-Pairó and Adrover (1966) was described on the basis of an enigmatic tooth from rocks of Neocomian age in Teruel Province, east-central Spain. From the name, one would suspect that satisfactory comparisons had been made with the type of *Endotherium*. The figures of *Endotherium*, however, do not allow adequate comparisons, and there is no real evidence that *Parendotherium* is in any way related to the Manchurian animal. It seems equally probable that the type of *Parendotherium* may be an upper incisor of a multituberculate (Szalay, *in* McKenna, 1969, p. 225, footnote 13). Alternatively, Crusafont and Gibert (1976) have reaffirmed an earlier suggestion that the tooth is a premolar of a dryolestid eupantothere.

Fox (1970) described, but did not name, an isolated upper molar from the upper part of the Milk River Formation ("Aquilan") of Alberta, Canada. He believed the tooth was of a eutherian mammal more advanced than *Pappotherium* (here placed in Theria of metatherian-eutherian grade) in the possession of a narrower stylar shelf, a smaller stylocone, stronger conules, larger protocone and metacone, and an incipient hypocone. Fox (1974) suggested that the tooth most closely resembles the "Lancian" arctocyonid condylarth *Protungulatum*, but noted also the resemblance to early "erinaceoid" insectivores (*e.g.*, *Leptacodon*; also see Szalay, 1968). Fox (1972) indicated in a faunal list the presence of two additional genera ("A" and "B") of insectivores, but these were not described and thus cannot yet be discussed.

Reliable designations of the affinities of the animals discussed above must await recovery of more complete and better documented specimens.

Proteutheria

The unquestioned Eutheria of the Cretaceous are dominated by three groups which have, by various authors and at one time or another, been included in the heterogeneous Order Insectivora. These are the Leptictidae (but see below), the Palaeoryctidae, and the Zalambdalestidae, but condylarths and primates were also in existence at that time. Novacek (1976) elevated Romer's (1966) Suborder Proteutheria to ordinal rank, and this taxon includes the above three families together with the Tertiary Apatemyidae, Ptolemaiidae, and Pantolestidae. The zalambdalestids are known exclusively from the Cretaceous, the palaeoryctids from the Late Cretaceous through the middle Eocene, and the leptictoids from the Late Cretaceous through the Oligocene. All known Cretaceous representatives of these groups were small mammals. *Cimolestes magnus*, a palaeoryctine, was the largest (P_4 anteroposterior length = 5.5 mm), and nearly attained the size of a marmot.

Gypsonictops (Fig. 12-13), from the Late Cretaceous of North America, has traditionally been considered a member of the predominantly early Tertiary Leptictidae (*e.g.*, Simpson, 1927, and Clemens, 1973a). Novacek (1977), however, concluded that although *Gypsonictops* is a member of the Superfamily Leptictoidea, it is in many characters more advanced than typical Cenozoic leptictids (*e.g.*, *Prodiacodon, Leptictis*), and thus should not be included in this family. Novacek (1977) suggested the elevation of Gypsonictopinae of Van Valen (1967) to family rank to accommodate *Gypsonictops*. In this book, however, we do not refine the classification of *Gypsonictops* beyond the Superfamily Leptictoidea.

A number of authors (*e.g.*, Kielan-Jaworowska, 1969; Lillegraven, 1969; McKenna, 1969; and Sloan, 1970) have suggested that the ?late Santonian and/or ?early Campanian (see Gradziński and others, 1977) Asiatic mammal *Kennalestes* (discussed earlier in chapter) is a leptictid or is related to the ancestry of that family. Kielan-Jaworowska (1969) originally assigned *Kennalestes* to the Superfamily Leptic-

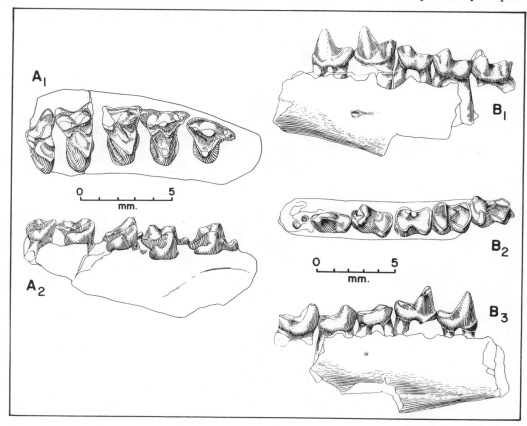

Figure 12-13. Cheek teeth of the North American Late Cretaceous species *Gypsonictops illuminatus*. *A*, $P^{3-4}M^{1-3}$ in occlusal (A_1) and lingual (A_2) views. *B*, $P_{3-4}M_{1-3}$ in labial (B_1), occlusal (B_2), and lingual (B_3) views. (After Lillegraven, 1969)

toidea, although with a query. She noted two characters in *Kennalestes* that are not shared by younger (and derived?) members of the Leptictidae *sensu stricto*. These are, first, the presence of non-molariform P^4_4, and second, nasals that are expanded posteriorly and in contact with the lacrimals. She did,

however, observe that the latter character appears to be a trait shared by Djadokhta eutherians in general, and may merely be a primitive feature.

McKenna (1969) believed *Kennalestes* to have been close to the origin of leptictids, but not far from the ancestry of the palaeoryctids as well. Kielan-

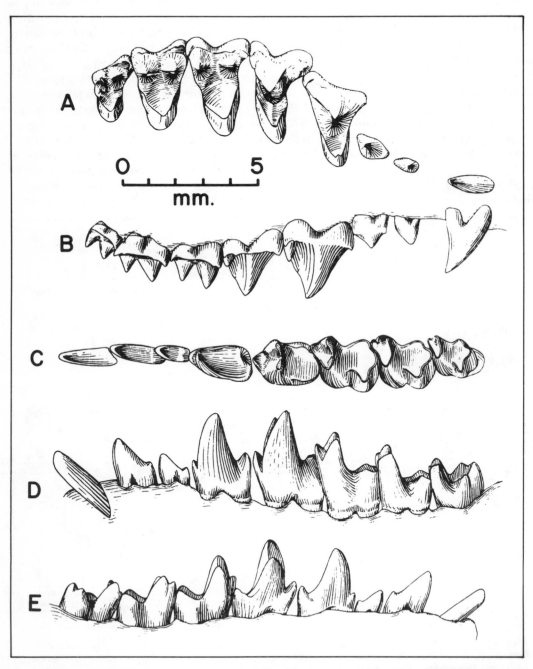

Figure 12-14.   Canines and cheek teeth of *Zalambdalestes lechei*. Right upper dentition in occlusal (A) and labial (B) views. Left lower dentition in occlusal (C), labial (D), and lingual (E) views. (From Kielan-Jaworowska, 1969)

Jaworowska (1969) suggested that *Kennalestes* may also have given rise to *Cimolestes* (Palaeoryctidae). Sloan (1970) believed that North American *Gypsonictops* (Leptictoidea) was a plausible derivative of *Kennalestes*. *Gypsonictops* (Fig. 11-13) has been interpreted to be a likely candidate for the ancestry of leptictine insectivores (or proteutherians; see Sloan, 1970; McKenna, 1969; Clemens, 1973a; and Novacek, 1977), and a somewhat less satisfactory precursor for the tupaiids, erinaceoid insectivores, soricoid insectivores (McKenna, 1969), and primates (McKenna, 1969; Sloan, 1970). Sloan (1970) suggested that *Gypsonictops* may have given rise to the earliest known primate, *Purgatorius ceratops*. This thesis, however, has been abandoned by Clemens (1973a) and Novacek (1977).

A second major group of Cretaceous insectivores was the Zalambdalestidae (Figs. 12-1, 12-8, 12-14), a wholly Asian Late Cretaceous family that contains two known genera, *Zalambdalestes* and its possible descendant, *Barunlestes*. Kielan-Jaworowska (1969, 1975a, *in press*) diagnosed the Zalambdalestidae upon the following criteria; comparatively large insectivores, skull varying from 4 to 5 cm in length; rostrum strongly constricted in front of P¹, snout long, tubular; zygoma strongly expanded laterally; choanae narrow; posterior palatine foramina large, suboval; three (?) upper incisors, upper canine double-rooted in *Zalambdalestes* but single-rooted in *Barunlestes*; P¹ and P² small (P¹ lost in *Barunlestes*); P³ large with prominent paracone; upper molars strongly elongated transversely with incipient conules, pre- and postcingula lacking; I₁ strongly enlarged; I₂₋₃ and lower canine semiprocumbent; P₂ lost in *Barunlestes*; lower molars with trigonids narrower than talonids, paraconid and metaconid connate at bases, paraconid smallest cusp of trigonid, protoconid the tallest; lower molar talonids strongly basined; postcranial skeleton of similar proportions with present-day Macroscelididae; hindlimbs long with fused tibia and fibula; feet very long; tibial trochlea on the astragalus well developed; calcaneal fibular facet wanting; sacrum composed of two vertebrae; epipubic bones probably present; and axis vertebra with long spinous process.

Clemens (1973a) suggested that the large number of characters shared by *Zalambdalestes* and the lep-

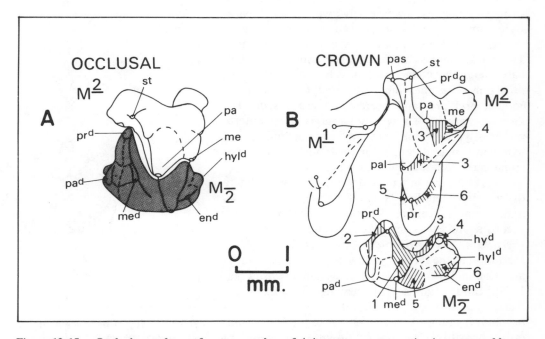

Figure 12-15. Occlusion and wear facets on molars of *Asioryctes nemegetensis*. *A*, **upper and lower (shaded) second molars as shown in oblique view during occlusion.** *B*, **crown views of part of M¹ and complete M₂ showing matching shearing surfaces (*1-6*) and identifications of main dental parts. Abbreviations are:** *en^d*, **entoconid;** *hy^d*, **hypoconid;** *hyl^d*, **hypoconulid;** *me*, **metacone;** *me^d*, **metaconid;** *pa*, **paracone;** *pa^d*, **paraconid;** *pal*, **paraconule;** *pas*, **parastyle;** *pr*, **protocone;** *pr^d*, **protoconid;** *pr^d g*, **groove for protoconid; and** *st*, **stylocone. (After Crompton and Kielan-Jaworowska, 1977; used with permission of Academic Press Inc. Limited)**

tictids reflects a close community or origin that warrants their inclusion within the same superfamily. Szalay and McKenna (1971) placed the Zalambdalestidae and the Tertiary Pseudictopidae, Anagalidae, and Eurymylidae in a new order, the Anagalida (the concept of which was emended by McKenna in 1975). McKenna (1969) and Van Valen (1964) had earlier suggested that *Zalambdalestes* was close to the ancestry of Asian Tertiary anagalids and lagomorphs. Kielan-Jaworowska (1975b; *in press*), working with newly discovered postcranial remains, demonstrated that zalambdalestids were not ancestral to the Pseudictopidae or the Anagalidae, and probably not to the eurymylids. The tibia and fibula are fused in Cretaceous zalambdalestids (see Fig. 12-8), and are unfused in the Pseudictopidae and Anagalidae. The apparent similarities between the Zalambdalestidae and Lagomorpha are only superficial.

The Superfamily Palaeoryctoidea is perhaps the least coherent of present groupings of Cretaceous "insectivores." Kielan-Jaworowska (1975b) assigned *Asioryctes*, from the (?middle Campanian) Barun Goyot Formation of Mongolia, to the Palaeoryctidae. Upper molars of *Asioryctes* (Fig. 12-15) are strongly elongated transversely, with a large parastyle, smaller stylocone, deep ectoflexus, large metastyle, and a comparatively narrow stylar shelf. The paracone and metacone are connate at their bases, and the metacone is much shorter than the paracone. The paraconule is larger than the metaconule, and pre- and postcingula are absent. The lower molars have a trigonid that is short anteroposteriorly, with the entoconid, hypoconulid, and hypoconid placed rather far posteriorly. The hypoconid is the tallest talonid cusp.

If *Asioryctes* is a palaeoryctid, the family had a distribution including North America, central Asia, and, possibly, Europe ("Champ-Garimond tooth," according to McKenna, 1969). Reference of *Deltatheridium, Deltatheroides*, and probably *Hyotheridium* to the Palaeoryctidae is rejected (see Butler and Kielan-Jaworowska, 1973; Kielan-Jaworowska, 1975b; and Chapter 10), leaving threadbare the Asiatic record of this family. *Asioryctes* thus becomes the oldest known member of the family and, quite possibly, the only known occurrence of palaeoryctids in Asia. Kielan-Jaworowska (1975a) demonstrated that *Asioryctes* would probably not have been in the ancestry of known North American palaeoryctid genera, because the reduction of the

metacone and the metaconule are specialized in comparison with known North American forms.

More typical representatives of the Palaeoryctoidea are abundant in latest Cretaceous rocks of North America with *Cimolestes, Procerberus*, and *Batodon*. North American Cretaceous and early Tertiary Palaeoryctidae have been separated into three subfamilies, the Didelphodontinae, the Procerberinae, and the Palaeoryctinae. To the first subfamily are referred *Cimolestes* and possibly *Batodon* (although McKenna in 1975 allied *Batodon* with the Insectivora, Erinaceomorpha, and Soricomorpha). *Procerberus* (Fig. 12-16), the sole known member of the Procerberinae, was originally diagnosed by Sloan

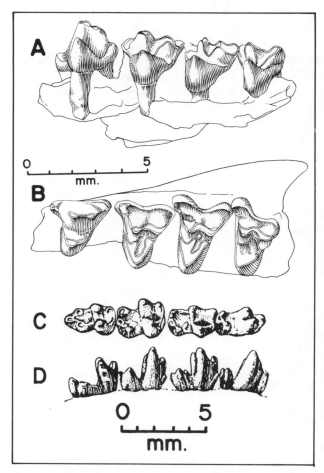

Figure 12-16.   Cheek teeth of the North American Late Cretaceous species *Procerberus formicarum*. Left maxillary fragment with P^4M^{1-3} in lingual (*A*) and occlusal (*B*) views (after Lillegraven, 1969). Right P_4M_{1-3} (reconstructed) in occlusal (*C*) and labial (*D*) views (from Sloan and Van Valen, 1965; copyright 1965 by the American Association for the Advancement of Science).

and Van Valen (1965) as a leptictid. *Procerberus* was removed from the Leptictidae by Lillegraven (1969) and placed in the Palaeoryctidae. The Palaeoryctinae, including *Palaeoryctes* (Paleocene) and *Pararyctes* (Paleocene and Eocene), is a strictly Tertiary group characterized, among other features, by tall trigonids, essentially premolariform P_4^4, and high, acute cusps on molars.

Cimolestes (Fig. 12-17) is believed to have given rise to *Procerberus* (see Sloan and Van Valen, 1965, and Lillegraven, 1969), and according to Lillegraven

(1969), *Procerberus* is the most probable candidate for the ancestry of the Taeniodonta of the early Tertiary. *Cimolestes* may also have shared a close common ancestry with the arctocyonid condylarth *Protungulatum* (? = *Loxolophus*). Szalay (1968) awarded *Cimolestes* and/or *Procerberus* to the ancestry of the Creodonta and Apatemyoidea, and McKenna (1969) felt that either or both genera may have been related to the ancestry of the true carnivores, the Taeniodonta, and the earliest known condylarth (*Protungulatum*). Van Valen (1969) sug-

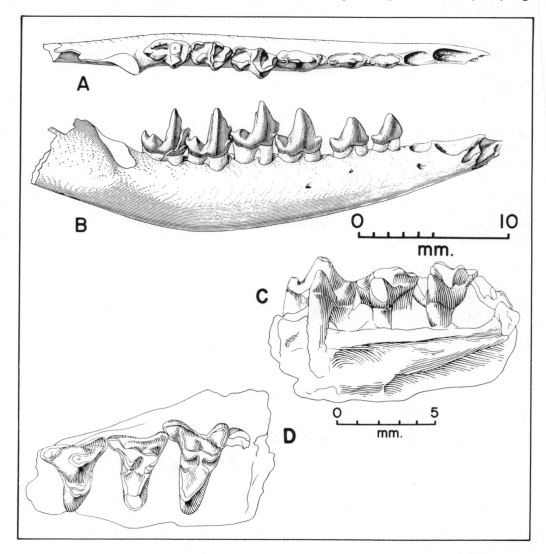

Figure 12-17.   Cheek teeth of the North American Late Cretaceous species *Cimolestes incisus*. Right mandible with alveoli for canine and P_1 plus complete $P_{2-4}M_{1-3}$ in occlusal (*A*) and labial (*B*) views (from Clemens, 1973a; copyright © 1973 by The Regents of the University of California). Left maxillary fragment with P^4M^{1-2} and fragment of M^3 in occlusal (*C*) and lingual (*D*) views (after Lillegraven, 1969).

gested derivation both of the Carnivora and the Palaeoryctidae from the Procerberinae, a group that he (following Sloan and Van Valen, 1965) included with the leptictids. The palaeoryctids, according to Van Valen (1969), gave rise to the creodont Oxyaenidae and Hyaenodontidae.

Batodon tenuis (see Fig. 12-18) is a minuscule palaeoryctid similar in most respects to *Cimolestes incisus.* Although Van Valen (1967) allied *Batodon* with *Deltatheridium* and *Hyotheridium* (Deltatheridiidae, here considered as Theria of metatherian-eutherian grade), the eutherian assignment seems more secure. Szalay and Decker (1974) suggested an "erinaceotan, nyctitheriid" affinity of *Batodon.*

Telacodon laevis is another small form, represented only by a mandibular fragment with P_{2-4}. The few teeth suggest similarities with other palaeoryctids, and probable distinctness from *Batodon* (see Clemens, 1973a).

A single lower molar, the "Champ-Garimond tooth" (late Senonian) from France (Ledoux and others, 1966), originally was tentatively assigned to the Condylarthra. McKenna (1969), however, offered the view that it more probably represents a palaeoryctid. Striking features of this tooth include the relatively great length of the trigonid, a lingually

placed paraconid, and an entoconid that is well removed posteriorly from the metaconid. Simpson (1971) was conservative in discussing this specimen and acknowledged the tooth only to be eutherian.

Condylarthra

Mesozoic representatives of the Condylarthra include "Lancian" *Protungulatum* and, with considerable doubt, *Perutherium. Protungulatum* (Fig. 12-19) occurs in latest Cretaceous deposits in Montana, and probably in Puercan (early Paleocene) rocks in northern Wyoming disguised under the appellation of *Loxolophus.* In addition to *Protungulatum donnae,* Sloan and Van Valen (1965) noted, but did not name or describe, four additional species. Sloan and Van Valen (1965) and Lillegraven (1969) favored a palaeoryctid origin for the genus, but Fox (1970) argued that condylarths probably descended from eutherians with molars that were less transverse than those of known palaeoryctid insectivores. *Protungulatum,* as the earliest known condylarth, is believed to have given rise to later members of that order and, through them, to at least some of the diversity of Cenozoic "ungulates."

Teeth of *Protungulatum donnae* are character-

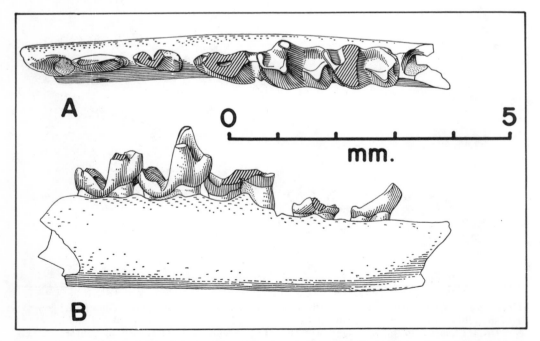

Figure 12-18.   Left mandibular fragment of the North American Late Cretaceous species *Batodon tenuis,* **showing** P_2, **broken** P_{3-4}, **and** M_{1-2}. *A* **, occlusal and** *B* **, lingual views. (From Clemens, 1973a;**

ized by P³⁻⁴ that possess a relatively narrow paracone (transversely), small on P³ and larger on P⁴. A small metacone is usually present on P³⁻⁴. M_2^2 are transversely wider than M_1^1, but all of the upper molars are transverse with the hypocone weak or absent. Labial cingula occur on P³⁻⁴, and lingual cingula are present on M¹⁻³. In the lower dentition, P_4 is sub-molariform with a low, but distinct, paraconid and metaconid; the talonid of P_4, however, is simple. The lower molars possess short and relatively narrow talonids and weak labial cingula. Lingual cingula are lacking. The paraconids of M_{1-3} are moderately large and lingually placed. M_3 is narrower than M_2, and has a large, posteriorly projecting hypoconulid.

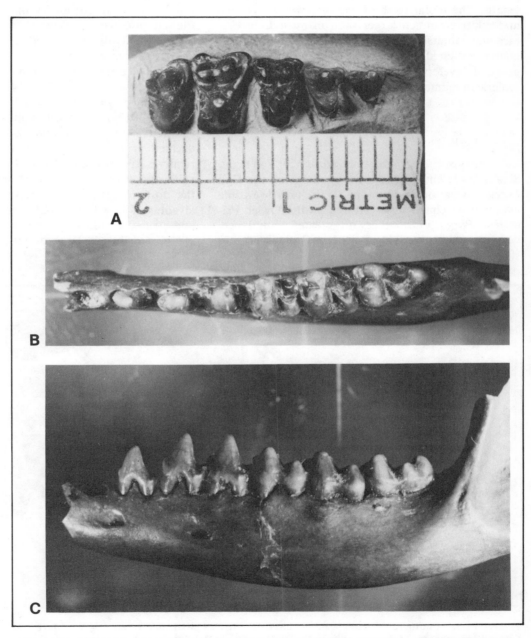

Figure 12-19.   Photographs of cheek teeth of the North American Late Cretaceous species *Protungulatum donnae*. *A*, **reconstructed right tooth row including P³⁻⁴M¹⁻³, as seen in occlusal view. Left mandible with alveolus for P₁ and complete P₂₋₄M₁₋₃, seen in occlusal (B) and labial (C) views.**

Perutherium (see Grambast and others, 1967, and Sigé, 1971, 1972) may be referable to the Condylarthra, but specimens and evidence are scanty (see Chapter 2). It is represented by a solitary fragment of a mandible that preserves the talonid of M_1 and the trigonid of M_2. The trigonid of M_2 is only slightly elevated above the level of the M_1 talonid, and the tooth is relatively wide transversely with respect to length. The molar teeth of *Perutherium* are crested and relatively much larger than in most Late Cretaceous mammals. These features, in addition to the characters cited above, suggest a more advanced grade of development than that exemplified by North American mammals of presumed similar antiquity.

Primates

The type of *Purgatorius ceratops* Van Valen and Sloan, 1965, an isolated lower molar from the Hell Creek Formation of Montana, is the only Mesozoic mammal specimen now referred to the Order Primates. *Purgatorius* occurs in greater abundance, however, in the overlying Paleocene Tullock Forma-

tion (see Clemens, 1974). The genus was assigned to the Paromomyidae by Van Valen and Sloan (1965) and by most subsequent authors. The paromomyids were reviewed by Bown and Rose (1976), who transferred most paromomyids *sensu lato* to the Microsyopidae. *Purgatorius* was regarded by them to be a plesiadapiform prosimian, but with so few shared and derived characters in common with the families of that infraorder that it was assigned to Plesiadapiformes, *incertae sedis*. *Purgatorius* seems to be sufficiently generalized to have been a possible ancestor for any known plesiadapiform family. Critical evidence from intermediate forms, however, is lacking.

Teeth of *Purgatorius* (as known from *P. unio*, an early Paleocene species) illustrate a number of characters (Figs. 12-20 and 12-21) that can only be deemed primitive in relation to its closest known relatives among the Paleocene primates. The lower canine appears to have been as large as the largest of the posterior lower incisors. Only the base of the alveolus of I_1 is known (Clemens, *in prep.*). Its size and structure indicate that I_1 was a relatively large tooth, possibly as large or larger than the canine.

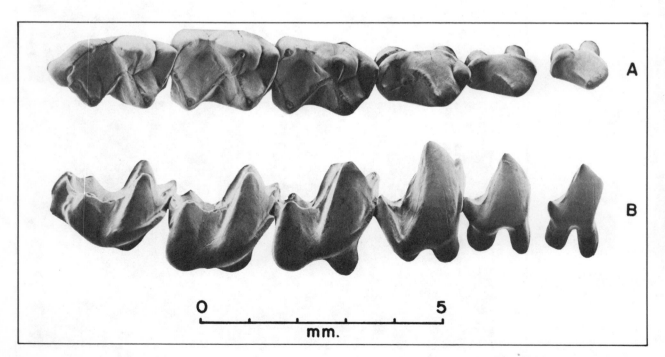

Figure 12-20.   Photographs from scanning electron microscope of right lower cheek teeth ($P_{2-4}M_{1-3}$) of *Purgatorius unio* within a jaw recovered from the Tullock Formation of early Paleocene age in Montana. The morphology probably does not differ greatly from the latest Cretaceous, *P. ceratops*. *A*, occlusal and *B*, labial views. (From Clemens, 1974; copyright 1974 by the American Association for the Advancement of Science)

There are three incisors and four premolars; P_{2-4} are two-rooted. P_4 possesses a strong paraconid, but only weak thickenings of the enamel in the vicinity of the metaconid (Clemens, 1974). The paraconid is large, rather medially placed on all lower molars, and the anterior inclination of the cusp increases progressively from M_1 through M_3. P_4M_{1-3} do not have well-developed cingulids, except that a minor descending cingulid is present on the anterolabial margin of the trigonid. Provisionally identified upper cheek teeth from the Garbani locality in eastern Montana show that the upper molars have, relative to those of later primates, a primitively broad external cingulum. The conules are well developed, as are the precingulum and postcingulum. Development of the postprotocingulum (= *Nannopithex*-fold) is variable. On the teeth of one individual (Fig. 12-21), it links the protocone and rudimentary hypocone of M^1. A postprotocingulum is absent on M^2, however, and the minute hypocone is separated from the wall of the protocone by a distinct cleft. P^4 is sub-molariform with a large protocone and small metacone (Clemens, *in prep.*). Clemens (1974) reviewed arguments favoring a leptictoid or a palaeoryctid origin for the primates, and concluded that known Late Cretaceous members of either group are too specialized to be considered as likely primate ancestors. The derivation of the order thus remains uncertain.

PHYLOGENY

The more important historical interpretations of phylogenetic relationships of described genera of Cretaceous eutherians were summarized in the section immediately above. In the present section, we provide our own interpretations, admittedly biased, using Figure 12-22 as a foundation for discussion. Also included in Figure 12-22 are the various genera which we here refer to the Theria of metatherian-eutherian grade (see Chapter 10).

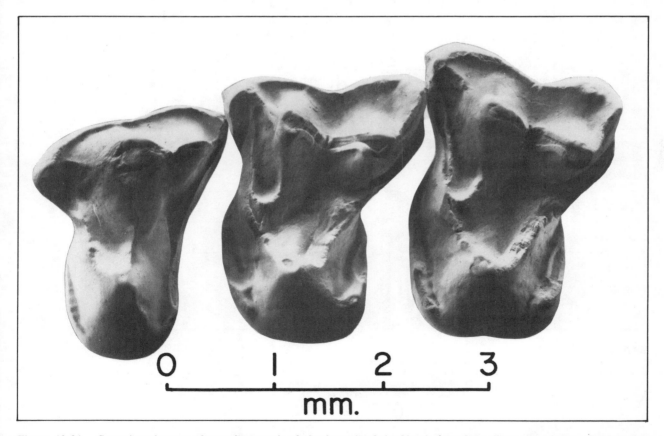

Figure 12-21.   Scanning electron photomicrograph of cheek teeth of the North American, Puercan primate, *Purgatorius unio*. Occlusal view of P^4M^{1-2} preserved in a fragment of left maxilla found at the Garbani locality, Tullock Formation, Garfield County, Montana (from Clemens, *in prep.*, with support from National Science Foundation grant DEB 75-21017).

We believe that all Cretaceous advanced therians were derived from an ancestor having lower molars similar to those seen in *Aegialodon*. We make no claim, however, that *Aegialodon* was itself the ancestor.

Endotherium is so poorly known that reference even to the Eutheria is uncertain. We include it here only to complete the roster.

"*Prokennalestes*," although unfigured and undescribed, is known to have a dental morphology similar in most respects to *Kennalestes*. "*Prokennalestes*" is a morphological intermediate between an ancestral type represented by *Aegialodon* and the

variety of known Late Cretaceous eutherians. Nothing can be said of "*Prozalambdalestes*," and its validity as represented by specimens in collections is here questioned.

The Late Cretaceous eutherian record is thus left without a solid understanding of possibly ancestral forms. As a result, most ideas concerning relationships and trends in Late Cretaceous mammals have developed from "hindsight," by the extrapolation backwards of trends seen in the phylogeny of early Tertiary mammals. Even these sorts of interpretations are made difficult, however, because of the nearly worldwide paucity of early Paleocene faunas

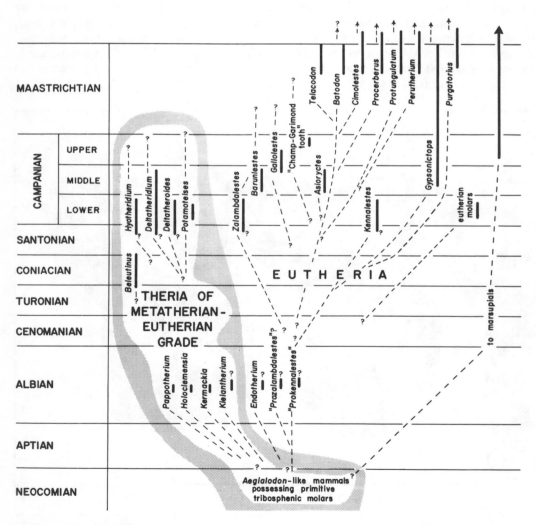

Figure 12-22.   Postulated phylogram of known genera of Cretaceous eutherians and therians of metatherian-eutherian grade. As indicated by the large number of queries, great uncertainty exists from several points of view. See Figure 2-1 for presumed equivalencies of the classic European stages with North American "land mammal ages."

(see Lillegraven, 1972b). Questions of endemism or directions of intercontinental dispersal cannot yet be confidently resolved (see Chapter 14).

Zalambdalestes and *Barunlestes* probably had an ancestor-descendant relationship, but other descendants from either genus are unknown. The pair certainly had nothing to do with the ancestry of lagomorphs, and probably not with the eurymylids.

Kennalestes is dentally primitive, and its ancestral stock may have been the stem for a variety of more advanced eutherians. It is possible, but not proven, that such disparate forms as *Gypsonictops* (Proteutheria) and *Purgatorius* (Primates) had a reasonably close common ancestry with *Kennalestes.*

The upper molar described by Fox (1970) from the upper part of the Milk River Formation shows no particular affinities with any other known group of placentals. The undescribed genera "A" and "B" from the same formation (Fox, 1972), although tantalizing, cannot be discussed with respect to their probable relationships with other forms. Thus pre-"Judithian" mammals from North America identified as eutherians cannot yet be linked with any other groups.

The affinities of *Gallolestes* and the "Champ-Garimond tooth" are unknown, though both seem closer in dental morphology to the North American palaeoryctids than to any other known group.

Asioryctes seems to have had a close common ancestry with more definite palaeoryctids, but there are some marked differences between them.

Species of *Telacodon, Batodon,* and *Cimolestes* show close affinities with one another, and all may have had a slightly more distant common ancestry with *Procerberus.* It is possible that Late Cretaceous *Batodon,* like *Cimolestes,* had descendant species in the early Tertiary. It is probable that the true Carnivora (Miacidae) and "creodonts" had their origins from descendants of *Cimolestes. Procerberus* was probably ancestral to the peculiar early Tertiary Order Taeniodonta.

The Order Condylarthra had its first appearance with the arctocyonid *Protungulatum,* and, possibly, *Perutherium.* The origin of the condylarths is quite unknown, but *Protungulatum* shares more features with the palaeoryctids than with any other known Late Cretaceous group. Features of the dentition of *Protungulatum* are those expected in the ultimate ancestry of most of the diverse early Tertiary condylarths (and their "ungulate" descendants, the perissodactyls and artiodactyls). The genus is probably well named in terms of its phylogenetic significance.

Known species of *Gypsonictops* apparently were not directly ancestral to Cenozoic leptictid proteutherians or their close allies. The genus was probably a sister-group of the leptictines, a group as yet unknown from the Cretaceous. The dental anatomy of *Gypsonictops* suggests no particular community of origin with *Purgatorius* of the early primates (*contra* Lillegraven, 1969). *Purgatorius* has dental characters that could be expected in the ancestry of any later primate group.

Although few definite statements can be made with respect to Cretaceous ancestries of particular eutherian groups, it is quite certain that ordinal differentiation was well under way by latest Cretaceous time. The likelihood is good that, among *living* orders, the evolutionary roots of at least the modern Insectivora, Carnivora (including the "pinnipeds"), Perissodactyla-Artiodactyla, and Primates have been distinct since late in the Mesozoic. Earliest members of the Dermoptera, Chiroptera, Rodentia, and Cetacea probably became differentiated immediately thereafter, but from as yet uncertain sources. The progenitors of the Edentata, Pholidota, Tubulidentata, Lagomorpha, Hyracoidea, Proboscidea, and Sirenia are completely unknown and, at least for the first four of these orders, may also have had stems distinct since the late Mesozoic. Thus it is clear that an understanding of relationships of modern eutherian groups requires further research into the world's Late Cretaceous fossil record.

ECOLOGY

The Problems

Speculations on life habits of extinct species of vertebrates depend primarily upon comparisons, by analogy with modern situations, of: (1) anatomical specializations that are characteristic of particular ways of coping with the environment (especially with respect to locomotory and dietary capabilities); (2) interpretation of clues from the sedimentological-geochemical record of the fossil-bearing rocks that might suggest the local environment at the time of deposition; and (3) largely intuitive analysis of the composition of the ancient local biotic community as shown by associated fossil remains of other life forms. Interpretation of probable ecological roles of most presently known Cretaceous eutherian species by use of available data from these three categories must be considered, at best, tentative; the reasons are summarized below. The discussion will be restricted to those formations known to contain eutherian mammals as defined within the present chapter.

The specimens from the Hsinchiu Coal Field ("Manchuria"), Khovboor (Mongolia), Champ-Garimond (France), and Laguna Umayo (Peru) are fragmentary, poorly represented, or undescribed, and provide little useful ecological information as based upon anatomy. The eutherians from the Late Cretaceous Djadokhta and Barun Goyot formations (Mongolia) are represented by excellent dental, cranial, and articulated postcranial material, and the animals show specializations interpretable to particular ways of life. The described Late Cretaceous eutherian record from North America, however, is restricted (except for a few foot bones) to dental remains and a few fragments of crania.

Detailed sedimentological-geochemical data are not available for the Early Cretaceous eutherian-bearing localities at the Hsinchiu Coal Field or Khovboor. Similarly, no such data are known to us for use in interpretation of the Late Cretaceous eutherians from Champ-Garimond or Laguna Umayo. Sedimentological studies useful for our purposes have been made, however, for the Djadokhta and Barun Goyot formations of Mongolia (see Lefeld, 1971, and Gradziński and Jerzykiewicz, 1974) and several of the formations in North America (see Schile, 1974, and Archibald, 1977).

Biotic analyses adequate for even the most generalized interpretation of mammalian ecological roles are available only from Late Cretaceous settings in Mongolia (for which a complete synthesis has yet to be completed and published) and for a short interval of the latest Cretaceous, from the western coastal region of the great Western Interior Seaway of North America (see Chapter 14).

The difficulties summarized above illustrate the magnitude of research remaining before all but the most rudimentary understanding of the biological aspects of eutherian life during the Cretaceous can be attained. Virtually all discussion of ecological adaptations of Cretaceous placentals must be restricted to those known from late in the period from central Asia and western North America.

Adaptations

Nothing is known of the ecological roles of Early Cretaceous eutherians other than the fact that some had sharp-cusped tribosphenic teeth that prob-

ably functioned best in insectivory. In contrast, the structural differentiation seen in the dentitions and postcranial skeletons of Late Cretaceous forms suggests the existence of diversified habits. For example, the teeth of North American species show a spectrum of adaptations that could be interpreted as representing insectivory (e.g., Cimolestes incisus, C. propalaeoryctes, and Batodon tenuis), perhaps some degree of carnivory upon larger prey (e.g., Cimolestes magnus), and omnivory or frugivory (e.g., various species of Gypsonictops and Purgatorius ceratops). Still other genera had dentitions the functions of which are extremely difficult to interpret (e.g., Procerberus and Gallolestes). As known from the study of modern small mammals, however, examination of the teeth alone usually cannot be used as a definitive guide to the animals' food habits; rodents participate to a large degree in carnivory, and most members of the Insectivora eat nearly anything organic that can be stuffed into their mouths and chewed. Thus little faith can be placed in attempts at interpretation of detailed dietary roles of the Cretaceous eutherians. All we really know is that the dental structural differentiation was considerable.

Remains of North American Late Cretaceous eutherians have been found almost exclusively in rocks representing conditions of floodplain lowlands that were somewhat swampy, with varying degrees of forestation (see Estes, 1964, and Estes and Berberian, 1970). Also, most were not far from the shores of epicontinental seas. The "El Gallo Formation" of Mexico was deposited in a similar environmental setting, but on the eastern coast of the Pacific Ocean. The only Cretaceous mammal-bearing locality in North America known to represent fully interior continental conditions is in the Newark Canyon Formation of Nevada, from which eutherians have not yet been discovered. Thus a very serious ecological bias exists on that continent with respect to the sampling of eutherians from varied environmental settings.

It seems probable that Late Cretaceous placental mammals in North America exhibited wide adaptive diversification, filling such roles as "generalists," climbers, jumpers, and diggers. In the absence of information from the postcranial skeletons, however, such a concept must reside within the realm of speculation.

The situation is in some respects better in the Asiatic Late Cretaceous record. Although the taxonomic diversity of known eutherians is less than that of North America, direct information from postcranial skeletons definitely shows the existence of functionally differentiated body types. At least two different life habits can be documented. One was developed in insectivorous mammals that possibly were shrew-like in general appearance. This group includes *Asioryctes* and, possibly, *Kennalestes*. A second, and physically larger, type of mammal is represented by the Zalambdalestidae. Kielan-Jaworowska (*in press*) demonstrated that the locomotion of the zalambdalestids was probably similar to present-day macroscelidids, which is a quadrupedal walk, run, or jump. Molar adaptations were for crushing and shearing, and the animals probably were largely insectivorous. It is possible that they occasionally used the procumbent, strongly enlarged first lower incisors for picking insects from crevices. No wholly fossorial Cretaceous eutherians have (knowingly) yet been discovered.

The apparent lower degree of mammalian diversity observed in the Late Cretaceous fossil-bearing rocks of Mongolia may be an artifact of the local environment in which the animals lived. The area was on the central Asiatic craton, and would have been some hundreds of kilometers from the nearest marine waters (see Fig. 14-5); it was a true continental interior situation. According to Lefeld (1971) and Gradziński and Jerzykiewicz (1974), analysis of rocks of the Djadokhta and Barun Goyot formations suggest aeolian-lacustrine deposition in a rather arid, semidesert environment. The Asiatic settings are extremely different from those existing at roughly the same time intervals on the verdant shores of the Western Interior Seaway of North America. Therefore, the samples from both Asia and North America are seriously biased from environmental points of view, but in different directions. It is presently uncertain as to what extent the differences in land vertebrate faunas between the two areas reflect the disparities of environmental setting in which the animals lived.

REFERENCES CITED

Altner, G., 1971, Histologische und vergleichend-anatomische Untersuchungen zur Ontogenie und Phylogenie des Handskeletts von *Tupaia glis* (Diard 1820) und *Microcebus murinus* (J. F. Miller 1777): Folia Primat., v. 14, suppl., p. 1-106.

Archibald, J. D., 1977, Fossil Mammalia and testudines of the Hell Creek Formation, and the geology of the Tullock and Hell Creek formations, Garfield County, Montana [Ph.D. thesis]: Berkeley, California, Univ. California.

Barnett, C. H., and Napier, J. R., 1953, The rotary mobility of the fibula in eutherian mammals: Jour. Anat., v. 87, p. 11-21.

Beliajeva, E. I., Trofimov, B. A., and Reshetov, V. J., 1974, General stages in evolution of late Mesozoic and early Tertiary mammalian fauna in central Asia, *in* Kramarenko, N. N., and others, eds., Mesozoic and Cenozoic faunas and biostratigraphy of Mongolia: Moscow, Joint Soviet-Mongol. Paleont. Exped. (Trans., v. 1), p. 19-45 (in Russian with English summary).

Bensley, B. A., 1901a, On the question of an arboreal ancestry of the Marsupialia and the interrelationships of the mammalian subclasses: Amer. Natur., v. 35, p. 117-138.

_____1901b, A theory of the origin and evolution of the Australian Marsupialia: *ibid.*, v. 35, p. 245-269.

Bown, T. M., and Rose, K. D., 1976, New early Tertiary primates and a reappraisal of some Plesiadapiformes: Folia Primat., v. 26, p. 109-138.

Brown, J. C., 1964, Observations on the elephant-shrews (Macroscelididae) of equatorial Africa: Zool. Soc. London Proc., v. 143, p. 103-119.

Brown, J. C., and Yalden, D. W., 1973, The description of mammals—2. Limbs and locomotion of terrestrial mammals: Mammal Rev., v. 3, p. 107-134.

Butler, P. M., and Kielan-Jaworowska, Z., 1973, Is *Deltatheridium* a marsupial?: Nature, v. 245, p. 105-106.

Clemens, W. A., 1971, Mammalian evolution in the Cretaceous, *in* Kermack, D. M., and Kermack, K. A., eds., Early mammals: Linn. Soc. Zool. Jour., v. 50, suppl. 1, p. 165-180.

_____1973a, Fossil mammals of the type Lance Formation, Wyoming. Part III. Eutheria and summary: Univ. California Publs. Geol. Sci., v. 94, *vi* + 102 p.

_____1973b, The roles of fossil vertebrates in interpretation of Late Cretaceous stratigraphy of the San Juan Basin, New Mexico: Four Corners Geol. Soc. Memoir Book, 1973, p. 154-167.

_____1974, *Purgatorius*, an early paromomyid primate (Mammalia): Science, v. 184, p. 903-905.

Clemens, W. A., and Russell, L. S., 1965, Mammalian fossils from the Upper Edmonton Formation, *in* Vertebrate paleontology in Alberta: Univ. Alberta Bull. (Geol. 2), p. 32-40.

Cope, E. D., 1881, A new type of Perissodactyla: Amer. Natur., v. 15, p. 1017-1018.

Crompton, A. W., 1974, The dentitions and relationships of the southern African Triassic mammals, *Erythrotherium parringtoni* and *Megazostrodon rudnerae*: Brit. Mus. (Nat. Hist.) Bull. (Geol.), v. 24, p. 397-437.

Crompton, A. W., and Kielan-Jaworowska, Z., 1978, Molar structure and occlusion in Cretaceous therian mammals, *in* Butler, P. M., and Joysey, K. A., eds., Studies in the development, function and evolution of teeth: London and New York, Academic Press, p. 249-287.

Crusafont-Pairó, M., and Adrover, R., 1966, El primer representante de la clase mamíferos hallado en el Mesozoico de España: Teruel, v. 35, p. 139-143.

Crusafont, M., and Gibert, J., 1976, Los primeros Multituberculados de España (Nota preliminar): Acta Geologica Hispanica, Año 11, p. 57-64.

Dashzeveg, D., 1975, New primitive therian from the Early Cretaceous of Mongolia: Nature, v. 256, p. 402-403.

Dollo, L., 1899, Les ancêtres des Marsupiaux étaient-ils arboricoles?: Trav. Stat. Zool. Wimereux, v. 7, p. 188-203.

Estes, R. D., 1964, Fossil vertebrates from the Late Cretaceous Lance Formation, eastern Wyoming: Univ. California Publs. Geol. Sci., v. 49, 180 p.

Estes, R. D., and Berberian, P., 1970, Paleoecology of a Late Cretaceous vertebrate community from Montana: Breviora (Harvard Univ.), no. 343, 35 p.

Evans, F. G., 1942, The osteology and relationships of elephant shrews: Amer. Mus. Nat. Hist. Bull., v. 80, p. 85-125.

Fox, R. C., 1970, Eutherian mammal from the early Campanian (Late Cretaceous) of Alberta, Canada: Nature, v. 227, p. 630-631.

———1972, A primitive therian mammal from the Upper Cretaceous of Alberta: Canad. Jour. Earth Sci., v. 9, p. 1479-1494.

———1974, *Deltatheroides*-like mammals from the Upper Cretaceous of North America: Nature, v. 249, p. 392.

———1975, Molar structure and function in the Early Cretaceous mammal *Pappotherium*: evolutionary implications for Mesozoic Theria: Canad. Jour. Earth Sci., v. 12, p. 412-442.

Gidley, J. W., 1919, Significance of divergence of the first digit in the primitive mammalian foot: Washington Acad. Sci. Jour., v. 9, p. 273-280.

Gill, T. N., 1872, Arrangement of the families of mammals and synoptical tables of characters of the subdivisions of mammals: Smithson. Misc. Coll., no. 230, *vi* + 98 p.

Gradziński, R., and Jerzykiewicz, T., 1974, Sedimentation of the Barun Goyot Formation, *in* Kielan-Jaworowska, Z., ed., Results Polish-Mongol. Palaeont. Expeds., pt. V: Palaeontologia Polonica, no. 33, p. 111-146.

Gradziński, R., Kielan-Jaworowska, Z., and Maryańska, T., 1977, Upper Cretaceous Djadokhta, Barun Goyot and Nemegt formations of Mongolia, including remarks on previous subdivisions: Acta Geol. Polonica, v. 27, p. 281-318.

Grambast, L., Martinez, M., Mattauer, M., and Thaler, L., 1967, *Perutherium altiplanense*, nov. gen., nov. sp., premier Mammifère mésozoïque d'Amérique du Sud: Acad. Sci. Paris C. R., sér. D, v. 264, p. 707-710.

Gregory, W. K., and Simpson, G. G., 1926, Cretaceous mammal skulls from Mongolia: Amer. Mus. Novitates, no. 225, 20 p.

Haines, R. W., 1958, Arboreal or terrestrial ancestry of placental mammals: Quart. Rev. Biol., v. 33, p. 1-23.

Hatt, R. T., 1931, The vertebral columns of richochetal rodents: Amer. Mus. Nat. Hist. Bull., v. 63, p. 599-738.

Howell, A. B., 1926, Anatomy of the wood rat: Amer. Soc. Mammal. Monog., v. 1, p. 1-225.

Huxley, T. H., 1880, On the application of the laws of evolution to the arrangement of the Vertebrata, and more particularly of the Mammalia: Zool. Soc. London Proc., 1880, p. 649-662.

Illiger, C., 1811, *Prodromus systematis mammalium et avium additis terminis zoographicus utriudque classis*: Berlin, C. Safeld, 301 p.

Jenkins, F. A., Jr., 1969, The evolution and development of the dens of the mammalian axis: Anat. Rec., v. 164, p. 173-184.

———1971, The postcranial skeleton of African cynodonts: Peabody Mus. Nat. Hist. (Yale Univ.) Bull., no. 36, 216 p.

———1974, Tree-shrew locomotion and primate arborealism, *in* Jenkins, F. A., Jr., ed., Primate locomotion: New York, Academic Press, p. 85-115.

Jenkins, F. A., Jr., and Parrington, F. R., 1976, The postcranial skeletons of the Triassic mammals *Eozostrodon, Megazostrodon* and *Erythrotherium*: Roy. Soc. London Philos. Trans., B (Biol. Sci.), v. 273, p. 387-431.

Kermack, K. A., Lees, P. M., and Mussett, F., 1965, *Aegialodon dawsoni*, a new trituberculosectorial tooth from the Lower Wealden: Roy. Soc. London Proc., B (Biol. Sci.), v. 162, p. 535-554.

Kielan-Jaworowska, Z., 1969, Preliminary data on the Upper Cretaceous eutherian mammals from Bayn Dzak, Gobi Desert, *in* Kielan-Jaworowska, Z., ed., Results Polish-Mongol. Palaeont. Expeds., pt. I: Palaeontologia Polonica, no. 19, p. 171-191.

———1975a, Preliminary description of two new eutherian genera from the Late Cretaceous of Mongolia, *in ibid.*, pt. VI: *ibid.*, no. 33, p. 5-16.

———1975b, Evolution of the therian mammals in the Late Cretaceous of Asia. Part I. Deltatheridiidae, *in ibid.*, pt. VI: *ibid.*, no. 33, p. 103-132.

———1975c, Late Cretaceous mammals and dinosaurs from the Gobi Desert: Amer. Sci., v. 63, p. 150-159.

———1975d, Possible occurrence of marsupial bones in

Cretaceous eutherian mammals: Nature, v. 255, p. 698-699.

_____1977, Evolution of the therian mammals in the Late Cretaceous of Asia. Part II. Postcranial skeleton in *Kennalestes* and *Asioryctes*, in Kielan-Jaworowska, Z., ed., Results Polish-Mongol. Palaeont. Expeds., pt. VII: Palaeontologia Polonica, no. 37, p. 65-84.

_____in press, Evolution of the therian mammals in the Late Cretaceous of Asia. Part III. Postcranial skeleton in the Zalambdalestidae, *in ibid.*, pt. VIII: *ibid.*, no. 38, p. 5-41.

Ledoux, J.-C., Hartenberger, J.-L., Michaux, J., Sudre, J., and Thaler, L., 1966, Découverte d'un Mammifère dans le Crétacé supérieur à Dinosaures de Champ-Garimond près de Fons (Gard): Acad. Sci. Paris, C. R., sér. D, v. 262, p. 1925-1928.

Lefeld, J., 1971, Geology of the Djadokhta Formation at Bayn Dzak (Mongolia), in Kielan-Jaworowska, Z., ed., Results Polish-Mongol. Palaeont. Expeds., pt. III: Palaeontologia Polonica, no. 25, p. 101-127.

Lessertisseur, J., and Saban, R., 1967, Squelette appendiculaire, in Grassé, P. P., ed., Traité de zoologie, v. 16, pt. 1: Paris, Masson & Cie, p. 709-1078.

Lewis, O. J., 1964, The evolution of the long flexor muscles of the leg and foot: Internat. Rev. Gen. Exp. Zool., v. 1, p. 165-185.

Lillegraven, J. A., 1969, Latest Cretaceous mammals of upper part of Edmonton Formation of Alberta, Canada, and review of marsupial-placental dichotomy in mammalian evolution: Univ. Kansas Paleont. Contribs., Art. 50 (Vertebrata 12), 122 p.

_____1972a, Preliminary report on Late Cretaceous mammals from the El Gallo Formation, Baja California del Norte, Mexico: Nat. Hist. Mus. Los Angeles Co. Contribs. Sci., no. 232, 11 p.

_____1972b, Ordinal and familial diversity of Cenozoic mammals: Taxon, v. 21(2/3), p. 261-274.

_____1974, Biogeographical considerations of the marsupial-placental dichotomy: Ann. Rev. Ecol. Syst., v. 5, p. 263-283.

_____1975, Biological considerations of the marsupial-placental dichotomy: Evolution, v. 29, p. 707-722.

_____1976, A new genus of therian mammal from the Late Cretaceous "El Gallo Formation," Baja California, Mexico: Jour. Paleont., v. 50, p. 437-443.

Linnaeus, C., 1758, *Systema naturae per regna tria naturae, secundum classis, ordines, genera, species cum characteribus, differentiis, synonymis locis*: Stockholm, Edito decoma, reformata, Laurentii Salvii, v. 1, 824 p.

MacIntyre, G. T., 1972, The trisulcate petrosal pattern of mammals, in Dobzhansky, T., Hecht, M. K., and Steere, W. C., eds., Evolutionary biology: New York, Appleton-Century-Crofts, v. 6, p. 275-302.

McKenna, M. C., 1969, The origin and early differentiation of therian mammals: New York Acad. Sci. Ann., v. 167, p. 217-240.

_____1975, Toward a phylogenetic classification of the Mammalia, in Luckett, W. P., and Szalay, F. S., eds., Phylogeny of the primates: New York, Plenum Press, p. 21-46.

McKenzie, W., 1911, Some observations on the comparative anatomy of the fibula: Roy. Soc. Victoria Proc., v. 23, p. 358-367.

Marsh, O. C., 1889, Discovery of Cretaceous Mammalia: Amer. Jour. Sci., ser. 3, v. 38, p. 81-92.

_____1892, Discovery of Cretaceous Mammalia, III: *ibid.*, ser. 3, v. 48, p. 249-262.

Martin, R. D., 1968, Towards a new definition of primates: Man, v. 3, p. 377-401.

Matthew, W. D., 1904, The arboreal ancestry of the Mammalia: Amer. Natur., v. 38, p. 811-818.

_____1909, The Carnivora and Insectivora of the Bridger Basin, Middle Eocene: Amer. Mus. Nat. Hist. Mem., v. 9, p. 289-567.

_____1937, Paleocene faunas of the San Juan Basin, New Mexico: Amer. Philos. Soc. Trans., new ser., v. 30, p. 1-510.

Mills, J. R. E., 1961, The correlation of form, function, and phylogeny in the teeth of mammals [Ph.D. thesis]: Manchester, Univ. Manchester.

_____1971, The dentition of *Morganucodon, in* Kermack, D. M., and Kermack, K. A., eds., Early mammals: Linn. Soc. Zool. Jour., v. 50, suppl. 1, p. 29-63.

Murray, A., 1866, The geographic distribution of mammals: London, Day and Son, 420 p.

Napier, J. R., 1961, Prehensibility and opposability in the hands of primates: Zool. Soc. Symp., v. 5, p. 115-132.

Novacek, M. J., 1976, Insectivora and Proteutheria of the later Eocene (Uintan) of San Diego County, California: Nat. Hist. Mus. Los Angeles Co. Contribs. Sci., no. 283, 52 p.

_____1977, A review of Paleocene and Eocene Leptictidae (Eutheria: Mammalia) from North America: Paleobios, no. 24, 42 p.

Parrington, F. R., 1971, On the Upper Triassic mammals: Roy. Soc. London Philos. Trans., B (Biol. Sci.), v. 261, p. 231-272.

Patterson, B., 1956, Early Cretaceous mammals and the evolution of mammalian molar teeth: Fieldiana (Geol.), v. 13, p. 1-105.

Romer, A. S., 1966, Vertebrate paleontology (3rd ed.): Chicago, Univ. Chicago Press, *ix* + 468 p.

Rüeger, J., 1938, Zur Osteologie der beiden ersten Halswirbel der Säugetiere: Vierteljahrschrift Naturf. Ges. Zürich, v. 83, Beiblatt no. 30, p. 25-56.

Sahni, A., 1972, The vertebrate fauna of the Judith River Formation, Montana: Amer. Mus. Nat. Hist. Bull., v. 147, p. 321-412.

Schile, C. A., 1974, Sedimentology of the "El Gallo Formation" (Upper Cretaceous), El Rosario, Baja California, Mexico [M.S. thesis]: San Diego, California, San Diego State Univ., *xi* + 120 p.

Shikama, T., 1947, *Teilhardosaurus* and *Endotherium*, new Jurassic Reptilia and Mammalia from the Husin Coal-field, South Manchuria: Japan Acad. Proc., v. 23, p. 76-84.

Sigé, B., 1971, Les Didelphoidea de Laguna Umayo (formation Vilquechico, Crétacé supérieur, Pérou), et le peuplement marsupial d'Amérique du Sud: Acad. Sci. Paris C. R., v. 273, p. 2479-2481.

_____1972, La faunule de mammifères du Crétacé supérieur de Laguna Umayo (Andes péruviennes): Mus. Natl. Hist. Natur. Bull., 3e sér., no. 99, Sciences de la Terre 19, p. 375-409.

Simons, E. L., 1972, Primate evolution: an introduction to man's place in nature: New York, Macmillan Press Ltd., 322 p.

Simpson, G. G., 1927, Mammalian fauna of the Hell Creek Formation of Montana: Amer. Mus. Novitates, no. 267, 7 p.

_____1928, Further notes on Mongolian Cretaceous mammals: *ibid.*, no. 329, 14 p.

_____1931, A new classification of mammals: Amer. Mus. Nat. Hist. Bull., v. 59, p. 259-293.

_____1971, Concluding remarks: Mesozoic mammals revisited, *in* Kermack, D. M., and Kermack, K. A., eds., Early mammals: Linn. Soc. Zool. Jour., v. 50, suppl. 1, p. 181-198.

Sisson, S., and Grossman, J. D., 1953, The anatomy of the domestic animals (4th ed.): Philadelphia, W. B. Saunders Co., 972 p.

Slijper, E. J., 1946, Comparative biologic-anatomical investigations on the vertebral column and spinal musculature of mammals: Verh. Kon. Neder. Akad. Wetensch. Afd. Natur. Kunde, v. 42, p. 1-128.

Slaughter, B. H., 1965, A therian from the Lower Cretaceous (Albian) of Texas: Postilla (Yale Univ.), no. 93, 18 p.

_____1971, Mid-Cretaceous (Albian) therians of the Butler Farm local fauna, Texas, *in* Kermack, D. M., and Kermack, K. A., eds., Early mammals: Linn. Soc. Zool. Jour., v. 50, suppl. 1, p. 131-143.

Sloan, R. E., 1970, Cretaceous and Paleocene terrestrial communities of western North America: N. Amer. Paleont. Conv. Proc., Part E, p. 427-453.

Sloan, R. E., and Van Valen, L., 1965, Cretaceous mammals from Montana: Science, v. 148, p. 220-227.

Steiner, H., 1965, Die vergleichend-anatomische und oekologische Bedeutung der rudimentären Anlage eines selbständigen fünften Carpale bei *Tupaia*. Betrachtungen zum Homologieproblem: Israel Jour. Zool., v. 14, p. 221-233.

Szalay, F. S., 1968, Origins of the Apatemyidae (Mammalia, Insectivora): Amer. Mus. Novitates, no. 2352, 11 p.

Szalay, F. S., and Decker, R. L., 1974, Origins, evolution, and function of the tarsus in the Late Cretaceous Eutheria and Paleocene primates, *in* Jenkins, F. A., Jr., ed., Primate locomotion: New York, Academic Press, p. 223-259.

Szalay, F. S., and McKenna, M. C., 1971, Beginning of the age of mammals in Asia: the Late Paleocene Gashato fauna, Mongolia: Amer. Mus. Nat. Hist. Bull., v. 144, p. 269-318.

Trouessart, E. L., 1885, Catalogue des mammifères vivants et fossiles. Carnivores: Soc. Études Sci. Angers Bull., v. 14, p. 1-108.

Van Valen, L., 1964, A possible origin for rabbits: Evolution, v. 18, p. 484-491.

_____1966, Deltatheridia, a new order of mammals: Amer. Mus. Nat. Hist. Bull., v. 132, p. 1-126.

_____1967, New Paleocene insectivores and insectivore classification: *ibid.*, v. 135, p. 217-284.

_____1969, The multiple origins of the placental carnivores: Evolution, v. 23, p. 118-130.

Van Valen, L., and Sloan, R. E., 1965, The earliest primates: Science, v. 150, p. 743-745.

Winge, H., 1917, Udsigt over Insektaedernes indbyrdes Slaegtskab.: Vidensk. Meddel. Dansk Naturh. Foren., v. 68, p. 83-203.

Yalden, D. W., 1972, The form and function of the carpal bones in some arboreally adapted mammals: Acta Anat., v. 82, p. 383-406.

CHAPTER 13

REPRODUCTION IN MESOZOIC MAMMALS

Jason A. Lillegraven

CONTENTS

INTRODUCTION

Few features of the mammalian skeleton or dentition provide clues to reproductive patterns either in living or in fossil forms. One unifying diagnostic complex of characteristics of the Mammalia, however, is the presence of functional mammary glands in the female and lactation, and there is indirect evidence that the approximate time of its origin can be determined from fossils. Detailed comparative morphology of mammary tissue is essentially identical between living therians and monotremes and strongly suggests the presence of such tissue in their last common ancestor (probably Late Triassic; see Fig. 13-1). Hopson (1973) suggested that the elimination of reptilian polyphyodonty in certain Triassic cynodonts (in favor of the mammalian reduction in amount of tooth replacement) heralded the development of significant maternal care and lactation.

The above idea was reiterated by Pond (1977) in stating that suckling, which requires flexible lips and specializations of the neonatal tongue and pharyngeal area (but which can occur in the absence of erupted teeth), was important in allowing the delayed development in young, growing mammals of adult-sized teeth that are capable of precise occlusal relationships soon after eruption. She further pointed out (*ibid.*, p. 191) that lactation was

. . . directly related to the evolution of the following mammalian characteristics: 1. Very rapid postnatal growth, particularly of skull and jaws; early attainment of skeletal and sexual maturity. 2. Feeding mechanisms which depend upon mechanical processing of food in the mouth with accurately occlusible teeth; diphyodonty. 3. All members of a species can specialize upon a narrow range of food sources or feeding techniques. 4. Programmed, age specific "time-tally" growth and development; loss of ability to recover completely from starvation in early life. 5. Timing of reproduction can be partially independent of supply of abundant or specialized foods. 6. Species can persist in impoverished, disturbed or rapidly changing habitats. 7. Mutualistic social behavior among adults and subadults.

Thus the development of lactation was probably a key feature in the origin and later success of mammals in adapting to the changing environments of the Mesozoic and Cenozoic, and was unquestionably fully functional well before the end of the Triassic.

The other important steps in the evolution of mammalian reproductive features such as the development of viviparity and trophoblastic tissue, however, did not correlate in time with the advent of lactation and left no known (or at best very equivocal) traces in preservable skeletal or dental anatomy. Thus determination of the timing of these events depends entirely upon a combination of: (1)

knowledge from fossils implying sequences of phylogenetic divergences; and (2) comparative morphogenetic studies of living descendants. As the preceding parts of the book show, the known fossil record of mammals in the Mesozoic is inadequate to provide documentation of detailed phylogenetic sequences. Knowledge of the time of origin of nonlactational reproductive features is therefore vague, and understanding of reproduction of Mesozoic mammals is mainly dependent upon comparative information extrapolated backward through time from modern descendants. Unfortunately, the methods of reproduction employed by totally extinct forms such

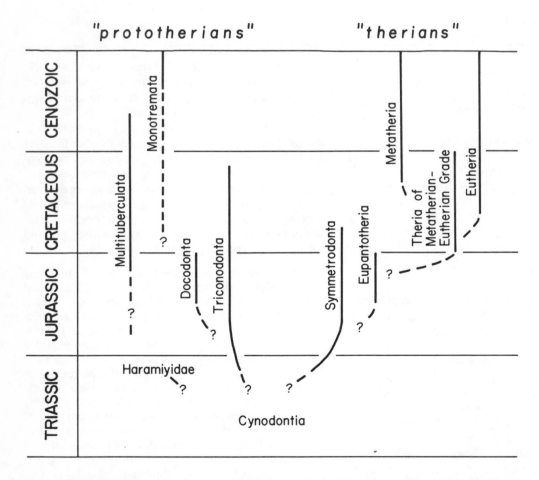

Figure 13-1.   Tentative range chart and phylogram, designed to suggest the uncertainties of evolutionary relationships among the major groups of mammals.

as nonmorganucodontid triconodonts, the docodonts, multituberculates, symmetrodonts, and most
eupantotheres may remain forever in doubt.

THE EARLIEST MAMMALS

As was discussed in Chapter 1, a key feature of
practically all mammals known from Mesozoic rocks
is their small body size; most of the Late Triassic
species rank among the smallest known from all of
mammalian history. Hopson (1973) presented the
case that the phenomena of nocturnal behavior, endothermy, dense pelage, small body size, reduced
egg-size and -energy content, increased maternal
care, greater maternal dependence by ectothermic
young, and lactation developed in concert to form
the integrated suite of physiological-behavioral
features diagnostic of mammalian reproduction. Although the nature of the selective pressures during
the Triassic that brought about this complex is uncertain, the following sequence of causes and effects
seems reasonable. The role of hunting for insects
during nighttime hours was open to animals that
could remain active under conditions of cooler temperatures, that had keen senses of sight, hearing, and
touch, and that had appropriate locomotory, masticatory, and digestive ability to capture and process
the prey. The pelage probably served double duty. It
was originally useful for the provision of tactile
orientation to nocturnal animals in a three-
dimensionally complex environment, but later became mandatory for reducing the loss of body heat
from small, endothermic, insectivorous (hunting)
animals.

Small body size would have been optimal for the
procurement of food in the form of arthropods and
for safety by hiding in a predator-rich world. It
would also have mandated, however, that reproducing females commit less energy reserves to the egg
and somehow dole out over a longer period of time
energy supplies required by the developing young.
The complex of a small, comparatively energy-poor
(on typical sauropsid standards) egg with post-
hatching lactation and maternal care for extremely
altricial young proved an admirable solution. The
evolution of genetically heritable elements of maternal behavior (of benefit to young individuals and
ultimately to the species as a whole) must have
developed concomitantly with lactation. The advent

of ultrasonic communication and silent communication that was effective over distance and time by
pheromones from various kinds of skin glands was
also probably important to the evolution of other
forms of social behavior. The latter, especially, also
resulted in general development of the brain's
neopallium in the form of increased degrees of
forebrain neuronal integration and, ultimately,
greater potential for intelligence.

Although the phylogenetic source of the
Monotremata is quite uncertain (see Fig. 13-1), the
group has, with little doubt, been genetically
separated from the Theria since the Late Triassic.
Most classification schemes of the Mammalia include
the monotremes, but MacIntyre (1972) supports a
minority opinion in arguing that the living prototherians (and all of the extinct and extremely
heterogeneous nontherian groups) should be considered reptiles. Following the usual definition of a
"mammal," however, the survival of monotremes
today shows that the egg-laying habit persisted in
time well beyond the reptile-mammal transition.
There is little reason to suspect that the process of
development of the young seen in living monotremes
differs greatly from that present in the Late Triassic
ancestral stock of all mammals; embryogenesis is
similar in most respects to that of living sauropsids
(reptiles and birds). Thus the earliest mammals were
small and hairy, they laid eggs, lactated, and had at
least the minimum level of sociality common to all
mammals (male-female pair-bonding and maternal care of offspring at least until weaning). Viviparity developed later, but the timing of its advent is
uncertain.

REPRODUCTIVE EVOLUTION
IN THE THERIA

The sequence of steps in the evolution of
viviparity in mammals may never be known, but it
probably resembled the pattern postulated by
Packard and others (1977) for reptiles. They suggested progressive delay (over many generations) of
oviposition such that more and more advanced
young were developed within the mother and less
time was needed to pass between egg-laying and
hatching. Eventually, the process of oviposition
could be lost permanently, if the neonates could
somehow be nourished and protected either in a nest

or, as in marsupials, semipermanently attached to a maternal teat. Potential advantages of viviparity are several, including: (1) development at a sustained maternal body temperature optimal to enzymatic activity allowing rapid morphogenesis; (2) provision of an essentially unlimited water supply to the developing embryo, even during dry seasons; (3) ability to discharge embryonic nitrogenous metabolic wastes into oviductal fluids; (4) ready availability of certain nutritional materials for the embryo in oviductal fluids that could be absorbed via the vascularization of the yolk sac and/or allantoic vesicle; and (5) maternal protection of embryos internally against possible microbial infection, predation, or parasitism upon egg clutches. Effective intrauterine gas exchange and food absorption by larger, more rapidly metabolizing embryos would have required development of an effective "placenta" beyond those rather simple membranes found associated with the embryos of most oviparous or incipiently viviparous amniotes. Nevertheless, as long as the neonates were extremely altricial, the modifications of extraembryonic membranes necessary to allow ovoviviparity or viviparity were not profound, and the amount of maternal energy committed to the formation of yolk and albumen could be greatly curtailed. Sharman (1976) pointed out the necessity to the evolution of mammalian viviparity of: (1) development of control by the maternal corpus luteum over uterine secretions (embryotrophe or "uterine milk") of nutritive value to the embryo; and (2) the development of discrete teats on the mammary glands and concomitant modifications of the neonatal mouth for firm attachment thereto.

All living therian mammals (marsupials and placentals) are viviparous, but marsupial development shows a series of features such as a thin eggshell and vestigial egg-tooth that strongly indicates a previously oviparous habit. The early development of placentals, on the other hand, is so profoundly specialized that one might never suspect their ultimate oviparous origin if living reptiles, birds, monotremes, and marsupials were not available for purposes of comparison. The great specializations seen in eutherian development have led to a series of discussions concerning comparisons of relative fitness of marsupial and placental reproductive strategies. The following section summarizes the most important similarities and differences between marsupial and placental reproduction (see Lillegraven, 1969 and 1975, for additional detail and pertinent references), and is designed to set the stage for consideration of what I see to be the fundamental evolutionary advantages of the eutherian pattern of development of the young.

REPRODUCTIVE COMPARISONS OF THERIANS

All marsupials are born at a stage of anatomical and physiological development characteristic of "embryos" of placentals. The duration of marsupial active embryogenesis is always significantly shorter than the estrous cycle typical for the species (even though, in a few cases, the duration of pregnancy slightly exceeds that of the estrous cycle). Neonates must crawl under their own power a distance up the mother's belly from the vulva to a teat upon which they remain attached for several months. The more generalized marsupials at birth lack cranial nerves II-IV and VI, eyelids (a protective periderm covers the eyes), eye pigments, and cerebral commissures. The hindlimb is little more than a bud, and the forelimb skeletal parts are precartilaginous; synovial cavities are developed only for the humerus. Heart ventricles are still unseparated, and the lungs are simple vascularized sacs. Respiration is probably in part cutaneous. Mesonephric kidneys are functional, and lack glomeruli. Placentals generally, on the other hand, are born at more advanced anatomical-physiological levels, and their period of active intrauterine morphogenesis is extended in time, sometimes dramatically so. Some form of pouch is found in females of most species of marsupials, but probably was derived independently in several lineages from primitively pouchless forms (Sharman, 1976; Kirsch, 1977a). Pouches are unknown in placentals and, although attachment of young to a teat occurs for a short time in some species, long-term attachment is unknown.

There are few recognizable hormonal, anatomical, or physiological differences in the marsupial uterine wall between a normal nonpregnant estrous cycle and pregnancy. Evidence is scanty for maternal physiological recognition of pregnancy in marsupials (see Sharman, 1976); thus the young must evacuate the uterus before or soon after the normal regressive phase begins. In many species of eutherians, however, uterine walls show incredible histological-circulatory features of "cooperation" with the placenta to benefit a developing fetus through a prolonged pregnancy. Early marsupial embryogenesis utilizes a small amount of yolk and mucoid materials ("albumens") for energy, but soon shifts to an embryotrophe, secreted by the uterine wall. Placentals (with some exceptions) lack yolk and significant amounts of mucoids. Thus they are dependent from the beginning upon embryotrophe, or, in some species, upon histiotrophic food materials derived from products of necrosis of the uterine wall during implantation. Rudiments of the definitive "chorioallantoic" placenta soon take over the function of fetal nutrition, gas exchange, and waste removal through two-way exchanges with the maternal circulation. Although physical erosion of the maternal uterine wall through metabolic activities of the developing young is rare in marsupials, the phenomenon is known in a number of quite distinct lineages of eutherians. Shell membranes are unknown in placentals, but persist until about the last one-third of pregnancy in marsupials; intrauterine "hatching" then occurs.

Early embryogenesis and extraembryonic membrane development in marsupials differs little from the sequence seen in reptiles, birds, and monotremes. Although the great reduction in yolk quantity dictates that morphogenesis occur from a cystlike rather than a discoid early embryonic structure, all essential features are otherwise the same. Eutherians, however, differ markedly from all other amniotes from their earliest developmental stages in the formation of trophoblastic versus inner cell mass (ICM) tissues.[1] Only the ICM is involved in the formation of the embryo proper; other parts of the ICM plus all of the trophoblast form extraembryonic membranes that become involved in protection, nourishment, gas exchange, and waste disposal for the fetus. The extraembryonic membrane development (amnion and yolk sac) in many species of eutherians also is unique among the amniotes in that it develops by delamination within the ICM rather than by the usual methods of folding and germ layer overgrowth.

The usual type of placenta in marsupials is a comparatively simple, partly vascularized yolk sac with rather low surface area that makes loose contact with the uterine wall. The allantoic vesicle typically is not externally exposed for contact with maternal epithelium (but see Padykula and Taylor, 1976, for a classic exception), and acts as a storage reservoir for nitrogenous wastes. Eutherian placentation in early

stages is also of the yolk sac nature (also fully functional), but soon shifts to the "chorioallantoic" variety with heavy vascularization and usually much closer contact with the endometrium. The "chorioallantoic" placenta of many eutherians becomes a structure of vast surface area and an important endocrine organ, essential to the prolonged maintenance of the secretory nature and rich vascularization of the uterine wall. Certain Australian marsupials have independently developed a chorioallantoic placenta that functions in conjunction with the yolk sac placenta, but the surface area and endocrinological functions of marsupial placentae are comparatively minor.

Except in those species which exhibit embryonic diapause or delayed implantation, eutherians tend to maximize the time available for internal gestation by rapid morphogenesis throughout pregnancy. Quite in contrast, marsupial zygotes or blastocysts usually spend a major part of the short gestation period in a morphogenetically quiescent state before beginning embryogenesis. Although marsupial pregnancy is known to vary in length from eleven to thirty-eight days, anatomical and physiological development in the long-duration species is only slightly greater than in short-duration species; most differences are in body size. In addition to the period of postfertilization "quiescence," the long-duration marsupials show developmental slowdowns or even standstills during pregnancy, thus not taking full morphogenetic advantage of the time of gestation. Related to this, Müller (1972-1973 and earlier papers cited therein) recognized two contrasting phenomena: (1) phylogenetic *extensions* (phylogenetischer Tragzeitverlängerung) of the period of gestation; and (2) phylogenetic *expansions* (phylogenetischer Tragzeitdehnung).

"Phylogenetic extensions" refer to evolutionary increases in intrauterine development time in which corresponding refinements in stages of anatomical development at birth occur. "Phylogenetic expansions," on the other hand, refer to the situation in which, even though the duration of pregnancy may be increased, it is *not* accompanied by increased anatomical organization of the young at birth. Marsupials seem capable only of "expansions," thus leading to the concept of "evolutionary stagnation" within the group; eutherian intrauterine development is rampant with examples of "extensions."

The fundamental difference in degree of morphogenetic exploitation of internal gestation time

---

1. See note added in proof, p. 275.

between marsupials and placentals cited above probably is a result of immunological factors (see Moors, 1974). As mentioned earlier, developing marsupials remain inside a thin shell membrane until late in pregnancy. The physiologically inert shell and inner mucoid coats (of maternal origin) are permeable to large molecules of a wide variety (nutrients, hormones, enzymes, antibodies, etc.) and thus allow essential materials from embryotrophe to reach the developing embryo. These outer coatings do not, however, allow physical contact of the embryo (partly of paternal genotype, thus with potentially antigenic tissues) with antigen-sensing lymphocytes in the uterine wall and lumenal fluids. Marsupials thus avoid the possibility of immunological attack upon the embryo during pregnancy by retaining it within a protective shell until a late date; intrauterine hatching (required by the increasing size of the embryo and its need for increased placental surface area) probably does not occur until the time at which it is too late for a full immunological response to be mounted. Marsupials "dare not" develop to advanced anatomical states in the intrauterine environment because of the following sequence: (1) the energy requirements and oxygen utilization of marsupial young are known to skyrocket as they approach developmental stages attained at birth; (2) if the animal were to be retained intrauterinely, the increased energy needs would require more intimate and elaborate placentation than the comparatively simple yolk sac can provide; and (3) the increased time and surface area of fetal-maternal contact would heighten the possibility of immunological attack and resultant damage or death of the young. Thus the system (i.e., an inert shell) used by marsupials to thwart immunological responses against embryonic tissues is unsophisticated, and does not lend itself to the possibility for development of anatomically advanced neonates.

The eutherians, quite in contrast, have developed a spectacular and unique solution to the above problem with the evolution of the trophoblast. Trophoblastic tissues and their derivatives are truly amazing in their diversity of functions. They include: (1) passive and active exchanges between the fetus and the mother of gases, wastes, and other inorganic and organic materials; (2) the formation, modification, and secretion of a variety of hormones; (3) the synthesis and secretion of certain prostaglandins; and (4) perhaps most important, control of the maternal immune response against fetal tissues, the uterine "invasion" by which may last many months. Most

mechanisms of trophoblastic action with respect to immunological function are not understood, but enough is known to indicate that its activities are immensely complex (see Scott and Jones, 1976). Trophoblast, except for certain kinds of leakages (especially at the time of birth) and limited fetal-maternal fusions and poorly understood migrations into the maternal bloodstream, always separates maternal tissues from those of the embryo (bearing potentially antigenic tissues), and is thus a highly sophisticated "eggshell-equivalent" with respect to fetal immunological protection. It differs greatly from the metatherian and prototherian shell, however, in its plethora of metabolically active roles that function to the direct benefit of rapidly developing, anatomically- and physiologically-advanced offspring; "phylogenetic extensions" can thus be facilitated. Certainly, the evolution of trophoblastic function was not an easy matter; and even its elementary roles probably developed slowly over many millions of years, probably during the Early Cretaceous. It seems most unlikely that such a complex system would have happened at all were there not definite selective advantages to animals possessing it, a speculative point pursued in more detail in the last section of the present chapter.

Because of the extremely immature level of development characteristic of marsupials at birth, their eyes, ears, and mouth region require specialized forms of protection. For example, some marsupials are born before the formation of eyelids. Thus a keratinous "periderm" covers the eyeball shortly before birth. Additionally, a specialized "filling substance" forms between the developing eyelids themselves that maintains a protective seal against desiccation until the time of eye-opening (which correlates with a particular level of brain and eye development). The external ear openings in marsupials are similarly plugged just before birth with a transitory cellular filling substance for protection against drying. Most interesting is the temporary seal seen around the margins of the mouth. Marsupials have a reptile-like gape at birth in that true cheeks have not yet formed. An anteriorly terminalized mouth opening, however, develops just before birth by the formation of filling substance along the lateral mouth margins such that the opening is just large enough to accept a maternal teat. The filling substance acts to seal the mouth's lateral margins to help hold the neonate onto the teat and to prevent the passage of air or leakage of milk until the true cheeks form. The tongue-driven "pumpsucking" mode of nursing characteristic of therian neonates can thus occur (in the absence of mandibular movement) by the motion of the dorsally grooved tongue and by the intranasopharyngeal positioning of the epiglottis. The true cheeks develop shortly thereafter, and the filling substance disappears *after* the time that the malleus completely detaches from the remainder of Meckel's cartilage.

All marsupials are also born with a reptile-like articular-quadrate jaw joint. Müller proposed that successful morphogenesis of a dentary-squamosal ("mammalian") jaw joint in therians depends upon a virtual absence of movement of the upper and lower jaws. She argued that the transitory lip closure is thus admirably designed for three basic functions in: (1) sealing the mouth for suckling; (2) holding the neonate onto the nipple (an absolute requirement in pouchless varieties); and (3) allowing the jaws to be held motionless for proper development of the dentary-squamosal joint. An interesting implication is that the dentary-squamosal jaw articulation and triossicular middle ear system in therian mammals may have been dependent in its evolution upon a suckling (nonchewing) nutritive mode in the young. It seems clear that the triossicular middle ear structure in monotremes was independently derived from the single-boned reptilian condition (see Hopson, 1966, and Allin, 1975) in parallel with therians. The cause-and-effect sequence behind this adaptation in monotremes, however, may have been quite different from that resulting in the therian middle ear. The comparison deserves further investigation.

The functional significance of the three forms of transitory closures discussed above is clear for the delicate neonates of marsupials. Most interesting, however, are Müller's observations that very similar closures also develop at comparable stages of morphogenesis in the eyes, ears, and mouth of eutherian mammals *intra*uterinely; these regress before birth in precocious forms, but retain some function in the most altricial species. The transitory seals in eutherians develop after the completion of the secondary palate and, as in newborn marsupials, after the intranasopharyngeal positioning of the epiglottis. Seal timing also correlates with the level of motor development characteristic of neonatal marsupials. Additionally, using the time of origin of recognizable endoderm as a marker, the advent of lid closure occurs between ten and eleven days thereafter in a variety of altricial eutherians. Such closely-timed forma-

tions of transitory closures in eutherians, especially in precocial species, would seem mysterious unless one postulates that they represent ontogenetic recapitulations of functionally valuable features in ancient forms that were born, as are marsupials today, in extremely altricial anatomical states.

Even if one accepts the evidence presented above that the primaeval eutherians were born in an extremely altricial form, a question remains of the reproductive mode of the last common ancestor (therian of metatherian-eutherian grade) of marsupials and placentals. Were they: (1) oviparous with the independent evolution of viviparity in the Metatheria and Eutheria as suggested by Sharman (1970, 1976); or (2) were they viviparous in the marsupial sense with an extremely short gestation period? Although we may never certainly know the answer, I believe the latter possibility to be somewhat more likely than the former. If Müller's suggestion that the therian dentary-squamosal jaw joint (and, ergo, the triossicular middle ear apparatus) depended for its development upon lip closures and immobile jaws, independent evolution of viviparity within the Theria would then mean that the jaw and middle ear features seen in common between marsupials and placentals would also have to be independent evolutionary derivations; I know of no evidence that would support such a possibility. Although the Late Jurassic eupantothere *Peramus* was off the "main line" toward therians of metatherian-eutherian grade, it probably was not greatly distant from it. *Peramus tenuirostris*, which almost certainly predated the marsupial-placental dichotomy in mammalian evolution, already had the dentary-squamosal jaw joint and, probably, a triossicular middle ear. For these reasons and others dealing with the extreme similarities seen within marsupial and placental development (after the time of earliest embryogenesis), I prefer the interpretation that the last common ancestor of surviving therian mammals was viviparous in the fashion of marsupials. Unfortunately, existing data from the paleobiogeography of Cretaceous therians, or from world paleogeography itself (see Chapter 14), cannot be used to muster effective circumstantial support for either interpretation.

Although marked differences in the comparative spatial architecture of marsupial and placental urogenital ducts exist (most obvious in the female), the differences are readily explained by rather minor modifications in the course of embryonic growth of the metanephric duct (see Lillegraven, 1969, and Sharman, 1976). In essence, the marsupial duct arrangement, except for the specialization of the pseudovaginal canal in the female, is basically similar to that of all other noneutherian amniotes; the eutherian condition, however, is unique with the metanephric ducts (ureters) placed lateral to the derivatives of the Müllerian ducts. Such an arrangement is "necessary" in eutherians so that advanced degrees of caudal fusion of the Müllerian ducts can occur to form a single vagina and variously fused uteri to accommodate the greatly expanding fetal masses developed during prolonged pregnancy and to allow an unobstructed path for birth. Except for the peculiarity of the pseudovaginal canal, there is no firm reason to suspect that the basic marsupial duct arrangement is anything other than primitive for the living Theria.

Speculative conclusions on the former modes of reproduction of extinct mammals may be drawn from study of the structure of pelves. The shape of the ischial arc and the form of fusion of ventral edges of the pubes and ischia provide relevant information. According to Kielan-Jaworowska (1975), the ischial arc is U-shaped in monotremes (oviparous), V-shaped and narrow in marsupials and altricial eutherians, and V-shaped and wide in precocial eutherians. Pelvic structure is unknown for most Mesozoic mammals, but a few species from the Late Cretaceous of Asia can be studied, including the eutherian *Barunlestes* and certain multituberculates. The ischial arc in *Barunlestes* is very narrow, which possibly indicates the birth of altricial young (see Kielan-Jaworowska, *ibid.*). Similarly, the structure of presently undescribed but well-preserved pelves of Cretaceous multituberculates may have precluded the laying of large eggs, and may also suggest birth of altricial young (Kielan-Jaworowska, research in preparation). Many pitfalls, however, await the worker who is willing to overextend the certainty of these interpretations.

The presence of epipubic ("marsupial") bones in mammals unfortunately provides no information useful to the interpretation of ancient reproductive modes. The existence of such bones has now been recognized in certain advanced therapsids, multituberculates (Chapter 6), eupantotheres (Henkel and Krebs, 1977), monotremes, marsupials (Chapter 11), and, perhaps, certain Late Cretaceous Asiatic eutherians (Chapter 12). They are found in both sexes, in oviparous and viviparous species, and in pouched and pouchless females. Their existence seems to be a primitive mammalian feature, and appears to be related to abdominal and hind leg musculature (see Lillegraven, 1969) in both sexes; it certainly cannot be used to interpret the presence or absence of a pouch in extinct species (see Kühne, 1975). Epipubic bones are unknown from post-Cretaceous eutherians and, recognizing the marked degree of abdominal swelling during advanced pregnancy seen in many modern representatives of the group, their loss would certainly be expected from mechanical considerations alone. A most interesting possibility was raised by Jellison (1945) concerning a possible new use in eutherians for the old epipubic bones as the baculum and os clitoridis. His bases for the hypothesis are that the baculum: (1) is endochondral (as are the epipubic bones); (2) is widespread throughout many lineages of eutherians but absent in all other groups of mammals; and (3) develops in some species from paired centers of ossification that secondarily fuse into a single shaft.

COMPARATIVE ADAPTIVENESS OF THERIAN REPRODUCTIVE MODES

As shown above, marsupials and placentals have modes of reproduction that provide curious contrasts of basic similarities and marked differences. The two groups are dentally distinguishable in the fossil record of the later Cretaceous (*i.e.*, Campanian-Maastrichtian ages and apparent correlatives). By this time the radiation of modern eutherian orders had already begun. Thus the differences in reproductive patterns probably were developed much earlier in the Cretaceous. At this point one should question what selective advantages, if any, would be gained by either of the two systems. Pond (1977, p. 193), for example, argued that ". . . placental mammals are more successful than marsupials in spite of their lack of a pouch, relatively long gestation and short lactation, not because of it." Further, she said (*ibid.*): "Whether the early embryonic development takes place in an egg, in a nest or pouch, or within the mother is shown to be of minor importance in determining other features of the anatomy and growth processes."

In a similar vein, Parker (1977; also see Kirsch, 1977a and 1977b) provided a formalized hypothesis stating that, from developmental and ecological points of view, marsupials and placentals are energetically equivalent and that their differences in reproduction simply represent alternative numerical values for terms within an energetic equation for which the resultant in survival is virtually identical. That is, the reproductive differences between the two groups provide no overall superiority in survival to either group, but rather only represent alternative approaches to coping with the rigors of life. Pond based her arguments, for the most part, upon the influence that the development of lactation has had upon mammalian morphology and lifestyle. Parker, on the other hand, worked mainly from concepts of the energetics of "reproductive investments" on the part of the female. I shall, in the paragraphs that follow, attempt to show on the basis of other lines of reasoning that the eutherian reproductive plan provides a variety of significant adaptive advantages over that common to the Marsupialia.

Recent work has been significant on the relationships: (1) between early brain development and morphogenesis; and (2) between the maturation of brain chemistry and its probable control over the development of functions of the remainder of the body and its aging processes. The studies provide information directly pertinent to the interpretation of relationships between modes of early development and potential adaptations of the organism to various environmental settings. Before looking at the ecological application of this new body of knowledge, some background on the subject must be provided.

Huggett and Widdas (1951), using information from a variety of mammalian species, showed that there exists a general linear relation between the cube root of neonatal *body* weight and the age of the animal from conception (a mammalian fetal growth curve). The data, however, cover a wide range, showing variability to the order of a factor of ten. Variation is considerable within and among orders. Sacher and Staffeldt (1974), using data from ninety-one eutherian species representing twelve orders, found a similar, but much tighter, relationship between the cube root of neonatal *brain* weight and gestation time; variability among species and among orders was shown in most cases to be less than a factor of two. Thus there exists a remarkably close linear relationship, seemingly independent of taxonomic position, between total volumetric brain growth and the duration of pregnancy in placental mammals. Using the time of first appearance of recognizable endoderm in marsupial development as a marker, the rate of brain development up to the time of birth is

also quite uniform throughout that group (see various papers by Müller).

Sacher and Staffeldt (1974) did not incorporate into their analysis most data from species that show: (1) delayed implantation; (2) delayed fertilization; or (3) maternal heterothermy during pregnancy. The study by Sacher and Staffeldt utilized the procedures of multiple regression analysis and compared the factors of: (1) gestation time; (2) litter size; (3) neonatal brain weight; (4) neonatal body weight; (5) adult brain weight; (6) adult body weight; (7) brain advancement; and (8) body advancement. By such a technique, they were able to estimate the independent contribution made by each of these factors to the total reproductive variation. Their analyses show that neonatal brain weight is far and away the most important variable. "Brain advancement,"[2] however, is a significant secondary factor (although brain weights at birth may be identical, precocial species have longer gestation periods than closely related altricial species). Litter size is also important to some extent in that gestation time generally decreases with an increase in the number of neonates. The other five factors show varying degrees of correlation, but are far less important than those discussed above.

From these sorts of analyses, Sacher and Staffeldt (1974) proposed a "general phenomenological theory of mammalian growth," the essence of which is held in the following hypotheses (*ibid.*, p. 604):

> . . . (1) the brain is the slowest-growing organ in the mammal; (2) the brain is, furthermore, the pacemaker for growth of all other somatic tissues, which are constrained to grow at its pace; and (3) brain growth proceeds at the maximum rate allowed by its nutrition and its intrinsic growth laws, and if nutrition is not rate limiting, then growth of all mammalian brains is governed by a general law leading to a single functional relation among attained size, advancement, and time.

There is little question that hypothesis 1 above is correct; the maturational refinement of detailed brain

---

[2]The "advancement factor" or "increase factor" (see Portmann, 1965 and earlier, and Mangold-Wirz, 1966 and earlier) is the number by which the weight of brain substance at birth must be multiplied to reach that of the adult. The value of the factor in altricial (nidicolous) birds and mammals is always more than five and in precocious (nidifugous) forms is always less than five. It is thus useful in the discrimination of altricial and precocial species, in contrast to an analogous "body advancement factor" which has no such power of discrimination (Sacher and Staffeldt, 1974).

architecture lags well behind the time at which other organs of the body have achieved morphological sophistication characteristic of the adult. Evidence for hypothesis 2 grows daily (*e.g.*, see Chiappa and Fink, 1977; Finch, 1976; Gross and Baker, 1977; and Jost and others, 1970) as understanding increases of the functional-endocrinological relationships among the fetal brain proper, hypophysis, and general body target tissues. A variety of sources of information suggest that the fetal brain is, indeed, a "pacemaker" in control of the other elements of the developing body. The questions come with hypothesis 3 because: (1) the nature of genetic or intrinsic control of brain development is as yet unknown; and (2) because there seems to be a significant difference in the intrinsic rates of cerebralization (see below) between marsupials and placentals.

What is the importance of the above to considerations of the relative successes of adaptations of marsupials and placentals to the environments in which they live? The following line of reasoning seems basic to the question and to much of the discussion that follows. All marsupials are born at an extremely altricial stage and, presumably because of their lack of ability to thwart the process of immunological rejection mediated by the mother's hematopoietic system, are incapable of significant embryological "extensions" (see above section); active morphogenesis (probably controlled early-on by brain development) is thus delayed following fertilization until the "last minute" at which a neonate can be assembled that is capable of autolocomotion to the teat. Eutherians, on the other hand, are born either at an altricial (but in all studied cases anatomically more advanced than any marsupial) or precocial stage. Speaking teleologically, the brain (once early stages are formed) in eutherians "knows" of the trophoblastic protection of the conceptus from immunological attack and thus "allows" morphogenesis to begin immediately and to continue at a high rate throughout the extended duration of pregnancy.

Müller (1969a, 1969b) showed that the eutherian cerebral cortex develops significantly more rapidly, in greater volume, and in greater complexity (with these factors being combined under the term "cerebralization") than in marsupials (for general features of the marsupial brain see Johnson, 1977). The comparisons were made among species at equivalent levels of development of the skeleton, sensory organs, and urogenital system. Citing Portmann's earlier studies, she pointed out that the degree of general body development and cerebralization are rather independent of each other, and that the amount of increase in the extent of cerebralization is critically dependent upon the duration of *intra*uterine development that involves "extensions." Placentals thus show greater rates and degrees of cerebralization than marsupials, and although the mechanisms are not understood, the empirical correlation between effective brain increase and available prenatal developmental time seems real. Much exciting basic research remains to be done before we can fully understand relationships between the fetal brain as a morphogenetic control-unit, the importance of morphogenesis in intrauterine life, and the resultant degree of cerebralization and its influence upon potential intelligence. Beyond that, of course, remain difficult questions of the relative adaptive significance of various forms of intelligence to survival. Unfortunately, very little is known about the relative intelligence of marsupials (see Kirkly, 1977) and placentals.

An immediate benefit of the eutherian system of reproduction is speed of generation, because the delay common to marsupials before the advent of morphogenesis from the time of fertilization need not exist. Thus placentals can, with full metabolic-enzymatic benefit of a maternal high core body temperature, take morphogenetic advantage of nearly the total duration of pregnancy. It is well known that developmental rates of externally carried marsupial young are slower than in intrauterine placentals for equivalent stages, thus prolonging still more the duration of intimate contact of developing young (of ever-increasing mass) with the mother.

Parker (1977) has argued that the investment of energy by the mother to the young during pregnancy in eutherians far exceeds that in marsupials. The more rapid postnatal maturation rate common in placentals also requires a more rapid rate of resource utilization, while marsupials usually prolong the growth period well into adulthood. Furthermore, she contends that reproducing placentals have less responsiveness to changes in the local external environment than marsupials, and are therefore committed to pregnancy in most cases once implantation has occurred (although appreciation continues to grow for the considerable taxonomic distribution among eutherians of the ability of intrauterine absorption of embryos under environmental conditions seriously unfavorable to the mother). The eutherian mother surrenders, in part, physiological-endocrinological control of her own body to activities of the placenta, which can work to the detriment of the mother's overall physical well-being in such ways as liberating elements vital to fetal welfare from the maternal skeleton.

From the point of view of energetics, marsupial pregnancy differs little from a nonpregnant estrous cycle, and growing young can be terminated at the nipple by starvation or, at older stages, be dumped from the pouch when the mother is being pressed by a predator. The process of birth is more costly in terms of time, possible trauma, and resultant weakness in placentals than in marsupials, and osteological modifications of the eutherian maternal pelvis before birth probably do have at least a slight energy "cost" to the mother. I believe Parker is correct in these points and that the marsupial mother does, indeed, suffer less of an energetic expenditure in reproduction (during and after gestation) than would be exhibited in most species of placentals. The question remains, however, whether the system seen in either group has adaptive advantages in life over the other. Do differences in energetic costs of reproduction necessarily relate to differences in overall fitness to the environment and ultimate survival?

I believe the situation is more complex than was discussed previously, and requires thought beyond a consideration of maternal energetics during pregnancy and during maternal care of offspring. Comparative analysis must also involve integration of features from the disciplines of immunology, karyology, behavior, and ecological settings.

The element of speed of reproduction in eutherians mentioned above could be highly advantageous in species of small body size which suffer heavy predation (*e.g.*, many microtine rodents). Because of the nature of their mode of reproduction, most marsupials do not have the ability for ultrarapid development of new generations (the effective use of embryonic diapause to this end in macropodids, although often cited, is the exception, not the rule, among the marsupials).

Certain adaptive limitations are placed upon the marsupials simply because of the nature of their state of development at birth and the necessity for the young to migrate under their own power to the teat. For example, the evolution of fully aquatic marsupials would be quite impossible because the young must breathe air and must be large enough to withstand cold stress from heat loss to the water.

Neonatal travel to the pouch area is done by the grasping of maternal hairs by separated fingers, each of which has a claw. The claws are usually deciduous, but in some species they represent early stages of development of the definitive adult structures. The nature of the claws is probably immaterial; the important thing is that separated fingers, with appropriate musculature and innervation, are essential to grasping. It is possibly for this reason that no species among the marsupials has developed single-toed horse-like forefeet or nongrasping hooklike claws on nonopposable fingers as are seen in tree sloths.

Marsupials seemingly would also be incapable of developing front flippers, as do cetaceans, pinnipeds, and sirenians, in which the individual fingers are united throughout their development. Heavily clawed forefeet (such as in *Notoryctes*, the "marsupial mole") perhaps could be allowed in species of small body size by proper positioning of the maternal body at birth such that the neonate falls more or less into the mammary area (but birth has never been observed in *Notoryctes*). The point remains, however, that diversity of forelimb design, intimately associated with locomotion and many other daily functions, *is* comparatively limited in marsupials; perhaps the limitation is because of the anatomical requirements of the birth process. Hairless or armored marsupials also could not develop. Because of these considerations, it seems that the allowable degree of "experimentation" and morphological heterochrony would be higher during embryonic development in placentals than in marsupials, especially in features related to locomotion.

Although it would be extremely difficult to test, the suggestion has been made that the evolutionary flexibility of marsupials may also be limited in part by their uniformly low diploid chromosome number (see Hayman, 1977) in comparison with that of most eutherians. The question revolves about mammalian abilities to coordinate the activities of unlinked genes, and upon selective pressures that might favor higher degrees of linkage. Lillegraven (1975, p. 719) couched the possibility as follows:

> One cannot help but wonder . . . if the generally reduced number of linkage groups (through lowered chromosome numbers) seen in marsupials might not have some complementary evolutionary relationship with their lower degree of flexibility of embryogenesis in comparison with placentals. Is it not possible that the rigid precision of embryological development

necessary to produce an immature neonate capable of independent travel to the nipple has been facilitated through selection of means to reduce excessive variation through segregation?

Additional karyological features of evolutionary importance will be discussed below.

The requirements for successful birth in marsupials may extend beyond canalization of forelimb design to an upper restriction in adult body size. Marsupials, except for rather modest and short-lived experiments in Australia by a few extinct macropodids and *Diprotodon*, have all been of small to moderate body size. Gigantism among marsupials would be most difficult for several reasons such as: (1) physically the mother would have to get into the proper position so that there would be possible the typical neonatal basally-supported, uphill climb from the vagina to the mammary area; (2) the physical distance of the crawlpath from the vagina (assuming a typical positioning) to the teats would have to be great in order to place the latter safely ahead of the legs; and (3) unless the young grew to relatively enormous size within the pouch (to the point that great gravitational stresses would be placed on the teats and/or pouch), the young-at-foot would have marked difficulty in reaching the teat for continued suckling or would have to be completely weaned upon departure from the pouch. The implications associated with either possibility allow one's imagination to run full reign. Clearly, the development of gigantism as seen in living proboscideans, rhinos, hippos, giraffes, camels, and even large bovids is made possible by prolonged internal gestation and the birth of large, anatomically advanced young. Such adaptations are difficult, at best, among the marsupials.

A more subtle advantage of certain eutherians over marsupials revolves around cooperative social behavior. Although long-term pair-bonding or harem development is common among the eutherians, I know of no marsupial species that shows these behavioral phenomena. Social behavior and stabilizing hierarchies are in general much less developed among marsupials than among placentals (see Kaufmann, 1974a, 1974b, and Wilson, 1975). Even modest territorial behavior in marsupials is a comparative rarity. As an hypothesis, I suggest that these significant distinctions again go back, at least in part, to reproductive considerations, especially dealing with the immune response. A finite length of time is required to develop antibodies against newly introduced antigens. Once the antibody synthesis begins, however, that specific antigen is often added to the individual's long-term immunological "library" of materials recognized as foreign ("nonself"). Subsequent introduction of the same antigen can result in accelerated antibody reaction. Thus, in marsupials, a second insemination of a female by the same (or closely related) male (with his antigens cropping out in the embryonic tissues) could result in increased embryonic mortality through a more quickly heightened maternal immune response. Marsupials are dominantly promiscuous, and probably are so for good reason. "Experiments" among marsupials in long-term societal behavior in the form of pair-bonding, harem development, or other social forms that would encourage polygamy could suffer through selection against the embryo. It is possible that genetically heritable control over close social order could not develop among marsupials—apparently it hasn't yet.

The above hypothesis is weakened, however, by the recent findings of Walker and Tyndale-Biscoe (1978) that repeated inseminations of Kangaroo Island female tammar wallabies by the same males does not affect their overall reproductive efficiency. They state (*ibid*., p. 180) that ". . . in general it appears that the tammar foetus is well protected from any deleterious immunological effects which might result from maternal sensitization to male histocompatibility antigens." Nevertheless, as far as I am aware the tammar (involving insular populations, members of which may possess unusually high immunological tolerances to paternal antigens in reproduction) is the only species of marsupial for which studies of this type have yet been completed; we have much to learn about the comparative immunology of reproduction in marsupials, and the hypothesis should not be summarily rejected for all of the Marsupialia. It would be expected that difficulties in combating histoincompatibility in marsupial reproduction would increase as the duration of post-"hatching" intrauterine development increases (a range of only three to eight days in species studied to date).

Because of the sophisticated trophoblastic function of immunoprotection of the developing fetus in placentals, protracted pregnancy combined with long-term or even permanent pair-bonding with multiple inseminations is commonly allowed. The adaptive advantages of refinement in cooperative behavior and learning through experience are many and well known. The sharing of labors in the form of providing food, shelter, and protection are to the survival benefit of individual offspring and, ultimately, to the species. Heightened social activities often result in a sort of emergent evolution in the training of offspring, the benefits of which in terms of potential flexibility may be more than the sum of its parts.

It can be argued (*e.g.*, Parker, 1977) that instinctive behavior is equally adaptive, and perhaps is energetically more efficient with less risk to the individual than learned behavior associated with intelligence, curiosity, and play behavior. Nevertheless, I believe, for example, that although the marsupial thylacine and the highly socially cooperative African wild dogs have had equal times to evolve as active predators, there would be little doubt as to the outcome were the two species thrust into direct competition. Heritable elements of advanced social behavior are also powerful molding influences on evolution through natural selection, and are ultimately expressed morphologically (especially in most forms of sexual dimorphism), ecologically (as, for example, in the partial sexual division of habitat and resources by certain species of sexually dimorphic pinnipeds), in communication (visual, olfactory, auditory, and postural), and even in physical "beauty" and culture (see review by Jewell, 1976). All of these phenomena have positive feedback loops among one another, and all ultimately can have their benefits expressed through the fitness of offspring.

Wilson and others (1975) and Bush and others (1977) spotlight the importance of social behavior upon speciation and the evolution of morphological (organismal) diversity within the Eutheria. They argued that most classical taxonomy has been developed on the basis of degrees of difference of morphology. That is, members of genera within a given family are structurally less different from one another than they are from members of other families, and so forth through the hierarchy of Linnean classification. Wilson and others (1975) then chose living genera (each with a known fossil record) of a wide variety of vertebrates (1,230 species) including 21 species of marsupials and 606 of placentals. The morphology of the karyotypes of each genus was reviewed in terms of its chromosome number and arm number, and it was found that an obvious correlation exists between karyotypic evolution and morphological evolution (the latter as shown by taxonomic distance). Further, they showed, with statistically highly significant data, that although

marsupials show karyotypic evolution (in estimated rates per units of million years) differing little from most other noneutherian vertebrates, the placental mammals show rates in arm number changes roughly five times that of most vertebrates, and rates in chromosome number changes about six times that of most vertebrates (average data used throughout).[3] When the data for eutherian mammals were further broken down into genera of various body sizes, it was found that those of large body size and bats (*i.e.*, animals of unusual mobility) showed somewhat less karyotypic variability (evolution) than most other eutherians, but still more than marsupials. Thus there is: (1) something about the Eutheria that provides for them greater evolutionary plasticity than other vertebrates; and (2) something about high vagility that reduces it.

Wilson and others (1975) made the case that eutherian societal behavior makes them evolutionarily unique among the vertebrates. This is because small groups of individuals develop that may retain their cohesiveness away from the parent population for several generations—long enough that mutations, which in large outbreeding populations would probably remain heterozygous and rather rare, would have increased opportunity for becoming homozygous. The homozygote (speaking now of chromosomal rearrangements) usually has less difficulty in pairing alignment during the process of meiosis, and thereby has greater fecundity. It the mutation provides some sort of adaptive advantage to the individual, it then has an increased opportunity to become fixed within the population. Thus family social bonds, dominance hierarchies (which would increase polygamy), and effective small population size should result in increased rates of fixation of mutations (at both the gene and chromosomal levels), and the expected result would be increased evolutionary rates. High mobility, on the other hand, would be expected to slow down the process, because it would decrease the likelihood of isolation of small

---

3. A similar approach was used by Bush and others (1977) using a broader sampling of species and somewhat different methods of data analysis. The revised results show greater differences in rates of chromosomal number and arm number evolution between nonmammalian vertebrates and therian mammals in general. Nevertheless, the new evaluations suggest even more strongly the relative slowness of marsupial karyotypic change in comparison with that of most placental groups; among the eutherian mammals tested, only carnivores, bats, and whales (all with unusually high capabilities of dispersal) show rates of karyotypic change less than those of marsupials.

groups from the main parent population; the size of the effective breeding population would be greater. Wilson and others again argued, however, that societal behavior operates even in the eutherians of high vagility, and the tendency for group bonding still operates to the benefit of genetic change. Thus, although most vertebrates depend for speciation principally upon geographic isolation (type I speciation of Bush, 1975), in eutherians ". . . speciation occurs in social units which generally persist for only a few generations. This type of speciation (type II . . .) is necessarily more rapid than type Ib [by the 'founder principle'] speciation because the number of small social units in a placental species is greater than the number of founder populations in a nonplacental species" (Wilson and others, 1975, p. 5064).

The unique evolutionary plasticity for the eutherians described by Wilson and others is dependent upon the ability of these animals to inbreed within small populations and thereby provide quick homozygosity for mutational innovations. I believe that such a phenomenon may, in turn, have been dependent upon the physiological refinement of the trophoblast and the protection that it provides against immunological attack upon developing embryos. Inbreeding within small populations of marsupials could have resulted in marked selection against "hatched" intrauterine young by a heightened antibody response to paternal antigens that would be more quickly recognized by the mother's "immunological memory." If true, the great evolutionary success of placental mammals results from a most interesting interplay of immunological, behavioral, and mutational factors.

Although marsupial young during gestation cost the mother no extra mechanical effort, the postnatal individuals certainly do. Not only are they normally attached to the mother's nipples for several months, but they also comprise a significant volume and weight in later months that is placed outside of the mother's usual center of gravity. It is questionable to what extent this burden can quickly be eliminated should the mother be surprised by a predator.

Placental fetuses, on the other hand, are kept in a firm support sling very near the mother's center of gravity and balance. She is still usually capable of high rates of activity involving hunting, running, turning, and great migrations, even when at near term stages of pregnancy. I have seen few data sug-

gesting that predation is significantly higher in pregnant eutherians than in nonpregnant individuals; most predation is upon the very young, the old, the crippled, and the diseased. Females in the most advanced stages of pregnancy (and vulnerability) may compensate by secretive behavior or by the seeking of protection within the depths of the herd. Once born, eutherian young can easily be abandoned if high stress situations so require. Thus, although a pregnant eutherian usually does have a noticeably swollen abdomen, the support of developing young is excellent, the overall locomotory fitness of the mother is not greatly reduced, the fetus is protected from desiccation, and the young is developed into an advanced morphological state at a sustained high rate under conditions of maternal core body temperature. All things considered, although the energetic drain on the eutherian mother does seem to exceed that seen among marsupials, the overall eutherian adaptive survival complex suggests superiority.

Many species of placentals are born in precocial anatomical states, and the selective advantages of this are in some cases obvious. African bovids, for example, are often in advanced stages of pregnancy during the annual migratory phase coinciding with a dry season. The young must be able to keep up with the herd within a few hours after birth and to move along with the mother while she attempts to feed. Conditions of greatest rainfall and vegetation may be delayed significantly, and thus the newborn must be at a high level of somatic and motor development while being dependent upon the mother's abilities to draw from her own reserves for lactation. This, combined with a degree of social herd cooperation in the defense of the young, is developed only within the Eutheria. The syndrome has many advantages toward survival under conditions of intense predation among eutherian species of the dry open plains that do not exist for the Australian ungulate-equivalents, the macropodids. Advanced anatomical development at birth is the key, and the physiologically sophisticated trophoblast, in turn, is the important factor lacking in marsupials.

The adaptive significance of precocial development in some other eutherian species is less clear. It is interesting to note, however, that no known eutherian species gives rise to neonates as immature as those of any marsupial. The range of anatomical development at birth is vast among placentals, and one would expect that, if indeed the marsupial mode of reproduction were as adaptive as that of the eutherians, at least a part of the spectacular diversity of eutherians would today exhibit the "marsupial way." Could it be that placentals have become "evolutionarily canalized" to the extent that once the trophoblast was refined the group could not revert back to the metatherian level? This seems unlikely in light of the incredible array of reproductive variety known to have developed successfully within the Eutheria; even the necessary transitory seals for the eye, ear, and mouth persist for secondary use.

I believe that the extensive development of the eutherian trophoblastic function was unique and perhaps the single most important post-Jurassic evolutionary event within the Mammalia. It allowed the eutherians to develop precocial young, enter new habitats, foster advanced societal behavior, and ultimately make possible the evolution of culture and the historical record. Whole new realms of adaptation and behavior not possible within the marsupials became reality within the Eutheria because of this breakthrough in reproductive biology; there would seem to be little advantage in reverting to a more primitive level.

Unfortunately, the known Cretaceous mammalian record does not give a hint as to when the various eutherian reproductive advantages likely became influential. As pointed out in Chapter 11, the considerable diversity of North American marsupials practically became extinct at the end of the Cretaceous, concomitant with a significant evolutionary radiation of the eutherians. It was also the time of major extinction (but perhaps not total; see Van Valen and Sloan, 1977) of the dinosaurs. The causes of the Late Cretaceous extinctions of marsupials, however, are unknown. It is unclear whether it was climatic deterioration, the immigration of certain competing eutherians, some other biotic change, or perhaps a combination thereof that was the cause.

REFERENCES CITED

Allin, E. F., 1975, Evolution of the mammalian middle ear: Jour. Morph., v. 147, p. 403-438.

Bush, G. L., 1975, Modes of animal speciation: Ann. Rev. Ecol. Syst., v. 6, p. 339-364.

Bush, G. L., Case, S. M., Wilson, A. C., and Patton, J. L., 1977, Rapid speciation and chromosomal evolution in mammals: Natl. Acad. Sci. USA, Proc., v. 74, p. 3942-3946.

Chiappa, S. A., and Fink, G., 1977, Releasing factor and hormonal changes in the hypothalamic-pituitary-gonadotrophin and -adrenocorticotrophin systems before and after birth and puberty in male, female and androgenized female rats: Jour. Endocrinol., v. 72, p. 211-224.

Finch, C. E., 1976, The regulation of physiological changes during mammalian aging: Quart. Rev. Biol., v. 51, p. 49-83.

Gross, D. S., and Baker, B. L., 1977, Immunohistochemical localization of gonadotropin-releasing hormone (GnRH) in the fetal and early postnatal mouse brain: Amer. Jour. Anat., v. 148, p. 195-216.

Hayman, D. L., 1977, Chromosone number—constancy and variation, in Stonehouse, B., and Gilmore, D., eds., The biology of marsupials: London, Macmillan Press Ltd., p. 27-48.

Henkel, S., and Krebs, B., 1977, Der erste Fund eines Säugetier-Skelettes aus der Jura-Zeit: Umschau in Wissenschaft und Technik 77, p. 217-218.

Hopson, J. A., 1966, The origin of the mammalian middle ear: Amer. Zool., v. 6, p. 437-450.

_____1973, Endothermy, small size, and the origin of mammalian reproduction: Amer. Natur., v. 107, p. 446-452.

Hugget, A. St. G., and Widdas, W. F., 1951, The relationship between mammalian foetal weight and conception age: Jour. Physiol., v. 114, p. 306-317.

Jellison, W. L., 1945, A suggested homolog of the os penis or baculum of mammals: Jour. Mammal., v. 26, p. 146-147.

Jewell, P. A., 1976, Selection for reproductive success, in Austin, C. R., and Short, R. V., eds., Reproduction in mammals. Book 6, The evolution of reproduction: Cambridge, Cambridge Univ. Press, p. 71-109.

Johnson, J. I., Jr., 1977, Central nervous system of marsupials, *in* Hunsaker, D., II, ed., The biology of marsupials: New York, Academic Press, p. 157-278.

Jost, A., Dupouy, J. P., and Geloso-Meyer, A., 1970, Hypothalmo-hypophyseal relationships in the fetus, *in* Martini, L., Motta, M., and Fraschini, F., eds., The hypothalamus: New York, Academic Press, p. 605-615.

Kaufmann, J. H., 1974a, The ecology and evolution of social organization in the kangaroo family (Macropodidae): Amer. Zool., v. 14, p. 51-62.

———1974b, Social ethology of the whiptail wallaby, *Macropus parryi*, in northeastern New South Wales: Anim. Behav., v. 22, p. 281-369.

Kielan-Jaworowska, Z., 1975, Possible occurrence of marsupial bones in Cretaceous eutherian mammals: Nature, v. 255, p. 698-699.

Kirkly, R. J., 1977, Learning and problem-solving behaviour in marsupials, *in* Stonehouse, B., and Gilmore, D., eds., 1977, The biology of marsupials: London, Macmillan Press Ltd., p. 193-208.

Kirsch, J. A. W., 1977a, The six-percent solution: second thoughts on the adaptedness of the Marsupialia: Amer. Sci., v. 65, p. 276-288.

———1977b, Biological aspects of the marsupial-placental dichotomy: a reply to Lillegraven: Evolution, v. 31, p. 898-900.

Kühne, W. G., 1975, Marsupium and marsupial bone in Mesozoic mammals and in the Marsupionta: Problèmes actuels de paléontologie-évolution des vertébrés, Colloque internat. C. N. R. S., no. 218, p. 585-590.

Lillegraven, J. A., 1969, Latest Cretaceous mammals of upper part of Edmonton Formation of Alberta, Canada, and review of marsupial-placental dichotomy in mammalian evolution: Univ. Kansas Paleont. Contribs., Art. 50 (Vertebrata 12), 122 p.

———1972, Ordinal and familial diversity of Cenozoic mammals: Taxon, v. 21 (2/3), p. 261-274.

———1975, Biological considerations of the marsupial-placental dichotomy: Evolution, v. 29, p. 707-722.

MacIntyre, G. T., 1972, The trisulcate petrosal pattern of mammals, *in* Dobzhansky, T., Hecht, M. K., and Steere, W. C., eds., Evolutionary biology: New York, Appleton-Century-Crofts, v. 6, p. 275-303.

Mangold-Wirz, K., 1966, Cerebralisation und Ontogenesemodus bei Eutherien: Acta Anat., v. 63, p. 449-508.

Moors, P. J., 1974, The foeto-maternal relationship and its significance in marsupial reproduction: a unifying hypothesis: Austral. Mammal Soc. Jour., v. 1, p. 263-266.

Müller, F., 1969a, Verhaltnis von Körperentwicklung und Cerebralisation in Ontogenese und Phylogenese der Säuger. Versuch einer Übersicht des Problems: Verh. naturf. Ges. Basel, v. 80, p. 1-31.

———1969b, Zur fruhen Evolution der Säuger-Ontogenesetypen. Versuch einer Rekonstruktion aufgrund der Ontogenese-Verhaltnisse bei den Marsupialia: Acta Anat., v. 74, p. 297-404.

———1972-1973, Zur stammesgeschichtlichen Veränderung der *Eutheria*-Ontogenesen. Versuch einer Übersicht aufgrund vergleichend morphologischer Studien an *Marsupialia* und *Eutheria*. Rev. suisse Zool., v. 79. Einführung und 1. Teil: Zur Evolution der Geburtgestalt: Gestaltstadien der Eutheria. Fasc. 1, no. 1, 1972a, p. 1-97. 2. Teil: Ontogenesetypus und Cerebralisation. Fasc. 2, no. 17, 1972b, p. 501-566. 3. Teil: Zeitliche Aspekte in der Evolution der Ontogenesetypen. Fasc. 2, no. 18, 1972c, p. 567-611. 4. Spezieller Teil. Fasc. 4, no. 65, 1973, p. 1599-1685.

Packard, G. C., Tracy, C. R., and Roth, J. J., 1977, The physiological ecology of reptilian eggs and embryos, and the evolution of viviparity within the class Reptilia: Biol. Rev., v. 52, p. 71-105.

Padykula, H. A., and Taylor, J. M., 1976, Ultrastructural evidence for loss of the trophoblastic layer in the chorioallantoic placenta of Australian bandicoots (Marsupialia: Peramelidae): Anat. Rec., v. 186, p. 357-385.

Parker, P., 1977, An ecological comparison of marsupial and placental patterns of reproduction, *in* Stonehouse, B., and Gilmore, D., eds., The biology of marsupials: London, Macmillan Press Ltd., p. 273-286.

Pond, C. M., 1977, The significance of lactation in the evolution of mammals: Evolution, v. 31, p. 177-199.

Portmann, A., 1965, Über die Evolution der Tragzeit bei Säugetieren: Rev. suisse Zool., v. 72, p. 658-666.

Sacher, G. A., and Staffeldt, E. F., 1974, Relation of gestation time to brain weight for placental mammals: implications for the theory of vertebrate growth: Amer. Natur., v. 108, p. 593-615.

Scott, J. S., and Jones, W. R., 1976, Immunology of human reproduction: London, Academic Press, *xviii* + 476 p.

Sharman, G. B., 1970, Reproductive physiology of marsupials: Science, v. 167, p. 1221-1228.

———1976, Evolution of viviparity in mammals, *in* Austin, C. R., and Short, R. V., eds., Reproduction in mammals. Book 6, The evolution of reproduction: Cambridge, Cambridge Univ. Press, p. 32-70.

Van Valen, L., and Sloan, R. E., 1977, Ecology and the extinction of the dinosaurs: Evol. Theory, v. 2, p. 37-64.

Walker, K. Z., and Tyndale-Biscoe, C. H., 1978, Immunological aspects of gestation in the tammar wallaby, *Macropus eugenii*: Aust. Jour. Biol. Sci., v. 31, p. 173-182.

Wilson, A. C., Bush, G. L., Case, S. M., and King, M.-C., 1975, Social structuring of mammalian populations and rate of chromosomal evolution: Natl. Acad. Sci. USA, Proc., v. 72, p. 5061-5065.

Wilson, E. O., 1975, Sociobiology—The new synthesis: Cambridge, Belknap Press, *ix* + 697 p.

AUTHOR'S NOTE

After completion of Chapter 13 the author was notified of the imminent publication of a note by Taylor and Padykula (1978) which challenges the idea that trophoblast is an embryonic tissue restricted in its taxonomic distribution to the eutherian mammals. Opportunity to reply in the same journal was denied, thus this addendum was prepared to respond to the specific criticisms raised. The problem results for the most part from differences in terminology used by Lillegraven from that used by Taylor and Padykula.

It is well known that reptiles, birds, monotremes, and marsupials agree in fundamental aspects of early embryogenesis. They all form a true blastula with a true blastocoele; marsupials differ in blastular configuration in that they develop a blastocyst (rather than a blastodisc) as a result of apomorphic major reductions in relative yolk volume. The blastular cells in all these groups can be considered presumptively "protodermal" (*sensu* McCrady, 1938, and 1944) in that they ultimately will form the entirety of the embryo plus all of the extraembryonic membranes. Eutherian mammals, on the other hand, are embryogenetically unique among the vertebrates in that a morula forms that hollows out and differentiates into two histologically recognizable cell groups, the "inner cell mass" (ICM) and the "trophoblast." The ICM develops the entirety of the embryo plus parts of the extraembryonic membranes; the "trophoblast" is developmentally committed to the formation of extraembryonic membranes (parts of the "chorioallantoic" placenta and, in some groups, the external coating of the yolk sac). The cavity seen in early stages of development that is outside the ICM and inside the trophoblastic sphere quite possibly is, from developmento-spatial points of view, not the same as the true blastocoele seen in other amniotes.

It is probable that the peculiarly differentiated ICM and trophoblastic tissues of eutherians evolutionarily were derived from the protodermal blastular cells characteristic of monotremes and marsupials, but intermediate stages are uncertain. There is no differentiation of marsupial blastulae into "embryonic" versus "trophoblastic" areas. In McCrady's (1938, p. 46) words, and in contrast to the situation in eutherians, ". . . no line can ever be drawn between cells [of an opossum blastocyst]

which are to be retained in the definitive body and those which are to be discarded." Although McCrady (1944) tentatively suggested that the inner cell mass of eutherians represents the homologue of the medullary plate area of a marsupial gastrula, the completeness of the homology has not been confirmed. "Blastula" formation shows fundamental differences between marsupials and eutherians, and it is quite possible that the "trophoblast" of the latter group is a neomorphic development peculiar to the infraclass. It was in light of these uncertainties in homology and basic differences in "blastula" formation that I argued for the uniqueness of "trophoblast" (and, *ergo*, ICM) to eutherians. If: (1) a purely functional connotation for the term "trophoblast" (Gr.: *trophos*, one who feeds; *blastos*, a germ) is used for an ultrastructurally complex tissue of considerable metabolic activity involved in two-way exchanges across the feto-maternal boundary; and/or if (2) "trophoblast" is meant to be an equivalent term with "chorion," then I certainly agree that marsupials (and amniotes in general) have trophoblast. Usage of the term within the Theria should be the topic of a thorough review, and the questions of "blastular" homologies a subject of renewed research.

Beyond the academic questions of terminology and homology are the realities of comparisons between marsupials and eutherians with respect to: (1) degrees of placental-endometrial tissue interactions; and (2) relative development and function of placentation. Quite truly, I was incorrect in 1969 in stating unequivocally that erosion of maternal uterine epithelium does not occur in marsupials (although the error was corrected in my 1975 review, p. 713). Nevertheless, it must be admitted that the taxonomic distribution among marsupials of pronounced endometrial erosion during implantation shows this to be a comparative exception (see Hughes, 1974, for review) rather than a commonplace event as within the diversity of eutherians. It must also be accepted that, in light of the short period of shell-free intrauterine development characteristic of marsupials in general, the "trophoblastic" tissue and its derivatives do not approach the degree of hypertrophy or complexity of function seen in most eutherians.

In appreciation of the fact that the last common ancestor of marsupials and eutherians existed no less than 100 million years ago, one should expect to find considerable anatomical-physiological "experimentation" at the interface of the placenta and endometrium of various groups of living marsupials; they too would be "searching" for ways to increase the effectiveness of exchange across the fetomaternal barrier for the benefit of developing young. The sort of detailed work being done by Padykula and Taylor (1976) on marsupial placentae is to be applauded. Such studies will provide valuable information concerning marsupial parallelisms with eutherian development, and will lead to better understanding of evolutionary progress in placentation.

Jason A. Lillegraven

ADDITIONAL REFERENCES CITED

Hughes, R. L., 1974, Morphological studies on implantation in marsupials: Jour. Reprod. Fert., v. 39, p. 173-186.

McCrady, E., Jr., 1938, Embryology of the opossum: Amer. Anat. Mem., no. 16 (Wistar Inst. Anat. Biol., Philadelphia), 234 p.

_____1944, The evolution and significance of the germ layers: Tennessee Acad. Sci. Jour., v. 19, p. 240-251.

Taylor, J. M., and Padykula, H. A., 1978, Marsupial trophoblast and mammalian evolution: Nature, v. 271, p. 588.

CHAPTER 14

PALEOGEOGRAPHY OF THE WORLD OF THE MESOZOIC

Jason A. Lillegraven

Mary J. Kraus

Thomas M. Bown

INTRODUCTION

In the years since Matthew's *Climate and Evolution* was published (1915), the concept of the earth and its faunas through geologic time has changed from one of essential stasis to one of dynamism. For example, new data support the relatively old concept of continental drift. The recognition that land masses as well as faunal and floral elements were mobile in the past has introduced a new order of variability into interpretations and solutions of problems in paleobiogeography (see McKenna,

1973). Many old questions have been resolved, but at least as many new ones have arisen.

The main purpose of the present chapter is to summarize the sequence of changes in Mesozoic (specifically Late Triassic-Late Cretaceous) intercontinental land connections in order that reasonable constraints of probability, on the basis of physical geography, can be applied to interpretations of interrelationships of land vertebrate faunas. Major emphasis is put on: (1) the succession of separations of particular continental blocks; and (2) the barriers to dispersal provided by epicontinental seas. Information on paleoclimates and possible land vertebrate dispersal pathways is also presented.

The discussion of physical geography will use, as a basis, five maps (Figs. 14-1 through 14-5) developed from many sources by Lillegraven. The maps use the "Lambert equal-area" projection suggested for geological reconstructions by Briden and others (1974) and Smith and Briden (1977). As will be discussed in more detail below, several modifications of the continental arrangements used by Smith and Briden (1977) and Bullard and others (1965) have been introduced into the present maps.

The horizontal line that bisects the maps represents the paleoequator, and the vertical bisector is an arbitrary line of longitude that is held fixed in position through the five reconstructions. The intersections of the lesser diameter circle with the vertical line represent the approximate positions of the north and south rotational poles. Pole positions are based upon paleomagnetic data, using the assumption of a relatively stable axial geocentric dipole model for the major component of the earth's magnetic field that has approximated the earth's rotational axis through time. Mesozoic mammal localities discussed in Chapter 2 are shown by triangles. Several discrete but closely spaced localities described in Chapter 2 may be generalized here by a single triangle. Lines of latitude and longitude are plotted for continental areas in ten degree intervals as they occur on a model of today's world. Although care in placement of lines of latitude and longitude was taken throughout the process of map development, the maps should be used only in a general, qualitative sense. Configurations of continental borders are in some cases completely conjectural (e.g., southern Asia and northern India). The question of the origins of southeast Asia is ignored except to assume (along with Johnson and others, 1976) that it has been a part of the Northern Hemisphere since at least late Paleozoic

time. The toned pattern showing ancient seaways should, in almost all cases, be considered variable in extent throughout the interval of geologic time represented. The epicontinental seas depicted are in general indicative of their greatest known extent, but exceptions will be noted.

LATE TRIASSIC AND EARLIEST JURASSIC

Physical Geography

The reconstruction of continental positions for the Late Triassic (Fig. 14-1) differs from that provided by Bullard and others (1965) in several respects. Most important, the Gondwanan continents have been rotated clockwise about twenty degrees to effect the apposition of northern South America with the Gulf Coast region of North America. Such a reconstruction is favored by Van der Voo and others (1976), who have shown that agreement in positions of Permo-Triassic paleomagnetic poles for Gondwanan and northern continents is thereby strengthened, as are alignments between continents of older orogenic belts (see Hurley, 1974). To accommodate the proposed absence of a Gulf of Mexico during Triassic time, the continental block that today includes the Mexican-Honduran-Guatemalan region would have had to be farther west than it is today (relative to the remainder of North America), and rotated clockwise from its present position. This would indicate that the Paleozoic geosynclinal areas of Mexico had major northern connections with the mobile belts of western North America, rather than with the southwestern end of the Appalachian-Ouachita geosynclinal region as is more generally visualized. A review of the various possibilities of Paleozoic geological connections between Mexico and the remainder of North America was provided by Helwig (1975).

A second series of differences between Figure 14-1 and the reconstruction of Pangaea by Bullard and others (1965) is in the region of eastern Asia. Figure 14-1 shows three distinct blocks (Kolyma platform, Fig. 14-1, no. 2; Sikhote-Alin region, no. 4; and China-Siberia platform, no. 3) that are today joined together and make up most of eastern Asia. McElhinny (1973) summarized Mesozoic paleomagnetic data for the three areas, and showed independent paths of polar-wandering. The paths are distinct in the Triassic, converge in the Jurassic, and

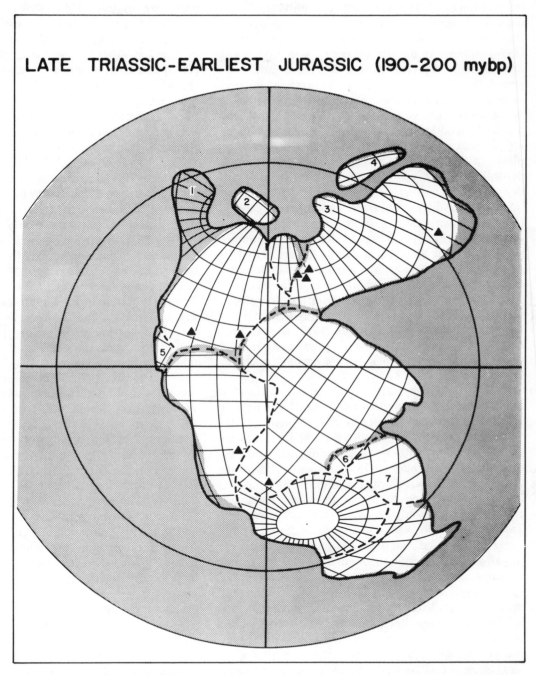

LATE TRIASSIC-EARLIEST JURASSIC (190-200 mybp)

Figure 14-1. Lambert equal-area projections (see text for explanation) of the world of the Late Triassic and earliest Jurassic. Stippled areas are marine waters, both oceanic and epicontinental. Triangles are generalizations of localities yielding fossil mammals that are discussed in more detail in Chapter 2. *1*, Combined block including western Alaska and parts of the Chukotsk and Kamchatka regions of modern Siberia; *2*, block encompassing most of the Kolyma region of modern Siberia; *3*, region of modern China-Siberia platform; *4*, block encompassing most of the Sikhote Alin region of modern eastern Asia; *5*, region including modern Mexico, Honduras, and Guatemala; *6*, region of modern Madagascar; and *7*, region of modern India. The heavy dashed lines mark the approximate boundaries of existing continents and do not imply that continental separation had begun by that interval of time.

tightly group in the Cretaceous; collisions of independent continental blocks are suggested, with final fusion in the Cretaceous. Herron and others (1974) summarized paleomagnetic and geological data for the Kolyma (Kolymski) block and suggested that, in the Triassic, the region was part of northern Canada. In the Jurassic, the Kolyma block broke away from North America and moved across a proto-Arctic basin, by means of sea-floor spreading, to make initial contact with the China-Siberia platform in the Early Cretaceous; the Verkhoyansk deformation belt was caused, at least in part, by this collision.

A third difference from Bullard and others' (1965) reconstruction is in the region of western Alaska. Churkin (1972) argued that the easternmost part of modern Siberia historically is part of North America, not Asia. The Alaska-Chukotsk-Kamchatka region is drawn in Figure 14-1 (no. 1) as a part of North America. As sea-floor spreading progressed through the Mesozoic in the North Atlantic basin (see Pitman and Talwani, 1972) the Alaska-Chukotsk-Kamchatka region gradually moved toward the Kolyma block with collision occurring late in the Cretaceous.

The Paleozoic-early Mesozoic foldbelts of South America, Antarctica, and eastern Australia are aligned as the arc-trench environment of the "Samfrau geosyncline" in the fashion suggested by De Wit (1977). Synthesis of paleomagnetic data by McElhinny and others (1976) from Karroo deposits (Late Carboniferous-Early Triassic) of Madagascar, South America, and Africa suggests that Madagascar was originally adjacent to Somalia, Kenya, and Tanzania; it is so placed in Figure 14-1 (no. 6).

It is assumed that Pangaea remained as an integral geographic unit through the Triassic; actual continental separation probably did not occur before the Early Jurassic. Considerable rifting that involved significant block-faulting, however, occurred along some lineations that were destined to be regions of separation between continents (e.g., the Triassic Newark Series of eastern North America). Such delays between the onsets of rifting and actual separation were common through geologic history. Although the Late Triassic represented a time of general continental emergence, the existence of some finger-like epicontinental seas has been documented. For example, parts of western Europe, including the region of Wales from which some of the earliest mammals were recovered, were progressively inundated by shallow seas during the Rhaeto-Liassic. The islands on which these animals lived became completely submerged before the end of the Liassic (see Robinson, 1971). Also, Burke (1975) discussed evaporite deposits in the Morocco-Nova Scotia-Newfoundland area that were developed from the incursion of Tethyan marine waters into developing grabens that marked initial rifting between northwestern Africa and eastern North America (for more detail see Dillon and Sougy, 1974; Van Houten, 1977; and Van Houten and Brown, 1977). Evaporite deposition continued into the Early Jurassic. Incursion of epeiric seas into the region that later became the Gulf of Mexico apparently did not begin until early in the Jurassic (see Arden, 1975). Rather poorly developed Late Triassic marine facies are known from East Greenland (Birkelund and others, 1974); marine and nonmarine conditions fluctuated during that time. Flores (1970) discussed the presence of marine Late Triassic strata along the western margin of Madagascar, indicating an incursion from Tethys.

It was apparently not until the Early Jurassic that significant continental separations occurred within Pangaea. The first breaks resulted from crustal spreading between the North American and West African regions (see Pitman and Talwani, 1972; Ager and Walley, 1977; and Mullins and Lynts, 1977), and presumably between North and South America. Spilling of marine waters, thought to be from the Pacific basin, initiated the accumulation of thick Jurassic evaporites in the developing Gulf of Mexico (Burke, 1975). The Gondwanan continents moved southeast by east (Ladd, 1976) and rotated counterclockwise relative to North America throughout the Jurassic as the southern part of the North Atlantic and the Caribbean basins increased in width (the controversy over the ultimate age of the Caribbean and Gulf of Mexico is discussed by Donnelly, 1975).

The connection between the North American and Eurasian plates remained throughout the Jurassic, thus during that time northern Africa would have had to move somewhat eastward relative to Europe along major zones of faulting and folding within the Tethyan region (see Rona and Fleming, 1973, and Dewey and others, 1973). Considerable marine bottom structural complexity in the Mediterranean region is suggested by Early Jurassic time (Vörös, 1977).

Although there is faunal evidence for continuity of waters between the eastern Pacific and Caribbean-Atlantic regions throughout the Jurassic (*e.g.*, see Imlay, 1965), the marine connection must have been restricted across the Mexican-Central American region until late in the period; Jurassic sedimentation in the Gulf of Mexico was characterized by poor circulation and widespread evaporite deposition. Marine faunal evidence suggests the possibility of a land connection between North and South America during the Bathonian, but it was less likely to have existed earlier in the Jurassic (see Imlay, 1968) and almost certainly was not present during Oxfordian to Tithonian time.

The Kolyma block presumably was free from North America and adrift in the Arctic Sea in the Early Jurassic, and perhaps the Sikhote-Alin block had begun to move toward the remainder of eastern Asia as a result of sea-floor spreading events in the Pacific basin (see Hilde and others, 1977).

Epicontinental seaway distribution changed little from the Late Triassic into the Early Jurassic (see Hallam, 1975).

Climates

Tillites are unknown from any Triassic stratigraphic sequence, indicating the probable lack of polar icecaps (Robinson, 1971, 1973). That, combined with the unique continental distribution of the Late Triassic (Fig. 14-1), is thought by many to have had a direct and profound effect upon the world's climate. Robinson (1971) suggested that mild temperatures may have extended as far north and south as 50° latitude, and that the polar regions may have been temperate during this ice-free period. Other authors (*e.g.*, Drewry and others, 1974), however, question whether the presence or absence of polar icecaps could have influenced atmospheric circulation patterns and caused significant latitudinal shifts of climatic belts.

Both Lotze (1964) and Meyerhoff (1970, 1971) considered the Triassic to have been a warmer and more arid period than today, as based upon the distribution of evaporite deposits. Meyerhoff observed that several intervals during the Mesozoic, including the Late Triassic, are notable for their extensive evaporites. He called such periods "evaporite maxima" and suggested that they were characterized by warm oceans and warm air temperatures, as well as arid land conditions. Meyerhoff

also noted the absence of extensive Late Triassic coal deposits (except at high latitudes), which he felt corroborated his conclusions.

Red beds, many of them associated with evaporites (*e.g.*, see Hubert, 1977), were also deposited over wide areas during the Late Triassic. In this regard, Van Houten (1964, p. 659) concluded that: "Red beds as a group accumulated in a warm-temperate to tropical climate, a broad range within which red beds as a group have no climatic significance." He (1961, 1964) also noted that red beds in themselves do not necessarily imply extremely dry depositional conditions, although when associated with evaporites or aeolian deposits, arid and warm conditions are probably indicated. Waugh (1973) noted the occurrence of red beds associated with evaporites in western Europe, North Africa, and the western United States. Paleomagnetic data show that these deposits were formed in the tropical belt, where dry conditions are not unusual. Evaporites are also known from Africa and southeast Asia, at somewhat higher (approximately 40°) latitudes (Robinson, 1971). Robinson observed that extensive Late Triassic aeolian deposits developed in the interiors of Gondwanaland and Laurasia, while Late Triassic coal deposits are more restricted in occurrence and are found primarily in the eastern, middle, and high latitude regions of the two supercontinents.

Faunal evidence hinting at Late Triassic climates is perhaps somewhat less conclusive than that of the sedimentary record. Cox (1973) demonstrated a worldwide distribution of land-dwelling vertebrates, but concluded that such a distribution is not strong evidence either that warm temperatures extended to higher latitudes at this time or that climates were very uniform. Westerman (1973), on the other hand, observed a large latitudinal distribution of a Middle-Late Triassic bivalve (*Monotis*) and concluded that ocean temperatures were quite equable and climates uniform during the Late Triassic.

Robinson (1971, 1973) stressed the probable climatic impact of the existence of unusually large continental masses and their nearly symmetrical distribution about the equator during the Late Triassic. She formulated an interpretation of the Late Triassic climates using a theoretical approach based upon modern climatology and sedimentologic evidence. She suggested that the large land areas both of Gondwanaland and of Laurasia created monsoonal conditions during their respective winter months. High pressure zones would have been formed in the continental interior during the winter months, and winds would have blown outward from the continental interior. Winds reaching the continental margins, having traveled only over land, would have accumulated little or no moisture and would have brought dry winter conditions to the continental margins. Air currents that passed over the Tethyan Sea to the low and middle latitudes of Laurasia, however, would have brought summer rainy conditions. Robinson believed that three general climatic zones emerged: (1) the central and western portions of each continent in the tropical latitudes would have experienced year round dry conditions; (2) the higher latitudes would have received moisture as a result of polar easterlies and westerlies; and (3) the eastern parts of both continental areas lying at middle and low latitudes would have had wet summers, alternating with dry winters. Robinson found that the occurrences of evaporites, red beds, coal deposits, and aeolian dune deposits in general corroborate this climatic model.

As noted earlier, a frequently encountered topic in paleoclimatologic studies is that of expanding or contracting climatic belts in response to the amount of polar ice, and the concomitant shifting of wind zones. Increased width of the tropical and subtropical belts has been suggested for the Late Triassic and, as will be seen, for the Jurassic as well. Drewry and others (1974), however, are doubtful that radical shifts of these belts have occurred in the past, or that it was even possible for such changes to have occurred. They cited the supporting works of several authors (e.g., Sawyer, 1966, and Lamb, 1972). Sawyer (1966) argued that it is the rotational velocity of the earth, its size, and related factors which influence the position of the subtropical high pressure zones, not the amount of ice present at the poles. Lamb (1972) demonstrated that in order for atmospheric angular momentum to be conserved, the areas that are covered by the surface westerly and easterly winds must be nearly equal. Consequently, the subtropical zone must consistently be at approximately 30° latitude, as it is today. If this belt were to expand to higher latitudes, Lamb concluded that regular wind patterns such as we have today (the easterlies and westerlies) would not be created; small, irregular winds would result. On the basis of these theoretical reasonings, Drewry and others (1974) argued that it is very unlikely that the climatic belts have shifted greatly through time, especially since the sedimentologic record shows that persistent trade winds did exist during the Mesozoic. Drewry and others (1974, p. 531) concluded, "Though rainfall and temperature have varied at a particular paleolatitude, marked equatorward shrinkage of the subtropical high-pressure belts during ice-sheet glaciations and marked poleward expansion during ice-free epochs is not evident from geological observations."

Faunas

A recent review of comparisons of Triassic intercontinental land vertebrate faunas by Cox (1974 and papers cited therein) shows that there were great similarities among all known areas of the time; a true "world fauna" existed. He stated (ibid., p. 82): "The clear implication is that not only were there no major geographical barriers between these areas, but also that there were no effective climatic barriers separating them." The mammals of the Late Triassic are so poorly known as to add little to the picture, except to say that the similarity of morganucodontids from China, Europe, and southern Africa are certainly consistent with other tetrapod resemblances.

A great deal of speculation about the origins of early groups of mammals has revolved about the study of *Morganucodon watsoni* and *Kuehneotherium praecursoris* from Wales. It is interesting to note, however, that known members of these species were island dwellers and that their homes were completely submerged by marine transgressions during the Liassic. Thus it is unlikely that they were themselves ancestral to any later mammalian lineages; the specimens are informative only in allowing a glimpse at the grades of evolution attained by the Rhaeto-Liassic.

MIDDLE JURASSIC

Physical Geography

The seaways and landmasses of the Middle Jurassic are diagrammed in Figure 14-2. No additional separations of continental blocks occurred beyond those seen earlier in the Jurassic. The width of the Caribbean-southern North Atlantic basins,

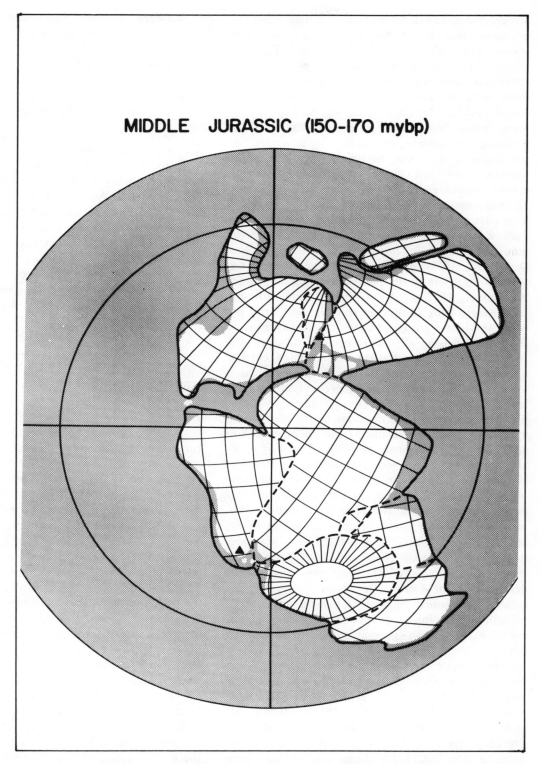

Figure 14-2. Lambert equal-area projection for the world of the Middle Jurassic. Symbols are as in Figure 14-1.

however, continued to increase through sea-floor spreading, and epeiric seas became somewhat more widespread. The North American and Eurasian plates were still joined, although epicontinental seaways at least intermittently inundated the eastern coast of Greenland (Birkelund and others, 1974; Surlyk, 1978). The East Greenland seaway showed considerable fluctuations in extent, and at times probably completely regressed. It generally increased in distribution, however, until late in the Jurassic, and comparison of fossils document marine faunal exchanges between the Arctic and Tethyan regions (see Callomon and others, 1972). A large part of western North America was covered by shallow seas that shifted complexly through Jurassic time (see Imlay, 1957, 1965, 1973, and Imlay and Detterman, 1973). Much of southern Europe was covered until late in the period (see summary maps by Hallam, 1975), but the seaway was probably archipelagic with complexly shifting shorelines between the island groups. Marine bivalves of Europe showed increasing diversity through most of the Jurassic in correlation with expansion of epicontinental seas, but extinction rates also increased toward the end of the period, perhaps in response to widespread marine regression (Hallam, 1976).

Marine deposition dominated the continental margin of West Africa during the Jurassic (Dillon and Sougy, 1974). Normal sea-floor spreading probably continued in the widening Caribbean (Fox and Heezen, 1975), with the ocean floor on either side of the midoceanic ridge becoming progressively deeper through time. The area from Cuba northward onto the margin of North America, however, appears to have acted as a shelf near sea level through the Jurassic (Pardo, 1975). The shallow shelf probably covered the northern third of the developing Gulf-Caribbean basin. Restricted circulation continued on the Cuban-Bahaman shelf with the deposition of evaporites until the close of the Jurassic, when general subsidence occurred (*ibid.*).

The western continental margin of South America was dominated by marine sedimentation throughout the Jurassic (Harrington, 1962). A volcanic chain developed during the Middle Jurassic in the region that is now part of the Antarctic Peninsula and contiguous southwestern South America (De Wit, 1977). Lavas and volcaniclastic debris accumulated in what was probably a shallow marginal marine environment. The volcanic activity

in that area continued throughout the remainder of the Jurassic as a result of melts at depth above an eastward-dipping subduction zone, originating somewhat to the west.

Climates and Faunas

As with the animals from the Rhaeto-Liassic fissure fills of Wales, known members of species from the Stonesfield Slate and Forest Marble formation probably were insular forms (see Hallam, 1975 and refs.). Again, although these animals have been important in the recognition of grades of evolution attained by the Middle Jurassic, they themselves may have had no direct relationships with later groups.

Additional brief interpretations of Jurassic climates and land vertebrate faunas will be discussed in the section below on "Late Jurassic-earliest Cretaceous."

LATE JURASSIC-EARLIEST CRETACEOUS
Physical Geography

The geological record beginning with the Late Jurassic is considerably more complete than that of earlier intervals, and more confidence can be placed in paleogeographic reconstructions. Figure 14-3 shows the probable distribution of lands and seas during the Late Jurassic and earliest Cretaceous.

After the end of the Middle Jurassic, the epicontinental seas of western North America showed considerable retreat from their previous extent. The initial incursion of sea water onto the area of the northern Canadian shield probably began during the earliest Cretaceous as a prelude to the major inundation that would divide the North American continent into eastern and western halves for most of the latter half of the Cretaceous. The East Greenland seaway had lost contiguity between the Arctic basin and Tethyan seaway before the end of the Jurassic (Tithonian-Volgian), and the marine faunas of the two areas increased in degree of endemism (see Hallam, 1975). As was discussed in Chapter 2, marine connections between Tethys and the boreal region of Europe were restored near the end of the Jurassic or very early in the Cretaceous (see Casey, 1971). East Greenland Cretaceous

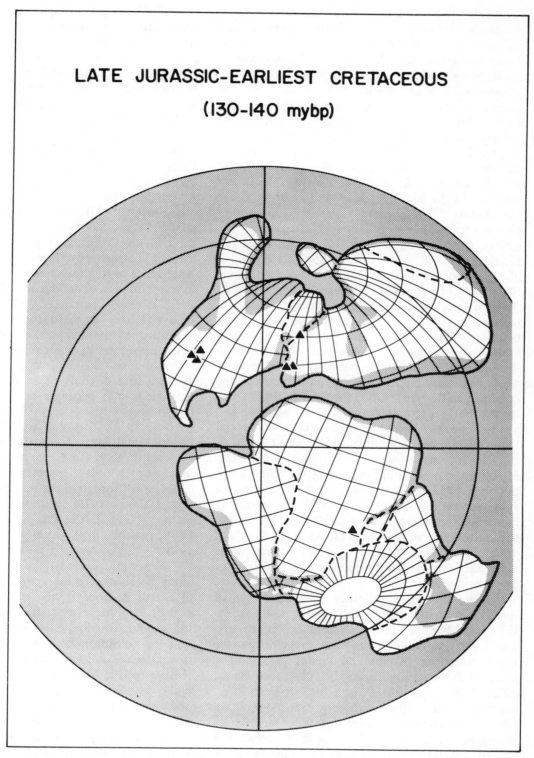

LATE JURASSIC-EARLIEST CRETACEOUS
(130-140 mybp)

Figure 14-3. Lambert equal-area projection for the world of the Late Jurassic and earliest Cretaceous. Symbols are as in Figure 14-1.

sediments are marine and dominantly clastics, with indications of several pulses of pronounced oceanic transgressions (Birkelund and others, 1974). Paleogeographic maps by Vereschagin and Ronov (1966) show major but laterally variable seaways across the Uralian region through most of the Cretaceous, but marine faunas suggest that the connection between boreal and Tethyan regions was not yet established by the end of the Jurassic.

Collision of the Sikhote-Alin block with the remainder of East Asia had probably occurred by the end of the Jurassic, and the Kolyma block was probably in the initial phase of contact in the Early Cretaceous.

The Tethyan seaway was very extensive by the earliest Cretaceous (see Hsü, 1976) and, from the faunal point of view, became the world's most discrete biogeographical unit of the Cretaceous (Kauffman, 1973); marine faunas of great generic similarity are seen until late in the Cretaceous all the way from Mexico to southern Asia. The seaway between North and South America became progressively broader and more open in circulation through the Cretaceous until late in the period, when secondary restrictions developed between the eastern Pacific and Gulf-Caribbean basins. Thus, by the Early Cretaceous, a relatively shallow and warm seaway bisected Pangaea near equatorial latitudes and was continuous with the vast extent of the Pacific. Such a seaway must have had profound effects upon moderating the continental climates of the time. The Cuba-Bahama platform underwent subsidence at this time (Pardo, 1975), thus probably increasing the rate of marine circulation throughout the entire Tethyan region. West Africa (Dillon and Sougy, 1974) and Africa's northern coastal areas were also predominantly marine through most of the Cretaceous.

There is still no indication of a separation of Africa and South America to form the South Atlantic Ocean by the earliest Cretaceous; continental and lacustrine deposits are widespread in eastern South American (Asmus and Ponte, 1973) and in equatorial western African (Franks and Nairn, 1973; Machens, 1973) Late Jurassic-Early Cretaceous basins. Similarly, there was at most only a minor extension northward of the Midatlantic spreading center to herald the incipient separation of North America and Eurasia. Although sea-floor spreading continued in the existing part of the Midatlantic ridge through the Late Jurassic and Early Cretaceous, the rate of crustal expansion was slow and did not increase until the Late Cretaceous (Pitman and Talwani, 1972). According to Ladd (1976), the movement of South America relative to North America shifted in the Early Cretaceous from east-southeast to a nearly due easterly direction; such a relative direction continued through most of the Cretaceous. The eastward movement of South America relative to North America beginning in the Early Cretaceous indicates that the Caribbean spreading center (previously continuous with the Midatlantic ridge) possibly became extinct (see Fox and Heezen, 1975). Fox and Heezen (1975, p. 461) stated: "From the Early Cretaceous on, the oceanic crust in the Caribbean region was caught between the differential movements of North and South America. The resultant compressive stresses resulted in the formation of subduction zones along much of the Caribbean perimeter." These are important points to keep in mind for even superficial consideration of the complexities of Caribbean island development during the Cretaceous.

Although the dating is uncertain, a Late Jurassic and/or Early Cretaceous major belt of volcanic islands began to develop in the region of the Nicaragua Rise (Fig. 14-5, no. 1) and Honduras (Arden, 1975). The geology of northern Central America and Mexico suggests that from the Late Jurassic through the Cretaceous the landscape was much as it is today, except for a persistent marine depositional trough along the eastern margin of the area (Dengo, 1975). Marine conditions prevailed across southern Central America and northern South America in the Early Cretaceous (see Geyer, 1973).

Harrington (1962) shows marine lithofacies along nearly the entire western continental margin of South America during the Late Jurassic, with significantly more extensive marine conditions in the earliest Cretaceous. It seems generally agreed that the volcanism initiated in the Middle Jurassic in southwestern South America and contiguous extensions of the Antarctic Peninsula continued to be highly active into the Early Cretaceous (see Dalziel and Elliot, 1973; De Wit, 1977; and Suárez, 1976). Shallow-water marine environments with accumulating graywacke volcanic debris extended over southeastern South America, the eastern part of the Antarctic Peninsula and region of Weddell Sea, and probably across parts of the southern end of Africa. Fingerlike epicontinental seas probably advanced slowly northward during the earliest Cretaceous along the developing rift basins that marked the future coasts of Africa and South America. No separation between continental units, however, is indicated until about 125-130 mybp (Ladd and others, 1973; Larson and Ladd, 1973), probably in the Valanginian.

Marine sediments representative of the Late Jurassic and Early Cretaceous are widespread along western Madagascar (Flores, 1970), indicating a persistent extension of Tethys southward as an epicontinental sea separating most of what would become Madagascar from eastern Africa. Relationship between Madagascar and India is unknown, but possibly they were one continuous land. Most of the western continental margin of Australia was covered by shallow seas during the Late Jurassic, with indication of more extensive and encroaching peripheral terrestrial environments during the earliest Cretaceous (see McWhae and others, 1958). Cretaceous marine sedimentation was widespread across a huge inland basin of Australia (Glaessner and Parkin, 1958), and across the northern coastal areas of the Australian block until late in the Cretaceous (Allen and others, 1960). The nature of the surface of Antarctica during the Cretaceous (or at virtually any other time in the geological past) is as yet a mystery.

It was not until after the earliest Cretaceous that separation began between India and the unit of Antarctica-Australia. According to Johnson and others (1976) and Veevers and McElhinny (1976), initial breakup through sea-floor spreading began about 130 mybp, during the Valanginian. The development of rift valleys (see Veevers and Cotterill, 1976) between future continental margins, however, began much earlier. The beginning of the destruction of Gondwanaland (see Embleton and Schmidt, 1977) by the dispersal of its continents was heralded at last.

Climates

The preponderance of evidence indicates that warm temperatures characteristic of the Late Triassic continued into the Jurassic. While conditions of continental aridity appear to have been alleviated in the Early and Middle Jurassic, aridity returned in the Late Jurassic.

Warm temperatures and equable conditions are interpretable from a number of independent sources. Tillites are unknown from Jurassic strata, implying ice-free polar regions (Hallam, 1975). Oxygen isotopes indicate relatively warm ocean temperatures (Bowen, 1966). The distribution of several marine invertebrate groups also suggests that ocean temperatures were more equable during the Jurassic than today. Stevens (1973) recognized a division, climatically controlled, of Jurassic belemnites into Boreal and Tethyan faunas. He suggested that widespread occurrence of given species in the Early Jurassic probably resulted from a latitudinally broadbanded, equable climate. Somewhat cooler ocean temperatures during the Callovian and early Oxfordian were interpreted from the southward spread of the Boreal belemnites; northward retreat of the Boreal group during the Kimmeridgian was taken to indicate return of warmer temperatures. Schaeffer (1970) found the Jurassic ceratodontid lungfishes, which were freshwater forms, to have been spread over a broad latitudinal area; today they are restricted to tropical or subtropical locales. A similar, worldwide distribution was observed for several actinopterygial fish families, including the macrosemiids and pycnodonts. Schaeffer concluded that uniform climatic conditions prevailed over wide expanses of the earth's surface.

Key evidence for warmer terrestrial conditions is also found in the floral world. Wesley (1973) observed that certain fern families, for example, the Matoniaceae and Dipteridaceae, were represented by several genera which had a widespread distribution in the Jurassic. Such ferns today are found only in the tropical Indo-Malaysian region. Barnard (1973, p. 180), in his study of Mesozoic floras, stated, "The considerable spread of the Middle Mesozoic flora at this time, as shown by the distribution of *Dictyophyllum*, to between 50° and 60° on either side of the equator is consistent with the argument that the Jurassic world had a warm and highly equable climate."

That the occurrence of moister conditions during the Early and Middle Jurassic was followed by a return to dryness in the Late Jurassic is indicated by several sedimentological factors. Hallam (1975) observed that coal seams are relatively widespread in Lower and Middle Jurassic strata; they are known from China, Australia, North America, Russia, and elsewhere. Late Jurassic coals, however, are less abundant and more restricted in their occurrence. Ironstones and bauxites show a similar decrease in the Late Jurassic, following a widespread distribution earlier (*ibid.*). Coal, ironstone, and bauxites all suggest moist depositional conditions (Kräusel, 1964; Robinson, 1973; Hallam, 1975), but their usefulness as temperature indicators is equivocal. Both Kräusel (1964) and Robinson (1973) noted that coal can form under a variety of temperatures. Bauxites are more temperature-restricted, and require warm conditions for formation.

The decrease in abundance of coals, ironstones, and bauxites in the Late Jurassic is accompanied by an increase in the distribution of evaporite deposits. Meyerhoff (1973) observed fewer evaporites during the Early and Middle Jurassic than in the Late Triassic, whereas the Late Jurassic through the Early Cretaceous was an evaporite maximum period. Lotze (1964) also noted the thick evaporite deposits of the Late Jurassic and reached the same conclusion as Meyerhoff's, that the Late Jurassic continental areas were more arid than during the Early and Middle Jurassic.

Hallam (1975) summarized paleoclimatic evidence for the Jurassic, and concluded that temperatures were warmer than today and that the tropical and subtropical belts had a broader latitudinal extent than now. Another approach, used by Drewry and others (1974), indicates that the climatic belts of the Jurassic did not, in fact, shift significantly. As mentioned earlier, these authors concluded that it is unlikely, on theoretical grounds reinforced with geological evidence, that the distribution of subtropical or other climatic belts has changed appreciably with time. They contended that the position of ancient trade-wind belts, and thus of subtropical high pressure zones, can be determined from the distribution of oceanic biogenic silica deposits. Siliceous ooze accumulates today in equatorial regions (as well as in Antarctic and Arctic belts) as the result of oceanic and atmospheric currents, which cause the upwelling of nutrient-laden waters in these zones. Drewry and others (1974) have found evidence for the existence of a silica zone of Jurassic age in the Pacific Ocean, which they attribute to an ancient trade-wind system. Similar equatorial belts of silica are known

in the Pacific and Indian Oceans from Cretaceous time through the Tertiary. From this evidence, they concluded that radical shifts of the trade-wind zones and climatic belts, as favored by some authors, have not occurred from Jurassic times to the present.

Faunas

Because of the persistent close proximity of continents, widespread dispersal of elements of the land vertebrate faunas throughout most of the Jurassic would have been expected. Vachrameev (1973) showed that the Jurassic was a time of exceptional floral uniformity at the generic level among continents. The land vertebrate fossil record is terribly biased for that period, however, as almost all known faunas are from Upper Jurassic rocks. Of the mammals, only the Tanzanian edentulous jaw representing *Brancatherulum* and the unidentified Argentinian footprints are known from the southern continents. Nevertheless, the summaries by Charig (1973) and Cox (1974) indeed do suggest considerable intercontinental exchange. The generic similarities of the dinosaur faunas of the Late Jurassic among eastern Africa, western Europe, and western North America (see Colbert, 1973) is rather surprising, however, in light of the seaways that presumably separated the northern and southern continents beginning in the Early Jurassic. As Cox (1974) suggested, intermittent land connections across a youthful Tethys between northern Africa and southern Europe may have occurred. Also, the possibility cannot be dismissed that some land connections occurred during parts of the Jurassic along the Cordillera between the Americas. Although there is no direct Mesozoic record of mammals in Australia, Lower Cretaceous fleas have been described (Riek, 1970) that may have been parasitic upon mammals (?monotremes).

The Late Jurassic mammalian faunas from Durlston Bay, England, and the Morrison Formation of the Rocky Mountains are generally considered to be quite similar. As the taxonomy is now accepted, however, only three and possibly four genera (all with different species) are in common from a total of about thirty-three named genera. Of the total of ten families represented, only four and possibly five are held in common. The physical distance between the two areas was great even in the Late Jurassic, and ecological differences were also probably significant. Thus the faunal dissimilarities seen between England and the Rockies should be fully expected, even if a complete land connection had been in existence.

"MIDDLE" CRETACEOUS
Physical Geography

The term "middle" Cretaceous will be loosely used here in a discussion of the major continental separations that occurred from the Early (but not earliest) Cretaceous through the early part of the Late Cretaceous. Although awkward in some respects, the usage will be convenient for purposes of the following paleogeographical discussion. The approximate positions of continental areas and their seaways are shown in Figure 14-4 for the interval of about 95-110 mybp (see Fig. 2-1). A great many very important events occurred during the "middle" Cretaceous from the point of view of facility of land vertebrate dispersal. Probably the greatest barriers to overland dispersal for all of the Mesozoic existed at that time. In addition to the dispersal of the Gondwanan continents, epeiric seas crossed entire continents, and Tethys was broad. Reference to evidence of greater detail is presented below.

Rocky Mountain Region of North America

The complex geological history of the Rocky Mountain and adjacent regions of North America described here mainly follows the summary by McGookey and others (1972). Nonmarine fluviatile sands and conglomeratic deposits characterize the earliest Cretaceous of the Rocky Mountain region. The environs of Utah and Idaho were undergoing mountain-building episodes at that time, but less turbulent conditions existed by the end of the Early Cretaceous. Large areas of Wyoming, Utah, and Montana were covered by lakes during much of the Early Cretaceous. The "Skull Creek Seaway" of the middle Albian represented the first marine transgression of the Cretaceous into the Rocky Mountain region, forming a rather narrow north-south seaway that connected Arctic and Gulf waters. Although there were minor intervals of marine regression thereafter, North America was essentially bisected into eastern and western parts by seaways throughout nearly all of the remainder of the Cretaceous.

The Skull Creek Seaway was short-lived, but a replacement by the "Mowry Sea" occurred soon afterward. It developed as a southward embayment from Arctic waters during the late Albian, and by the early Cenomanian was continuous with the Gulf of Mexico. The Mowry Sea regressed somewhat, leaving a land connection across west Texas and New Mexico between the eastern and western parts of North America. That land bridge was ephemeral, however, and for all but the very end of the Cretaceous ("Lancian") various transgressions of the "Western Interior Seaway" would have greatly restricted land vertebrate exchanges between east and west. As summarized by McGookey and others (1972), the Late Cretaceous of the Rocky Mountain region experienced four great transgressions and regressions that were widely variable in lateral extent (see Ryer, 1977). The transgressions, listed in chronological order of occurrence, are referred to as the "Greenhorn," "Niobrara," "Claggett," and "Bearpaw" seas. The first two were much broader in expanse and longer-lived (totalling about 30 my) than the last two (totalling about 13 my). Geological evidence suggests that the intervening regressive phases did not result in the separation of Arctic from Gulf waters. Distributional studies of clastic rocks within the seaway areas indicate that the lands to the east contributed sediments on a significant scale only during the Early Cretaceous and early Cenomanian. Most sediments were derived from highlands to the west, and during the Late Cretaceous the contribution of clastics from the west was on a grand scale (see Gilluly and others, 1970). Such differences in elevation between the eastern and western parts of North America suggest that significant differences in ecological conditions existed in the two areas, as is the case today.

The above interpretation of the Cretaceous history of central North America, although grossly incomplete, is better than can now be rendered for any of the other continents. It seems clear that, except for slightly more than the initial one-third of the Cretaceous, land vertebrate exchange between eastern and western North America would, at best, have been markedly restricted.

East Greenland, Europe, Western Asia, and Tethys

Scattered deposits along the coastal areas of East Greenland suggest the presence of relatively shallow marine conditions throughout the Cretaceous, and the included faunas show mixtures of Boreal, cosmopolitan, and Tethyan species (Birkelund and others, 1974). Thus eastern North American land vertebrates would have been restricted from distribution to the European region through virtually the entirety of the Cretaceous by a persistent seaway. Exceptions to this pattern may have occurred upon occasion (see Soper and others, 1976), but the biogeographical picture is certainly not one suggesting free exchange.

The history of Europe in post-Triassic time is one of incredible structural and stratigraphic complexity. Beyond the earliest part of the Cretaceous, the paleogeographic picture for the remainder of that period is one of an ever-changing landscape of large islands and oscillating shallow seas (see various references in Hallam, 1973, and Christensen, 1976). Details of land connections through the Jurassic and Cretaceous among the various parts of the archipelago are quite unknown. It would be expected, however, that land faunas would show high diversity as a result of genetic differentiation of isolated populations, followed later by exchanges with species in newly joined areas. Barriers to land vertebrate dispersal in the form of shallow, ephemeral seaways would have been important features of the faunal development of Europe throughout the Cretaceous.

European land vertebrates were probably somewhat restricted from free distribution into Asia by major north-south seaways, variable in width, that connected Arctic with Tethyan waters across European Russia and/or the Uralian-Western Siberian platform regions. These seas, according to maps by Vereschagin and Ronov (1966), separated western Europe from western Asia continuously from early in the Cretaceous through the Aptian, but became narrower in the Albian. From the Cenomanian through the remainder of the Cretaceous, intermittent land connections are shown between Europe and Asia, within the general areas of present latitudes 50°-55° N. This positive area may have separated a persistent and major epicontinental sea to the north (on the Western Siberian platform) from Tethys to the south. Information on these areas is difficult to extract from the literature, however, and data on the extent of the seaways (occasionally referred to as the "Turgay Strait" or "Obik Sea") through the Cretaceous is sorely in need of review (see Nalivkin, 1973).

As discussed in the section above on the physical geography of the Late Jurassic-earliest Cretaceous, the Tethyan region encompassed the most distinct of the marine biogeographical realms during all but the latest Cretaceous. Virtually unrestricted circumglobal marine circulation between the Gondwanan and northern continents dominated the Cretaceous until constrictions secondarily developed late in the period. Shallow marine conditions across northern Africa were common throughout the Cretaceous (Furon, 1963), and the northwestern half of Africa became largely inundated during parts of the Late Cretaceous (see Reyment, 1974, and Dillon and Sougy, 1974). Considering this known record, it seems unlikely that extensive dispersal of land vertebrates occurred across the Tethyan seaway between Eurasia and Africa during the Cretaceous until, perhaps, late in the period.

North Atlantic and Caribbean Basins

Sea-floor spreading continued at a slow rate along the Midatlantic ridge in the North Atlantic basin during the "middle" Cretaceous, but there was still no indication of its extension northward during that time into the present region of the Labrador Sea (Pitman and Talwani, 1972; Fitch and others, 1974). The Bay of Biscay may have begun to form in the "middle" Cretaceous as a spur developed from the Midatlantic ridge (Vigneaux, 1974). The southern part of the Midatlantic ridge had not yet extended into the juncture of South America and Africa in the region that would become the Gulf of Guinea, although there is ample evidence there for rifting and block faulting during the "middle" Cretaceous; variable fingerlike extensions of epicontinental marine waters penetrated the area from the Albian onward (Machens, 1973).

Faunal (Kauffman, 1973) and various geological evidences suggest that the "middle" Cretaceous Gulf of Mexico-Caribbean basin was a broad seaway with free connection to the eastern Pacific. It was merely the western extension of the great Tethyan seaway,

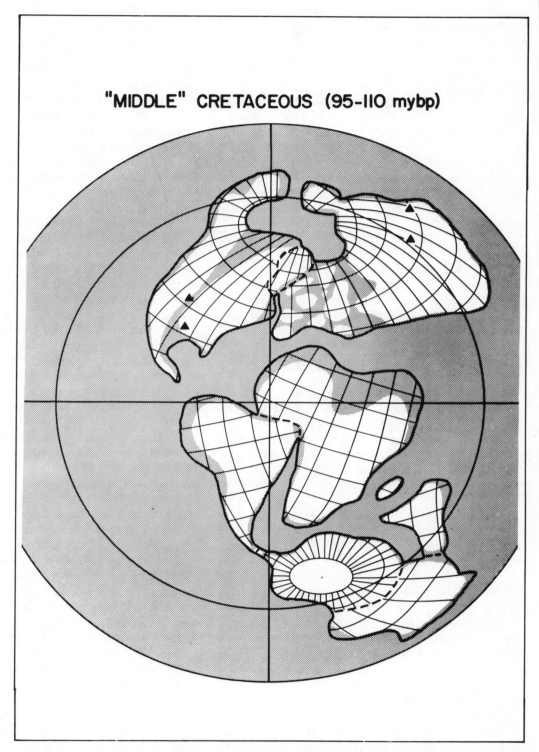

Figure 14-4. Lambert equal-area projection for the world of the "middle" Cretaceous. Symbols are as in Figure 14-1.

and there is little indication of restriction of marine circulation through the area. Island chains were undoubtedly developing in the Caribbean during the time as a result of various compressive and subductive zones (see various papers in Nairn and Stehli, 1975), but they seem not to have been significant until late in the Cretaceous (discussed below). There is no indication of land connection between Central America and South America (see Dengo, 1975), and rocks of marine facies representing the "middle" Cretaceous dominate the entirety of northwestern South America (Harrington, 1962). In short, it seems that the probability of dispersal of land vertebrates between North and South America during the "middle" Cretaceous was slight indeed.

Gondwanaland

Probably the most dramatic paleogeographic event of the Mesozoic began in the Early Cretaceous, with the destruction of Gondwanaland by the dispersal of the southern continents. Paleomagnetic data summarized by Larson and Ladd (1973) suggest that the initial breakup began during the Valanginian, about 125-130 mybp.

As shown in Figure 14-4, the initial opening of the South Atlantic basin was scissors-like; because the pole of spreading at that time was not far to the north of the developing South Atlantic, the southern part of the basin opened more rapidly than the northern part. Sea-floor spreading in the South Atlantic basin, however, progressed slowly throughout the Early Cretaceous.

Geological data summarized for Cretaceous coastal regions of eastern South America (Asmus and Ponte, 1973) and western Africa south of the equator (Machens, 1973; Franks and Nairn, 1973) tell a story of progressive south-to-north transitions from: (1) continental-lacustrine facies characteristic of rift-valleys; to (2) evaporitic facies indicating initial spills of marine waters under conditions of greatly restricted circulation (see Burke, 1975); to (3) marine facies that are more nearly normal, but still show pronounced indications of restricted circulation (see Thiede and Van Andel, 1977). Geological-paleontological data summarized by Reyment (1974 and papers cited therein) show a complex series of marine transgressions and regressions across the land connection between Brazil and the Guinean coast, starting in the late Aptian. According to Reyment, full marine connections between the North and South Atlantic basins did not develop until the middle

Turonian; marine incursions across the intervening areas between the late Aptian and middle Turonian were more in the form of spills into continental rift basins. Kennedy and Cooper (1975), however, reevaluated evidence from ammonite distributions and suggested the existence of open marine connections between the North and South Atlantic basins starting in late Albian time and probably continuing uninterrupted thereafter. Thus from the late Albian onward, remains of nektoplanktonic marine organisms indicate faunal contiguity between the North and South Atlantic basins, proclaiming the final separation of land areas of the continents of South America and Africa.

The rate of separation of South America and Africa apparently increased markedly through the earlier half of the Late Cretaceous, with the rate of crustal expansion in the south still exceeding the rate of expansion farther north. Although the southern part of the South Atlantic basin increased greatly in width, the distance between the developing south-facing coast of the Gulf of Guinea and the northern coast of Brazil remained fairly short (see Herz, 1977); separation of the continents between those two areas was due mainly to east-west transform faulting rather than marked sea-floor spreading. Nevertheless, the distance between the coasts seems to have made the probability remote that there was widespread intercontinental land vertebrate dispersal.

The oversea distance from the Cape of Good Hope to the coast of central Argentina is estimated to have been at least 3,000 km by 75 mybp (Maxwell and others, 1970). Despite the fact that the South Atlantic basin increased rapidly in width and depth through the Late Cretaceous, conditions of somewhat restricted circulation persisted in the basin north of the latitude of southern Brazil and Uruguay (Wardlaw and Nicholls, 1972; Theide and Van Andel, 1977). The restriction was probably caused by the presence of a submarine volcanic "hot-spot" complex involving the Rio Grande Rise and Walvis Ridge. This ridge-like complex was oriented east-west across the width of the South Atlantic basin (Neill, 1976), and presumably acted as a structural sill, partially blocking deep marine currents coming from the south.

New oceanic crust and shallow epicontinental seas developed around the entire curvature of southern Africa during the Early Cretaceous, and the whole area experienced considerable faulting (Dingle, 1973; Scrutton, 1973; Scrutton and Dingle, 1976). The Early Cretaceous molluscan fauna of the

South Atlantic, although somewhat depauperate because of restricted marine circulation, shows affinities with the Indo-Pacific region (Kauffman, 1973) rather than with the eastern Pacific basin. The reconstructions showing the steps in the evolution of southern South America and the Antarctic Peninsula by Dalziel and Elliot (1973), Suárez (1976), and De Wit (1977) suggest intensive volcanism in island chains through the area, with shallow water in marginal basins to the east during virtually the entire Cretaceous. That would explain the lack of similarity of Cretaceous marine faunas between the eastern Pacific and the South Atlantic. It would also imply the probability of some land connection for terrestrial vertebrate dispersal between South America and Antarctica (plus India and Australia) during the Cretaceous.

From what has been discussed above, it seems that dispersal of land vertebrates between the South American and African continents would have shown progressively greater restriction from the Valanginian onward. Direct overland exchange may have been possible intermittently, however, as late in the Cretaceous as the Turonian (see Kennedy and Cooper, 1975). Direct land vertebrate exchange between Africa and Antarctica would have had to be across a major seaway from the Valanginian onward. Thus, except by way of South America, it seems unlikely that there was land faunal communication between Africa and the Antarctic-Australia-India complex after the earliest Cretaceous. The South America-Antarctica connection during the Cretaceous by a volcanic arc would seem, at best, to have been a strongly restrictive land route for dispersal.

Australia remained a part of Antarctica until the end of the Paleocene (Veevers and McElhinny, 1976) or, perhaps, the Eocene. India, however, began to move northward in the Early Cretaceous (Johnson and others, 1976; Larson, 1977). As shown in Figures 14-1 through 14-4, the present eastern coast of India was probably adjacent to coastal Antarctica (see Norton and Molnar, 1977), and the eastern continental part of India (?Tibet) was juxtaposed to southwestern Australia. Paleomagnetic and geological information suggests that active sea-floor spreading between Antarctica and India began at about 130 mybp, along an east-trending ridge (Johnson and others, 1976). The date is virtually identical with that of the inception of spreading of the South Atlantic basin and its extension south of Africa. Because India, as it moved northward, remained close to Western Australia until about 105 mybp (*ibid.*),

geometrical considerations suggest that India was progressively separating from Africa-Madagascar throughout the Early Cretaceous by sea-floor spreading along the midoceanic ridge. Johnson and others (1976) argued that the present southern tip of India and Ceylon did not pass Enderby Land of Antarctica until about 110-120 mybp. Thus, it is probable that an ever-widening but landlocked sea of rectangular shape developed for 10 to 20 my in the new crustal floor south of India from about 130 mybp until full marine connection occurred with the embryonic Indian Ocean to the west. Pre-Cretaceous rifting in Western Australia is described by Veevers and Cotterill (1976). Shallow marine conditions with indications of nearby land dominated the environment of southwestern Australia during the Early Cretaceous, as is shown by the rocks in the Carnarvon and Perth basins (McWhae and others, 1958; also see Branson, 1978). Thus it seems that significant barriers (in the form of new sea floor and epicontinental seas) to the exchange of land vertebrates from any continent with India existed from the Early Cretaceous through the remainder of the Mesozoic.

The position of Madagascar during the Mesozoic has been a traditional point of controversy (see McElhinny and others, 1976, and Scrutton, 1978), but the reconstruction of its geology and that of the western border of the Mozambique Channel by Flores (1970) indicates the presence of persistent Cretaceous marine waters between Africa proper and Madagascar. The western coast of the Mozambique Channel is dominated throughout the Cretaceous section by marine rocks that grade westward into continental strata. According to Flores (1970, p. 11), "A characteristic of Cretaceous deposition in Madagascar is the abundance of intra-Cretaceous unconformities and hiatuses, which suggests frequent oscillations." Thus, although land conditions existed on Madagascar itself during Cretaceous time, it must have had the environment of an island from the earliest Cretaceous onward, with all attendant problems for the dispersal of land vertebrates.

Climates

Discussion of "middle" Cretaceous climates is deferred to the section below on the Late Cretaceous.

Faunas

The theme of the above section on the "middle" Cretaceous has been one of continental and subcontinental isolations by a variety of kinds of seaways. Intercontinental exchanges of land vertebrates during the time would have been especially unlikely, as barriers were the most pronounced of the entire Mesozoic era. It would be expected, as a corollary, that the greatest degree of land vertebrate endemism of the Mesozoic would also have developed during that time. We believe this idea to be particularly interesting in light of the fact that it was probably during the Early and "middle" Cretaceous that major radiations of "advanced" therian mammals (i.e., therians of metatherian-eutherian grade, marsupials, and placentals) occurred.

The "middle" Cretaceous mammalian record is completely Holarctic and limited to: (1) three undescribed bones from Wyoming; (2) the "Paluxian" assemblages and unidentified dental scraps from the Woodbine Formation in Texas; (3) the largely undescribed material from Khovboor, Mongolia; and, perhaps, (4) the enigmatic *Manchurodon* and *Endotherium* from southern "Manchuria." Thus the existing record for that time interval is so poor, and the biogeographical-evolutionary possibilities so many, that we can only look with anticipation toward research yet to be done. Several orders of mammals, some still living, quite probably had their roots of origin in the "middle" Cretaceous. Only further research on the fossil record of this interval will make possible an understanding of the evolutionary relationships of modern mammalian orders. Further remarks on Cretaceous land vertebrate faunas are deferred to the section below dealing with the Late Cretaceous.

LATE CRETACEOUS

Physical Geography

As the Mesozoic drew to a close, generally greater possibilities existed for intercontinental land vertebrate exchange. Also, the mammalian fossil record is somewhat more complete. The likelihood for accuracy in biogeographical interpretations, although still highly questionable, becomes the greatest for the Mesozoic.

"Beringia" (Arctic Western North America and Northeastern Asia)

The Kolyma block, which started its history as a part of northern Canada in the Triassic, apparently had made an initial collision with eastern Asia in the Early Cretaceous, and became an integral part of that continent before the Late Cretaceous (see Fujita, 1978, Herron and others, 1974, and McElhinny, 1973). Meanwhile, the Alaska-Chukotsk-Kamchatka region of western North America had been slowly moving in a roughly westward course toward northeastern Asia because of sea-floor spreading in the North Atlantic basin (see Pitman and Talwani, 1972). Presumably, a wide seaway existed until the Late Cretaceous through Beringia, thus allowing free exchange of waters between the Arctic and northern Pacific basins. Jurassic and Early Cretaceous marine faunas between the two areas document an open marine connection (Sachs and others, 1973). By the Late Cretaceous, however, the waterway through Beringia became constricted and perhaps even obliterated at times (Fig. 14-5). Pitman and Talwani (1972, Fig. 9) suggested more than 900 km of westerly movement of Alaska, to roughly its present western position, during the interval of 81 to 63 mybp. Cenozoic movement of Alaska (and its associated parts) relative to most of northeastern Asia was mainly transcurrent in a right-lateral sense to the south because of complex sea-floor spreading events in the North Atlantic and Arctic basins (see Herron and others, 1974).

Patton and others (1976) presented strong evidence for the existence of a narrow but direct land connection, in the form of a major volcanic (island?) belt, extending from Siberia to west-central Alaska across the Gulf of Anadyr and regions of St. Lawrence and St. Matthew islands. Marine, deepwater conditions existed immediately to the south. Cooper and others (1976) suggested that the now greatly diminished Kula plate was moving westnorthwest across what is now the Aleutian Basin before about 70 mybp; some subduction occurred near the present Bering Sea continental margin. The subduction would, in part, explain the volcanic chain immediately to the north. After 70 mybp, the zone of subduction shifted southward several hundred km from the edge of the Bering Shelf to what is now the position of the Aleutian Arc; intensive volcanism began there in the latest Cretaceous (Scholl and others, 1975).

Despite the complexity of interpretation of the detailed geological history of Beringia during the Late Cretaceous, the broad-brush picture of continental collision, intensive volcanism, and at least partial disruption of marine connections between the North Pacific and Arctic basins speaks positively for the possibility of overland vertebrate dispersal be-

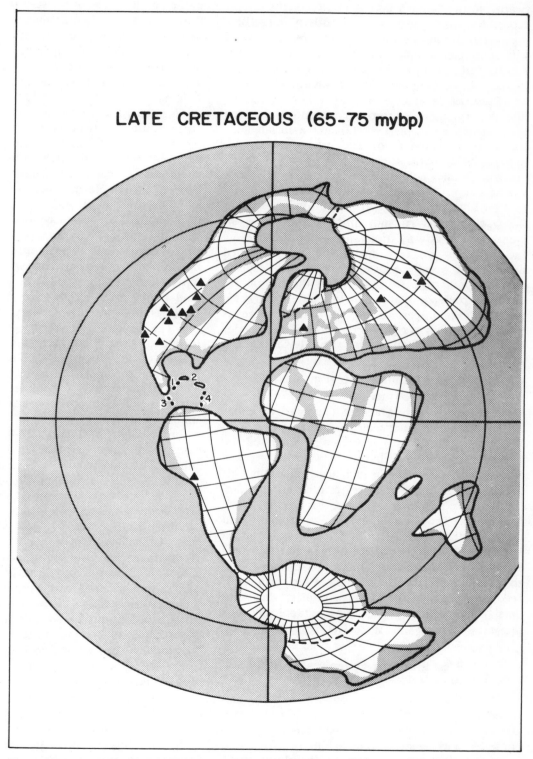

LATE CRETACEOUS (65-75 mybp)

Figure 14-5. Lambert equal-area projection for the world of the Late Cretaceous. *1*, Now-submerged Nicaragua Rise; *2*, Cuba and Hispaniola volcanic belts; *3*, Nicoya Complex; and *4*, now-submerged Aves Ridge. Other symbols are as in Figure 14-1.

tween North America and Asia late in the Cretaceous. A certain degree of continentality in the Bering region during the Late Cretaceous is consistent with progressive uplift at that time in northern Alaska (Detterman, 1973), increased volcanic activity in the Alaska-Aleutian range batholith (Lanphere and Reed, 1973), and the vast extent in northeastern Siberia of Late Cretaceous terrigenous deposits (Semenovich and others, 1973) and associated intrusive rocks (Vinogradov and others, 1973). Although Beringia was apparently at or very near the north rotational pole of the earth during the latest Cretaceous, paleontological information summarized by Lillegraven (1974, p. 275-276) suggests that the world's northern and southern polar environments were in no way frigid at the time. Despite the fact that the polar regions experienced prolonged darkness or greatly shortened day-lengths during winter months, the fossil floras of the regions indicate the presence of abundant vegetation; markedly fluctuating photoperiods probably acted more as biotic filters than as rigid barriers to the exchange of land life across Beringia during the Late Cretaceous.

Rocky Mountain Region of North America

The various transgressions (summarized above in the "middle" Cretaceous section) of the great Western Interior Seaway acted as a persistent barrier to land vertebrate distribution between eastern and western North America through nearly all of the Late Cretaceous, until the great regression during "Lancian" time. The area of transgression for North America, as shown in Figure 14-5, is roughly that characteristic of late "Lancian" time, and is much more limited than that of the Campanian and some earlier stages of the Late Cretaceous. Except for an ephemeral marine pulse extending as far north as the Dakotas from the Gulf of Mexico during Paleocene time, North America acted biogeographically as a single unified land area thereafter.

West and East Greenland, Europe, Western Asia, and Tethys

In addition to the Cretaceous seaway along East Greenland (see Birkelund and others, 1974) discussed above, a second connection between Arctic and North Atlantic waters appeared in the Late Cretaceous along West Greenland (see Birkelund, 1965). Possible major marine connections at various times in the Late Cretaceous between the Western Interior Seaway and the West Greenland seaway across the present area of Hudson Bay are discussed by Williams and Stelck (1975). Some sea-floor spreading may have occurred in the Davis Strait-Labrador Sea area during the Late Cretaceous (Fitch and others, 1974; also see Kristoffersen, 1978), but farther to the north in Baffin Bay probably only rifting covered by an epicontinental sea occurred (Martin, 1973). Thus the seaways along the borders of Greenland apparently continued throughout the remainder of the Cretaceous as barriers to land vertebrate exchange between eastern North America and Europe.

The archipelagic nature of Europe continued through the Late Cretaceous (see Hancock, 1975) with its shifting seas and probable variability in island connections. The Uralian and Western Siberian platform seaways similarly persisted as intermittent but probably significant barriers to Eurasian land faunal exchange through the Late Cretaceous (and well into the early Tertiary).

The structural geology of the Tethyan region throughout the Mesozoic represents an incredible mosaic of migrating plate boundaries, subduction zones, and spreading centers (see Dewey and others, 1973). Because of the complexity, movements of Africa relative to central Europe are difficult to unravel during the Mesozoic. Comparison of the reconstructions of Figures 14-4 and 14-5 suggest northward convergence of Africa toward Europe during the Late Cretaceous. Such an interpretation is admittedly speculative, but is consistent with compressive stresses developed during the latest Cretaceous and Cenozoic Alpine orogenic cycles of southern Europe (see, for example, Dietrich, 1976, and Channell and Horváth, 1976) and the increase in Tethyan marine invertebrate endemism late in the Cretaceous recognized by Kauffman (1973). Restriction in circulation of marine waters between Mediterranean Tethys and southern Asia is indicated late in the Cretaceous by comparisons of marine faunas (see Kauffman, 1973); intermittent dispersal of land vertebrates between archipelagic Europe and the great islands of North Africa seems a reasonable possibility.

North Atlantic and Caribbean Basins

According to the paleomagnetic information summarized by Ladd (1976), the North and South American continents diverged slightly from each other by an essentially north-south relative movement during the time interval from about 84 mybp to the Late Eocene. Nevertheless, because of igneous events within the Caribbean basin and Central America, land surfaces in the form of island chains became more prominent during the Late Cretaceous, increasing the possibility of terrestrial vertebrate dispersal between the Americas. For example, Dengo (1975) described a Late Cretaceous (?Campanian) volcanic chain (the Nicoya Complex) running through southern Central America southward into Ecuador (Fig. 14-5, no. 3). The rocks are pyroclastics, submarine basalts, volcanogenic conglomerates, cherts, and limestones, and probably represent a partially emergent line of Late Cretaceous islands (see Raven and Axelrod, 1974, Fig. 4, based upon Dengo's work). Kauffman (1973) showed that centers of endemism of benthonic marine invertebrates developed during the Late Cretaceous to the west and east of the Central American peninsula. The constriction of marine currents by the Nicoya volcanic chain across the region that is now the southern part of Central America may well have been the most important cause of that development of endemism. A broad, unbroken land connection between the Americas, however, is not indicated.

Geological evidence from Cuba (Pardo, 1975) suggests the existence of emergent islands in the region during the Late Cretaceous (Fig. 14-5, no. 2). Similarly, volcanic nonmarine conditions existed in parts of Honduras and the Jamaica-Nicaragua Rise region during the latest Cretaceous (Arden, 1975; Fig. 14-5, no. 1). This becomes especially intriguing when one considers the geological history of the now submerged "Aves Swell." It is an extinct volcanic mountain chain that runs northward about 500 km from the Venezuelan coast toward Puerto Rico (Fig. 14-5, no. 4). According to Tomblin (1975), volcanism probably continued from the mid-Cretaceous into the Miocene, resulting in a chain of emergent islands ("Aves Arc") during that time interval. The situation is seen to have been similar to that of today, 200 km eastward in the much younger Lesser Antilles. Volcanic island conditions also existed during the Late Cretaceous in Puerto Rico (Donnelly, 1975) and Hispaniola (Bowen, 1975), with the deposition of pyroclastic materials, volcaniclastic sediments, and limestones. Thus a complete chain of volcanic islands (Aves Arc-Puerto Rico-Hispaniola-Cuba-Jamaica-Nicaragua Rise) seems to have been present across the Caribbean at various times during the Late Cretaceous, in a magnitude probably significantly greater than seen today. Such a series of stepping-stones, in addition to the Nicoya volcanic arc described above, may well have been used for the chance dispersal of land organisms between the Americas during the Late Cretaceous. The paleogeographic picture, however, clearly does not support the interpretation of Caribbean biogeography proposed by Rosen (1975) that was based upon a "vicariance" model (see Croizat and others, 1974) requiring an original broad pan-American biotic continuity that was later disrupted by geographic barriers which allowed the allopatric diversification of modern species groups. Although details of Caribbean paleogeography are still sketchy, the general picture indicates with little doubt that chance dispersal across water barriers would have been the necessary mode of faunal interchange between the Americas from late in the Jurassic to the late Cenozoic.

Harrington (1962) reported the existence of marine deposition throughout most of the Late Cretaceous in northern and northwestern South America, from eastern Venezuela through Colombia, Ecuador, and Peru to the region of Lake Titicaca. Late Cretaceous volcanic belts more or less continuous with the position of the Nicoya Complex, however, have been recognized in Ecuador (Dengo, 1975), and the Aves volcanic chain was contiguous with the eastern Venezuelan coast. Harrington (1962) also documented a rather general regression of epicontinental seas from northwestern South America at the end of the Cretaceous.

Gondwanaland

Late Cretaceous continental movements and seaway developments pertinent to the story of possibilities for dispersal of land vertebrates between the southern landmasses were summarized above in the section on the "middle" Cretaceous of Gondwanaland.

Climates

Oxygen isotope determinations have shown that a larger thermal gradient existed between the poles and the equator during the Cretaceous than in the Triassic or Jurassic. Lotze (1964) and Meyerhoff (1970, 1973) both observed that the evaporite peak of the Late Jurassic continued into the Early Cretaceous, suggesting the continuation of relative aridity. The Cretaceous as a whole, however, had fewer evaporite deposits or red beds than either the Triassic or Jurassic.

The conditions of the Early Cretaceous did not continue unaltered through the Late Cretaceous. There are indications of more moisture over lands of the Late Cretaceous, and cooling temperatures. Sometime toward the end of the Cretaceous there was a general climatic "deterioration" (decrease in temperatures and worldwide equability). According to Savin (1977) ". . . it does seem clear that at least most of the world experienced a significant net cooling (perhaps as much as 8° or 10° C in both Northern Europe and the tropical Pacific Ocean) between Albian time and the end of the Cretaceous period."

Matsumoto (1973) found that many genera, and even some species, of Late Cretaceous ammonoids had a widespread distribution, from which he inferred mild and equable ocean temperatures (also see Berggren and Hollister, 1974). Oxygen isotopes indicate rising ocean temperatures in the Cenomanian, with temperatures reaching a peak in the Coniacian-Santonian, according to Lowenstam and Epstein (1954). They also reported, however, a worldwide decline in ocean temperatures in the Maastrichtian.

The record of land temperatures interpreted from floras is more variable, but a recognition of a general cooling trend emerges. North Africa had a rain forest vegetation in the Late Cretaceous, and Raven and Axelrod (1974) and Axelrod and Raven (1978) concluded that much of Africa, with the exception of the southern portion, had similar conditions. Dingle (1973) suggested that the southern Cape region of Africa experienced warm temperatures during the Late Cretaceous; the central and eastern portions were reasonably moist, but the western part was arid. Southern Africa did in fact become drier and undergo some climatic deterioration in the Late Cretaceous with the advent of the cold Benguela current off the western coast (Dingle, 1973). Krassilov (1973a), working in eastern Asia, observed both a temperate and a subtropical floral group in the Early Cretaceous. Through observations of floral diversity and cycadophyte distribution, he concluded that temperatures vacillated in this area. Temperatures rose from the Late Jurassic to the Berriasian and during the Aptian. Declining temperatures were indicated for the Berriasian through the Barremian, and a sharp decline occurred in the Albian. For the Late Cretaceous, Krassilov (1975) recognized warm

periods (by the expansion in distribution of angiosperms with entire-margined leaves) and cooler periods (by the spread of dicotyledons having platanoid leaves). He observed a trend of increasing temperatures from the Coniacian through the Campanian, followed by an interval of cooling through the end of the Cretaceous. Kobayashi and Shikama (1961) noted a tendency toward cooler temperatures in the Far East following the Neocomian; their conclusions were based upon the angiosperm assemblages.

Similar coolings in the climate of the Late Cretaceous have been recorded in a number of localities in North America. Hall and Norton (1967) concluded that a slight climatic change occurred between the Late Cretaceous and early Tertiary in Montana. They noted that both floral diversity and fern percentages declined, while the gymnosperm percentage showed an increase from the Hell Creek Formation (Upper Cretaceous) to the overlying Tullock Formation (Paleocene). Sloan (1970) discussed floral changes between the Lance-Hell Creek formations (Upper Cretaceous) and the Fort Union Formation (Paleocene) in Wyoming and Montana. He found a decrease in diversity of angiosperms with an associated increase in gymnosperm numbers, again indicating a climatic deterioration. Sloan correlated the changing climate in this area with the decline of dinosaur and North American marsupial populations. He noted that several additional studies have resulted in the discovery of similar occurrences, with the implication of climatic change at the end of the Cretaceous in South Dakota (Stanley, 1965), Alberta (Snead, 1969), and the Mississippi embayment (Tschudy, 1968).

The paleoclimate of the Gobi Desert of Mongolia is of special interest, because strata from this region have yielded many Late Cretaceous mammals. Faunal evidence (the presence of crocodile remains) indicates that the period during which the Djadokhta Formation was deposited was warm (Lefeld, 1971). Lefeld (1971) also suggested that semiarid periods alternated with more humid intervals on the basis of interbedded aeolian sands and calcareous strata. Gradziński and Jerzykiewicz (1974) suggested that the lower part of the Barun Goyot Formation was deposited under hot and probably semiarid conditions. Dunes developed, and the vegetation was patchy, occurring primarily along the margins of intermittent streams (also see Chapter 12).

A slightly different interpretation of Cretaceous

climates, the "radmax" hypothesis, was proposed by Hughes (1976). He argued that temperatures continued warm from the Jurassic into the Cretaceous and reached a peak either prior to or during the Maastrichtian. Temperatures may then have been the warmest in geologic history since the origin of land plants. Hughes relied heavily upon oxygen isotope data and evidence from paleobotany for his interpretation. The term "radmax" reflects Hughes' opinion that the thermal peak was related to increased intensities of solar energy. He suggested that the radmax may ultimately have been responsible for several notable biological events in the Cretaceous, such as the extinction of dinosaurs.

The collective evidence indicates that temperatures were warmer during the Late Cretaceous than they are today, and possibly reached a peak sometime during that interval. The abundant flora of the Late Cretaceous implies relatively moist conditions, as does the decline in evaporite deposits from their maximum accumulation in the Late Jurassic and Early Cretaceous. A cooling trend began toward the end of the Cretaceous and continued into the early Tertiary.

Faunas

Incomplete knowledge of the distributional histories of extant mammals has placed at a premium information about extinct groups. It is natural, and indeed desirable, to attempt explanations based upon the record of geology. It is, however, easy to become overzealous with the reconstruction of events from numerous bits of data that may: (1) be open to a number of interpretations; (2) be incomplete; or (3) individually be based upon unproven assumptions.

Reconstructions based upon geophysical data offer possibilities, but they do not necessarily provide biogeographical solutions. Likewise, although distributions of extant plants and animals are important to the understanding of Cenozoic and Mesozoic paleogeography, it must be admitted that confidence in theories of origins and dispersals can be acquired only through the use of a good fossil record.

In the past fifteen years, roughly threescore papers have dealt in particular or in general with mammalian evolution and/or distribution during the Cretaceous. A number of these have offered explanations for the geographic and temporal origins of certain mammalian groups, and others have attempted

to reconstruct ancient dispersal routes. What, we may well ask, is the nature of the record of Cretaceous fossil mammals that so inspires such a plethora of suggestions from students of paleontology? Table 14-1 summarizes existing geographic knowledge of Cretaceous mammals.

The notable lack of data from almost all of the world's Cretaceous landmass allows much "flexibility" in paleobiogeographical hypothesizing; it is not surprising that equally probable but contradictory alternatives exist with respect to reconstruction of mammalian dispersal histories. Recall, furthermore, that the mammalian record for the Cretaceous is the best for the three periods of the Mesozoic. We are, in most respects, still near "square one" in understanding the origin, differentiation, and dispersal of mammalian groups in the Cretaceous. All that really exist are tantalizing hints of the extent of mam-

TABLE 14-1   SUMMARY OF KNOWN OCCURRENCES OF CRETACEOUS MAMMALS ACROSS THE WORLD

	EARLY CRETACEOUS	LATE CRETACEOUS
western North America	no record	good record
eastern North America	small fauna, only partly described	no record
Central America	no record	no record
South America	no record	a few teeth
Europe	fair record	one tooth plus undescribed material
western Asia	no record	one enigmatic jaw
central Asia	mostly undescribed but potentially good record	good record
eastern Asia	poor record, two localities	no record
southeastern Asia and Indonesia	no record	no record
India	no record	no record
Africa	no record	no record
Madagascar	no record	no record
Australia	no record	no record
Antarctica	no record	no record

malian diversification attained by the end of the Cretaceous.

The distributional history of early marsupials can be used to illustrate the difficulties involved in interpreting Cretaceous directions and extents of dispersal (see reviews by Lillegraven, 1974, and Tedford, 1974). Of particular importance in this example is the temptation to equate "no present record" with "no probable occurrence" in particular geographic areas. Marsupials, living or extinct, are unknown from Africa and Antarctica. In view of the absence of known Mesozoic mammalian faunas from either continent, it seems surprising that most current authors accept the presence of marsupials during the Late Cretaceous in Antarctica, but deny their presence in Africa. It is a question of "need"; marsupials "must" have been in Antarctica, because it is necessary for them to have been there to fit commonly held ideas of late Mesozoic and early Tertiary biogeography. The reasoning suggesting the real absence of marsupials in Africa is based upon the facts that no marsupials are living in Africa today, nor are they known from the early Tertiary of that continent. An important point commonly not appreciated, however, is that the only African localities known to contain significant assemblages of early Tertiary mammals are in the Fayum deposits of Egypt. Although it does indeed seem unlikely from the point of view of mammalian access, it remains remotely possible that much of Africa was teeming with marsupials in the Late Cretaceous and that their extinction coincided with that of most of the North American forms. [Note added in proof: But see reference in Chapter 11 to recent work on early Paleocene mammals from Morocco by Cappetta and others (1978).]

The above hypothesis is not presented as a serious reconstruction of the Gondwanan dispersal of marsupial mammals in the Late Cretaceous. Rather, it is intended as an example of the reasoning that commonly has been used in hypotheses relevant to dispersal problems as based upon inadequate data. Similar problems exist in the analysis of the intercontinental distributional history of virtually all Cretaceous land vertebrate groups (see Cox, 1974). In fact, from evidence derived purely from land vertebrate faunas, only exchanges between central Asia and western North America during the Cretaceous can be studied with any degree of scientific confidence. Even in this case, however, major problems exist that are briefly discussed below.

The Late Cretaceous dinosaurian faunas of North America and Asia, as presently understood, do not show great similarities. The only genus so far recognized as being in common is *Saurolophus* (see Gradziński and others, 1977, for full references to Mongolian faunas). The dinosaurian Deinocheiridae and Therezinosauridae were apparently endemic to Asia. The Hypsilophodontidae, Ceratopsidae, Pachyrhinosauridae, and Panoplosauridae, rather common in North America, are unknown from Asia. Most familial resemblances are equivocal, and were based upon a systematic approach of "lumping." It is difficult to say, however, how many of the faunal differences are merely the result of biases from sampling quite different ancient environments (see above and Chapter 12).

Among the lizards, only members of the Polyglyphanodontidae are known from Upper Cretaceous rocks both in Asia and North America (Sulimski, 1975).

Known multituberculate faunas (Chapter 6) differ markedly between Asia and North America. The Neoplagiaulacidae, Ptilodontidae, and Cimolomyidae are unknown from Asia, and the Sloanbaataridae and Chulsanbaataridae were apparently endemic to Asia. *Gobibaatar* from the Djadokhta Formation and *Cimexomys* from North America will eventually be united within a new family (Kielan-Jaworowska, pers. comm. to Lillegraven, 1977). Additionally, the Taeniolabididae and Eucosmodontidae are common to the two continents (Kielan-Jaworowska, 1974). Kielan-Jaworowska and Sloan (*in press*) believe that the taeniolabidids *Catopsalis* (North America) and *Djadochtatherium* (Asia) are congeneric, with the former being the valid name. They visualize a phylogenetic sequence, based upon morphological-temporal trends, as *C. matthewi* to *C. catopsaloides* (both Asiatic) to *C. joyneri* ("Lancian" of North America) to species of the Cenozoic. Kielan-Jaworowska (1974) suggested that two, and possibly three, multituberculate lineages dispersed from Asia to North America during the Late Cretaceous (*Gobibaatar* to *Cimexomys*; *Catopsalis*; and eucosmodontids, but record is poor). According to her, the faunal exchange was only one-way, with no evidence of North American genera having successfully reached Asia.

Evidence from the Theria of metatherian-eutherian grade (Chapter 10) is not yet very helpful. Any similarities between the deltatheridiids of Asia (see Kielan-Jaworowska, 1975) and the isolated

"*Deltatheroides*-like" teeth from North America described by Fox (1974) are quite equivocal. It cannot yet be said whether this represents: (1) migrations of stocks from Asia to North America; (2) vice versa; (3) independent retention of primitive features from an ancient common ancestor; or (4) similarities resulting from convergent evolution.

Marsupials (Chapter 11), common in North American Upper Cretaceous rocks, are unknown (Cretaceous or Cenozoic) from Asia. The North American marsupials suffered major extinctions at the end of the Cretaceous (see Clemens, 1966), and this coincided with the time of major evolutionary radiation of placentals having affinities with those of the Cenozoic (see Lillegraven, 1969).

The Cretaceous record of eutherians is extremely difficult to evaluate and is filled with controversy (summarized in Chapter 12). Significant points, however, include: (1) the ancient and primitive nature of the eutherian "*Prokennalestes*" from Mongolia; (2) the paucity of pre-"Lancian" eutherians from North America; and (3) the similarities, vague though they may be, between leptictoids and palaeoryctids from Asiatic and North American deposits. Although no eutherian genera can yet be linked between the two continents, the diversity sampled to date on either continent is so low, and the ecological differences are so great, that the probability of finding common forms is slight indeed.

The Asiatic continent during the Cretaceous was enormous, being practically its present size. The effective land area of western North America during the Cretaceous, however, was much smaller. Figure 14-5 is somewhat deceptive for North America in showing an unusual restriction of Late Cretaceous epicontinental seas. The situation shown would be characteristic only of late in the "Lancian." Prior to that time, the epicontinental seas of the Late Cretaceous were far more widespread, commonly restricting the land areas of western North America to perhaps half of the areal extent shown on Figure 14-5. Although admittedly many pitfalls exist, Matthew's (1915) generalization seems to be valid that competitive success will usually be achieved by organisms from the larger of two newly joined continental areas. As a working hypothesis (based upon evidence from physical geography and the known Cretaceous fossil record of Asia and North America), we suggest that although greatly limited, land vertebrate exchanges occurred predominantly in the direction of Asia to North America following the Late Cretaceous continental collision in the region of Beringia. The nature of the restrictive filtering (*i.e.*, seasonal day length considerations, intermittent seaways, vegetational-edaphic factors, *etc.*) is unknown.

Until more material is collected containing *Beleutinus* (Kazakhstan), the species represented by the "Champ-Garimond tooth" (France), and the species from Laguna Umayo (Peru), the paleogeographic-phylogenetic significance of each must remain so speculative that virtually unlimited and equally reasonable hypotheses concerning their relationships may be proposed.

ANGIOSPERMS AND MAMMALS

It seems reasonably certain that fossil evidence (characteristic pollen and leaf morphology) for the existence of flowering plants as presently defined does not appear prior to the late Neocomian of the Early Cretaceous (see Hughes, 1976, Hickey and Doyle, 1977, and Muller, 1970). Although the review by Hughes (1976) emphasizes that the phyletic source of angiosperms, the place of origin, the causes of their development, and even whether the group was mono- or polyphyletic in origin are unsolved problems, Doyle (1977) is somewhat more optimistic. Most identifications made to date that were based upon gross leaf morphology are probably incorrect (see Dilcher, 1974), and much work remains to be done in relating the Mesozoic fossil record of plants with modern data on continental positions (see Raven and Axelrod, 1974, and Schuster, 1976).

Details of the above-listed problems matter little, however, in the present discussion of the evolutionary relationship of mammals to angiosperms. Flowering plants comprised the dominant land flora and were already diversified into recognizable geographic provinces by the "middle" Cretaceous (see Brenner, 1976). Stebbins (1976) and Regal (1977) emphasized that many of the selective advantages seen in angiosperms over their gymnospermous ancestors lay in reproductive rather than vegetative specializations. Related to these are adaptations of the flower to promote pollination (see Faegri and Van der Pijl, 1966) and a wide variety of modifications of virtually every part of the plant itself to effect dispersal (see Van der Pijl, 1972). Many adaptations related to both pollination and dispersal are closely linked to the life cycles of animals, and complex coadaptations between plants and animals are perhaps the rule. Insects, in particular, are regularly involved in key roles of angiosperm life cycles, and Krassilov (1973b) argued that the pistil of the angiosperm flower developed coadaptively with insect pollinators. Insects are also major "predators" upon angiosperms, and are known to be capable of attacking most parts of the plants (see review by Southwood, 1973). Close insect-spermatophyte relationships have existed since the late Paleozoic, and evolutionary radiations of the angiosperms and insects must also have been intimately linked (see Smart and Hughes, 1973, and Regal, 1977). Raven (1977) emphasized the likely selective advantages of insect pollination strategies for angiosperms during the "middle" Cretaceous. The density of the expansive, tropical lowland rainforests of the time would have rendered wind pollination less effective, especially where floral diversity was high and individuals of plant populations were scattered. Thus, although the Cretaceous insect fossil record is poor (see Carpenter, 1976, and Hughes, 1976, for reviews), one could expect that a considerable evolutionary radiation of insects would have characterized the latter two-thirds of the period, concomitant with the initial great diversification of flowering plants.

As was discussed in Chapter 1, mammals were small in body size throughout virtually all of the Mesozoic. Most were also carnivorous, with probable diets revolving mainly about available insects. Angiosperm-insect relationships undoubtedly were complicated by mammalian predators, and probably were regulated by them to some degree. Thus, successes in coadapted angiosperm-insect diversifications probably would have been directly beneficial to the opportunistic mammals of the day.

It is interesting to note that the mammalian fossil record, incomplete as it is, shows considerable radiation within the "modern" kinds of therian mammals (therians of metatherian-eutherian grade, marsupials, and placentals) during the latter two-thirds of the Cretaceous. The comparative homogeneity of dental morphology characteristic of the therians of the Jurassic was lost after the earliest Cretaceous, and it seems highly probable that the new mammalian diversification represented responses to emergent properties of flowering plant-insect coadaptations. Also, Krassilov (1973b) noted that some of the earliest known small angiospermous fruits possessed hooklets that seemingly would have been functional in tangling with mammalian fur as the animals foraged through the plants for prey or edible vegetal parts. If true, perhaps mammal-angiosperm coadaptations were even more direct during the Cretaceous than we now suspect. Quite possibly, early experimentation by flowering plants was already well under way before the end of the Mesozoic in such adaptations as the development of palatability and/or chemical attractants within fruits (or associated parts) for mammaliochoric seed dispersal, or attractants within flowers for mammalian pollination (see Sussman and Raven, 1978, for speculations on antiquity of this adaptation). Similar "middle" Cretaceous evolutionary radiations among dinosaurian faunas (see Colbert, 1973) and the herbivorous multituberculates (see Chapter 6) probably were also related to the diversification of angiosperms.

Coadaptive syndromes among plant, insect, and mammalian lineages probably were common through the long duration of the Cretaceous period, particularly in densely vegetated tropical areas where wind pollination would have been undependable. The warm, equable climates that dominated the world of the time probably allowed biotic diversification approaching that seen in tropical areas of today. The prevailing climate and restrictions to long-distance dispersal provided by marine barriers during the Cretaceous probably combined to allow the development in the terrestrial realm of great taxonomic diversity and considerable local endemism, both among plants and animals. It is undoubtedly within the latter two-thirds of the Cretaceous that the roots of many Cenozoic orders of mammals will eventually be found. Paleontological inquiry to date, however, has documented only a tiny fraction of these evolutionary radiations; we have much to learn.

REFERENCES CITED

Ager, D. V., and Walley, C. D., 1977, Mesozoic brachiopod migrations and the opening of the North Atlantic: Palaeogeog., Palaeoclimatol., Palaeoecol., v. 21, p. 85-99.

Allen, R. J., Day, R. W., Denmead, A. K., Hawthorne, W. L., Jenkins, T. G. H., de Jersey, N. J., Laing, A. C. M., Mott, W. D., Paten, R. J., Power, P. E., Reynolds, M. A., Siller, C. W., and Tweedale, G. W., 1960, Cretaceous, in Hill, D., and Denmead, A. K., eds., The geology of Queensland: Geol. Soc. Australia Jour., v. 7, p. 309-340.

Arden, D. D., Jr., 1975, Geology of Jamaica and the Nicaragua Rise, in Nairn, A. E. M., and Stehli, F. G., eds., The ocean basins and margins. Volume 3, The Gulf of Mexico and the Caribbean: New York, Plenum Press, p. 617-661.

Asmus, H. E., and Ponte, F. C., 1973, The Brazilian marginal basins, in Nairn, A. E. M., and Stehli, F. G., eds., The ocean basins and margins. Volume 1, The South Atlantic: New York, Plenum Press, p. 87-133.

Axelrod, D. I., and Raven, P. H., 1978, Late Cretaceous and Tertiary vegetation history of Africa, in Werger, M. J. A., and Van Bruggen, A. C., eds., Biogeography and ecology of southern Africa: The Hague, Dr. W. Junk b. b. Publishers, p. 77-130.

Barnard, P. D. W., 1973, Mesozoic floras, in Hughes, N. F., ed., Organisms and continents through time: Palaeont. Assoc. London Spec. Papers Palaeont. 12, p. 175-187.

Berggren, W. A., and Hollister, C. D., 1974, Paleogeography, paleobiogeography and the history of circulation in the Atlantic Ocean: Tulsa, Soc. Econ. Paleont. Mineral., Spec. Publ. 20, p. 126-186.

Birkelund, T., 1965, Ammonites from the Upper Cretaceous of West Greenland: Medd. Grønland, v. 179, no. 7, p. 1-192.

Birkelund, T., Perch-Nielsen, K., Bridgwater, D., and Higgins, A. K., 1974, An outline of the geology of the Atlantic coast of Greenland, in Nairn, A. E. M., and Stehli, F. G., eds., The ocean basins and margins. Volume 2, The North Atlantic: New York, Plenum Press, p. 125-159.

Bowen, R., 1966, Palaeotemperature analysis: Amsterdam, Elsevier Publ. Co., x + 265 p.

Bowin, C., 1975, The geology of Hispaniola, in Nairn, A. E. M., and Stehli, F. G., eds., The ocean basins and margins. Volume 3, The Gulf of Mexico and the Caribbean: New York, Plenum Press, p. 501-552.

Branson, J. C., 1978, Evolution of sedimentary basins from Mesozoic times in Australia's continental slope and shelf: Tectonophysics, v. 48, p. 389-412.

Brenner, G. J., 1976, Middle Cretaceous floral provinces and early migrations of angiosperms, in Beck, C. B., ed., Origin and early evolution of angiosperms: New York, Columbia Univ. Press, p. 23-47.

Briden, J. C., Drewry, G. E., and Smith, A. G., 1974, Phanerozoic equal area world maps: Jour. Geol., v. 82, p. 555-574.

Bullard, E. C., Everett, J., and Smith, A. G., 1965, A symposium on continental drift: Roy. Soc. London Philos. Trans., A (Math. Phys. Sci.), v. 258, p. 41-51.

Burke, K., 1975, Atlantic evaporites formed by evaporation of water spilled from Pacific, Tethyan, and southern oceans: Geology, v. 3, p. 613-616.

Callomon, J. H., Donovan, D. T., and Trümpy, R., 1972, An annotated map of the Permian and Mesozoic formations of East Greenland: Medd. Grønland, v. 168, no. 3, p. 1-35.

Carpenter, F. M., 1976, Geological history and evolution of the insects: XV Internat. Cong. Entomol. Proc., p. 63-70.

Casey, R., 1971, Facies, faunas and tectonics in late Jurassic-early Cretaceous Britain, in Middlemiss, F. A., Rawson, P. F., and Newall, G., eds., Faunal provinces in space and time: Geol. Jour. Spec. Issue 4, p. 153-168.

Channell, J. E. T., and Horváth, F., 1976, The African/Adriatic promontory as a palaeogeographical premise for Alpine orogeny and plate movements in the Carpatho-Balkan region: Tectonophysics, v. 35, p. 71-101.

Charig, A. J., 1973, Jurassic and Cretaceous dinosaurs, in Hallam, A., ed., Atlas of palaeobiogeography: New York, Elsevier Sci. Publ. Co., p. 339-352.

Christensen, W. K., 1976, Palaeobiogeography of Late Cretaceous belemnites of Europe: Paläont. Zeit., v. 50, p. 113-129.

Churkin, M., Jr., 1972, Western boundary of the North American continental plate in Asia: Geol. Soc. America Bull., v. 83, p. 1027-1036.

Clemens, W. A., 1966, Fossil mammals of the type Lance Formation, Wyoming. Part II. Marsupialia: Univ. California Publs. Geol. Sci., v. 62, vi + 122 p.

Colbert, E. H., 1973, Continental drift and the distribution of fossil reptiles, in Tarling, D. H., and Runcorn, S. K., eds., Implications of continental drift to the earth sciences: New York, Academic Press, NATO Adv. Study Inst., v. 1, p. 395-412.

Cooper, A. K., Scholl, D. W., and Marlow, M. S., 1976, Plate tectonic model for the evolution of the eastern Bering Sea Basin: Geol. Soc. America Bull., v. 87, p. 1119-1126.

Cox, C. B., 1973, Triassic tetrapods, in Hallam, A., ed., Atlas of palaeobiogeography: New York, Elsevier Sci. Publ. Co., p. 213-233.

———1974, Vertebrate palaeodistributional patterns and

continental drift: Jour. Biogeogr., v. 1, p. 75-94.

Croizat, L., Nelson, G., and Rosen, D. E., 1974, Centers of origin and related concepts: Syst. Zool., v. 23, p. 265-287.

Dalziel, I. W. D., and Elliot, D. H., 1973, The Scotia Arc and Antarctic margin, *in* Nairn, A. E. M., and Stehli, F. G., eds., The ocean basins and margins. Volume 1, The South Atlantic: New York, Plenum Press, p. 171-246.

Dengo, G., 1975, Paleozoic and Mesozoic tectonic belts in Mexico and Central America, *in* Nairn, A. E. M., and Stehli, F. G., eds., The ocean basins and margins. Volume 3, The Gulf of Mexico and the Caribbean: New York, Plenum Press, p. 283-323.

Detterman, R. L., 1973, Mesozoic sequence in Arctic Alaska, *in* Pitcher, M. G., ed., Arctic geology: Tulsa, Amer. Assoc. Petrol. Geol. Mem. 19, p. 376-387.

Dewey, J. F., Pitman, W. C., III, Ryan, W. B. F., and Bonnin, J., 1973, Plate tectonics and the evolution of the Alpine system: Geol. Soc. America Bull., v. 84, p. 3137-3180.

De Wit, M. J., 1977, The evolution of the Scotia Arc as a key to the reconstruction of southwestern Gondwanaland: Tectonophysics, v. 37, p. 53-81.

Dietrich, V. J., 1976, Evolution of the eastern Alps: a plate tectonics working hypothesis: Geology, v. 4, p. 147-152.

Dilcher, D. L., 1974, Approaches to the identification of angiosperm leaf remains: Bot. Rev., v. 40, p. 1-157.

Dillon, W. P., and Sougy, J. M. A., 1974, Geology of West Africa and Canary and Cape Verde islands, *in* Nairn, A. E. M., and Stehli, F. G., eds., The ocean basins and margins. Volume 2, The North Atlantic: New York, Plenum Press, p. 315-390.

Dingle, R. V., 1973, Mesozoic palaeogeography of the southern Cape, South Africa: Palaeogeog., Palaeoclimatol., Palaeoecol., v. 13, p. 203-213.

Donnelly, T. W., 1975, The geological evolution of the Caribbean and Gulf of Mexico—some critical problems and areas, *in* Nairn, A. E. M., and Stehli, F. G., eds., The ocean basins and margins. Volume 3, The Gulf of Mexico and the Caribbean: New York, Plenum Press, p. 663-689.

Doyle, J. A., 1977, Patterns of evolution in early angiosperms, *in* Hallam, A., ed., Patterns of evolution: Amsterdam, Elsevier Sci. Publ. Co., p. 501-546.

Drewry, G. E., Ramsay, A. T. S., and Smith, A. G., 1974, Climatically controlled sediments, the geomagnetic field, and trade wind belts in Phanerozoic time: Jour. Geol., v. 82, p. 531-553.

Embleton, B. J. J., and Schmidt, P. W., 1977, Revised palaeomagnetic data for the Australian Mesozoic and a synthesis of late Palaeozoic-Mesozoic results for Gondwanaland: Tectonophysics, v. 38, p. 355-364.

Faegri, K., and Van der Pijl, L., 1966, The principles of pollination ecology: Oxford, Pergamon Press, 248 p.

Fitch, F. J., Miller, J. A., Warrell, D. M., and Williams, S. C., 1974, Tectonic and radiometric age comparisons, *in* Nairn, A. E. M., and Stehli, F. G., eds., The ocean basins and margins. Volume 2, The North Atlantic: New York, Plenum Press, p. 485-538.

Flores, G., 1970, Suggested origin of the Mozambique Channel: Geol. Soc. South Africa Trans., v. 73, p. 1-16.

Fox, P. J., and Heezen, B. C., 1975, Geology of the Caribbean crust, *in* Nairn, A. E. M., and Stehli, F. G., eds., The ocean basins and margins. Volume 3, The Gulf of Mexico and the Caribbean: New York, Plenum Press, p. 421-466.

Fox, R. C., 1974, *Deltatheroides*-like mammals from the Upper Cretaceous of North America: Nature, v. 249, p. 392.

Franks, S., and Nairn, A. E. M., 1973, The equatorial marginal basins of West Africa, *in* Nairn, A. E. M., and Stehli, F. G., eds., The ocean basins and margins. Volume 1, The South Atlantic: New York, Plenum Press, p. 301-350.

Fujita, K., 1978, Pre-Cenozoic tectonic evolution of northeast Siberia: Jour. Geol., v. 86, p. 159-172.

Furon, R., 1963, Geology of Africa: New York, Hafner Publ. Co., *xii* + 377 p.

Geyer, O. F., 1973, Das präkretazische Mesozoikum von Kolumbien: Geol. Jahrb., B, no. 5, p. 1-155.

Gilluly, J., Reed, J. C., Jr., and Cady, W. M., 1970, Sedimentary volumes and their significance: Geol. Soc. America Bull., v. 81, p. 353-375.

Glaessner, M. F., and Parkin, L. W., 1958, The geology of South Australia: Geol. Soc. Australia Jour., v. 5, pt. 2, p. 1-163.

Gradziński, R., and Jerzykiewicz, T., 1974, Dinosaur- and mammal-bearing aeolian and associated deposits of the Upper Cretaceous in the Gobi Desert (Mongolia): Sediment. Geol., v. 12, p. 249-278.

Gradziński, R., Kielan-Jaworowska, Z., and Maryańska, T., 1977, Upper Cretaceous Djadokhta, Barun Goyot and Nemegt formations of Mongolia, including remarks on previous subdivisions: Acta Geol. Polonica, v. 27, 281-318.

Hall, J. W., and Norton, N. J., 1967, Palynological evidence of floristic change across the Cretaceous-Tertiary boundary in eastern Montana: Palaeogeog., Palaeoclimatol., Palaeoecol., v. 3, p. 121-131.

Hallam, A., ed., 1973, Atlas of palaeobiogeography: New York, Elsevier Sci. Publ. Co., *xii* + 531 p.

———1975, Jurassic environments: Cambridge, Cambridge Univ. Press, *ix* + 269 p.

———1976, Stratigraphic distribution and ecology of European Jurassic bivalves: Lethaia, v. 9, p. 245-259.

Hancock, J. M., 1975, The sequence of facies in the Upper Cretaceous of northern Europe compared with that in the Western Interior, *in* Caldwell, W. G. E., ed., The

Cretaceous System in the Western Interior of North America: Geol. Assoc. Canada Spec. Paper 13, p. 83-118.

Harrington, H. J., 1962, Paleogeographic development of South America: Amer. Assoc. Petrol. Geol. Bull., v. 46, p. 1773-1814.

Helwig, J., 1975, Tectonic evolution of the southern continental margin of North America from a Paleozoic perspective, in Nairn, A. E. M., and Stehli, F. G., eds., The ocean basins and margins. Volume 3, The Gulf of Mexico and the Caribbean: New York, Plenum Press, p. 243-255.

Herron, E. M., Dewey, J. F., and Pitman, W. C., III, 1974, Plate tectonics model for the evolution of the Arctic: Geology, v. 2, p. 377-380.

Herz, N., 1977, Timing of spreading in the South Atlantic: information from Brazilian alkalic rocks: Geol. Soc. America Bull., v. 88, p. 101-112.

Hickey, L. J., and Doyle, J. A., 1977, Early Cretaceous fossil evidence for angiosperm evolution: Bot. Rev., v. 43, p. 3-104.

Hilde, T. W. C., Uyeda, S., and Kroenke, L., 1977, Evolution of the western Pacific and its margin: Tectonophysics, v. 38, p. 145-165.

Hsü, K. J., 1976, Paleoceanography of the Mesozoic Alpine Tethys: Geol. Soc. America Spec. Paper 170, iii + 44 p.

Hubert, J. F., 1977, Paleosol caliche in the New Haven Arkose, Connecticut: record of semiaridity in Late Triassic-Early Jurassic time: Geology, v. 5, p. 302-304.

Hughes, N. F., 1976, Palaeobiology of angiosperm origins. Problems of Mesozoic seed-plant evolution: Cambridge, Cambridge Univ. Press, vii + 242 p.

Hurley, P. M., 1974, Pangeaic orogenic system: Geology, v. 2, p. 373-376.

Imlay, R. W., 1957, Paleoecology of Jurassic seas in the Western Interior of the United States, in Ladd, H. S., ed., Treatise on marine ecology and paleoecology: Geol. Soc. America Mem. 67, v. 2, Paleoecology, p. 469-504.

———1965, Jurassic marine faunal differentiation in North America: Jour. Paleont., v. 39, p. 1023-1038.

———1968, Lower Jurassic (Pliensbachian and Toarcian) ammonites from eastern Oregon and California: U. S. Geol. Surv. Prof. Paper 593-C, iii + 48 p.

———1973, Middle Jurassic (Bajocian) ammonites from eastern Oregon: U. S. Geol. Surv. Prof. Paper 756, iv + 100 p.

Imlay, R. W., and Detterman, R. L., 1973, Jurassic paleobiogeography of Alaska: U. S. Geol. Surv. Prof. Paper 801, 34 p.

Johnson, B. D., Powell, C. McA., and Veevers, J. J., 1976, Spreading history of the eastern Indian Ocean and greater India's northward flight from Antarctica and Australia: Geol. Soc. America Bull., v. 87, p. 1560-1566.

Kauffman, E. G., 1973, Cretaceous Bivalvia, in Hallam, A., ed., Atlas of palaeobiogeography: New York, Elsevier Sci. Publ. Co., p. 353-383.

Kielan-Jaworowska, Z., 1974, Migrations of the Multituberculata and the Late Cretaceous connections between Asia and North America: So. African Mus. Ann., v. 64, p. 231-243.

———1975, Evolution of the therian mammals in the Late Cretaceous of Asia. Part I. Deltatheridiidae, in Kielan-Jaworowska, Z., ed., Results Polish-Mongol. Palaeont. Expeds., pt. VI: Palaeontologia Polonica, no. 33, p. 103-132.

Kielan-Jaworowska, Z., and Sloan, R. E., in press, Catopsalis (Multituberculata) from Asia and North America and the problem of taeniolabidid dispersal in the Late Cretaceous: Acta Palaeont. Polonica, v. 24.

Kennedy, W. J., and Cooper, M., 1975, Cretaceous ammonite distributions and the opening of the South Atlantic: Geol. Soc. London Jour., v. 131, p. 283-288.

Kobayashi, T., and Shikama, T., 1961, The climatic history of the Far East, in Nairn, A. E. M., ed., Descriptive palaeoclimatology: New York, Interscience Publ. Inc., p. 292-306.

Krassilov, V. A., 1973a, Climatic changes in eastern Asia as indicated by fossil floras. I. Early Cretaceous: Palaeogeog., Palaeoclimatol., Palaeoecol., v. 13, p. 261-273.

———1973b, Mesozoic plants and the problem of angiosperm ancestry: Lethaia, v. 6, p. 163-178.

———1975, Climatic changes in eastern Asia as indicated by fossil floras. II. Late Cretaceous and Danian: Palaeogeog., Palaeoclimatol., Palaeoecol., v. 17, p. 157-172.

Kräusel, R., 1964, Introduction to the palaeoclimatic significance of coal, in Nairn, A. E. M., ed., Problems in palaeoclimatology: London, Interscience Publ., p. 53-56.

Kristoffersen, Y., 1978, Sea-floor spreading and the early opening of the North Atlantic: Earth Planet. Sci. Lett., v. 38, p. 273-290.

Ladd, J. W., 1976, Relative motion of South America with respect to North America and Caribbean tectonics: Geol. Soc. America Bull., v. 87, p. 969-976.

Ladd, J. W., Dickson, G. O., and Pitman, W. C., III, 1973, The age of the South Atlantic, in Nairn, A. E. M., and Stehli, F. G., eds., The ocean basins and margins. Volume 1, The South Atlantic: New York, Plenum Press, p. 555-573.

Lamb, H. H., 1972, Climate: present, past and future (Volume I. Fundamentals and climate now): London, Methuen & Co. Ltd., xxxi + 613 p.

Lanphere, M. A., and Reed, B. L., 1973, Timing of Mesozoic and Cenozoic plutonic events in circum-Pacific North America: Geol. Soc. America Bull., v. 84, p. 3773-3782.

Larson, R. L., 1977, Early Cretaceous breakup of Gondwanaland off western Australia: Geology, v. 5, p. 57-60.

Larson, R. L., and Ladd, J. W., 1973, Evidence for the opening of the South Atlantic in the Early Cretaceous: Nature, v. 246, p. 209-212.

Lefeld, J., 1971, Geology of the Djadokhta Formation at Bayn Dzak (Mongolia), in Kielan-Jaworowska, Z., ed., Results Polish-Mongol. Palaeont. Expeds., pt. III: Palaeontologia Polonica, no. 25, p. 101-127.

Lillegraven, J. A., 1969, Latest Cretaceous mammals of upper part of Edmonton Formation of Alberta, Canada, and review of marsupial-placental dichotomy in mammalian evolution: Univ. Kansas Paleont. Contribs., Art. 50 (Vertebrata 12), 122 p.

———1974, Biogeographical considerations of the marsupial-placental dichotomy: Ann. Rev. Ecol. Syst., v. 5, p. 263-283.

Lotze, F., 1964, The distribution of evaporites in space and time, in Nairn, A. E. M., ed., Problems in palaeoclimatology: London, Interscience Publ., p. 491-509.

Lowenstam, H. A., and Epstein, S., 1954, Paleotemperatures of the post-Aptian Cretaceous as determined by the oxygen isotope method: Jour. Geol., v. 62, p. 207-248.

McElhinny, M. W., 1973, Palaeomagnetism and plate tectonics: London, Cambridge Univ. Press, x + 358 p.

McElhinny, M. W., Embleton, B. J. J., Daly, L., and Pozzi, J.-P., 1976, Paleomagnetic evidence for the location of Madagascar in Gondwanaland: Geology, v. 4, p. 455-457.

McGookey, D. P., Haun, J. D., Hale, L. A., Goodell, H. G., McCubbin, D. G., Weimer, R. J., and Wulf, G. R., 1972, Cretaceous system, in Mallory, W. W., ed., Geologic atlas of the Rocky Mountain region: Denver, Rocky Mountain Assoc. Geol., p. 190-228.

McKenna, M. C., 1973, Sweepstakes, filters, corridors, Noah's arks, and beached Viking funeral ships in palaeogeography, in Tarling, D. H., and Runcorn, S. K., eds., Implications of continental drift to the earth sciences: New York, Academic Press, NATO Adv. Study Inst., v. 1, p. 295-308.

McWhae, J. R. H., Playford, P. E., Lindner, A. W., Glenister, B. F., and Balme, B. E., 1958, The stratigraphy of Western Australia: Geol. Soc. Australia Jour., v. 4, pt. 2, p. 1-161.

Machens, E., 1973, The geologic history of the marginal basins along the north slope of the Gulf of Guinea, in Nairn, A. E. M., and Stehli, F. G., eds., The ocean basins and margins. Volume 1, The South Atlantic: New York, Plenum Press, p. 351-390.

Martin, R., 1973, Cretaceous-early Tertiary rift basin of Baffin Bay—continental drift without sea-floor spreading, in Pitcher, M. G., ed., Arctic geology: Tulsa, Amer. Assoc. Petrol. Geol. Mem. 19, p. 500-505.

Matsumoto, T., 1973, Late Cretaceous Ammonoidea, in Hallam, A., ed., Atlas of palaeobiogeography: New York, Elsevier Sci. Publ. Co., p. 421-429.

Matthew, W. D., 1915, Climate and evolution: New York Acad. Sci. Ann., v. 24, p. 171-318.

Maxwell, A. E., Von Herzon, R. P., Andrews, J. E., Boyce, R. E., Milow, E. D., Hsü, K. J., Percival, S. F., and Saito, T., 1970, Initial reports of the Deep Sea Drilling Project, v. 3: Washington, D.C., U.S. Govt. Printing Office, xx + 806 p.

Meyerhoff, A. A., 1970, Continental drift: implications of palaeomagnetic studies, meteorology, physical oceanography, and climatology: Jour. Geol., v. 78, p. 1-51.

———1973, Mass biotal extinctions, world climate changes, and galactic motions, possible interrelations, in Logan, A., and Hills, L. V., eds., The Permian and Triassic systems and their mutual boundary: Canad. Soc. Petrol. Geol. Mem. 2, p. 745-758.

Muller, J., 1970, Palynological evidence on early differentiation of angiosperms: Biol. Rev., v. 45, p. 417-450.

Mullins, H. T., and Lynts, G. W., 1977, Origin of the northwestern Bahama Platform: review and reinterpretation: Geol. Soc. America Bull., v. 88, p. 1447-1461.

Nairn, A. E. M., and Stehli, F. G., eds., 1975, The ocean basins and margins. Volume 3, The Gulf of Mexico and the Caribbean: New York, Plenum Press, xvi + 706 p.

Nalivkin, D. V., 1973, Geology of the U.S.S.R.: Toronto, Univ. Toronto Press, xxviii + 855 p.

Neill, W. M., 1976, Mesozoic epeirogeny at the South Atlantic margin and the Tristan hot spot: Geology, v. 4, p. 495-498.

Norton, I., and Molnar, P., 1977, Implications of a revised fit between Australia and Antarctica for the evolution of the eastern Indian Ocean: Nature, v. 267, p. 338-340.

Pardo, G., 1975, Geology of Cuba, in Nairn, A. E. M., and Stehli, F. G., eds., The ocean basins and margins. Volume 3, The Gulf of Mexico and the Caribbean: New York, Plenum Press, p. 553-615.

Patton, W. W., Jr., Lanphere, M. A., Miller, T. P., and Scott, R. A., 1976, Age and tectonic significance of volcanic rocks on St. Matthew Island, Bering Sea, Alaska: U.S. Geol. Surv. Jour. Res., v. 4, p. 67-73.

Pitman, W. C., III, and Talwani, M., 1972, Sea-floor spreading in the North Atlantic: Geol. Soc. America Bull., v. 83, p. 619-646.

Raven, P. H., 1977, A suggestion concerning the Cretaceous rise to dominance of the angiosperms: Evolution, v. 31, p. 451-452.

Raven, P. H., and Axelrod, D. I., 1974, Angiosperm biogeography and past continental movements: Missouri Bot. Gard. Ann., v. 61, p. 539-673.

Regal, P. J., 1977, Ecology and evolution of flowering plant dominance: Science, v. 196, p. 622-629.

Reyment, R. A., 1974, Application des méthodes paléobiologiques à la théorie de la dérive des continents, illustrée par l'Atlantique Sud: Revue Géographie phys. Géologie dynam., v. 16, p. 61-70.

Riek, E. F., 1970, Lower Cretaceous fleas: Nature, v. 227, p. 746-747.

Robinson, P. L., 1971, A problem of faunal replacement on Permo-Triassic continents: Palaeontology, v. 14, p. 131-153.

———1973, Palaeoclimatology and continental drift, in Tarling, D. H., and Runcorn, S. K., eds., Implications of continental drift to the earth sciences: New York, Academic Press, NATO Adv. Study Inst., v. 1, p. 449-474.

Rona, P. A., and Fleming, H. S., 1973, Mesozoic plate motions in the eastern central North Atlantic: Marine Geol., v. 14, p. 239-252.

Rosen, D. E., 1975, A vicariance model of Caribbean biogeography: Syst. Zool., v. 24, p. 431-464.

Ryer, T. A., 1977, Patterns of Cretaceous shallow-marine sedimentation, Coalville and Rockport areas, Utah: Geol. Soc. America Bull., v. 88, p. 177-188.

Sachs, V. N., Basov, V. A., Dagis, A. A., Dagis, A. S., Ivanova, E. F., Meledina, S. V., Mesezhnikov, M. S., Nalnyayeva, T. I., Zakharov, V. A., and Shulgina, N. I., 1973, Paleozoogeography of Boreal-realm seas in Jurassic and Neocomian, in Pitcher, M. G., ed., Arctic geology: Tulsa, Amer. Assoc. Petrol. Geol. Mem. 19, p. 219-229.

Savin, S. M., 1977, The history of the earth's surface temperature during the past 100 million years: Ann. Rev. Earth Planet. Sci., v. 5, p. 319-355.

Sawyer, J. S., 1966, Possible variations of the circulation of the atmosphere: London, Roy. Meteorol. Soc. Quart. Jour., Spec. Vol., Proc. Internat. Conf. World Climate, 8,000-0 B.C., p. 218-229.

Schaeffer, B., 1970, Mesozoic fishes and climate: N. Amer. Paleont. Conv. Proc., Part D, p. 376-388.

Scholl, D. W., Buffington, E. C., and Marlow, M. S., 1975, Plate tectonics and the structural evolution of the Aleutian-Bering Sea region: Geol. Soc. America Spec. Paper 151, p. 1-31.

Schuster, R. M., 1976, Plate tectonics and its bearing on the geographical origin and dispersal of angiosperms, in Beck, C. B., ed., Origin and early evolution of angiosperms: New York, Columbia Univ. Press, p. 48-138.

Scrutton, R. A., 1973, Structure and evolution of the sea floor south of South Africa: Earth Planet. Sci. Lett., v. 19, p. 250-256.

———1978, Davie fracture zone and the movement of Madagascar: ibid., v. 39, p. 84-88.

Scrutton, R. A., and Dingle, R. V., 1976, Observations on the processes of sedimentary basin formation at the margins of southern Africa: Tectonophysics, v. 36, p. 143-156.

Semenovich, V. N., Gramberg, I. S., and Nesterov, I. I., 1973, Oil and gas possibilities in the Soviet Arctic, in Pitcher, M. G., ed., Arctic geology: Tulsa, Amer. Assoc. Petrol. Geol. Mem. 19, p. 194-203.

Sloan, R. E., 1970, Cretaceous and Paleocene terrestrial communities of western North America: N. Amer. Paleont. Conv. Proc., Part E, p. 427-453.

Smart, J., and Hughes, N. F., 1973, The insect and the plant: progressive palaeoecological integration, in Van Emden, H. F., ed., Insect/plant relationships: Roy. Entomol. Soc. London, Symp. 6, p. 143-155.

Smith, A. G., and Briden, J. C., 1977, Mesozoic and Cenozoic paleocontinental maps: Cambridge, Cambridge Univ. Press, 63 p.

Snead, R. G., 1969, Microfloral diagnosis of the Cretaceous-Tertiary boundary, central Alberta: Alberta Res. Council Bull., v. 25, p. 1-148.

Soper, N. J., Higgens, A. C., Downie, C., Matthews, D. W., and Brown, P. E., 1976, Late Cretaceous-early Tertiary stratigraphy of the Kangerdlugssuag area, east Greenland, and the age of the opening of the north-east Atlantic: Geol. Soc. London Jour., v. 132, p. 85-104.

Southwood, T. R. E., 1973, The insect/plant relationship—an evolutionary perspective, in Van Emden, H. F., ed., Insect/plant relationships: Roy. Entomol. Soc. London, Symp. 6, p. 3-30.

Stanley, E. A., 1965, Upper Cretaceous and Palaeocene plant microfossils and Paleocene dinoflagellates and hystricosphaerids from northwestern South Dakota: Amer. Paleont. Bull., v. 49, p. 179-384.

Stebbins, G. L., 1976, Seeds, seedlings, and the origin of angiosperms, in Beck, C. B., ed., Origin and early evolution of angiosperms: New York, Columbia Univ. Press, p. 300-311.

Stevens, G. R., 1973, Jurassic belemnites, in Hallam, A., ed., Atlas of palaeobiogeography: New York, Elsevier Sci. Publ. Co., p. 385-401.

Suárez, M., 1976, Plate-tectonic model for southern Antarctic Peninsula and its relation to southern Andes: Geology, v. 4, p. 211-214.

Sulimski, A., 1975, Macrocephalosauridae and Polyglyphanodontidae (Sauria) from the Late Cretaceous of Mongolia, in Kielan-Jaworowska, Z., ed., Results Polish-Mongol. Palaeont. Expeds., pt. VI: Palaeontologia Polonica, no. 33, p. 25-102.

Surlyk, F., 1978, Jurassic basin evolution of East Greenland: Nature, v. 274, p. 130-133.

Sussman, R. W., and Raven, P. H., 1978, Pollination by lemurs and marsupials: an archaic coevolutionary system: Science, v. 200, p. 731-736.

Tedford, R. H., 1974, Marsupials and the new paleogeography, in Ross, C. A., ed., Paleogeographic provinces and provinciality: Tulsa, Soc. Econ. Paleont. Mineral., Spec. Publ. 21, p. 109-126.

Thiede, J., and Van Andel, T. H., 1977, The paleoenvironment of anaerobic sediments in the late Mesozoic South Atlantic Ocean: Earth Planet. Sci. Lett., v. 33, p. 301-309.

Tomblin, J. F., 1975, The Lesser Antilles and Aves Ridge, *in* Nairn, A. E. M., and Stehli, F. G., eds., The ocean basins and margins. Volume 3, The Gulf of Mexico and the Caribbean: New York, Plenum Press, p. 467-500.

Tschudy, R. H., 1968, Palynology of the Cretaceous-Tertiary boundary in the Mississippi Embayment and northern Rocky Mountain regions (abstract): Geol. Soc. America Spec. Paper 101, p. 223.

Vachrameev, V. A., 1973, Mesozoic floras of the Southern Hemisphere and their relationship to the floras of the northern continents: Palaont. Jour. (Paleont. Zhur.), v. 6, p. 409-421.

Van der Pijl, L., 1972, Principles of dispersal in higher plants (2nd ed.): New York, Springer-Verlag, *xi* + 162 p.

Van Houten, F. B., 1961, Climatic significance of red beds, *in* Nairn, A. E. M., ed., Descriptive palaeoclimatology: New York, Interscience Publ. Inc., p. 89-139.

———1964, Origin of red beds—some unsolved problems, *in* Nairn, A. E. M., ed., Problems in palaeoclimatology: London, Interscience Publ., p. 647-661.

———1977, Triassic-Liassic deposits of Morocco and eastern North America: Amer. Assoc. Petrol. Geol. Bull., v. 61, p. 79-99.

Van Houten, F. B., and Brown, R. H., 1977, Latest Paleozoic-early Mesozoic paleography [*sic*], northwestern Africa: Jour. Geol., v. 85, p. 143-156.

Van der Voo, R., Mauk, F. J., and French, R. B., 1976, Permian-Triassic continental configurations and the origin of the Gulf of Mexico: Geology, v. 4, p. 177-180.

Veevers, J. J., and Cotterill, D., 1976, Western margin of Australia: a Mesozoic analog of the East African rift system: *ibid.*, v. 4, p. 713-717.

Veevers, J. J., and McElhinny, M. W., 1976, The separation of Australia from other continents: Earth-Sci. Rev., v. 12, p. 139-159.

Vereschagin, V. N., and Ronov, A. B., 1966, Paleogeographic maps of the Cretaceous of the USSR (Sheets 29-50), *in* Atlas of the lithological-paleogeographical maps of the USSR, Vol. III, Triassic, Jurassic and Cretaceous (1968): Moscow, Min. Geol. USSR, Akad. Nauk SSSR, 75 sheets (in Russian).

Vigneaux, M., 1974, The geology and sedimentation history of the Bay of Biscay, *in* Nairn, A. E. M., and Stehli, F. G., eds., The ocean basins and margins. Volume 2, The North Atlantic: New York, Plenum Press, p. 273-314.

Vinogradov, V. A., Gramberg, I. S., Pogrebitsky, Yu. E., Rabkin, M. I., Ravich, M. G., Sokolov, V. N., and Sorokov, D. S., 1973, Main features of geologic structure and history of north-central Siberia, *in* Pitcher, M. G., ed., Arctic geology: Tulsa, Amer. Assoc. Petrol. Geol. Mem. 19, p. 181-188.

Vörös, A., 1977, Provinciality of the Mediterranean Lower Jurassic brachiopod fauna: causes and plate-tectonic implications: Palaeogeog., Palaeoclimatol., Palaeoecol., v. 21, p. 1-16.

Wardlaw, N. C., and Nicholls, G. D., 1972, Cretaceous evaporites of Brazil and West Africa: 24th Internat. Geol. Congr., sec. 6, p. 43-58.

Waugh, B., 1973, The distribution and formation of Permian-Triassic red beds, *in* Logan, A., and Hills, L. V., eds., The Permian and Triassic systems and their mutual boundary: Canad. Soc. Petrol. Geol. Mem. 2, p. 678-693.

Wesley, A., 1973, Jurassic plants, *in* Hallam, A., ed., Atlas of palaeobiogeography: New York, Elsevier Sci. Publ. Co., p. 329-338.

Westermann, G. E. G., 1973, The Late Triassic bivalve *Monotis*: *ibid.*, p. 251-258.

Williams, G. D., and Stelck, C. R., 1975, Speculations on the Cretaceous palaeogeography of North America, *in* Caldwell, W. G. E., ed., The Cretaceous System in the Western Interior of North America: Geol. Assoc. Canada Spec. Paper 13, p. 1-20.

CHAPTER 15

NOTES ON THE MONOTREMATA

William A. Clemens

Modern monotremes, the echidna and platypus, exhibit curious combinations of primitive and highly derived features that have long intrigued systematists. Three genera of modern monotremes usually are recognized: *Tachyglossus*, the echidna of Australia, *Zaglossus*, the long-beaked echidna of New Guinea, and *Ornithorhynchus*, the platypus of Australia. All three are represented in Pleistocene deposits of Australia (see Mahoney and Ride, 1975, and Griffiths, 1968), but these fossils add little data toward solving the mystery of monotreme ancestry. Given this uncertainty concerning their forbears, why should a separate chapter on monotremes be included in a book devoted to Mesozoic mammals? Some systematists, noting the wealth of primitive (*i.e.*, reptile-like) characters in modern monotremes have interpreted the platypus and echidna as relicts of an early grade of mammalian evolution. Also particular orders of Mesozoic mammals have been cited as possibly part of the ancestry of the modern monotremes. The purpose of these notes is to briefly review the fossil record of pre-Pleistocene, Australian monotremes and to summarize and evaluate the current hypotheses concerning their Mesozoic ancestry.

Tertiary fossil record provides little information about the ancestry of monotremes. Stirton and others (1967) tentatively suggested that *Ektopodon serratus*, from the Australian Miocene, might have been a monotreme. Fossils collected subsequently indicate it probably is a highly specialized phalangeroid

marsupial and not a monotreme (Woodburne and Clemens, *in preparation*).

The one known Tertiary monotreme, *Obdurodon insignis* (Fig. 15-1) is represented by two isolated teeth found at disparate localities in South Australia that are thought to be of middle Miocene age (Woodburne and Tedford, 1975). The crowns of these teeth have relatively thin bases. In occlusal view, the crown is subrectangular in outline and dominated by two transverse lophs. The type preserves the six roots that supported the tooth. These are relatively short and end in bulbous tips, not unlike those of the taurodont roots of teeth of *Morganucodon*, a Rhaeto-Liassic triconodont (Chapter 4). Allocation of *Obdurodon* to the monotreme Family Ornithorhynchidae is based on a number of dental characters shared with ephemeral teeth of the platypus (see Simpson, 1929, and Green, 1937). Data on the microstructure of the enamel are presented in Chapter 11.

Recent hypotheses concerning the origins of monotremes can be ordered into three groups. The first includes those that recognize a basic evolutionary dichotomy subdividing the Mammalia into nontherian and therian lineages and allocate the monotremes to the nontherians without nominating a known Mesozoic order as their ancestral stock (see Chapter 3). Another group of hypotheses also recognizes the fundamental dichotomy between therian and nontherian mammals and allocates the monotremes to the nontherian group. Going farther, morphological similarities, particularly in cranial structure, are cited as indicating that among non-therian orders monotremes are most closely related to multituberculates (see Kermack and Kielan-Jaworowska, 1971, Kielan-Jaworowska, 1971 and 1974, and Chapter 6).

The third group of hypotheses suggests a special phylogenetic relationship between monotremes and marsupials. Citing a wide range of data and applying what he dubbed the "palimpsest" theory, Gregory (1947, p. 9) argued ". . . the monotremes have been derived, probably within the Australasian region and by relatively rapid divergence, from the ancestors of some of the Australian marsupials." He suggested this divergence might have occurred in the Tertiary. Kühne (1973 and 1977), primarily utilizing a cladistic analysis of patterns of dental ontogeny, concluded that marsupials and monotremes were derived from a common ancestral stock that was a sister group of the Eutheria (= placentals).

As is almost always the case in current speculations on phylogenetic interrelationships of mammalian orders, more data are needed before choices can be made among available hypotheses. However, they can be ranked in light of what information is available. The dichotomous taxonomic division of the Mammalia into therian and nontherian categories might be an oversimplification (see Chapters 3 and 4), but fundamental differences in structure of the braincase and pattern of occlusion of the cheek teeth still appear to characterize the major Mesozoic lineages (see Chapter 9). Marsupials and eutherians share many characters thought to be apomorphies distinguishing them from monotremes (see Chapters 9 and 13). This suggests the "palimpsest" theory and similar hypotheses probably are incorrect.

The other two groups of hypotheses concerning monotreme origins agree in associating them with the various lineages of nontherian mammals found in

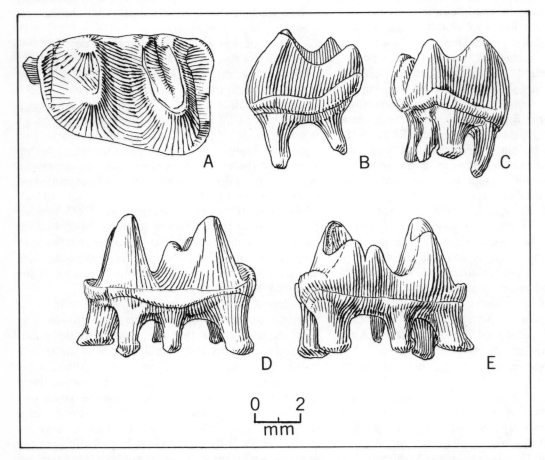

Figure 15-1. *Obdurodon insignis*, isolated right upper molar. *A*, occlusal view, anterior to right; *B*, anterior view; *C*, posterior view; *D*, lingual view, anterior to right; and *E*, labial view, anterior to left. (Illustrations prepared by M. O. Woodburne)

Mesozoic faunas. In some of these hypotheses no specific ancestor-descendant relationships are mooted, but in others (*e.g.*, Kermack and Kielan-Jaworowska, 1971) a special phylogenetic relationship between monotremes and multituberculates is proposed. In support of this thesis (*ibid.*, also see Kielan-Jaworowska, 1974) the following similarities between multituberculates and monotremes have been cited: (1) lateral broadening of the braincase resulting in ventral orientation of the foramen pseudovale; (2) great reduction of the alisphenoid; (3) multituberculate ectopterygoid and "Echidna

pterygoid" share a similar posterior position; and (4) absence of a jugal. These similarities could be the product of parallel or convergent evolution, and new data on the postcranial skeleton of multituberculates (Chapter 6 and Kielan-Jaworowska, pers. comm.) suggest major differences between the two lineages. Although it certainly cannot be falsified, the suggestion of multituberculate origins of the monotremes is not particularly compelling. The Mesozoic, non-therian ancestors of monotremes probably are still best regarded as unidentified or unknown.

REFERENCES CITED

Green, H. L. H. H., 1937, The development and morphology of the teeth of *Ornithorhynchus*: Roy. Soc. London Philos. Trans., B (Biol. Sci.), v. 288, p. 367-420.

Gregory, W. K., 1947, The monotremes and the palimpsest theory: Amer. Mus. Nat. Hist. Bull., v. 88, p. 1-52.

Griffiths, M., 1968, Echidnas: Oxford and New York, Pergamon Press, ix + 282 p.

Kermack, K. A., and Kielan-Jaworowska, Z., 1971, Therian and non-therian mammals, *in* Kermack, D. M., and Kermack, K. A., eds., Early mammals: Linn. Soc. Zool. Jour., v. 50, suppl. 1, p. 103-115.

Kielan-Jaworowska, Z., 1971, Skull structure and affinities of the Multituberculata, *in* Kielan-Jaworowska, Z., ed., Results Polish-Mongol. Palaeont. Expeds., pt. III: Palaeontologia Polonica, no. 25, p. 5-41.

_____1974, Multituberculate succession in the Late Cretaceous of the Gobi Desert (Mongolia), *in ibid.*, pt. V: *ibid.*, no. 30, p. 23-44.

Kühne, W. G., 1973, The systematic position of monotremes reconsidered (Mammalia): Zeit. Morph. Tiere, v. 75, p. 59-64.

_____1977, On the Marsupionta, a reply to Dr. Parrington: Jour. Nat. Hist., v. 11, p. 225-228.

Mahoney, J. A., and Ride, W. D. L., 1975, Index to the genera and species of fossil Mammalia described from Australia and New Guinea between 1838 and 1968 (including citations of type species and primary type specimens): West. Austral. Mus. Spec. Publ., no. 6, 250 p.

Simpson, G. G., 1929, The dentition of *Ornithorhynchus* as evidence of its affinities: Amer. Mus. Novitates, no. 390, 15 p.

Stirton, R. A., Tedford, R. H., and Woodburne, M. O., 1967, A new Tertiary formation and fauna from the Tirari Desert, South Australia: So. Austral. Mus. Rec., v. 15, p. 427-462.

Woodburne, M. O., and Tedford, R. H., 1975, The first Tertiary monotreme from Australia: Amer. Mus. Novitates, no. 2588, 11 p.

Designer: Jane Bernard
Compositor: Pioneer Printing & Stationery Co.
Printer: Malloy Lithographing
Binder: Malloy Lithographing
Text: Compugraphic English
Display: Compugraphic English
Cloth: Joanna Arrestox B41550
Paper: Williamsburg 60 lb.